Contents

Spark plug condition and bodywork repair colour pages between pages 32 and 33

Vauxhall Cavalier SRi 130

Vauxhall Cavalier L Estate

Vauxhall
Cavalier
Owners
Workshop
Manual

I M Coomber

Models covered
All Vauxhall Cavalier front-wheel-drive models with
petrol engines, including special/limited editions;
Saloon, Hatchback & Estate
1297 cc, 1598 cc, 1796 cc & 1998 cc

Covers major mechanical features of Convertible
Does not cover Diesel engine models, or 'new' Cavalier introduced
October 1988

(812-7U5)   ABC

Haynes Publishing Group
Sparkford Nr Yeovil
Somerset BA22 7JJ England

Haynes Publications, Inc
861 Lawrence Drive
Newbury Park
California 91320 USA

Acknowledgements

Thanks are due to Champion Spark Plug who supplied the illustrations showing spark plug conditions, to Holt Lloyd Limited who supplied the illustrations showing bodywork repair, and to Duckhams Oils who provided lubrication data. Certain other illustrations are the copyright of Vauxhall Motors Ltd., and are used with their permission. Thanks are also due to Sykes-Pickavant, who supplied some of the workshop tools, and all those people at Sparkford who assisted in the production of this manual.

A book in the **Haynes Owners Workshop Manual Series**

Printed by J. H. Haynes & Co. Ltd, Sparkford, Nr Yeovil, Somerset BA22 7JJ, England

ISBN 1 85010 542 1

British Library Cataloguing in Publication Data
Coomber, Ian, *1943-*
Vauxhall Cavalier owners workshop manual
1. Cars   Maintenance & repair - Amateurs' manuals
1. Title   II. Series
629.28'722
ISBN 1-85010-542-1

Restoring and Preserving our Motoring Heritage

Few people can have had the luck to realise their dreams to quite the same extent and in such a remarkable fashion as John Haynes, Founder and Chairman of the Haynes Publishing Group.

Since 1965 his unique approach to workshop manual publishing has proved so successful that millions of Haynes Manuals are now sold every year throughout the world, covering literally thousands of different makes and models of cars, vans and motorcycles.

A continuing passion for cars and motoring led to the founding in 1985 of a Charitable Trust dedicated to the restoration and preservation of our motoring heritage. To inaugurate the new Museum, John Haynes donated virtually his entire private collection of 52 cars.

Now with an unrivalled international collection of over 210 veteran, vintage and classic cars and motorcycles, the Haynes Motor Museum in Somerset is well on the way to becoming one of the most interesting Motor Museums in the world.

A 70 seat video cinema, a cafe and an extensive motoring bookshop, together with a specially constructed one kilometre motor circuit, make a visit to the Haynes Motor Museum a truly unforgettable experience.

Every vehicle in the museum is preserved in as near as possible mint condition and each car is run every six months on the motor circuit.

Enjoy the picnic area set amongst the rolling Somerset hills. Peer through the William Morris workshop windows at cars being restored, and browse through the extensive displays of fascinating motoring memorabilia.

From the 1903 Oldsmobile through such classics as an MG Midget to the mighty 'E' Type Jaguar, Lamborghini, Ferrari Berlinetta Boxer, and Graham Hill's Lola Cosworth, there is something for everyone, young and old alike, at this Somerset Museum.

Haynes Motor Museum

Situated mid-way between London and Penzance, the Haynes Motor Museum is located just off the A303 at Sparkford, Somerset (home of the Haynes Manual) and is open to the public 7 days a week all year round, except Christmas Day and Boxing Day.

About this manual

Its aim

The aim of this manual is to help you get the best value from your vehicle. It can do so in several ways. It can help you decide what work must be done (even should you choose to get it done by a garage), provide information on routine maintenance and servicing, and give a logical course of action and diagnosis when random faults occur. However, it is hoped that you will use the manual by tackling the work yourself. On simpler jobs it may even be quicker than booking the car into a garage and going there twice, to leave and collect it. Perhaps most important, a lot of money can be saved by avoiding the costs a garage must charge to cover its labour and overheads.

The manual has drawings and descriptions to show the function of the various components so that their layout can be understood. Then the tasks are described and photographed in a step-by-step sequence so that even a novice can do the work.

Its arrangement

The manual is divided into thirteen Chapters, each covering a logical sub-division of the vehicle. The Chapters are each divided into Sections, numbered with single figures, eg 5; and the Sections into paragraphs (or sub-sections), with decimal numbers following on from the Section they are in, eg 5.1, 5.2, 5.3 etc.

It is freely illustrated, especially in those parts where there is a detailed sequence of operations to be carried out. There are two forms of illustration: figures and photographs. The figures are numbered in sequence with decimal numbers, according to their position in the Chapter – eg Fig. 6.4 is the fourth drawing/illustration in Chapter 6. Photographs carry the same number (either individually or in related groups) as the Section or sub-section to which they relate.

There is an alphabetical index at the back of the manual as well as a contents list at the front. Each Chapter is also preceded by its own individual contents list.

References to the 'left' or 'right' of the vehicle are in the sense of a person in the driver's seat facing forwards.

Unless otherwise stated, nuts and bolts are removed by turning anti-clockwise, and tightened by turning clockwise.

Vehicle manufacturers continually make changes to specifications and recommendations, and these, when notified, are incorporated into our manuals at the earliest opportunity.

Whilst every care is taken to ensure that the information in this manual is correct, no liability can be accepted by the authors or publishers for loss, damage or injury caused by any errors in, or omissions from, the information given.

Project vehicles

The vehicles used in the preparation of this manual, and which appear in many of the photographic sequences, were: an early 1.3 Saloon, an early 1.6 Estate, an early 1.8 SRi Hatchback, and two 1987 models – a 1.6L and an SRi.

Introduction to the Vauxhall Cavalier

The front-wheel-drive (fwd) Cavalier was introduced in August 1981 and replaced the earlier range of rear-wheel-drive Cavalier models. The bodywork was also revised to distinguish it from the earlier models and was initially available in a two or four-door Saloon version, or a five-door Hatchback. The five-door Estate variant was introduced in 1983.

The engine and transmission on all models is transversely mounted. Initially available with a 1.3, 1.6 or 1.8 litre engine, the 2.0 version was added to the range for the 1987 model year. A 4 or 5-speed manual transmission, or a 3-speed automatic transmission will be fitted.

The 2-door Convertible variant was introduced in October 1985.

Various levels of trim and equipment are available depending upon the model selected from the range.

These vehicles should present few problems for the home mechanic. They are of straightforward construction with good access to all service points.

Vauxhall Cavalier Antibes

Vauxhall Cavalier Convertible

General dimensions, weights and capacities

For information applicable to later models see Supplement at end of manual

Dimensions

Overall length:
Saloon and Estate	4.366 m (171.9 in)
Hatchback	4.264 m (167.9 in)

Overall width:
All models	1.668 m (65.7 in)

Overall height:
Saloon	1.395 m (54.9 in)
Hatchback	1.385 m (54.5 in)
Estate	1.368 in (53.9 in)
Wheelbase	2.573 m (101.3 in)

Track – front:
1300	1.400 m (55.1 in)
1600 and 1800	1.406 m (55.4 in)
Track – rear (all models)	1.406 m (55.4 in)

Weights*

Kerb weight:	Manual	Automatic
1300 2-door	941 kg (2075 lb)	976 kg (2152 lb)
1300 4-door	961 kg (2119 lb)	996 kg (2196 lb)
1300 5-door	986 kg (2173 lb)	1021 kg (2251 lb)
1600 4-door	1011 kg (2229 lb)	1041 kg (2295 lb)
1600 5-door	1036 kg (2284 lb)	1066 kg (2350 lb)
1600 5-door Estate	1062 kg (2341 lb)	1060 kg (2337 lb)
1800 SRi 4-door	1070 kg (2359 lb)	1100 kg (2425 lb)
1800 CD 4-door	1031 kg (2273 lb)	1060 kg (2337 lb)
1800 SRi 5-door	1100 kg (2425 lb)	1130 kg (2491 lb)
1800 CD 5-door	1060 kg (2337 lb)	1090 kg (2403 lb)
Convertible	1085 kg (2392 lb)	

Permissible caravan/trailer towing weight:	Braked trailer	Unbraked trailer
1300 manual	950 kg (2094 lb)	475 kg (1047 lb)
1300 automatic	650 kg (1433 lb)	475 kg (1047 lb)
1600 manual and automatic	1100 kg (2425 lb)	500 kg (1102 lb)
1800 manual	1300 kg (2866 lb)	500 kg (1102 lb)
1800 automatic	1100 kg (2425 lb)	500 kg (1102 lb)

Maximum roof rack load:
Saloon and Hatchback	80 kg (176 lb)
Estate	50 kg (110 lb)

* The kerb weights and maximum permissible towing weights given are for general reference. The weights can differ according to model and year, therefore, if specific weight requirements are wanted for a particular model, consult your vehicle handbook or a Vauxhall dealer

Capacities (approximate)

Engine oil (with filter change):
1.3	3.00 litres (5.28 pints)
1.6	3.50 litres (6.16 pints)
1.8	3.55 litres (6.25 pints)

Cooling system:	Manual transmission	Automatic transmission
1.3	6.3 litres (11.1 pints)	7.1 litres (12.5 pints)
1.6	7.9 litres (13.9 pints)	7.7 litres (13.6 pints)
1.8	7.6 litres (13.4 pints)	7.4 litres (13.0 pints)

Fuel tank	61 litres (13.4 gallons)

Manual transmission:
F10 and F10.4	1.7 litres (3.0 pints)
F10.5	1.8 litres (3.2 pints)
F16 and F16.4	2.0 litres (3.5 pints)
F16.5	2.1 litres (3.7 pints)
Automatic transmission	7.0 litres (12.3 pints)

Jacking, towing and wheel changing

Jacking

Use the jack supplied with the vehicle only for wheel changing during roadside emergencies (photos). Chock the wheel diagonally opposite the one being removed.

When raising the vehicle for repair or maintenance, preferably use a trolley jack with a wooden block as an insulator to prevent damage to the underbody. Place the jack below the sill at a point midway between the wheel arch and the vehicle jack engagement point. Never raise the vehicle by jacking up under the engine sump, transmission casing or rear axle.

To avoid repetition, the procedure for raising the vehicle in order to carry out work under it is not included before each relevant operation described in this manual.

It is to be preferred and is certainly recommended that the vehicle is positioned over an inspection pit or raised on a lift. Where such equipment is not available, use ramps or jack up the vehicle as previously described, but always supplement the lifting device with axle stands.

Towing

Towing hooks are welded to the front and the rear of the vehicle and should only be used in an emergency, as their designed function is as lash-down hooks, for use during transportation (photos).

When towing vehicles equipped with automatic transmission, restrict the distance towed to 70 miles (100 km) and the towing speed to 50 mph (80 kmh). If these conditions are likely to be exceeded, then the front wheels will have to be raised off the road.

When being towed, remember to insert the ignition key and turn it to Position 1. Expect to apply greater pressure to the footbrake, as servo assistance will not be available after the first few brake applications.

Wheel changing

To change a roadwheel, first prise off the hub cap and remove the roadwheel bolt plastic caps (photo).

If the car is fairly new, the roadwheels and tyres will have been balanced on the vehicle during production. In order to maintain this balance then the position of the roadwheel in relation to the mounting hub must be marked before removing the wheel.

Release but do not remove each roadwheel bolt (photo) and then raise the vehicle with the jack. Remove the bolts and take off the wheel.

Refit the wheel by locating it in its original balanced position. Obviously, if the spare wheel is being fitted this cannot be done and is not essential as the wheel will have been balanced off the vehicle.

Screw in the roadwheel bolts and then lower the jack. Fully tighten the bolts, refit the bolt caps and the hub cap (photo).

Sill jacking points – arrowed

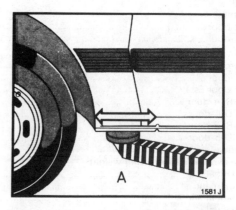

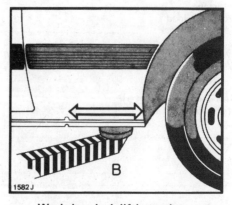

Workshop jack lifting points

A   Front   B   Rear

Jack and spare wheel location

Tool kit jack in use

Front towing hook

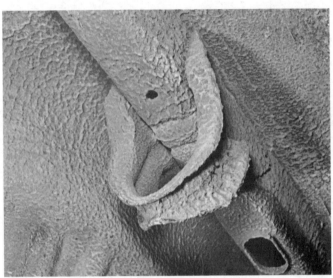

Rear towing hook

Hub cap removal

Releasing a wheel nut

Wheel nut plastic cap

Buying spare parts and vehicle identification numbers

Buying spare parts

Spare parts are available from many sources, for example: Vauxhall garages, other garages and accessory shops, and motor factors. Our advice regarding spare part sources is as follows:

Officially appointed Vauxhall garages – This is the best source of parts which are peculiar to your car and otherwise not generally available (eg complete cylinder heads, transmission components, badges, interior trim etc). It is also the only place at which you should buy parts if your vehicle is still under warranty – use of non-Vauxhall components may invalidate the warranty. To be sure of obtaining the correct parts it will always be necessary to give the storeman your car's vehicle identification number, and if possible, to take the 'old' parts along for positive identification. Remember that many parts are available on a factory exchange scheme – any parts returned should always be clean! It obviously makes good sense to go straight to the specialists on your car for this type of part for they are best equipped to supply you.

Other garages and accessory shops – These are often very good places to buy materials and components needed for the maintenance of your car (eg oil filters, spark plugs, bulbs, drivebelts, oils and greases, touch-up paint, filler paste etc). They also sell general accessories, usually have convenient opening hours, charge lower prices and can often be found not far from home.

Motor factors – Good factors will stock all of the more important components which wear out relatively quickly (eg clutch components, pistons, valves, exhaust systems, brake cylinders/pipes/hoses/seals/shoes and pads etc). Motor factors will often provide new or reconditioned components on a part exchange basis – this can save a considerable amount of money.

Vehicle identification numbers

The Vehicle Identification Number is located inside the engine compartment on top of the front end panel (photo). The plate is marked with the vehicle chassis and designation number and the colour code. Also shown is the maximum gross weight for the car.

The engine number is stamped on a flat machined on the engine cylinder block (photo).

The chassis number is stamped on the body floor panel between the driver's seat and the door sill (photo).

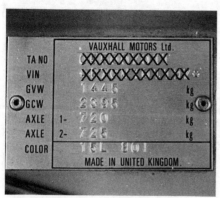

Vehicle identification plate

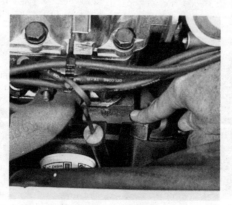

Engine number

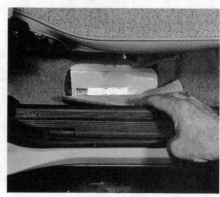

Chassis number

General repair procedures

Whenever servicing, repair or overhaul work is carried out on the car or its components, it is necessary to observe the following procedures and instructions. This will assist in carrying out the operation efficiently and to a professional standard of workmanship.

Joint mating faces and gaskets

Where a gasket is used between the mating faces of two components, ensure that it is renewed on reassembly, and fit it dry unless otherwise stated in the repair procedure. Make sure that the mating faces are clean and dry with all traces of old gasket removed. When cleaning a joint face, use a tool which is not likely to score or damage the face, and remove any burrs or nicks with an oilstone or fine file.

Make sure that tapped holes are cleaned with a pipe cleaner, and keep them free of jointing compound if this is being used unless specifically instructed otherwise.

Ensure that all orifices, channels or pipes are clear and blow through them, preferably using compressed air.

Oil seals

Whenever an oil seal is removed from its working location, either individually or as part of an assembly, it should be renewed.

The very fine sealing lip of the seal is easily damaged and will not seal if the surface it contacts is not completely clean and free from scratches, nicks or grooves. If the original sealing surface of the component cannot be restored, the component should be renewed.

Protect the lips of the seal from any surface which may damage them in the course of fitting. Use tape or a conical sleeve where possible. Lubricate the seal lips with oil before fitting and, on dual lipped seals, fill the space between the lips with grease.

Unless otherwise stated, oil seals must be fitted with their sealing lips toward the lubricant to be sealed.

Use a tubular drift or block of wood of the appropriate size to install the seal and, if the seal housing is shouldered, drive the seal down to the shoulder. If the seal housing is unshouldered, the seal should be fitted with its face flush with the housing top face.

Screw threads and fastenings

Always ensure that a blind tapped hole is completely free from oil, grease, water or other fluid before installing the bolt or stud. Failure to do this could cause the housing to crack due to the hydraulic action of the bolt or stud as it is screwed in.

When tightening a castellated nut to accept a split pin, tighten the nut to the specified torque, where applicable, and then tighten further to the next split pin hole. Never slacken the nut to align a split pin hole unless stated in the repair procedure.

When checking or retightening a nut or bolt to a specified torque setting, slacken the nut or bolt by a quarter of a turn, and then retighten to the specified setting.

Locknuts, locktabs and washers

Any fastening which will rotate against a component or housing in the course of tightening should always have a washer between it and the relevant component or housing.

Spring or split washers should always be renewed when they are used to lock a critical component such as a big-end bearing retaining nut or bolt.

Locktabs which are folded over to retain a nut or bolt should always be renewed.

Self-locking nuts can be reused in non-critical areas, providing resistance can be felt when the locking portion passes over the bolt or stud thread.

Split pins must always be replaced with new ones of the correct size for the hole.

Special tools

Some repair procedures in this manual entail the use of special tools such as a press, two or three-legged pullers, spring compressors etc. Wherever possible, suitable readily available alternatives to the manufacturer's special tools are described, and are shown in use. In some instances, where no alternative is possible, it has been necessary to resort to the use of a manufacturer's tool and this has been done for reasons of safety as well as the efficient completion of the repair operation. Unless you are highly skilled and have a thorough understanding of the procedure described, never attempt to bypass the use of any special tool when the procedure described specifies its use. Not only is there a very great risk of personal injury, but expensive damage could be caused to the components involved.

Tools and working facilities

Introduction

A selection of good tools is a fundamental requirement for anyone contemplating the maintenance and repair of a motor vehicle. For the owner who does not possess any, their purchase will prove a considerable expense, offsetting some of the savings made by doing-it-yourself. However, provided that the tools purchased meet the relevant national safety standards and are of good quality, they will last for many years and prove an extremely worthwhile investment.

To help the average owner to decide which tools are needed to carry out the various tasks detailed in this manual, we have compiled three lists of tools under the following headings: *Maintenance and minor repair, Repair and overhaul,* and *Special.* The newcomer to practical mechanics should start off with the *Maintenance and minor repair* tool kit and confine himself to the simpler jobs around the vehicle. Then, as his confidence and experience grow, he can undertake more difficult tasks, buying extra tools as, and when, they are needed. In this way, a *Maintenance and minor repair* tool kit can be built-up into a *Repair and overhaul* tool kit over a considerable period of time without any major cash outlays. The experienced do-it-yourselfer will have a tool kit good enough for most repair and overhaul procedures and will add tools from the *Special* category when he feels the expense is justified by the amount of use to which these tools will be put.

It is obviously not possible to cover the subject of tools fully here. For those who wish to learn more about tools and their use there is a book entitled *How to Choose and Use Car Tools* available from the publishers of this manual.

Maintenance and minor repair tool kit

The tools given in this list should be considered as a minimum requirement if routine maintenance, servicing and minor repair operations are to be undertaken. We recommend the purchase of combination spanners (ring one end, open-ended the other); although more expensive than open-ended ones, they do give the advantages of both types of spanner.

> *Combination spanners - 10, 11, 12, 13, 14 & 17 mm*
> *Adjustable spanner - 9 inch*
> *Spark plug spanner (with rubber insert)*
> *Spark plug gap adjustment tool*
> *Set of feeler gauges*
> *Brake bleed nipple spanner*
> *Screwdriver - 4 in long x $^1/4$ in dia (flat blade)*
> *Screwdriver - 4 in long x $^1/4$ in dia (cross blade)*
> *Combination pliers - 6 inch*
> *Hacksaw (junior)*
> *Tyre pump*
> *Tyre pressure gauge*

> *Oil can*
> *Fine emery cloth (1 sheet)*
> *Wire brush (small)*
> *Funnel (medium size)*

Repair and overhaul tool kit

These tools are virtually essential for anyone undertaking any major repairs to a motor vehicle, and are additional to those given in the *Maintenance and minor repair* list. Included in this list is a comprehensive set of sockets. Although these are expensive they will be found invaluable as they are so versatile - particularly if various drives are included in the set. We recommend the $^1/2$ in square-drive type, as this can be used with most proprietary torque wrenches. If you cannot afford a socket set, even bought piecemeal, then inexpensive tubular box spanners are a useful alternative.

The tools in this list will occasionally need to be supplemented by tools from the *Special* list.

> *Sockets (or box spanners) to cover range in previous list*
> *Reversible ratchet drive (for use with sockets)*
> *Extension piece, 10 inch (for use with sockets)*
> *Universal joint (for use with sockets)*
> *Torque wrench (for use with sockets)*
> *'Mole' wrench - 8 inch*
> *Ball pein hammer*
> *Soft-faced hammer, plastic or rubber*
> *Screwdriver - 6 in long x $^5/16$ in dia (flat blade)*
> *Screwdriver - 2 in long x $^5/16$ in square (flat blade)*
> *Screwdriver - 1$^1/2$ in long x $^1/4$ in dia (cross blade)*
> *Screwdriver - 3 in long x $^1/8$ in dia (electricians)*
> *Pliers - electricians side cutters*
> *Pliers - needle nosed*
> *Pliers - circlip (internal and external)*
> *Cold chisel - $^1/2$ inch*
> *Scriber*
> *Scraper*
> *Centre punch*
> *Pin punch*
> *Hacksaw*
> *Valve grinding tool*
> *Steel rule/straight-edge*
> *Allen keys (inc. splined/Torx type if necessary)*
> *Selection of files*
> *Wire brush (large)*
> *Axle-stands*
> *Jack (strong trolley or hydraulic type)*

Special tools

The tools in this list are those which are not used regularly, are expensive to buy, or which need to be used in accordance with their manufacturers' instructions. Unless relatively difficult mechanical jobs are undertaken frequently, it will not be economic to buy many of these tools. Where this is the case, you could consider clubbing together with friends (or joining a motorists' club) to make a joint purchase, or borrowing the tools against a deposit from a local garage or tool hire specialist.

The following list contains only those tools and instruments freely available to the public, and not those special tools produced by the vehicle manufacturer specifically for its dealer network. You will find occasional references to these manufacturers' special tools in the text of this manual. Generally, an alternative method of doing the job without the vehicle manufacturers' special tool is given. However, sometimes, there is no alternative to using them. Where this is the case and the relevant tool cannot be bought or borrowed, you will have to entrust the work to a franchised garage.

> Valve spring compressor (where applicable)
> Piston ring compressor
> Balljoint separator
> Universal hub/bearing puller
> Impact screwdriver
> Micrometer and/or vernier (caliper) gauge
> Dial gauge
> Stroboscopic timing light
> Dwell angle meter (contact breaker only)/tachometer
> Universal electrical multi-meter
> Cylinder compression gauge
> Lifting tackle
> Trolley jack
> Light with extension lead

Buying tools

For practically all tools, a tool factor is the best source since he will have a very comprehensive range compared with the average garage or accessory shop. Having said that, accessory shops often offer excellent quality tools at discount prices, so it pays to shop around.

There are plenty of good tools around at reasonable prices, but always aim to purchase items which meet the relevant national safety standards. If in doubt, ask the proprietor or manager of the shop for advice before making a purchase.

Care and maintenance of tools

Having purchased a reasonable tool kit, it is necessary to keep the tools in a clean serviceable condition. After use, always wipe off any dirt, grease and metal particles using a clean, dry cloth, before putting the tools away. Never leave them lying around after they have been used. A simple tool rack on the garage or workshop wall, for items such as screwdrivers and pliers is a good idea. Store all normal wrenches and sockets in a metal box. Any measuring instruments, gauges, meters, etc, must be carefully stored where they cannot be damaged or become rusty.

Take a little care when tools are used. Hammer heads inevitably become marked and screwdrivers lose the keen edge on their blades from time to time. A little timely attention with emery cloth or a file will soon restore items like this to a good serviceable finish.

Working facilities

Not to be forgotten when discussing tools, is the workshop itself. If anything more than routine maintenance is to be carried out, some form of suitable working area becomes essential.

It is appreciated that many an owner mechanic is forced by circumstances to remove an engine or similar item, without the benefit of a garage or workshop. Having done this, any repairs should always be done under the cover of a roof.

Wherever possible, any dismantling should be done on a clean, flat workbench or table at a suitable working height.

Any workbench needs a vice: one with a jaw opening of 4 in (100 mm) is suitable for most jobs. As mentioned previously, some clean dry storage space is also required for tools, as well as for lubricants, cleaning fluids, touch-up paints and so on, which become necessary.

Another item which may be required, and which has a much more general usage, is an electric drill with a chuck capacity of at least 5/16 in (8 mm). This, together with a good range of twist drills, is virtually essential for fitting accessories such as mirrors and reversing lights.

Last, but not least, always keep a supply of old newspapers and clean, lint-free rags available, and try to keep any working area as clean as possible.

Spanner jaw gap comparison table

Jaw gap (in)	Spanner size
0.250	1/4 in AF
0.276	7 mm
0.313	5/16 in AF
0.315	8 mm
0.344	11/32 in AF; 1/8 in Whitworth
0.354	9 mm
0.375	3/8 in AF
0.394	10 mm
0.433	11 mm
0.438	7/16 in AF
0.445	3/16 in Whitworth; 1/4 in BSF
0.472	12 mm
0.500	1/2 in AF
0.512	13 mm
0.525	1/4 in Whitworth; 5/16 in BSF
0.551	14 mm
0.563	9/16 in AF
0.591	15 mm
0.600	5/16 in Whitworth; 3/8 in BSF
0.625	5/8 in AF
0.630	16 mm
0.669	17 mm
0.686	11/16 in AF
0.709	18 mm
0.710	3/8 in Whitworth; 7/16 in BSF
0.748	19 mm
0.750	3/4 in AF
0.813	13/16 in AF
0.820	7/16 in Whitworth; 1/2 in BSF
0.866	22 mm
0.875	7/8 in AF
0.920	1/2 in Whitworth; 9/16 in BSF
0.938	15/16 in AF
0.945	24 mm
1.000	1 in AF
1.010	9/16 in Whitworth; 5/8 in BSF
1.024	26 mm
1.063	11/16 in AF; 27 mm
1.100	5/8 in Whitworth; 11/16 in BSF
1.125	11/8 in AF
1.181	30 mm
1.200	11/16 in Whitworth; 3/4 in BSF
1.250	11/4 in AF
1.260	32 mm
1.300	3/4 in Whitworth; 7/8 in BSF
1.313	15/16 in AF
1.390	13/16 in Whitworth; 15/16 in BSF
1.417	36 mm
1.438	17/16 in AF
1.480	7/8 in Whitworth; 1 in BSF
1.500	11/2 in AF
1.575	40 mm; 15/16 in Whitworth
1.614	41 mm
1.625	15/8 in AF
1.670	1 in Whitworth; 11/8 in BSF
1.688	111/16 in AF
1.811	46 mm
1.813	113/16 in AF
1.860	11/8 in Whitworth; 11/4 in BSF
1.875	17/8 in AF
1.969	50 mm
2.000	2 in AF
2.050	11/4 in Whitworth; 13/8 in BSF
2.165	55 mm
2.362	60 mm

Safety first!

Professional motor mechanics are trained in safe working procedures. However enthusiastic you may be about getting on with the job in hand, do take the time to ensure that your safety is not put at risk. A moment's lack of attention can result in an accident, as can failure to observe certain elementary precautions.

There will always be new ways of having accidents, and the following points do not pretend to be a comprehensive list of all dangers; they are intended rather to make you aware of the risks and to encourage a safety-conscious approach to all work you carry out on your vehicle.

Essential DOs and DON'Ts

DON'T rely on a single jack when working underneath the vehicle. Always use reliable additional means of support, such as axle stands, securely placed under a part of the vehicle that you know will not give way.

DON'T attempt to loosen or tighten high-torque nuts (e.g. wheel hub nuts) while the vehicle is on a jack; it may be pulled off.

DON'T start the engine without first ascertaining that the transmission is in neutral (or 'Park' where applicable) and the parking brake applied.

DON'T suddenly remove the filler cap from a hot cooling system – cover it with a cloth and release the pressure gradually first, or you may get scalded by escaping coolant.

DON'T attempt to drain oil until you are sure it has cooled sufficiently to avoid scalding you.

DON'T grasp any part of the engine, exhaust or catalytic converter without first ascertaining that it is sufficiently cool to avoid burning you.

DON'T allow brake fluid or antifreeze to contact vehicle paintwork.

DON'T syphon toxic liquids such as fuel, brake fluid or antifreeze by mouth, or allow them to remain on your skin.

DON'T inhale dust – it may be injurious to health (see *Asbestos* below).

DON'T allow any spilt oil or grease to remain on the floor – wipe it up straight away, before someone slips on it.

DON'T use ill-fitting spanners or other tools which may slip and cause injury.

DON'T attempt to lift a heavy component which may be beyond your capability – get assistance.

DON'T rush to finish a job, or take unverified short cuts.

DON'T allow children or animals in or around an unattended vehicle.

DO wear eye protection when using power tools such as drill, sander, bench grinder etc, and when working under the vehicle.

DO use a barrier cream on your hands prior to undertaking dirty jobs – it will protect your skin from infection as well as making the dirt easier to remove afterwards; but make sure your hands aren't left slippery. Note that long-term contact with used engine oil can be a health hazard.

DO keep loose clothing (cuffs, tie etc) and long hair well out of the way of moving mechanical parts.

DO remove rings, wristwatch etc, before working on the vehicle – especially the electrical system.

DO ensure that any lifting tackle used has a safe working load rating adequate for the job.

DO keep your work area tidy – it is only too easy to fall over articles left lying around.

DO get someone to check periodically that all is well, when working alone on the vehicle.

DO carry out work in a logical sequence and check that everything is correctly assembled and tightened afterwards.

DO remember that your vehicle's safety affects that of yourself and others. If in doubt on any point, get specialist advice.

IF, in spite of following these precautions, you are unfortunate enough to injure yourself, seek medical attention as soon as possible.

Asbestos

Certain friction, insulating, sealing, and other products – such as brake linings, brake bands, clutch linings, torque converters, gaskets, etc – contain asbestos. *Extreme care must be taken to avoid inhalation of dust from such products since it is hazardous to health.* If in doubt, assume that they *do* contain asbestos.

Fire

Remember at all times that petrol (gasoline) is highly flammable. Never smoke, or have any kind of naked flame around, when working on the vehicle. But the risk does not end there – a spark caused by an electrical short-circuit, by two metal surfaces contacting each other, by careless use of tools, or even by static electricity built up in your body under certain conditions, can ignite petrol vapour, which in a confined space is highly explosive.

Always disconnect the battery earth (ground) terminal before working on any part of the fuel or electrical system, and never risk spilling fuel on to a hot engine or exhaust.

It is recommended that a fire extinguisher of a type suitable for fuel and electrical fires is kept handy in the garage or workplace at all times. Never try to extinguish a fuel or electrical fire with water.

Note: *Any reference to a 'torch' appearing in this manual should always be taken to mean a hand-held battery-operated electric lamp or flashlight. It does NOT mean a welding/gas torch or blowlamp.*

Fumes

Certain fumes are highly toxic and can quickly cause unconsciousness and even death if inhaled to any extent. Petrol (gasoline) vapour comes into this category, as do the vapours from certain solvents such as trichloroethylene. Any draining or pouring of such volatile fluids should be done in a well ventilated area.

When using cleaning fluids and solvents, read the instructions carefully. Never use materials from unmarked containers – they may give off poisonous vapours.

Never run the engine of a motor vehicle in an enclosed space such as a garage. Exhaust fumes contain carbon monoxide which is extremely poisonous; if you need to run the engine, always do so in the open air or at least have the rear of the vehicle outside the workplace.

If you are fortunate enough to have the use of an inspection pit, never drain or pour petrol, and never run the engine, while the vehicle is standing over it; the fumes, being heavier than air, will concentrate in the pit with possibly lethal results.

The battery

Never cause a spark, or allow a naked light, near the vehicle's battery. It will normally be giving off a certain amount of hydrogen gas, which is highly explosive.

Always disconnect the battery earth (ground) terminal before working on the fuel or electrical systems.

If possible, loosen the filler plugs or cover when charging the battery from an external source. Do not charge at an excessive rate or the battery may burst.

Take care when topping up and when carrying the battery. The acid electrolyte, even when diluted, is very corrosive and should not be allowed to contact the eyes or skin.

If you ever need to prepare electrolyte yourself, always add the acid slowly to the water, and never the other way round. Protect against splashes by wearing rubber gloves and goggles.

When jump starting a car using a booster battery, for negative earth (ground) vehicles, connect the jump leads in the following sequence: First connect one jump lead between the positive (+) terminals of the two batteries. Then connect the other jump lead first to the negative (–) terminal of the booster battery, and then to a good earthing (ground) point on the vehicle to be started, at least 18 in (45 cm) from the battery if possible. Ensure that hands and jump leads are clear of any moving parts, and that the two vehicles do not touch. Disconnect the leads in the reverse order.

Mains electricity and electrical equipment

When using an electric power tool, inspection light etc, always ensure that the appliance is correctly connected to its plug and that, where necessary, it is properly earthed (grounded). Do not use such appliances in damp conditions and, again, beware of creating a spark or applying excessive heat in the vicinity of fuel or fuel vapour. Also ensure that the appliances meet the relevant national safety standards.

Ignition HT voltage

A severe electric shock can result from touching certain parts of the ignition system, such as the HT leads, when the engine is running or being cranked, particularly if components are damp or the insulation is defective. Where an electronic ignition system is fitted, the HT voltage is much higher and could prove fatal.

Routine maintenance

The maintenance intervals recommended are those specified by the manufacturer. They are necessarily something of a compromise, since no two vehicles operate under identical conditions. The DIY mechanic, who does not have labour costs to consider, may wish to shorten the service intervals. Experience will show whether this is necessary.

Where the vehicle is used under severe operating conditions (extremes of heat or cold, dusty conditions, or mainly stop-start driving), more frequent oil changes may be desirable. If in doubt consult your dealer.

With old or high-mileage vehicles, more frequent inspection of components and systems is advisable, particularly in safety-related areas.

View of engine compartment (1.3)

1	Wiper motor	6	Washer fluid reservoir	11	Oil filler cap
2	Heater blower motor	7	Fuel pump	12	Distributor
3	Suspension strut turret	8	Alternator	13	Battery
4	Air cleaner	9	Cooling system expansion bottle	14	Radiator electric cooling fan
5	Brake servo/master cylinder	10	Intake air temperature valve vacuum unit	15	Bonnet support strut

View from underside of front end (1.3)

1 Suspension control arm support	5 Driveshaft inboard joint	8 Sump	11 Brake hose
2 Exhaust pipe	6 Engine/transmission mounting bracket	9 Radiator	12 Brake pipes
3 Suspension control arm	7 Flywheel housing cover plate	10 Oil filter	13 Fuel pipe
4 Final drive cover plate			14 Anti-roll bar

View from underside of rear end (1.3)

1 Fuel contents sender unit	4 Rear suspension trailing arm	7 Fuel tank filler/breather hoses	10 Brake pipes
2 Fuel tank	5 Rear axle member	8 Spare wheel recess	11 Handbrake cable
3 Exhaust pipe	6 Exhaust silencer	9 Fuel pipe	

18

View of engine
compartment (pre-1987 1.8)

1 Wiper motor
2 Heater blower motor
3 Washer fluid reservoir
4 Cooling system expansion
  bottle
5 Fuel injection system control
  relay
6 Ignition coil
7 Electronic ignition control
  unit
8 Battery
9 Battery negative terminal
10 Radiator cooling fan
11 Distributor
12 Engine oil dipstick
13 Oil filler cap
14 Thermostat housing
15 Air cleaner
16 Airflow sensor
17 Idle mixture bypass screw
18 Suspension strut mounting
19 Alternator
20 Throttle valve housing
21 Throttle valve switch
22 Auxiliary air valve
23 Fuel pressure regulator
24 Brake master cylinder/fluid
   reservoir

19

View from underside of front end (pre-1987 1.8)

1 Suspension control arm support
2 Exhaust pipe
3 Suspension control arm
4 Final drive cover plate
5 Driveshaft inboard joint
6 Sump drain plug
7 Flywheel housing cover plate
8 Brake pipes
9 Fuel pipes
10 Brake hose
11 Anti-roll bar

View from underside of rear end (pre-1987 1.8)

1 Fuel tank
2 Exhaust expansion box
3 Spare wheel recess
4 Fuel level sender unit
5 Anti-roll bar
6 Fuel filler pipe
7 Rear axle member
8 Suspension trailing arm
9 Fuel filter
10 Electric fuel pump and regulator
11 Towing hook
12 Brake pipes
13 Handbrake cable
14 Fuel return pipe
15 Fuel delivery pipe

Weekly, or before a long journey

Engine (Chapter 1)
Check the oil level

Cooling system (Chapter 2)
Check coolant level

Braking system (Chapter 9)
Check the hydraulic fluid level

Suspension (Chapter 10)
Check the tyre pressures (cold) – do not forget the spare

Electrical system (Chapter 12)
Check the operation of all lights, washer systems and horn
Check the battery electrolyte level or state of charge (maintenance-free type)
Check the washer system(s) fluid levels, adding a screen wash such as Turtle Wax High Tech Screen Wash

MODELS UP TO 1982

Every 9000 miles (15 000 km) or 6 months, whichever comes first

Engine (Chapter 1)
Renew the engine oil and filter

Cooling system (Chapter 2)
Check the tension and condition of the drivebelt(s)

Fuel and exhaust systems (Chapter 3)
Check idle speed and mixure adjustments
Clean the fuel pump filter screen (carburettor models)
Check the exhaust system for condition and security
Check the throttle cable adjustment

Ignition system (Chapter 4)
Clean or renew the contact breaker points. Check the dwell angle (early 1.3 models)
Lubricate the distributor (early 1.3 models)
Clean and regap the spark plugs
Check the ignition timing

Transmission (Chapter 6)
Check the oil/fluid level

Driveshafts (Chapter 7)
Check the CV joints and bellows for condition

Braking system (Chapter 9)
Check the pads/shoes and discs/drums for wear
Check the hydraulic pipes and hoses for condition and security
Check the rear brake adjustment

Suspension and steering (Chapters 8 and 10)
Check the tyres for wear and damage
Check the front wheel alignment
Check all components for condition and security

Every 18 000 miles (30 000 km) or 12 months, whichever comes first

In addition to, or instead of, the earlier service tasks

Cooling system (Chapter 2)
Check the coolant antifreeze concentration

Fuel and exhaust systems (Chapter 3)
Renew the fuel filter (fuel injection models)

Ignition system (Chapter 4)
Renew the spark plugs

Clutch (Chapter 5)
Check the pedal adjustment

Braking system (Chapter 9)
Renew the hydraulic fluid (annually, regardless of mileage)
Check the handbrake adjustment
Check the handbrake cable linkages for condition

Suspension and steering (Chapters 8 and 10)
Check the rear wheel bearings adjustment
Check the power steering fluid level

Electrical system (Chapter 12)
Check the headlamp alignment

Every 27 000 miles (45 000 km) or 18 months, whichever comes first

In addition to, or instead of, the earlier service tasks

Fuel and exhaust systems (Chapter 3)
Renew the air cleaner element
Renew the fuel pump filter screen (carburettor models)

Every 2 years (regardless of mileage)

Cooling system (Chapter 2)
Renew the coolant

Every 54 000 miles (90 000 km) or 3 years, whichever comes first

In addition to, or instead of, the earlier service tasks

Transmission (Chapter 6)
Renew the automatic transmission fluid and screen

MODELS FROM 1983

Every 9000 miles (15 000 km) or 6 months, whichever comes first

Engine (Chapter 1)
Renew the engine oil and filter

Every 9000 miles (15 000 km) or 12 months, whichever comes first

In addition to the earlier service tasks

Cooling system (Chapter 2)
Check the coolant antifreeze concentration
Check the tension and condition of the drivebelt(s)

Fuel and exhaust systems (Chapter 3)
Check the idle speed and mixture adjustments (not fuel injection models from 1987)
Check the exhaust system for condition and security
Check the throttle cable adjustment

Ignition system (Chapter 4)
Clean and regap, or renew, the spark plugs

Clutch (Chapter 5)
Check the pedal adjustment

Transmission (Chapter 6)
Check the oil/fluid level

Driveshafts (Chapter 7)
Check the CV joints and bellows for condition

Braking system (Chapter 9)
Check the pads/shoes and discs/drums for wear
Check the hydraulic pipes and hoses for condition and security
Renew the hydraulic fluid (annually, regardless of mileage)
Check the rear brake adjustment (if applicable)

Suspension and steering (Chapters 8 and 10)
Check the tyres for wear and damage
Check all components for condition and security
Check the front wheel alignment

Electrical system (Chapter 12)
Check the headlamp alignment

General
Lubricate all controls and hinges

Every 18 000 miles (30 000 km) or 2 years, whichever comes first

In addition to, or instead of, the earlier service tasks

Cooling system (Chapter 2)
Renew the coolant (every 2 years, regardless of mileage)

Fuel and exhaust systems (Chapter 3)
Renew the air cleaner element
Renew the fuel filter (fuel injection models) (every 2 years, regardless of mileage)
Renew the carburettor fuel inlet strainer (if applicable)

Braking system (Chapter 9)
Check the handbrake adjustment
Check the handbrake cable linkages for condition

Suspension and steering (Chapters 8 and 10)
Check the power steering fluid level

Every 36 000 miles (60 000 km) or 4 years, whichever comes first

In addition to, or instead of, the earlier service tasks

Transmission (Chapter 6)
Renew the automatic transmission fluid and screen

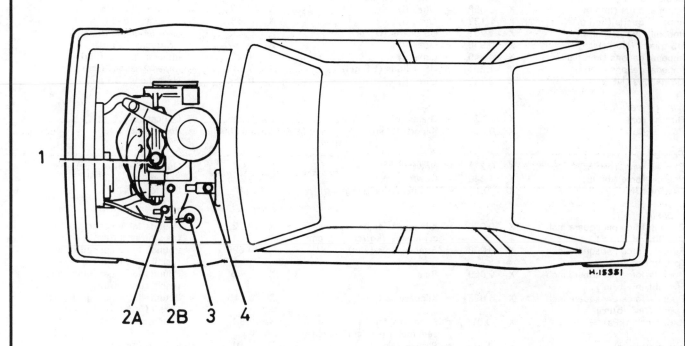

Recommended lubricants and fluids

Component or system	Lubricant type/specification	Duckhams recommendation
1 Engine	Multigrade engine oil, viscosity range SAE 10W/40 to 20W/50, to API SF/CC or SE/CC	Duckhams QXR, Hypergrade or 10W/40 Motor Oil
2A Manual transmission	Gear oil, viscosity SAE 80EP, or GM gear oil 90 188 629	Duckhams Hypoid 80, or Hypoid 75W/90S
2B Automatic transmission	Dexron II type ATF	Duckhams D-Matic
3 Cooling system	Ethylene glycol based antifreeze	Duckhams Universal Antifreeze and Summer Coolant
4 Brake hydraulic system	Hydraulic fluid to SAE J1703F or DOT 4	Duckhams Universal Brake and Clutch Fluid
Power assisted steering	Dexron II type ATF	Duckhams D-Matic

Conversion factors

Length (distance)

	X			X		
Inches (in)	X	25.4	= Millimetres (mm)	X	0.0394	= Inches (in)
Feet (ft)	X	0.305	= Metres (m)	X	3.281	= Feet (ft)
Miles	X	1.609	= Kilometres (km)	X	0.621	= Miles

Volume (capacity)

	X			X		
Cubic inches (cu in; in³)	X	16.387	= Cubic centimetres (cc; cm³)	X	0.061	= Cubic inches (cu in; in³)
Imperial pints (Imp pt)	X	0.568	= Litres (l)	X	1.76	= Imperial pints (Imp pt)
Imperial quarts (Imp qt)	X	1.137	= Litres (l)	X	0.88	= Imperial quarts (Imp qt)
Imperial quarts (Imp qt)	X	1.201	= US quarts (US qt)	X	0.833	= Imperial quarts (Imp qt)
US quarts (US qt)	X	0.946	= Litres (l)	X	1.057	= US quarts (US qt)
Imperial gallons (Imp gal)	X	4.546	= Litres (l)	X	0.22	= Imperial gallons (Imp gal)
Imperial gallons (Imp gal)	X	1.201	= US gallons (US gal)	X	0.833	= Imperial gallons (Imp gal)
US gallons (US gal)	X	3.785	= Litres (l)	X	0.264	= US gallons (US gal)

Mass (weight)

	X			X		
Ounces (oz)	X	28.35	= Grams (g)	X	0.035	= Ounces (oz)
Pounds (lb)	X	0.454	= Kilograms (kg)	X	2.205	= Pounds (lb)

Force

	X			X		
Ounces-force (ozf; oz)	X	0.278	= Newtons (N)	X	3.6	= Ounces-force (ozf; oz)
Pounds-force (lbf; lb)	X	4.448	= Newtons (N)	X	0.225	= Pounds-force (lbf; lb)
Newtons (N)	X	0.1	= Kilograms-force (kgf; kg)	X	9.81	= Newtons (N)

Pressure

	X			X		
Pounds-force per square inch (psi; lbf/in²; lb/in²)	X	0.070	= Kilograms-force per square centimetre (kgf/cm²; kg/cm²)	X	14.223	= Pounds-force per square inch (psi; lbf/in²; lb/in²)
Pounds-force per square inch (psi; lbf/in²; lb/in²)	X	0.068	= Atmospheres (atm)	X	14.696	= Pounds-force per square inch (psi; lbf/in²; lb/in²)
Pounds-force per square inch (psi; lbf/in²; lb/in²)	X	0.069	= Bars	X	14.5	= Pounds-force per square inch (psi; lbf/in²; lb/in²)
Pounds-force per square inch (psi; lbf/in²; lb/in²)	X	6.895	= Kilopascals (kPa)	X	0.145	= Pounds-force per square inch (psi; lbf/in²; lb/in²)
Kilopascals (kPa)	X	0.01	= Kilograms-force per square centimetre (kgf/cm²; kg/cm²)	X	98.1	= Kilopascals (kPa)
Millibar (mbar)	X	100	= Pascals (Pa)	X	0.01	= Millibar (mbar)
Millibar (mbar)	X	0.0145	= Pounds-force per square inch (psi; lbf/in²; lb/in²)	X	68.947	= Millibar (mbar)
Millibar (mbar)	X	0.75	= Millimetres of mercury (mmHg)	X	1.333	= Millibar (mbar)
Millibar (mbar)	X	0.401	= Inches of water (inH₂O)	X	2.491	= Millibar (mbar)
Millimetres of mercury (mmHg)	X	0.535	= Inches of water (inH₂O)	X	1.868	= Millimetres of mercury (mmHg)
Inches of water (inH₂O)	X	0.036	= Pounds-force per square inch (psi; lbf/in²; lb/in²)	X	27.68	= Inches of water (inH₂O)

Torque (moment of force)

	X			X		
Pounds-force inches (lbf in; lb in)	X	1.152	= Kilograms-force centimetre (kgf cm; kg cm)	X	0.868	= Pounds-force inches (lbf in; lb in)
Pounds-force inches (lbf in; lb in)	X	0.113	= Newton metres (Nm)	X	8.85	= Pounds-force inches (lbf in; lb in)
Pounds-force inches (lbf in; lb in)	X	0.083	= Pounds-force feet (lbf ft; lb ft)	X	12	= Pounds-force inches (lbf in; lb in)
Pounds-force feet (lbf ft; lb ft)	X	0.138	= Kilograms-force metres (kgf m; kg m)	X	7.233	= Pounds-force feet (lbf ft; lb ft)
Pounds-force feet (lbf ft; lb ft)	X	1.356	= Newton metres (Nm)	X	0.738	= Pounds-force feet (lbf ft; lb ft)
Newton metres (Nm)	X	0.102	= Kilograms-force metres (kgf m; kg m)	X	9.804	= Newton metres (Nm)

Power

	X			X		
Horsepower (hp)	X	745.7	= Watts (W)	X	0.0013	= Horsepower (hp)

Velocity (speed)

	X			X		
Miles per hour (miles/hr; mph)	X	1.609	= Kilometres per hour (km/hr; kph)	X	0.621	= Miles per hour (miles/hr; mph)

Fuel consumption*

	X			X		
Miles per gallon, Imperial (mpg)	X	0.354	= Kilometres per litre (km/l)	X	2.825	= Miles per gallon, Imperial (mpg)
Miles per gallon, US (mpg)	X	0.425	= Kilometres per litre (km/l)	X	2.352	= Miles per gallon, US (mpg)

Temperature

Degrees Fahrenheit = (°C x 1.8) + 32   Degrees Celsius (Degrees Centigrade; °C) = (°F - 32) x 0.56

*It is common practice to convert from miles per gallon (mpg) to litres/100 kilometres (l/100km), where mpg (Imperial) x l/100 km = 282 and mpg (US) x l/100 km = 235

Fault diagnosis

Introduction

The vehicle owner who does his or her own maintenance according to the recommended schedules should not have to use this section of the manual very often. Modern component reliability is such that, provided those items subject to wear or deterioration are inspected or renewed at the specified intervals, sudden failure is comparatively rare. Faults do not usually just happen as a result of sudden failure, but develop over a period of time. Major mechanical failures in particular are usually preceded by characteristic symptoms over hundreds or even thousands of miles. Those components which do occasionally fail without warning are often small and easily carried in the vehicle.

With any fault finding, the first step is to decide where to begin investigations. Sometimes this is obvious, but on other occasions a little detective work will be necessary. The owner who makes half a dozen haphazard adjustments or replacements may be successful in curing a fault (or its symptoms), but he will be none the wiser if the fault recurs and he may well have spent more time and money than was necessary. A calm and logical approach will be found to be more satisfactory in the long run. Always take into account any warning signs or abnormalities that may have been noticed in the period preceding the fault – power loss, high or low gauge readings, unusual noises or smells, etc – and remember that failure of components such as fuses or spark plugs may only be pointers to some underlying fault.

The pages which follow here are intended to help in cases of failure to start or breakdown on the road. There is also a Fault Diagnosis Section at the end of each Chapter which should be consulted if the preliminary checks prove unfruitful. Whatever the fault, certain basic principles apply. These are as follows:

Verify the fault. This is simply a matter of being sure that you know what the symptoms are before starting work. This is particularly important if you are investigating a fault for someone else who may not have described it very accurately.

Don't overlook the obvious. For example, if the vehicle won't start, is there petrol in the tank? (Don't take anyone else's word on this particular point, and don't trust the fuel gauge either!) If an electrical fault is indicated, look for loose or broken wires before digging out the test gear.

Cure the disease, not the symptom. Substituting a flat battery with a fully charged one will get you off the hard shoulder, but if the underlying cause is not attended to, the new battery will go the same way. Similarly, changing oil-fouled spark plugs for a new set will get you moving again, but remember that the reason for the fouling (if it wasn't simply an incorrect grade of plug) will have to be established and corrected.

Don't take anything for granted. Particularly, don't forget that a 'new' component may itself be defective (especially if it's been rattling round in the boot for months), and don't leave components out of a fault diagnosis sequence just because they are new or recently fitted. When you do finally diagnose a difficult fault, you'll probably realise that all the evidence was there from the start.

Electrical faults

Electrical faults can be more puzzling than straightforward mechanical failures, but they are no less susceptible to logical analysis if the basic principles of operation are understood. Vehicle electrical wiring exists in extremely unfavourable conditions – heat, vibration and chemical attack – and the first things to look for are loose or corroded connections and broken or chafed wires, especially where the wires pass through holes in the bodywork or are subject to vibration.

All metal-bodied vehicles in current production have one pole of the battery 'earthed', ie connected to the vehicle bodywork, and in nearly all modern vehicles it is the negative (–) terminal. The various electrical components – motors, bulb holders etc – are also connected to earth, either by means of a lead or directly by their mountings. Electric current flows through the component and then back to the battery via the bodywork. If the component mounting is loose or corroded, or if a good path back to the battery is not available, the circuit will be incomplete and malfunction will result. The engine and/or gearbox are also earthed by means of flexible metal straps to the body or subframe; if these straps are loose or missing, starter motor, generator and ignition trouble may result.

Assuming the earth return to be satisfactory, electrical faults will be due either to component malfunction or to defects in the current supply. Individual components are dealt with in Chapter 12. If supply wires are broken or cracked internally this results in an open-circuit, and the easiest way to check for this is to bypass the suspect wire temporarily with a length of wire having a crocodile clip or suitable connector at each end. Alternatively, a 12V test lamp can be used to verify the presence of supply voltage at various points along the wire and the break can be thus isolated.

If a bare portion of a live wire touches the bodywork or other earthed metal part, the electricity will take the low-resistance path thus formed back to the battery: this is known as a short-circuit. Hopefully a short-circuit will blow a fuse, but otherwise it may cause burning of the insulation (and possibly further short-circuits) or even a fire. This is why it is inadvisable to bypass persistently blowing fuses with silver foil or wire.

Spares and tool kit

Most vehicles are supplied only with sufficient tools for wheel changing; the *Maintenance and minor repair* tool kit detailed in *Tools*

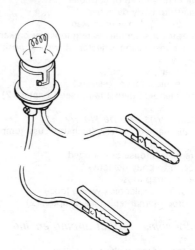

Simple test lamp is useful for tracing electrical faults

and working facilities, with the addition of a hammer, is probably sufficient for those repairs that most motorists would consider attempting at the roadside. In addition a few items which can be fitted without too much trouble in the event of a breakdown should be carried. Experience and available space will modify the list below, but the following may save having to call on professional assistance:

> *Spark plugs, clean and correctly gapped*
> *HT lead and plug cap – long enough to reach the plug furthest from the distributor*
> *Distributor rotor, condenser and contact breaker points (1.3 before Sept 1982)*
> *Drivebelt(s) – emergency type may suffice*
> *Spare fuses*
> *Set of principal light bulbs*
> *Tin of radiator sealer and hose bandage*
> *Exhaust bandage*
> *Roll of insulating tape*
> *Length of soft iron wire*
> *Length of electrical flex*
> *Torch or inspection lamp (can double as test lamp)*
> *Battery jump leads*
> *Tow-rope*
> *Ignition water dispersant aerosol*
> *Litre of engine oil*
> *Sealed can of hydraulic fluid*
> *Emergency windscreen (only required on 1.3 models)*
> *Worm drive clips*

If spare fuel is carried, a can designed for the purpose should be used to minimise risks of leakage and collision damage. A first aid kit and a warning triangle, whilst not at present compulsory in the UK, are obviously sensible items to carry in addition to the above.

When touring abroad it may be advisable to carry additional spares which, even if you cannot fit them yourself, could save having to wait while parts are obtained. The items below may be worth considering:

> *Clutch and throttle cables*
> *Cylinder head gasket*
> *Alternator brushes*
> *Tyre valve core*

One of the motoring organisations will be able to advise on availability of fuel etc in foreign countries.

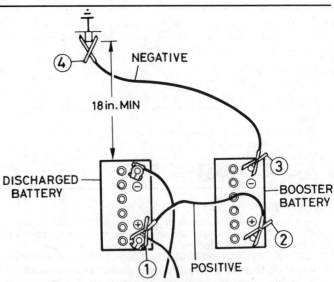

Jump start lead connections for negative earth vehicles – connect leads in order shown

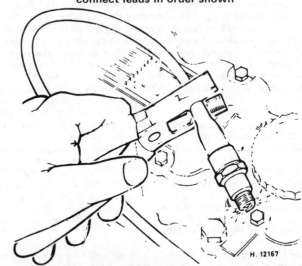

Crank engine and check for a spark. Note use of insulated tool
Use a spare plug – not one from the engine (fire risk)

Engine will not start

Engine fails to turn when starter operated
    Flat battery (recharge, use jump leads, or push start)
    Battery terminals loose or corroded
    Battery earth to body defective
    Engine earth strap loose or broken
    Starter motor (or solenoid) wiring loose or broken
    Automatic transmission selector in wrong position, or inhibitor switch faulty
    Ignition/starter switch faulty
    Major mechanical failure (seizure)
    Starter or solenoid internal fault (see Chapter 12)

Starter motor turns engine slowly
    Partially discharged battery (recharge, use jump leads, or push start)
    Battery terminals loose or corroded
    Battery earth to body defective
    Engine earth strap loose
    Starter motor (or solenoid) wiring loose
    Starter motor internal fault (see Chapter 12)

Starter motor spins without turning engine
    Flat battery
    Starter motor pinion sticking on sleeve
    Flywheel gear teeth damaged or worn
    Starter motor mounting bolts loose

Engine turns normally but fails to start
    Damp or dirty HT leads and distributor cap (crank engine and check for spark) – try moisture dispersant such as Holts Wet Start
    Dirty or incorrectly gapped distributor points (1.3 before Sept 1982)
    No fuel in tank (check for delivery)
    Excessive choke (hot engine) or insufficient choke (cold engine)
    Fouled or incorrectly gapped spark plugs (remove, clean and regap)
    Other ignition system fault (see Chapter 4)
    Other fuel system fault (see Chapter 3)
    Poor compression
    Major mechanical failure (eg camshaft drive)

Engine fires but will not run
    Insufficient choke (cold engine)
    Air leaks at carburettor or inlet manifold
    Fuel starvation (see Chapter 3)
    Ballast resistor defective, or other ignition fault (see Chapter 4)

Engine cuts out and will not restart

Engine cuts out suddenly – ignition fault
    Loose or disconnected LT wires

Wet HT leads or distributor cap (after traversing water splash)
Coil or condenser failure (check for spark) – 1.3 before Sept 1982
Other ignition fault (see Chapter 4)

Engine misfires before cutting out – fuel fault

Fuel tank empty
Fuel pump defective or filter blocked (check for delivery)
Fuel tank filler vent blocked (suction will be evident on releasing cap)
Carburettor needle valve sticking
Carburettor jets blocked (fuel contaminated)
Other fuel system fault (see Chapter 3)

Engine cuts out – other causes

Serious overheating
Major mechanical failure (eg camshaft drive)

Engine overheats

Coolant loss due to internal or external leakage (see Chapter 2)
Thermostat defective
Low oil level
Brakes binding
Radiator clogged externally or internally
Electric cooling fan not operating correctly
Engine waterways clogged
Ignition timing incorrect or automatic advance malfunctioning
Mixture too weak

Note: *Do not add cold water to an overheated engine or damage may result*

Low engine oil pressure

Gauge reads low or warning light illuminated with engine running

Oil level low or incorrect grade
Defective gauge or sender unit

Wire to sender unit earthed
Engine overheating
Oil filter clogged or bypass valve defective
Oil pressure relief valve defective
Oil pick-up strainer clogged
Oil pump worn or mountings loose
Worn main or big-end bearings

Note: *Low oil pressure in a high-mileage engine at tickover is not necessarily a cause for concern. Sudden pressure loss at speed is far more significant. In any event, check the gauge or warning light sender before condemning the engine.*

Engine noises

Pre-ignition (pinking) on acceleration

Incorrect grade of fuel
Ignition timing incorrect
Distributor faulty or worn
Worn or maladjusted carburettor
Excessive carbon build-up in engine

Whistling or wheezing noises

Leaking vacuum hose
Leaking carburettor or manifold gasket
Blowing head gasket

Tapping or rattling

Worn valve gear
Worn timing chain or belt
Broken piston ring (ticking noise)

Knocking or thumping

Unintentional mechanical contact (eg fan blades)
Worn drivebelt
Peripheral component fault (generator, water pump etc)
Worn big-end bearings (regular heavy knocking, perhaps less under load)
Worn main bearings (rumbling and knocking, perhaps worsening under load)
Piston slap (most noticeable when cold)

Carrying a few spares can save you a long walk

Chapter 1 Engine

For modifications, and information applicable to later models, see Supplement at end of manual

Contents

Specifications

General

Type .... Four-cylinder, in-line, water-cooled, single overhead camshaft, transversely mounted

Engine:	Code	Capacity	Bore	Stroke	Compression ratio
1.3 litre	13S	1297 cc	75.0 mm	73.4 mm	9.2:1
1.6 litre	16S	1598 cc	80.0 mm	79.5 mm	9.2:1
1.8 litre	18E	1796 cc	84.8 mm	79.5 mm	9.5:1

Firing order .... 1–3–4–2 (No 1 cylinder at timing belt cover end)

Cylinder block (crankcase)

Material	Cast-iron
Maximum cylinder bore out of round	0.013 mm
Maximum permissible taper	0.013 mm
Maximum rebore oversize	0.5 mm

Crankshaft

	1.3	**1.6 and 1.8**
Number of main bearings	5	5
Main bearing journal diameter	54.972 to 54.985 mm	57.982 to 57.995 mm
Crankpin diameter	42.971 to 42.987 mm	48.971 to 48.987 mm
Undersizes	0.25 and 0.50 mm	0.25 and 0.50 mm
Crankshaft endfloat	0.1 to 2.0 mm	0.07 to 0.3 mm
Main bearing running clearance	0.025 to 0.05 mm	0.015 to 0.04 mm
Big-end running clearance	0.019 to 0.071 mm	0.019 to 0.063 mm
Big-end side-play	0.11 to 0.24 mm	0.07 to 0.24 mm
Bearing shell identification:	**Top (all engines)**	**Bottom (all engines)**
Main bearings, standard	Brown	Green
Main bearings, 0.25 mm undersize	Brown/blue	Green/blue
Main bearings, 0.5 mm undersize	Brown/white	Green/white
Big-end bearings, standard	None	None
Big-end bearings, 0.25 mm undersize	Blue	Blue
Big-end bearings, 0.5 mm undersize	White	White

Camshaft

Identification code:		
1.3	B	
1.6	A	
1.8	B	
Endfloat	0.09 to 0.21 mm	
Camshaft journal diameters:	**1.3**	**1.6 and 1.8**
No 1	39.435 to 39.450 mm	42.455 to 42.470 mm
No 2	39.685 to 39.700 mm	42.705 to 42.720 mm
No 3	39.935 to 39.950 mm	42.955 to 42.970 mm
No 4	40.125 to 40.200 mm	43.205 to 43.220 mm
No 5	40.435 to 40.450 mm	43.455 to 43.470 mm
Camshaft bearing (direct in housing) diameters:		
No 1	39.500 to 39.525 mm	42.500 to 42.525 mm
No 2	39.750 to 39.775 mm	42.750 to 42.775 mm
No 3	40.000 to 40.025 mm	43.000 to 43.025 mm
No 4	40.250 to 40.275 mm	43.250 to 43.275 mm
No 5	40.550 to 40.525 mm	43.500 to 43.525 mm

Pistons and rings

Type	Alloy, recessed head	
Number of piston rings	2 compression, 1 oil control	
Ring end gap:		
Compression	0.3 to 0.5 mm	
Oil control (rail)	0.40 to 1.40 mm	
Ring gap offset (to gap of adjacent ring)	180°	
Gudgeon pin-to-piston clearance:		
1.3	0.007 to 0.010 mm	
1.6 and 1.8	0.011 to 0.014 mm	
Piston grades – 1.3:	**Diameter (mm)**	**Marking**
Production grade 1	74.93	5
	74.94	6
	74.95	7
	74.96	8
Production grade 2	74.97	99
	74.98	00
	74.99	01
	75.00	02
	75.01	03
	75.02	04
Production grade 3	75.03	05
	75.04	06
	75.05	07
	75.06	08
Production grade 4	75.07	09
	75.08	1
Oversize (0.5 mm)	75.45	7 + 0.5
	75.46	8 + 0.5
	75.47	9 + 0.5
	75.48	0 + 0.5

Piston grades – 1.6:

Production grade 1	79.935 to 79.945	5
	79.945 to 79.955	6
	79.955 to 79.965	7
	79.965 to 79.975	8
Production grade 2	79.975 to 79.985	99
	79.985 to 79.995	00
	79.995 to 80.005	01
	80.005 to 80.015	02
Production grade 3	80.015 to 80.025	03
	80.025 to 80.035	04
	80.035 to 80.045	05
	80.045 to 80.055	06
Production grade 4	80.055 to 80.065	07
	80.065 to 80.075	08
	80.075 to 80.085	09
	80.085 to 80.095	1
Oversize (0.5 mm)	80.455 to 80.465	7 + 0.5
	80.465 to 80.475	8 + 0.5
	80.475 to 80.485	9 + 0.5
	80.485 to 80.495	0 + 0.5

Piston grades – 1.8:

Production grade 1	84.735 to 84.745	5
	84.745 to 84.755	6
	84.755 to 84.765	7
	84.765 to 84.775	8
Production grade 2	84.775 to 84.785	99
	84.785 to 84.795	00
	84.795 to 84.805	01
	84.805 to 84.815	02
Production grade 3	84.815 to 84.825	03
	84.825 to 84.835	04
	84.835 to 84.845	05
	84.845 to 84.855	06
Production grade 4	84.855 to 84.865	07
	84.865 to 84.875	08
	84.875 to 84.885	09
	84.885 to 84.895	1
Oversize (0.5 mm)	85.255 to 85.265	7 + 0.5
	85.265 to 85.275	8 + 0.5
	85.275 to 85.285	9 + 0.5
	85.285 to 85.295	0 + 0.5

Piston-to-bore clearance:
New engine .... 0.02 mm
After rebore:
  1.3 .... 0.01 to 0.03 mm
  1.6 and 1.8 .... 0.02 to 0.04 mm

Cylinder head

	1.3	1.6 and 1.8
Material	Light alloy	Light alloy
Maximum permissible distortion of sealing face	0.025 mm	0.025 mm
Overall height of cylinder head	95.9 to 96.1 mm	95.75 to 96.25 mm
Valve seat width:		
Inlet	1.3 to 1.4 mm	1.3 to 1.4 mm
Exhaust	1.7 to 1.8 mm	1.7 to 1.8 mm

Valves

	1.3	1.6 and 1.8
Valve clearance	Automatic by hydraulic valve lifters (cam followers)	
Valve stem-to-guide clearance:		
Inlet	0.02 to 0.05 mm	0.015 to 0.042 mm
Exhaust	0.04 to 0.07 mm	0.03 to 0.06 mm
Valve seat angle	44°	44°
Valve guide installed height	80.85 to 81.25 mm	80.95 to 81.85 mm
Valve stem diameter:		
Inlet	7.000 to 7.010 mm	7.795 to 7.985 mm
Exhaust	6.980 to 6.990 mm	7.957 to 7.970 mm
Oversizes	0.075, 0.150, 0.250 mm	0.075, 0.150, 0.250 mm
Valve guide bore diameter	7.030 to 7.050 mm	8.000 to 8.017 mm

Flywheel

Maximum thickness reduction at driven plate and pressure plate cover
contact surfaces .... 0.3 mm

Lubrication

Oil type/specification	Multigrade engine oil, viscosity range SAE 10W/40 to 20W/50, to API SF/CC or SE/CC (Duckhams QXR, Hypergrade, or 10W/40 Motor Oil)
Oil pump:	
Tooth play (gear to gear)	0.1 to 0.2 mm
Gear-to-housing clearance (endfloat):	
1.3	0.08 to 0.15 mm
1.6 and 1.8	0.03 to 0.10 mm
Oil pressure at idle (engine at operating temperature)	1.5 bar (21.75 lbf/in^2)
Oil capacity (with filter change) – approximate:	
1.3	3.00 litres (5.28 pints)
1.6	3.50 litres (6.16 pints)
1.8	3.55 litres (6.25 pints)
Oil filter:	
1.3 (UNF fitting)	Champion G103
All other models	Champion G102

Torque wrench settings

	Nm	lbf ft
Flywheel to crankshaft:		
1.3	60	44
1.6 and 1.8 (in two stages)	50 then +25 to 35°	37 then +25 to 35°
Driveplate to crankshaft	60	44
Main bearing cap bolts:		
1.3, 1.6 and 1.8	65	48
Oil pump mounting bolts	6	4
Oil pump relief valve cap	30	22
Oil filter to engine	15	11
Oil pressure switch	30	22
Oil pump bolts	6	4
Oil drain plug	45	33
Sump pan bolts	5	4
Big-end cap bolts:		
1.3	28	21
1.6 and 1.8 (in two stages)	35 then +45°	26 then +45°
Cylinder head bolts (1.3):		
Stage 1	25	18
Stage 2	Turn bolt through 60°	
Stage 3	Turn bolt through 60°	
Stage 4	Turn bolt through 30°	
Stage 5	Tighten a further 30° after warm up	
Cylinder head bolts (1.6 and 1.8):		
Stage 1	25	18
Stage 2	Turn bolt through 60°	
Stage 3	Turn bolt through 60°	
Stage 4	Turn bolt through 60°	
Stage 5	Tighten a further 30° after warm up	
Camshaft sprocket bolt	45	33
Crankshaft pulley bolt:		
1.3	55	41
1.6 and 1.8 (fillister type)	20	15
Crankshaft sprocket bolt (1.6 and 1.8):		
Stage 1	130	96
Stage 2	Tighten a further 40° to 50°	Tighten a further 40° to 50°
Starter motor bolts:		
1.3	25	18
1.6 and 1.8	45	33
Manifold nuts and bolts:		
1.3	20	15
1.6 and 1.8	22	16
Engine mounting bracket to crankcase	50	37
Engine mounting bracket to transmission	30	22
Engine mountings to bodyframe	40	30
Alternator bracket to block	40	30
Fuel pump to camshaft housing	18	13
Water pump to cylinder block:		
1.3	8	6
1.6 and 1.8	25	18

1 General description

The engine is of four-cylinder, in-line, overhead camshaft type, mounted transversely at the front of the car.

The crankshaft is supported in five shell-type main bearings. Thrustwashers are incorporated in the centre main bearing, to control crankshaft endfloat.

The connecting rods are attached to the crankshaft by horizontally-split shell-type big-end bearings, and to the pistons by gudgeon pins, which are an interference fit in the connecting rod small-end bore. The aluminium alloy pistons are fitted with three piston rings: two compression rings and an oil control ring.

The camshaft is driven by a toothed composite rubber belt from the crankshaft, and operates the valves via rocker arms. The rocker arms are supported at their pivot end by hydraulic self-adjusting valve lifters (tappets) which automatically take up any clearance between the camshaft, rocker arm and valve stems. The inlet and exhaust valves are

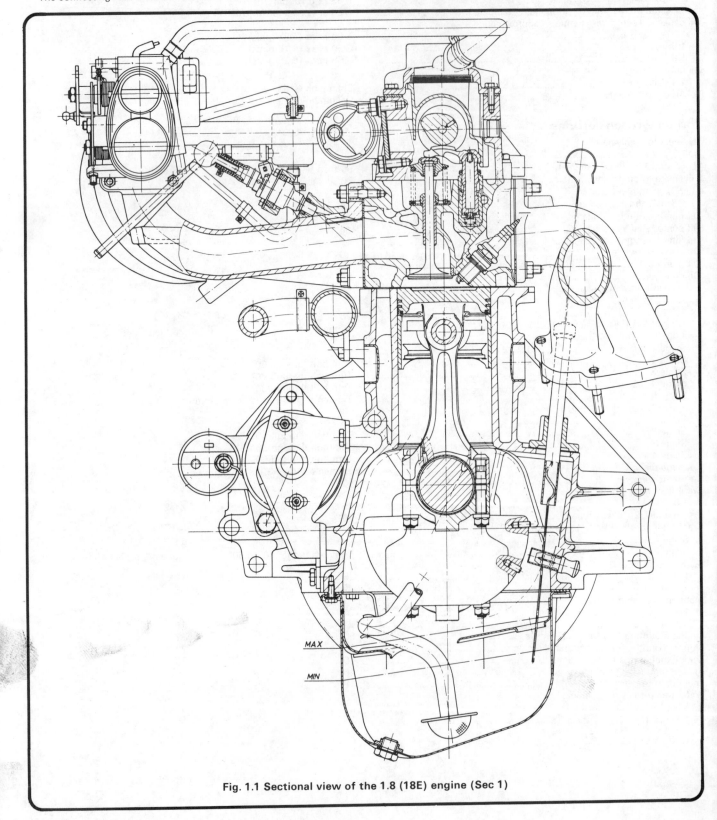

MAX

MIN

Fig. 1.1 Sectional view of the 1.8 (18E) engine (Sec 1)

Are your plugs trying to tell you something?

Normal.
Grey-brown deposits, lightly coated core nose. Plugs ideally suited to engine, and engine in good condition.

Heavy Deposits.
A build up of crusty deposits, light-grey sandy colour in appearance.
Fault: Often caused by worn valve guides, excessive use of upper cylinder lubricant, or idling for long periods.

Lead Glazing.
Plug insulator firing tip appears yellow or green/yellow and shiny in appearance.
Fault: Often caused by incorrect carburation, excessive idling followed by sharp acceleration. Also check ignition timing.

Carbon fouling.
Dry, black, sooty deposits.
Fault: over-rich fuel mixture.
Check: carburettor mixture settings, float level, choke operation, air filter.

Oil fouling.
Wet, oily deposits. Fault: worn bores/piston rings or valve guides; sometimes occurs (temporarily) during running-in period.

Overheating.
Electrodes have glazed appearance, core nose very white – few deposits. Fault: plug overheating. Check: plug value, ignition timing, fuel octane rating (too low) and fuel mixture (too weak).

Electrode damage.
Electrodes burned away; core nose has burned, glazed appearance. Fault: pre-ignition. Check: for correct heat range and as for 'overheating'.

Split core nose.
(May appear initially as a crack). Fault: detonation or wrong gap-setting technique. Check: ignition timing, cooling system, fuel mixture (too weak).

WHY DOUBLE COPPER IS BETTER FOR YOUR ENGINE.

Unique Trapezoidal Copper Cored Earth Electrode — 50% Larger Spark Area — Copper Cored Centre Electrode

Champion Double Copper plugs are the first in the world to have copper core in both centre <u>and</u> earth electrode. This innovative design means that they run cooler by up to 100°C – giving greater efficiency and longer life. These double copper cores transfer heat away from the tip of the plug faster and more efficiently. Therefore, Double Copper runs at cooler temperatures than conventional plugs giving improved acceleration response and high speed performance with no fear of pre-ignition.

TRAPEZOIDAL COPPER CORED EARTH ELECTRODE
NEW TRAPEZOIDAL COPPER CORED EARTH ELECTRODE
CONVENTIONAL SOLID NICKEL ALLOY EARTH ELECTRODE
50% INCREASE IN SPARK AREA

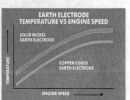

EARTH ELECTRODE TEMPERATURE VS ENGINE SPEED
SOLID NICKEL EARTH ELECTRODE
COPPER CORED EARTH ELECTRODE
TEMPERATURE
ENGINE SPEED

Champion Double Copper plugs also feature a unique trapezoidal earth electrode giving a 50% increase in spark area. This, together with the double copper cores, offers greatly reduced electrode wear, so the spark stays stronger for longer.

 FASTER COLD STARTING

 FOR UNLEADED OR LEADED FUEL

 ELECTRODES UP TO 100°C COOLER

 BETTER ACCELERATION RESPONSE

 LOWER EMISSIONS

 50% BIGGER SPARK AREA

 THE LONGER LIFE PLUG

Plug Tips/Hot and Cold.
Spark plugs must operate within well-defined temperature limits to avoid cold fouling at one extreme and overheating at the other.
Champion and the car manufacturers work out the best plugs for an engine to give optimum performance under all conditions, from freezing cold starts to sustained high speed motorway cruising.
Plugs are often referred to as hot or cold. With Champion, the higher the number on its body, the hotter the plug, and the lower the number the cooler the plug. For the correct plug for your car refer to the specifications at the beginning of this chapter.

Plug Cleaning
Modern plug design and materials mean that Champion no longer recommends periodic plug cleaning. Certainly don't clean your plugs with a wire brush as this can cause metal conductive paths across the nose of the insulator so impairing its performance and resulting in loss of acceleration and reduced m.p.g.
However, if plugs are removed, always carefully clean the area where the plug seats in the cylinder head as grit and dirt can sometimes cause gas leakage.
Also wipe any traces of oil or grease from plug leads as this may lead to arcing.

CHAMPION

DOUBLE COPPER

This photographic sequence shows the steps taken to repair the dent and paintwork damage shown above. In general, the procedure for repairing a hole will be similar; where there are substantial differences, the procedure is clearly described and shown in a separate photograph.

First remove any trim around the dent, then hammer out the dent where access is possible. This will minimise filling. Here, after the large dent has been hammered out, the damaged area is being made slightly concave.

Next, remove all paint from the damaged area by rubbing with coarse abrasive paper or using a power drill fitted with a wire brush or abrasive pad. 'Feather' the edge of the boundary with good paintwork using a finer grade of abrasive paper.

Where there are holes or other damage, the sheet metal should be cut away before proceeding further. The damaged area and any signs of rust should be treated with Turtle Wax Hi-Tech Rust Eater, which will also inhibit further rust formation.

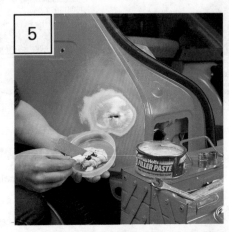

For a large dent or hole mix Holts Body Plus Resin and Hardener according to the manufacturer's instructions and apply around the edge of the repair. Press Glass Fibre Matting over the repair area and leave for 20-30 minutes to harden. Then ...

... brush more Holts Body Plus Resin and Hardener onto the matting and leave to harden. Repeat the sequence with two or three layers of matting, checking that the final layer is lower than the surrounding area. Apply Holts Body Plus Filler Paste as shown in Step 5B.

For a medium dent, mix Holts Body Plus Filler Paste and Hardener according to the manufacturer's instructions and apply it with a flexible applicator. Apply thin layers of filler at 20-minute intervals, until the filler surface is slightly proud of the surrounding bodywork.

For small dents and scratches use Holts No Mix Filler Paste straight from the tube. Apply it according to the instructions in thin layers, using the spatula provided. It will harden in minutes if applied outdoors and may then be used as its own knifing putty.

Use a plane or file for initial shaping. Then, using progressively finer grades of wet-and-dry paper, wrapped round a sanding block, and copious amounts of clean water, rub down the filler until glass smooth. 'Feather' the edges of adjoining paintwork.

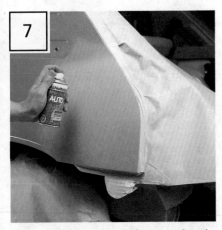

Protect adjoining areas before spraying the whole repair area and at least one inch of the surrounding sound paintwork with Holts Dupli-Color primer.

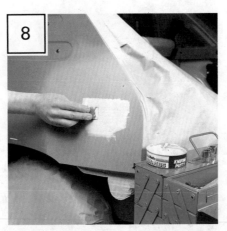

Fill any imperfections in the filler surface with a small amount of Holts Body Plus Knifing Putty. Using plenty of clean water, rub down the surface with a fine grade wet-and-dry paper – 400 grade is recommended – until it is really smooth.

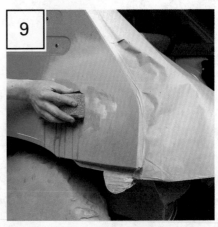

Carefully fill any remaining imperfections with knifing putty before applying the last coat of primer. Then rub down the surface with Holts Body Plus Rubbing Compound to ensure a really smooth surface.

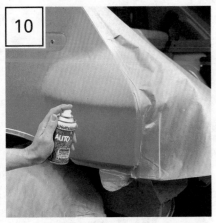

Protect surrounding areas from overspray before applying the topcoat in several thin layers. Agitate Holts Dupli-Color aerosol thoroughly. Start at the repair centre, spraying outwards with a side-to-side motion.

If the exact colour is not available off the shelf, local Holts Professional Spraymatch Centres will custom fill an aerosol to match perfectly.

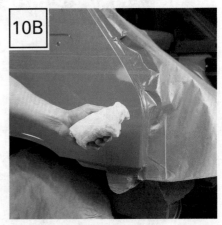

To identify whether a lacquer finish is required, rub a painted unrepaired part of the body with wax and a clean cloth.

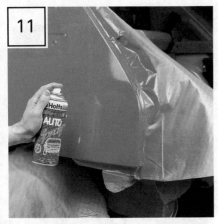

If *no* traces of paint appear on the cloth, spray Holts Dupli-Color clear lacquer over the repaired area to achieve the correct gloss level.

The paint will take about two weeks to harden fully. After this time it can be 'cut' with a mild cutting compound such as Turtle Wax Minute Cut prior to polishing with a final coating of Turtle Wax Extra.

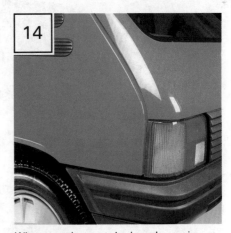

When carrying out bodywork repairs, remember that the quality of the finished job is proportional to the time and effort expended.

HAYNES No1 for DIY

Haynes publish a wide variety of books besides the world famous range of *Haynes Owners Workshop Manuals*. They cover all sorts of DIY jobs. Specialist books such as the *Improve and Modify* series and the *Purchase and DIY Restoration Guides* give you all the information you require to carry out everything from minor modifications to complete restoration on a number of popular cars. In addition there are the publications dealing with specific tasks, such as the *Car Bodywork Repair Manual* and the *In-Car Entertainment Manual*. The *Household DIY* series gives clear step-by-step instructions on how to repair everyday household objects ranging from toasters to washing machines.

Whether it is under the bonnet or around the home there is a Haynes Manual that can help you save money. Available from motor accessory stores and bookshops or direct from the publisher.

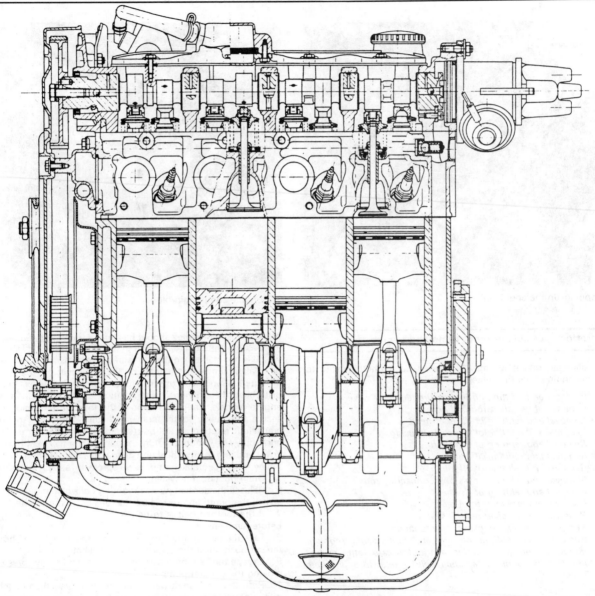

Fig. 1.2 Sectional view of the 1.8 (18E) engine (Sec 1)

each closed by a single spring, and operate in guides pressed into the cylinder head.

Engine lubrication is by a gear-type pump, located in a housing attached to the front of the cylinder block. The oil pump is driven by the crankshaft, while the fuel pump (on carburettor models) and the distributor are driven by the camshaft.

2 Routine maintenance – engine

The following maintenance procedures must be carried out at the specified intervals given at the front of this manual.

1   Check the engine oil level with the vehicle parked on level ground. If possible, allow the engine to cool off before checking the oil level which must be kept between the minimum and maximum markings on the dipstick. Withdraw the dipstick, wipe it clean and fully reinsert it. Withdraw the dipstick and now observe the oil level reading. If required top up the oil level through the filler neck on the rocker cover. Do not overfill (photos).

2   To change the oil, position a suitable container beneath the sump drain plug. Unscrew the plug and allow the oil to drain into the container (photo).

3   Refit and tighten the plug when draining is completed. If the oil filter is to be renewed, do this before topping-up the engine/transmission oil. Use only the correct grade and quantity of oil.

4   Renew the oil filter at the specified intervals, referring to Section 28 for details.

5   Occasionally check the engine and associated components for signs of oil, fuel and coolant leaks and make any repairs as necessary.

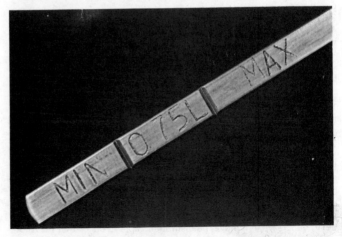

2.1A Engine oil dipstick level markings

2.1B Topping-up the engine oil

2.2 Engine sump drain plug

3 Operations possible without removing engine

The following operations may be carried out without having to remove the engine from the vehicle:

    (a) *Removal and refitting of oil pressure regulator valve*
    (b) *Renewal of camshaft toothed belt*
    (c) *Removal and refitting of cylinder head*
    (d) *Removal and refitting of camshaft housing*
    (e) *Removal and refitting of camshaft*
    (f) *Removal and refitting of sump*
    (g) *Removal and refitting of oil pump*
    (h) *Removal and refitting of pistons/connecting rods*
    (j) *Removal and refitting of flywheel*
    (k) *Renewal of crankshaft front oil seal*
    (l) *Renewal of crankshaft rear oil seal*
    (m) *Renewal of engine/transmission mountings*
    (n) *Removal and refitting of ancillary components (coolant pump, fuel pump, manifolds, distributor, carburettor or fuel injection components (as applicable) – refer to appropriate Chapters).*

4 Oil pressure regulator valve – removal and refitting

1   From just to the rear of the crankshaft pulley, unscrew the pressure regulator valve plug and extract the spring and plunger.
2   Renew the spring if it is distorted or weak (compare it with a new one if possible).
3   If the plunger is scored, renew it.
4   Clean out the plunger hole and reassemble. Use a new plug sealing washer on 1.3 engines.

5 Camshaft toothed belt – renewal

1   Release the alternator adjustment link and mounting bolts, push the alternator in towards the engine and slip the drivebelt from the pulleys.
2   Unscrew the bolts and remove the timing belt cover. Remove the air cleaner unit for improved access on fuel injection models (Chapter 5).
3   Using a socket spanner on the crankshaft pulley bolt, turn the crankshaft until No 1 piston is rising on its compression stroke. To check that this is the compression stroke, either remove No 1 spark plug and place a finger over the plug hole to feel the compression being generated or remove the distributor cap and check that the rotor is aligned with No 1 spark plug contact in the cap. The notch in the rim

of the crankshaft pulley should be aligned with the timing pointer, and represents ignition timing at the specified degrees BTDC **not** TDC which is not marked on these engines. The camshaft sprocket mark will be in alignment with the mark on the belt cover backplate (photo).
4   On 1.3 engines, unscrew the crankshaft pulley bolt without disturbing the previously set position of the crankshaft. On larger engine models, undo and remove the four fillister head bolts which secure the pulley to the crankshaft drive sprocket. To prevent the crankshaft rotating as the bolt(s) are removed, either engage a gear and apply the handbrake fully, or remove the flywheel housing lower cover and jam the flywheel ring gear with a suitable tool. Withdraw the pulley from the crankshaft or drive sprocket (as applicable) (photo).
5   Drain the cooling system.
6   Release the coolant pump mounting bolts just enough to be able to swivel the pump and to release the tension of the toothed belt.
7   If the toothed belt is to be used again, note its running direction before removing it.
8   Take the belt off the sprockets and fit the new one without moving the set position of the camshaft or crankshaft.
9   Engage the new belt over the sprockets and apply some tension by moving the coolant pump.
10   Refit the crankshaft pulley into position and then check that the pulley notch is still in alignment with the timing pointer and that the camshaft sprocket mark is aligned with the groove in the plate behind it. If not, release the belt tension and readjust the position of the sprockets as necessary.
11   The belt tension should now be adjusted in the following way if the official tool is not available. Partially tighten the clamping screws on the coolant pump and, using the thumb and forefinger, twist the belt through 90°. If, with moderate effort, the belt twists too easily or will not reach the full 90°, increase or decrease the tension as necessary by moving the coolant pump; a hexagon is moulded into the pump to turn it with a spanner. If the belt is overtightened, it will usually be heard to hum when the engine is running. Fully tighten the coolant pump bolts (photos).
12   Remove the crankshaft pulley, then fit the timing belt cover into position.
13   Refit the crankshaft pulley.
14   Refit the alternator drivebelt and adjust the tension as described in Chapter 2.

6 Camshaft front oil seal – renewal (engine in car)

1   The camshaft front oil seal may be renewed without removing the camshaft. Proceed as follows.
2   Remove the camshaft toothed belt, as described in Section 5.
3   Hold the camshaft stationary using a spanner on the flats provided. Unscrew the camshaft sprocket retaining bolt and pull off the sprocket.

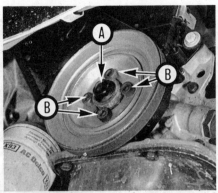

5.3 Camshaft sprocket timing marks

5.4 Crankshaft pulley on a 1.6 engine
A   Torsional damper and crankshaft sprocket retaining bolt
B   Pulley retaining bolts (fillister type)

5.11A Checking the timing belt tension

5.11B Adjusting the timing belt tension

5.11C Tightening the coolant pump bolt after tightening the timing belt

4   Punch or drill a small hole in the centre of the oil seal. Screw in a self-tapping screw and pull on the screw with pliers to extract the seal.
5   Clean out the oil seal seat wth a wooden or plastic scraper. Grease the lips of the new seal and fit it, lips inwards, using a piece of tube and a mallet to drive it home. Take care not to damage the seal lips during fitting; if a protective sleeve is supplied with the new seal, use it.
6   Refit the camshaft sprocket and tighten its securing bolt to the specified torque (see Specifications).
7   Refit and tension the camshaft toothed belt, as described in Section 5. Renew the belt if the old one was contaminated with oil.

7   Camshaft – removal (engine in car)

1   The procedure for camshaft renewal is given in Sections 8 and 9. While it is not strictly necessary to remove the cylinder head, there is no doubt that it is good practice to renew the head gasket since the joint may be disturbed during removal of the camshaft housing.
2   When fitting the new camshaft, coat the cam lobes and followers with molybdenum disulphide paste, or with special cam lube if supplied with the camshaft.
3   When the engine is first started after camshaft renewal, observe the following running-in schedule:

   (a)   1 minute at 2000 rpm
   (b)   1 minute at 1500 rpm
   (c)   1 minute at 3000 rpm
   (d)   1 minute at 2000 rpm

4   Change the engine oil (but not the filter) after 600 miles (1000 km).

8   Cylinder head – removal and refitting

The cylinder head can be removed together with the inlet/exhaust manifolds and associated fuel system components or, if preferred, these items can be detached prior to the removal of the cylinder head itself. The method to be employed should be considered prior to starting and is dependent on the extent to which the cylinder head is to be dismantled once removed from the car. The following text (and photos) describes the removal and refitting of the cylinder head on a carburettor engine model. For more detailed procedures concerning the removal of such items as the fuel injection components, refer to the appropriate Sections in Chapter 3.

1   The cylinder head should only be removed from an engine that has completely cooled off. Removal from a warm engine could cause distortion.
2   Disconnect the battery earth lead.
3   Drain the coolant (Chapter 2) and retain it for further use if required.
4   On carburettor models, remove the air cleaner unit. On fuel injection models disconnect the air intake duct at the throttle housing.
5   Disconnect the fuel supply lines to the fuel pump (carburettor models) or the fuel manifold and pressure regulator (fuel injection models) as applicable. Be prepared for fuel spillage.
6   Disconnect the control cables and electrical leads from the carburettor or throttle housing as applicable.
7   Disconnect the heater hoses and vacuum pipe from the inlet manifold.
8   Disconnect the lead from the temperature sensor on the inlet manifold or throttle housing as applicable (photo).

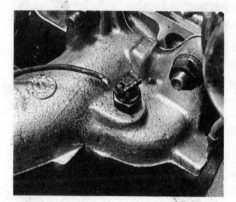

8.8 Coolant temperature switch leads
(1.3)

8.26 Using an angular torque gauge to
measure cylinder head bolt angular rotation

8.28 Spark plug lead clip on camshaft
housing cover

9 Remove the alternator drivebelt (Chapter 2).
10 Remove the cover from the camshaft belt then set No 1 piston on the firing stroke as described in Section 5.
11 Remove the distributor or disconnect the cap and low tension lead harness connector. On later fuel injection models, detach the HT cable at the coil to remove the distributor with the cylinder head.
12 Remove the camshaft cover.
13 Check that the mark on the camshaft sprocket is in alignment with the one on the camshaft housing.
14 Disconnect the exhaust downpipe from the manifold.
15 Release the coolant pump bolts, move the pump to relieve the tension on the toothed belt and slip the belt from the sprockets.
16 Remove the cylinder head bolts in the reverse sequence to that shown in Fig. 1.3; loosening all the bolts first by a 1/4 turn each, and then by 1/2 turn increments, still using the same sequence, until all tension is removed from the bolts. This procedure is important to avoid distortion of the cylinder head or camshaft housing.
17 Lift off the camshaft housing. This is located on dowels. Lift straight upwards.
18 Lift off the cylinder head. If it is stuck, tap it gently with a plastic-faced hammer.
19 Peel away the cylinder head gasket and discard it.
20 Remove the rocker arms and thrust pads from the cylinder head. Withdraw the hydraulic valve lifters and immerse them in a container of clean engine oil to avoid any possibility of them draining. Keep all components in their original order. If full dismantling and valve grinding is to be carried out, refer to Section 30. Check the head for distortion.
21 Clean the cylinder block and the cylinder head free from carbon and old pieces of gasket by careful scraping. Take care not to damage the cylinder head, which is made of light alloy and is easily scored. Cover the coolant passages and other openings with masking tape or rag to prevent dirt and carbon falling in. Mop out oil from the bolt holes; hydraulic pressure could crack the block when the bolts are screwed in if oil is left in the holes.
22 When all is clean, locate a new gasket on the block so that the word OBEN can be read from above.

23 Refit the hydraulic lifters, thrust pads and rocker arms to the cylinder head in their original order. If new hydraulic lifters are being used, initially immerse each one in a container of clean engine oil and compress it (by hand) several times to charge it.
24 With the mating surfaces scrupulously clean, locate the cylinder head on the block so that the positioning dowels engage in their holes.
25 Apply jointing compound to the mating flanges of the cylinder head and the camshaft housing and refit the camshaft housing to the cylinder head (camshaft sprocket marks in alignment).
26 Refit the cylinder head bolts, and tighten them in a spiral pattern, as shown in Fig. 1.3, following the stages given in the Specifications. Note that the bolts are tightened initially to the stage 1 torque wrench setting, and then to an angular measurement in four further stages. The required angular measurement can be marked on a card, and then placed over the bolt as a guide to the movement of the bolt. Alternatively, an angular torque gauge can be used to accurately determine the required movement (photo). Gauges of this type are readily available from motor factors at modest cost, or it may be possible to hire one from larger DIY outlets.
27 Fit and tension the toothed belt as described in Section 5, then refit the belt cover.
28 Fit the camshaft cover, using a new gasket (photo).
29 Fit and tension the alternator drivebelt (Chapter 2).
30 The remainder of the refitting details are a reversal of the removal procedures. On completion, refill the cooling system and bleed it as described in Chapter 2.
31 When the engine is restarted check for signs of fuel and cooling system leaks. Once the engine is warmed up to its normal operating temperature, check and if necessary adjust the idle speed with reference to Chapter 3, and retighten the head bolts (Stage 5).

9 Camshaft housing and camshaft – dismantling and reassembly

1 With the camshaft housing removed from the cylinder head, as described in Section 8, remove any ancillary items such as the fuel pump, distributor, injector rail etc, according to model. Fit an open-ended spanner to the flats on the camshaft. Hold the camshaft from turning and unscrew the camshaft sprocket retaining bolt. Pull off the sprocket.
2 At the opposite end of the camshaft housing, use an Allen key to unscrew the two screws which retain the camshaft lockplate.
3 Withdraw the lockplate.
4 Remove the camshaft carefully out of the distributor end of the camshaft housing taking care not to damage the camshaft bearing surfaces.
5 Before refitting the camshaft, oil the bearings.
6 Fit the camshaft retaining plate with fixing screws and then check the camshaft endfloat. If it exceeds the specified limit, renew the retaining plate.
7 Renew the seal in its retainer (photo).
8 Hold the camshaft from rotating while the sprocket bolt is tightened to specified torque.

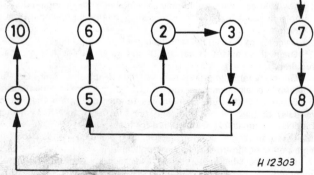

Fig. 1.3 Cylinder head bolt tightening sequence – work in
the spiral pattern shown (Sec 8)

Fig. 1.4 Distributor mounting nuts (1.6) – arrowed (Sec 9)

Fig. 1.5 Camshaft lockplate securing screws – arrowed (Sec 9)

9.7 Camshaft bearing retainer housing oil seal

10.6 Tightening a sump bolt (engine inverted)

10 Sump – removal and refitting

1 Unscrew the drain plug and allow the engine oil to drain from the sump into a container. Refit and tighten the drain plug.
2 On 1.3 engines, unbolt and remove the sump guard plate, where fitted.
3 Disconnect the exhaust downpipes from the manifold and at the ball coupling, and remove the front exhaust section from the vehicle.
4 Unscrew and remove the sump fixing bolts and lower the sump. Scrape off the old gasket and clean the mating surfaces.
5 To refit the sump, apply jointing compound to the seams in the crankcase jointing face and stick the gasket in position after having applied a thin film of compound to both sides of the gasket.
6 Offer up the sump and screw in the fixing bolts, which should have jointing compound applied to their threads (photo).
7 Refit the exhaust pipe, using a new gasket at the manifold/downpipe flange joint.
8 Fill the engine with oil.
9 Refit the guard plate (if applicable).

11 Oil pump – removal and refitting

1 Remove the camshaft toothed belt as described in Section 5. Remove the belt cover backplate.
2 Remove the crankshaft sprocket centre bolt, where applicable. Using two screwdrivers as levers, prise off the belt sprocket from the front end of the crankshaft. Remove the Woodruff key.
3 Remove the sump as described in Section 10.
4 Remove the oil pump pick-up pipe and strainer.
5 Unbolt the oil pump from the cylinder block and remove it.
6 Refer to Section 29 for details of oil pump overhaul.
7 Before refitting the oil pump, steps must be taken to protect the seal lips from damage or turning back on the shoulder at the front end of the crankshaft. To do this, grease the seal lips and then bind tape around the crankshaft to form a gentle taper. Locate a new gasket.
8 Refit the oil pump and unwind and remove the tape.
9 Tighten the bolts to the specified torque and fit the belt sprocket.
10 Refit the pick-up pipe and strainer, the sump and the timing belt and its cover as previously described.

11 Refit the crankshaft pulley and the drivebelt and fill the engine with oil.

12 Pistons/connecting rods – removal and refitting

1   Remove the cylinder head (Section 8).
2   Remove the sump (Section 10).
3   Remove the oil pump pick-up pipe and filter screen.
4   Check that the rods and caps are marked with their position in the crankcase. If they are not, centre-punch them at adjacent points either side of the cap/rod joint. Note to which side of the engine the marks face.
5   Unscrew the big-end cap bolts from the first rod and remove the cap. If the bearing shells are to be used again, tape the cap and shell together.
6   Check the top of the cylinder bores for a wear ridge. If evident, carefully scrape it away with a ridge reaming tool, otherwise as the piston is pushed out of the block, the piston top ring may jam against it.
7   Place the wooden handle of a hammer against the bottom of the connecting rod and push the piston/rod assembly up and out of the cylinder bore.
8   Remove the remaining three assemblies in a similar way. Rotate the crankshaft as necessary to bring the big-end bolts to the most accessible position.
9   If the piston must be separated from its rod, leave this job to your dealer as special tools and a press will be required.
10 Commence reassembly by laying the piston/connecting rod assemblies out in their correct order, complete with bearing shells, ready for refitting into their respective bores in the cylinder block. Make sure that the seats for the shells are absolutely clean and then fit the shells into the seats.
11 Wipe out the bores and oil them. Oil the piston rings liberally. Ensure that the ring gaps are correctly positioned (see Section 34, paragraph 16).
12 Fit a piston ring compressor to the first assembly to be installed.
13 Insert the rod and piston into the top of the bore so that the base of the compressor stands on the block. Check that the rod markings are towards the side of the engine as noted before dismantling. Although there are no marks on the piston crowns, different contours on their undersides can be used to identify which way round they are fitted (photo).
14 Apply the wooden handle of a hammer to the piston crown and tap the assembly into the bore, at the same time releasing the compressor (photo).

15 Guide the big-end of the connecting rod near to the crankpin and then pull it firmly onto the crankpin which should have been oiled liberally.
16 Fit the cap and bolts and tighten to the specified torque.
17 Repeat the operations on the other pistons/rods.
18 Refit the cylinder head, the pick-up pipe and filter and the sump, all as described in earlier Sections of this Chapter.

13 Flywheel – removal and refitting

1   Refer to Chapter 5 and remove the clutch.
2   Although the flywheel bolt holes are offset so that it can only be fitted one way, it will make fitting easier if its relationship to the crankshaft flange is marked before removal.
3   Remove the clutch release bearing and guide sleeve, again referring to Chapter 5.
4   Jam the flywheel starter ring gear and using a ring spanner or socket, unscrew the bolts from the flywheel. As the heads of these bolts are very shallow, if a chamfered type of socket is being used it is best to grind it flat to ensure more positive engagement.
5   Remove the flywheel.
6   Refit by reversing the removal operations, but apply thread locking compound to the bolts.

14 Crankshaft front (pulley end) oil seal – renewal

1   It is possible to renew the oil seal without the need to remove the oil pump.
2   Remove the timing belt as described in Section 5.
3   On 1.6 and 1.8 models, undo the torsional damper/sprocket retaining bolt. Remove the bolt and damper.
4   Using two screwdrivers as levers, prise the sprocket from the crankshaft. Remove the Woodruff key.
5   Punch or drill a small hole in the metal face of the oil seal and screw in a self-tapping screw. Use the head of the screw to lever out the seal.
6   Fill the lips of the new seal with grease and tape the step on the crankshaft as described in Section 11.
7   Using a piece of tubing, tap the oil seal into position. Refit the Woodruff key.
8   Refit the crankshaft sprocket.
9   Refit the timing belt as described in Section 5.

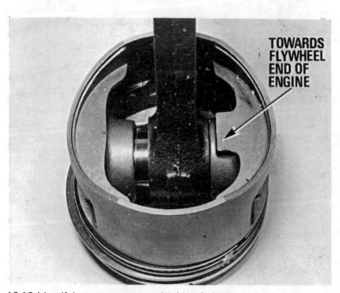

12.13 Identifying contour on underside of piston

12.14 Fitting a piston to cylinder block

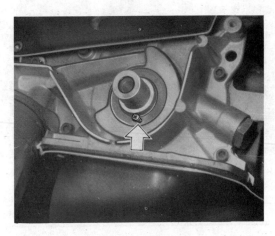

Fig. 1.6 Screw inserted into crankshaft front (pulley end) oil seal – arrowed (Sec 14)

Fig. 1.7 Prising out crankshaft front (pulley end) oil seal (Sec 14)

15 Crankshaft rear (flywheel end) oil seal – renewal

1 Remove the clutch (Chapter 5).
2 Remove the flywheel (Section 13).
3 The defective rear oil seal can now be prised off the crankshaft using a suitably hooked tool.
4 Grease the lips of the new seal before installing it. As there is very little space to tap the seal into position, it is better to use a bolt with a thick nut and a piece of tubing inserted between the outer face of the seal and the clutch release bearing guide. If the nut is then unscrewed to effectively increase the overall length of the bolt, the seal will be pressed into its seat.
5 Refit the flywheel and clutch by reversing the removal operations.

16 Engine/transmission mountings – renewal

1 The engine/transmission flexible mountings can be renewed if they have hardened or been compressed. Take the weight of the engine/transmission on either a hoist or a jack and a wooden block used as an insulator.
2 Unbolt the mounting brackets from the crankcase or transmission casing and the body frame member and separate the brackets from the flexible member.

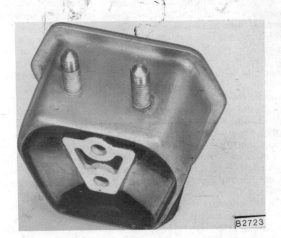

Fig. 1.8 Engine mounting flexible member (Sec 16)

3 Refit the mountings with the new flexible components, but have the bolts only 'nipped up' initially.
4 Once the hoist or jack has been removed, tighten all bolts to the specified torque with the weight of the engine/transmission on the mountings.

17 Engine – methods of removal

1 It is possible to remove the engine on its own or to remove it complete with transmission.
2 It is much easier to remove the engine independently and this should be done if overhaul of the transmission is not required at the same time.
3 Both methods are described in the following Sections.

18 Engine – removal (leaving manual transmission in the vehicle)

1 Disconnect the battery earth lead.
2 With the help of an assistant, unbolt and remove the bonnet (Chapter 11).
3 Remove the air cleaner and preheater ducting (carburettor models). On fuel injection models, disconnect the air intake trunking between the air cleaner unit and the airflow manifold.
4 Drain the cooling system and remove the radiator (Chapter 2).
5 Disconnect the brake servo vacuum hose from the intake manifold.
6 Disconnect the throttle linkage from the carburettor also the choke operating cable or automatic choke electrical lead. On versions equipped with fuel injection disconnect the wiring harness plugs and the brake servo pipe from the throttle housing. Pull off the distributor vacuum pipe and disconnect the fuel pipes noting that the one with the white band is attached to the distribution pipe stub nearest the alternator. Disconnect the crankcase ventilation hose and the throttle housing coolant hoses. Disconnect the injector wiring harness (No 4 nearest clutch bellhousing). Remove the throttle housing/intake manifold assembly after reference to Chapter 3.
7 Disconnect the fuel supply hose to the fuel pump (carburettor models) or the fuel rail manifold. Similarly detach the fuel return pipes and plug them to prevent fuel leakage. Be prepared for fuel spillage.
8 Disconnect the electrical leads from:

(a) The alternator
(b) The starter motor
(c) The distributor

18.8 Engine oil pressure switch lead

18.22 Flywheel housing front cover plate

19.17 Engine-to-underbody earth strap

(d) The coolant temperature sensor
(e) The oil pressure switch (photo)
(f) The inductive pulse sensor (fuel injection models)
(g) The injector nozzles

Unclip and move the leads out of the way.

9   Raise and support the front end of the vehicle securely or position it over an inspection pit.

10 Disconnect the exhaust downpipe from the manifold, also disconnect the pipe at the spring-loaded ball coupling.

11 Unscrew the threaded plug from the transmission casing end cover.

12 Remove the retaining circlip now exposed.

13 A screw will now be observed which has a splined recess in its head. A twelve-point splined key will be required to unscrew it. Accessory shops can supply a socket adaptor for this purpose, or sometimes an Allen key will do the job.

14 Unscrew and remove the screw.

15 As described in more detail in Chapter 5, the input shaft can be slid out of engagement with the clutch driven plate. To do this, the vehicle makers supply a special tool (KM449-1 and 22-1), but a substitute can be used by borrowing one of the four bolts which secure the gearchange mechanism cover to the top of the transmission casing. Screw this bolt into the end of the input shaft. Grip the head of the bolt and pull the shaft out of engagement with the splined hub of the clutch driven plate. Don't forget to refit the bolt to the gearchange mechanism cover. The foregoing substitute method of withdrawing the input shaft may not always be possible with 5-speed transmissions as the shaft is often very tight requiring the use of the special tool or even a slide hammer.

16 Connect a hoist to the engine and just take its weight. Support the transmission on a jack.

17 Remove the alternator and its bracket in order to provide access to the right rear engine mounting bracket.

18 Disconnect the right front engine mounting bracket from both the engine and the flexible member of the mounting.

19 Remove the right rear engine mounting bracket from both the engine and the flexible member of the mounting. This engine bracket incorporates the alternator mounting lugs.

20 Unbolt and remove the starter motor.

21 On 1.6 and 1.8 engines remove the pulley from the front end of the crankshaft (four bolts). The engine will have to be locked in order to unscrew these four bolts. In order to do this, jam the starter ring gear by inserting a suitable lever into the starter motor aperture.

22 Unbolt and remove the cover plate from the bottom of the flywheel housing. This is the plate which faces towards the timing belt end of the engine (photo).

23 Support the transmission on a jack.

24 Unscrew all the engine to transmission connecting bolts from the flywheel housing flange. Note the clips for the starter motor and clutch cables held by the two upper bolts.

25 Disconnect the engine earth strap.

26 Pull the engine from the transmission just enough to clear the positioning dowels, turn the unit slightly so that the timing belt cover moves towards the engine compartment rear bulkhead.

27 Lift the engine straight up, taking care not to damage adjacent components and remove it from the engine compartment.

19 Engine – removal (complete with manual transmission)

1   Proceed as described in paragraphs 1 to 8 inclusive in Section 18, then proceed as follows.

2   Disconnect the gearchange rod from the transmission (Chapter 6).

3   Disconnect the clutch operating cable.

4   Disconnect the speedometer cable from the transmission, also the reverse lamp switch leads.

5   The front end of the vehicle should now be raised and safely supported to provide sufficient clearance under the front to be able to withdraw the engine transmission once it has been lowered to the floor (see paragraph 22).

6   Connect a suitable hoist to the engine and just take the weight of the engine and transmission.

7   Disconnect the exhaust downpipe from the manifold, also disconnect the pipe at its spring-loaded balljoint coupling.

8   Mark the fitted position of the front left-hand roadwheel on its hub. This is necessary to prevent altering the wheel balance which will have been carried out on the car during production. Marking can be done by applying a dab of paint to one wheel bolt hole and to the corresponding bolt hole on the hub.

9   Remove the left-hand front roadwheel.

10 Remove the nut lock or split pin from the driveshaft hub castellated nut and unscrew the nut. To prevent the hub from rotating, use a length of flat steel as a lever, either bolting it to the hub after having drilled two holes, or simply by screwing in two roadwheel bolts and passing the lever between them. Take care not to damage the threads of the roadwheel bolts.

11 The suspension control arm and support must now be disconnected as described in Chapter 10.

12 Make sure that the body is well supported under the jacking points with the suspension hanging free before starting operations.

13 Press the driveshaft from the hub. This can usually be done using hand pressure. If tight, use a plastic-faced hammer or engage a two or three-legged puller and use its centre screw as a press.

14 Release the left-hand driveshaft from the transmission as described in Chapter 7, then pull the hub/stub axle carrier with suspension lower arm outwards until the shaft can be removed from the vehicle.

15 Unbolt the right rear engine mounting bracket from its flexible member.

16 Unbolt the left rear mounting bracket from its flexible member.

17 Disconnect the earth straps from the transmission casing also the engine crankcase (photo).

18 Unbolt the right rear engine mounting from the bodyframe side member (photo).

19 Unbolt the engine/transmission front mountings (photos).

20 Check that the engine/transmission is now hanging free on the hoist with all leads, hoses and controls disconnected.

21 Carefully lower the engine/transmission at the same time swivelling it so that the right-hand driveshaft can be released from the transmission. Do not allow the shaft to drop to the floor.

22 With the engine/transmission on the floor, disconnect the hoist and use it to raise the front end of the vehicle, if necessary, to provide room for the assembly to be withdrawn from under the vehicle. Alternatively, use a jack and axle stands placed under the bodyframe side-members.

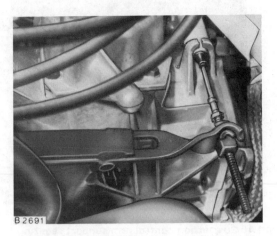

Fig. 1.9 Clutch cable connection to release lever (Sec 19)

Fig. 1.10 Hoist connected to engine (Sec 19)

Fig. 1.11 Exhaust connecting flange (Sec 19)

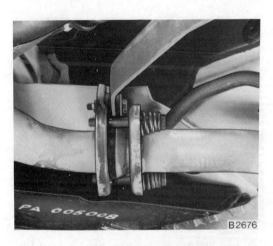

Fig. 1.12 Exhaust spring-loaded balljointed coupling (Sec 19)

Fig. 1.13 Hub nut lock (Sec 19)

Fig. 1.14 Releasing driveshaft/hub nut (Sec 19)

42

Fig. 1.15 Track rod end balljoint extractor (Sec 19)

Fig. 1.16 Suspension control arm support securing bolts (1.3 and some 1.6 – refer to Chapter 10) – arrowed (Sec 19)

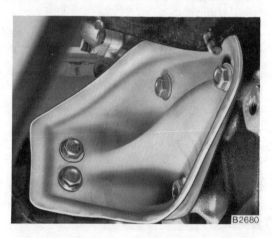

Fig. 1.17 Right rear mounting bracket (Sec 19)

Fig. 1.18 Left rear mounting pad nuts – arrowed (Sec 19)

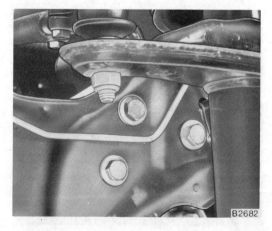

Fig. 1.19 Right rear engine mounting bracket to bodyframe (Sec 19)

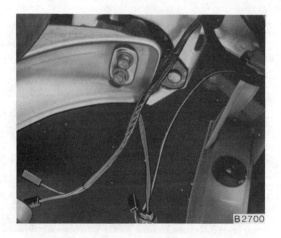

Fig. 1.20 Left front mounting (Sec 19)

19.18 Right rear engine mounting

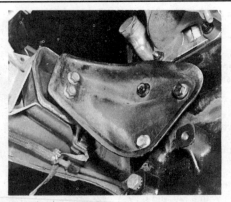

19.19A Right front engine mounting bracket

19.19B Left front transmission mounting bracket

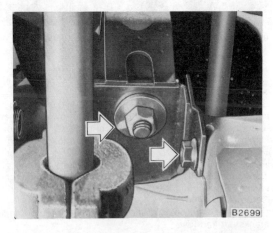

Fig. 1.21 Engine front mounting nuts – arrowed (Sec 19)

20 Engine/manual transmission – separation after removal

1   With the combined assembly removed from the vehicle, clean away external dirt using paraffin or a water soluble solvent, and a stiff brush.
2   Unbolt and remove the starter motor.
3   Unbolt and remove the clutch cover plate.
4   Support the transmission and unbolt the engine/transmission connecting bolts.
5   Withdraw the transmission from the engine without allowing the weight of the transmission to hang upon the input shaft while it is in engagement with the clutch driven plate.

21 Engine – removal (leaving automatic transmission in the vehicle)

1   Carry out the operations described in Section 18 for engine removal leaving manual transmission in vehicle (paragraphs 1 to 8).
2   Disconnect the kickdown cable from the carburettor/throttle housing as applicable.
3   Unbolt and withdraw the starter motor.
4   Unscrew and remove the torque converter cover plate. On 1.6 and 1.8 engines only, unbolt and remove the torsional damper from the crankshaft.
5   Unbolt the engine driveplate from the torque converter. Hold the driveplate from rotating by jamming the starter ring gear with a heavy screwdriver blade. New connecting bolts must be used at re-connection.
6   Support the transmission on a jack.
7   Attach a suitable hoist to the engine and just take its weight.
8   Unbolt the engine from the transmission.

9   Disconnect the engine mountings.
10 Separate the engine and transmission just enough to clear the positioning dowels and then turn the engine slightly until it can be lifted from the engine compartment.

22 Engine – removal (complete with automatic transmission)

1   Carry out the operations described in paragraphs 1 to 8 of Section 18.
2   Disconnect the kickdown cable from the carburettor (or throttle housing as applicable) and the transmission.
3   Disconnect the speed selector lever cable (see Chapter 6).
4   Disconnect the speedometer drive cable from the transmission, also the reverse lamp switch leads.
5   Withdraw the oil level dipstick and oil filler tube.
6   Disconnect the anti-roll bar from the suspension lower control arm (Chapter 10).
7   Disconnect the oil cooler hoses and plug them.
8   Carry out the operations described in Section 19, paragraphs 5 and 6.
9   Disconnect the exhaust downpipe from the manifold, also disconnect its bracket from the transmission. Swing the bracket upwards.
10 Carry out the operations described in Section 19, paragraphs 8 to 14.
11 Disconnect the engine and transmission mountings, noting that the left-hand rear mounting is accessible from below.
12 Disconnect the transmission earth strap.
13 Check that the engine and transmission are now free with all leads, hoses and controls disconnected and then lower the complete assembly to the floor. Swivel the unit as it is lowered so that the right-hand driveshaft can be released from the transmission. Do not allow the shaft to drop to the floor.
14 With the engine/transmission on the floor, disconnect the hoist and use it to raise the front end of the vehicle if necessary to provide room for the assembly to be withdrawn from under the vehicle.
15 Alternatively, use a jack and axle stands placed under the bodyframe side members.

23 Engine/automatic transmission – separation after removal

1   With the combined assembly removed from the vehicle, clean away external dirt using paraffin or a water soluble solvent, and a stiff brush.
2   Unbolt and remove the starter motor.
3   Unscrew and remove the torque converter cover plate.
4   Unbolt the driveplate from the torque converter. To prevent the driveplate from rotating as the bolts are unscrewed, jam the starter ring gear with a heavy screwdriver blade. New connecting bolts must be used at reassembly.
5   Unscrew and remove the engine-to-transmission connecting bolts.
6   Withdraw the transmission from the engine, at the same time retaining the torque converter fully within its housing.

24 Engine dismantling – general

1   It is best to mount the engine on a dismantling stand, but if this is not available, stand the engine on a strong bench at a comfortable working height. Failing this, it will have to be stripped down on the floor.

2   During the dismantling process, the greatest care should be taken to keep the exposed parts free from dirt. As an aid to achieving this thoroughly clean down the outside of the engine, first removing all traces of oil and congealed dirt.

3   A good grease solvent will make the job much easier, for, after the solvent has been applied and allowed to stand for a time, a vigorous jet of water will wash off the solvent and grease wth it. If the dirt is thick and deeply embedded, work the solvent into it with a strong stiff brush.

4   Finally, wipe down the exterior of the engine with a rag and only then, when it is quite clean, should the dismantling process begin. As the engine is stripped, clean each part in a bath of paraffin.

5   Never immerse parts with oilways in paraffin (eg crankshaft and camshaft). To clean these parts, wipe down carefully with a paraffin-dampened rag. Oilways can be cleaned out with wire. If an air line is available, all parts can be blown dry and the oilways blown through as an added precaution.

6   Re-use of old gaskets is false economy. To avoid the possibility of trouble after the engine has been reassembled **always** use new gaskets throughout.

7   Do not throw away the old gaskets, for sometimes it happens that an immediate replacement cannot be found and the old gasket is then very useful as a template.

8   To strip the engine, it is best to work from the top down. When the stage is reached where the crankshaft must be removed, the engine can be turned on its side and all other work carried out with it in this position.

9   Wherever possible, refit nuts, bolts and washers finger tight from wherever they were removed. This helps to avoid loss and muddle. If they cannot be fitted then arrange them in a sequence that ensures correct reassembly.

10 Make sure that you have a valve grinding tool and a valve spring compressor.

25 Engine ancillary components – removal

1   Before engine dismantling begins, it is necessary to remove the following ancillary components:

    (a) *Alternator (Chapter 12)*
    (b) *Fuel pump (Chapter 3)*
    (c) *Thermostat (Chapter 2)*
    (d) *Inlet manifold and carburettor (Chapter 3)*
    (e) *Throttle housing, injectors and associated fuel injection system components (Chapter 3)*
    (f) *Distributor (Chapter 4)*
    (g) *Coolant pump (Chapter 2)*
    (h) *Exhaust manifold (Chapter 3)*

    Refer to the Chapters concerned for the removal procedures of the items listed.

26 Engine – complete dismantling

1   With the engine removed from the vehicle and suitably positioned on a solid working surface, carry out the following sequence of operations.

2   Refer to earlier Sections of this Chapter and remove the following:

    (a) *Camshaft toothed belt*
    (b) *Cylinder head*
    (c) *Sump*
    (d) *Oil pump and oil pick-up pipe*
    (e) *Pistons, connecting rods*
    (f) *Clutch and flywheel*

3   Invert the engine so that it is standing on the top surface of the cylinder block.

26.4 A main bearing cap showing identification number

4   The main bearing caps are numbered 1 to 4 from the timing belt end of the engine. The rear (flywheel end) cap is not marked. To ensure that the caps are refitted the correct way round, note that the numbers are read from the coolant pump side when the crankcase is inverted (photo).

5   Unscrew and remove the main bearing cap bolts and tap off the caps. If the bearing shells are to be used again, keep them with their respective caps. The original shells are colour-coded and if used again must be returned to their original locations.

6   Note that the centre bearing shell incorporates thrust flanges to control crankshaft endfloat.

7   Lift the crankshaft from the crankcase. Extract the upper half shells and again identify their position in the crankcase if they are to be used again.

8   Refer to Section 30 for details of dismantling and decarbonising the cylinder head and pistons, and to Section 9 for removal of the camshaft.

9   Unbolt and remove the timing belt cover backing plate.

10 The rubber plug located adjacent to the bellhousing flange on the crankcase covers the aperture for installation of a TDC sensor. This sensor when connected to a suitable monitoring unit, indicates TDC from the position of the contact pins set in the crankshaft counterbalance weight.

27 Engine lubrication and crankcase ventilation systems – description and maintenance

1   Oil pressure for all moving components is provided by a gear type oil pump which is driven from the front end of the crankshaft. The crankshaft has flats for this purpose.

2   The pump draws oil from the sump through a pick-up pipe and strainer and pumps it through the oil filter and oil galleries to the engine friction surfaces.

3   A pressure regulator valve is screwed into the body of the oil pump. A relief valve, located in the oil filter mounting base opens should the filter block due to clogging caused by neglected servicing. An oil pressure switch is screwed into the pump casing (photo).

4   The cylinder bores are lubricated by oil splash from the sump.

5   The hydraulic valve lifters are pressurised with oil to maintain optimum valve clearance at all times, and this pressure is stabilised on 1.6 and 1.8 engines by an oil pressure regulating valve in the cylinder head (photo).

6   The crankcase ventilation system is designed to draw oil fumes and blow-by gas (combustion gas which has passed the piston rings) from the crankcase into the air cleaner, whence they are drawn into the engine and burnt during the normal combustion cycles.

7 On 1.3 engines, the ventilation system incorporates an oil separator bolted to the block. Although it is not a specified maintenance task, the separator can be removed for cleaning (photo).

8 On 1.6 and 1.8 engines, one of the crankcase ventilation hoses is attached to the camshaft cover (photo). Inside the cover is a filter, which should be cleaned in paraffin periodically.

9 On all engines, the breather hoses should be cleaned out periodically, and renewed if necessary.

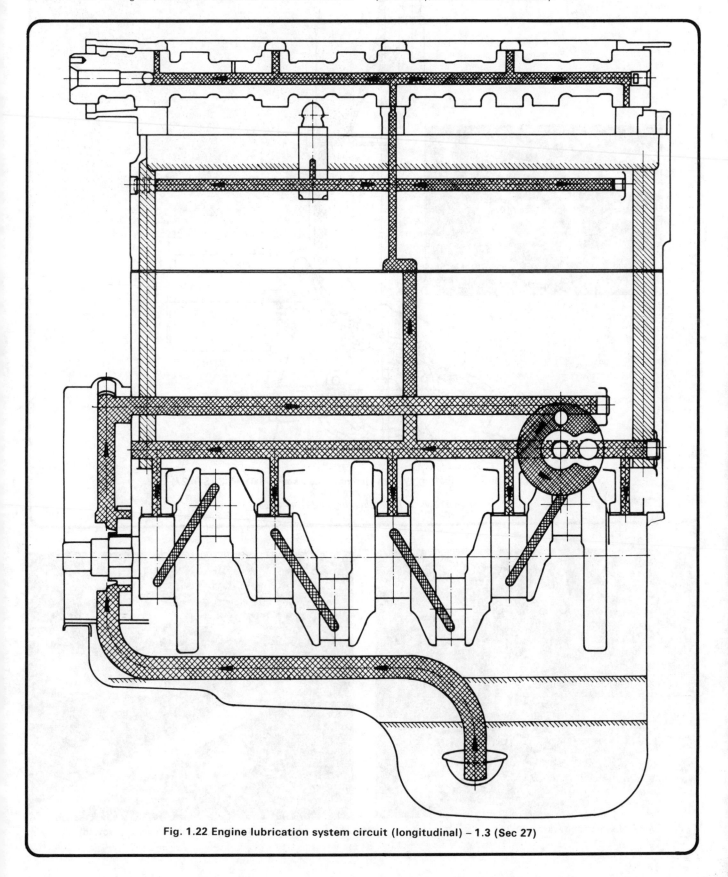

Fig. 1.22 Engine lubrication system circuit (longitudinal) – 1.3 (Sec 27)

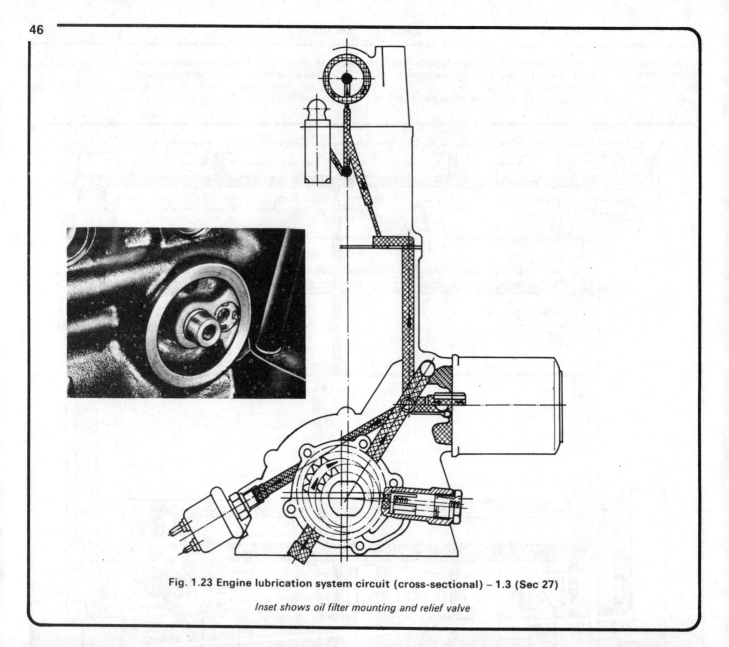

Fig. 1.23 Engine lubrication system circuit (cross-sectional) – 1.3 (Sec 27)

Inset shows oil filter mounting and relief valve

27.3 Oil pressure switch and washer (1.3)

27.5 Cylinder head oil pressure regulating valve (arrowed)

27.7 Crankcase vent system oil separator

27.8 Crankcase ventilation hose attached to camshaft cover (1.6/1.8)

28.1 Engine oil filter

28 Oil and filter – renewal

1 The engine oil and filter should be renewed at the intervals specified in *Routine Maintenance* at the beginning of this Manual (photo).
2 The author recommends that on vehicles fitted wth a replacement engine only, the oil and engine oil filter should be renewed after 1000 km (600 miles).
3 Always drain the oil hot after a run which will ensure that all impurities are flushed out more effectively.
4 Unscrew the oil filler cap.
5 Place a large bowl or other suitable container under the sump drain plug and then unscrew the plug. Allow the oil to drain completely. Refit the drain plug.
6 On 1.3 engines, the oil filter is located adjacent to the exhaust downpipes on the side of the crankcase. When changing the filter beware of hot exhaust pipes. All 1.3 models produced from October 1985 have an oil filter with a metric thread and it is therefore essential to be specific on which type is required when obtaining the replacement.
7 On 1.6 and 1.8 engines, the oil filter is positioned below the alternator lower mounting bracket at the side of the crankshaft pulley.
8 The oil filters are of disposable cartridge type and are not interchangeable between engine sizes.
9 An oil filter strap or chain type removal tool will almost certainly be required to unscrew the old filter.
10 Alternatively, drive a screwdriver through the oil filter casing near its end and use this as a lever to unscrew it. Be prepared for some loss of oil in this case.
11 Wipe the crankcase mating flange and smear the rubber sealing ring on the filter with grease.
12 Screw on the filter using hand pressure only.
13 Refill the engine with oil by pouring it into the hole in the camshaft housing cover.

14 Refit the cap.
15 Use only the specified type and quantity of oil.
16 Start the engine when it will take a few seconds for the oil warning lamp to go out. This is normal and is due to the time taken to fill the empty oil filter cartridge with oil.
17 Switch off the engine, wait a few minutes and check the oil level by withdrawing the dipstick, wiping it clean, re-inserting it and withdrawing it again. The level may have fallen slightly, some having been absorbed by the new filter. Top up as necessary, but never over fill now or at any time when topping-up as oil foaming at high speed may occur.
18 An oil level maintained between the two marks on the dipstick is acceptable.

Oil filter relief valve renewal

19 The oil filter relief valve is located under the oil filter, in the oil filter mounting block. If it is wished to remove the valve, screw an M10 tap into it and extract the valve.
20 The new valve should be driven into position up to its stop, using a drift, approximately 15 mm (0.6 in) in diameter.

29 Oil pump – overhaul

1 With the oil pump removed from the vehicle, withdraw the rear cover. The cross-head fixing screws are very tight and an impact driver will be required to remove them (photo).
2 Check the clearance between the inner and outer gear teeth, and the endfloat between the gear edges and the housing (photo).
3 If any of the clearances are outside the specified tolerance, renew the components as necessary. Note that the outer gear face is marked

29.1 Removing the oil pump rear cover retaining screws

29.2A Checking the oil pump gear tooth clearance

29.2B Checking oil pump gear endfloat

29.3 Oil pump gear positioning mark (arrowed)

29.4 Exploded view of oil pump pressure regulator valve (1.3)

29.6 Oil pump seal

for position (photo).

4   The pressure regulator valve can be unscrewed from the oil pump housing and the components cleaned and examined (photo).

5   Note that the valve components are not identical for both engines. The copper washer used on the 1.3 valve must be renewed when reassembling.

6   Always renew the oil seal; a socket is useful to remove and install it (photo).

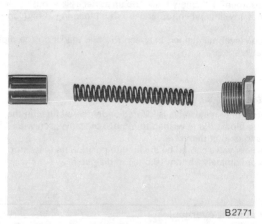

Fig. 1.24 Pressure regulating valve – 1.6 (Sec 29)

30 Cylinder head – dismantling, examination, renovation and decarbonising

1   With the cylinder head removed, clean away external dirt.

2   To remove the valves, the springs will have to be compressed to allow the split collets to be released from the groove in the upper section of the valve stems. A valve spring compressor will therefore be necessary.

3   Locate the compressor to enable the forked end of the arm to be positioned over the valve spring collar whilst the screw part of the clamp is situated squarely on the face of the valve.

4   Screw up the clamp to compress the spring and release the pressure of the collar acting on the collets. If the collar sticks, support the head and clamp frame and give the end of the clamp a light tap with a hammer to help release it.

5   Extract the two collets and then release the tension of the clamp. Remove the clamp, withdraw the collar and spring and extract the valve.

6   As they are released and removed, keep the valves in order so that if they are to be refitted they will be replaced in their original positions in the cylinder head. A piece of stiff card with eight holes punched in it is a sure method of keeping the valves in order.

7   Bearing in mind that the cylinder head is of light alloy construction and is easily damaged, use a blunt scraper or rotary wire brush to clean all traces of carbon deposits from the combustion spaces and the ports. The valve head stems and valve guides should also be freed from any

carbon deposits. Wash the combustion spaces and ports down with paraffin and scrape the cylinder head surface free of any foreign matter with the side of a steel rule, or a similar article.

8   If the engine is installed in the car, clean the pistons and the top of the cylinder bores. If the pistons are still in the block, then it is essential that great care is taken to ensure that no carbon gets into the cylinder bores as this could scratch the cylinder walls or cause damage to the pistons and rings. To ensure this does not happen, first turn the crankshaft so that two of the pistons are at the top of their bores. Stuff rag into the other two bores or seal them off with paper and masking tape. The waterways should also be covered with small pieces of masking tape to prevent particles of carbon entering the cooling system and damaging the coolant pump.

9   Press a little grease into the gap between the cylinder walls and the two pistons which are to be worked on With a blunt scraper carefully scrape away the carbon from the piston crown, taking great care not to scratch the aluminium. Also scrape away the carbon from the surrounding lip of the cylinder wall. When all carbon has been removed, scrape away the grease which will now be contaminated with carbon particles, taking care not to press any into the bores. To assist prevention of carbon build-up the piston crown can be polished with a metal polish. Remove the rags or masking tape from the other two cylinders and turn the crankshaft so that the two pistons which were at the bottom are now at the top. Place rag or masking tape in the cylinders which have been decarbonised, and proceed as just described.

10   Examine the head of the valves for pitting and burning, especially the heads of the exhaust valves. The valve seatings should be examined at the same time. If the pitting on the valve and seat is very slight, the marks can be removed by grinding the seats and valves together with coarse, and then fine, valve grinding paste.

11   Where bad pitting has occurred to the valve seats it will be necessary to recut them and fit new valves. This latter job should be entrusted to the local agent or engineering works. In practice it is very seldom that the seats are so badly worn. Normally it is the valve that is too badly worn for refitting, and the owner can easily purchase a new set of valves and match them to the seats by valve grinding.

12   Valve grinding is carried out as follows. Smear a trace of coarse carborundum paste on the seat face and apply a suction grinder tool to the valve head. With a semi-rotary motion, grind the valve head to its seat, lifting the valve occasionally to redistribute the grinding paste. When a dull matt even surface is produced on both the valve seat and the valve, wipe off the paste and repeat the process with fine carborundum paste, lifting and turning the valve to redistribute the paste as before. A light spring placed under the valve head will greatly ease this operation. When a smooth unbroken ring of light grey matt finish is produced, on both valve and valve seat faces, the grinding operation is complete. Carefully clean away every trace of grinding compound, taking great care to leave none in the ports or in the valve guides. Clean the valves and valve seats with a paraffin-soaked rag, then with a clean rag, and finally, if an air line is available, blow the valves, valve guides and valve ports clean.

13   Check that all valve springs are intact. If any one is broken, all should be renewed. Check the free height of the springs against new ones. If some springs are not long enough, replace them all. Springs suffer from fatigue and it is a good idea to renew them even if they look serviceable.

14 The cylinder head can be checked for warping either by placing it on a piece of plate glass or using a straight-edge and feeler blades. If there is any doubt or if its block face is corroded, have it re-faced by your dealer or motor engineering works.

15 On 1.6 and 1.8 models, always renew the sealing ring between the cylinder head and the thermostat housing when the head is removed for overhaul. Reference to Chapter 2 will show that a considerable amount of work is involved if it is wished to renew the sealing ring with the cylinder head installed.

16 If the oil pressure regulating valve in the cylinder head is to be renewed, access is gained via the circular plug covering the end of the valve. The old valve must be crushed, then its remains extracted, and a thread (M10) cut in the valve seat to allow removal using a suitable bolt. A new valve and plug can then be driven into position. In view of the intricacies of this operation, it is probably best to have the valve renewed by a GM dealer if necessary.

31 Engine – examination and renovation, general

1 With the engine stripped and all parts thoroughly cleaned, every component should be examined for wear. The items listed in the following Sections should receive particular attention and where necessary be renewed or renovated.

2 So many measurements of engine components require accuracies down to tenths of a thousandth of an inch. It is advisable therefore to check your micrometer against a standard gauge occasionally to ensure that the instrument zero is set correctly.

3 If in doubt as to whether or not a particular component must be renewed, take into account not only the cost of the component, but the time and effort which will be required to renew it if it subsequently fails at an early date.

32 Engine components – examination and renovation

Crankshaft

1 Examine the crankpin and main journal surfaces for signs of scoring or scratches, and check the ovality and taper of the crankpins and main journals. If the bearing surface dimensions do not fall within the tolerance ranges given in the Specifications at the beginning of this Chapter, the crankpins and/or main journals will have to be reground.

2 Big-end and crankpin wear is accompanied by distinct metallic knocking, particularly noticeable when the engine is pulling from low revs, and some loss of oil pressure.

3 Main bearing and main journal wear is accompanied by severe engine vibration rumble – getting progressively worse as engine revs increase – and again by loss of oil pressure.

4 If the crankshaft requires regrinding take it to an engine reconditioning specialist, who will machine it for you and supply the correct undersize bearing shells.

Big-end and main bearing shells

5 Inspect the big-end and main bearing shells for signs of general wear, scoring, pitting and scratches. The bearings should be matt grey in colour. With lead-indium bearings, should a trace of copper colour be noticed, the bearings are badly worn as the lead bearing material has worn away to expose the indium underlay. Renew the bearings if they are in this condition or if there are any signs of scoring or pitting. **You are strongly advised to renew the bearings – regardless of their condition at time of major overhaul. Refitting used bearings is a false economy.**

6 The undersizes available are designed to correspond with crankshaft regrind sizes. The bearings are in fact, slightly more than the stated undersize as running clearances have been allowed for during their manufacture.

7 Main and big-end bearing shells can be identified as to size by the marking on the back of the shell. Standard size shell bearings are marked STD or .00, undersize shells are marked with the undersize such as 0.020 u/s. This marking method applies only to replacement bearing shells and not to those used during production.

Cylinder bores

8 The cylinder bores must be examined for taper, ovality, scoring and scratches. Start by carefully examining the top of the cylinder bores. If they are at all worn a very slight ridge will be found on the thrust side. This marks the top of the piston ring travel. The owner will have a good indication of the bore wear prior to dismantling the engine, or removing the cylinder head. Excessive oil consumption accompanied by blue smoke from the exhaust is a sure sign of worn cylinder bores and piston rings.

9 Measure the bore diameter across the block and just below any ridge. This can be done with an internal micrometer or a dial gauge. Compare this with the diameter of the bottom of the bore, which is not subject to wear. If no measuring instruments are available, use a piston from which the rings have been removed and measure the gap between it and the cylinder wall with a feeler gauge. Refer to the Specifications. If the cylinder wear exceeds the permitted tolerances then the cylinders will need reboring, in which case note the following points:

(a) *Piston and cylinder bores are closely matched in production. The actual diameter of the piston is indicated by numbers on its crown; the same numbers stamped on the crankcase indicate the bore diameter*

(b) *After reboring has taken place, the cylinder bores should be measured accurately and oversize pistons selected from the grades available to give the specified piston-to-bore clearance*

(c) *For grading purposes, the piston diameter is measured across the bottom of the skirt*

10 If the wear is marginal and within the tolerances given, new special piston rings can be fitted to offset the wear.

Connecting rods

11 Examine the mating faces of the big-end caps to see if they have ever been filed in a mistaken attempt to take up wear. If so, the offending rods must be renewed.

12 Check the alignment of the rods visually, and if all is not well, take the rods to your local agent for checking on a special jig.

13 The gudgeon pins are an interference (shrink) fit in the connecting rod small end. As previously explained, removal and refitting of pistons to rods is a job for your dealer, as would be any remedial action required if the gudgeon pin is no longer an interference fit in the rod.

Pistons and piston rings

14 If the pistons and/or rings are to be re-used, remove the rings from the pistons. Three strips of tin or 0.38 mm (0.015 in) feeler gauges should be prepared and the top ring then sprung open just sufficiently to allow them to be slipped behind the ring. The ring can then be slid off the piston upwards without scoring or scratching the piston lands.

15 Repeat the process for the second and third rings.

16 Mark the ring or keep them in order so they may be refitted in their original location. The top ring may be fitted either way up. The second ring is marked TOP on its upper facing side.

17 Inspect the pistons to ensure that they are suitable for re-use. Check for cracks, damage to the piston ring grooves and lands, and scores or signs of picking-up on the piston walls.

18 Clean the ring grooves using a piece of old piston ring ground to a suitable width and scrape the deposits out of the grooves, taking care not to remove any metal or score the piston lands. Protect your fingers – piston rings are sharp (photo).

19 Check the rings in their respective bores. Press the ring down to the unworn lower section of the bore (use a piston to do this, and keep the ring square in the bore). Measure the ring end gap and check that it is within the tolerance allowed (see Specifications). If this measurement exceeds the specified tolerance the rings will have to be renewed, and if the ring grooves in the pistons are worn new pistons may be needed.

20 If genuine spares are used, new pistons and rings are not supplied separately; however, if the pistons are in good condition, new rings can be obtained from specialist suppliers who will also undertake any machining work necessary to modify the pistons to suit the new rings.

21 If new rings (or pistons and rings) are to be fitted to an existing bore the top ring must be stepped to clear the wear ridge at the top of the bore, or the bore must be de-ridged.

22 Check the end gap of any new rings as described in paragraph 19. If a ring is slightly tight in its groove it may be rubbed down using an oilstone or a sheet of carborundum paper laid on a sheet of glass. If the end gap is inadequate the ring can be carefully ground until the specified clearance is achieved.

32.18 Cleaning a piston ring groove

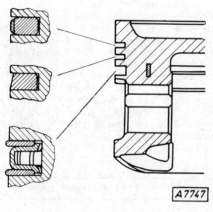

Fig. 1.25 Piston ring fitting diagram (Sec 32)

23 If new pistons are to be installed they will be selected from the grades available, after measuring the bores as described in paragraph 9. Normally the appropriate oversize pistons are supplied by the repairer when the block is rebored. Whenever new piston rings are being installed, the glaze on original cylinder bores should be 'broken' using either abrasive paper or a glaze removing tool in an electric drill. If abrasive paper is used, use strokes at 60° to the bore centre line to create a cross hatching effect.

Flywheel

24 If the teeth on the flywheel starter ring are badly worn, or if some are missing, then it will be necessary to remove the ring and fit a new one.

25 The old ring can be split with a cold chisel after making a cut with a hacksaw blade between two gear teeth. Take great care not to damage the flywheel during this operation, and use eye protectors at all times. Once the ring has been split, it will spread apart and can be lifted from the flywheel.

26 The new ring gear must be heated to 180 to 230°C (356° to 446°F) and unless facilities for heating by oven or flame are available, leave the fitting to your dealer or motor engineering works. The new ring gear must not be overheated during this work or the temper of the metal will be altered.

27 The ring should be tapped gently down onto its register and left to cool naturally when the contraction of the metal on cooling will ensure that it is a secure and permanent fit.

28 If the driven plate contact surface of the flywheel is scored or on close inspection shows evidence of small hair cracks, caused by overheating, it may be possible to have the flywheel surface ground provided the overall thickness of the flywheel is not reduced too much. Consult your specialist engine repairer and if it is not possible, renew the flywheel complete.

29 If the needle bearing in the centre of the crankshaft flange is worn, fill it with grease and tap in a close-fitting rod. Hydraulic pressure will remove it. Alternatively, a very small extractor having a claw type leg may be used. When tapping the new bearing into position, make sure that the chamfered side of the bearing enters first. After Engine No. 14089444 the crankshaft does not incorporate a needle bearing.

Driveplate (automatic transmission)

30 Should the starter ring gear on the driveplate require renewal, renew the driveplate complete.

Camshaft

31 With the camshaft removed, examine the bearings for signs of obvious wear and pitting. If evident, a new camshaft housing will probably be required.

32 The camshaft itself should show no marks or scoring on the journal or cam lobe surfaces. If evident, renew the camshaft. Where the camshaft has to be renewed then the camshaft housing should be modified (if an early production model – 1.3 and 1.6) to improve lubrication. To do this, temporarily fit the old camshaft into the housing without its retaining plate. Centre punch the housing at the point shown on the circumference of the camshaft journal according to the engine type (1.3 or 1.6). Now drill a hole 16.0 mm (0.630 in) deep using a 3.0 mm (0.118 in) diameter drill into the housing. On no account drill deeper than specified depth (Figs. 1.27 and 1.28).

33 The retaining plate should appear unworn and without grooves. In any event, check the camshaft endfloat and fit a new plate where necessary.

34 The housing front oil seal should always be renewed at major overhaul. A filter is incorporated in the camshaft housing cover on 1.6 and 1.8 models. Remove it and wash thoroughly in petrol and allow to dry (Fig. 1.29).

Camshaft toothed belt

35 Closely inspect the belt for cracking, fraying or tooth deformation. Where evident, renew the belt.

36 If the belt has been in use for 30 000 miles (48 000 km) or more, it is recommended that it is renewed even if it appears in good condition.

37 Whenever the original belt is to be removed, but is going to be used again, always note its running direction before removing it. It is even worthwhile marking the tooth engagement points on each sprocket. As the belt will have worn in a set position, refitting it in exactly the same way will prevent any increase in noise which might otherwise occur when the engine is running.

Valve lifters, rockers and thrust pads

38 Any signs of wear in a hydraulic valve lifter can only be rectified by renewal, the unit cannot be dismantled.

39 Inspect the rockers and thrust pads for wear or grooving. Again, renew if evident.

Cylinder block and core plugs

40 Ensure that the cylinder block is thoroughly cleaned inside and out. Check the core plugs for signs of corrosion. If the engine has covered a high mileage it is advisable to renew them irrespective of their condition.

41 To remove the old core plugs, drill them through then insert a suitable rod and prise them out using the rod as a lever.

42 Clean the plug orifice thoroughly then carefully drive the new plug into position taking care not to distort it. Apply some suitable sealant around the periphery of the plug when fitting to ensure a good seal. Use aluminium coated plugs where possible.

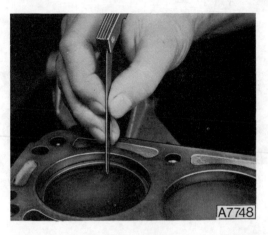

Fig. 1.26 Checking piston ring end gap (Sec 32)

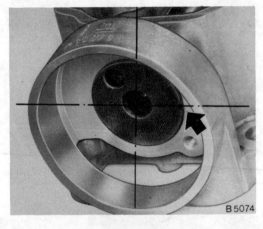

Fig. 1.27 Camshaft housing drilling point – 1.3 (Sec 32)

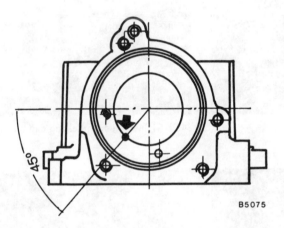

Fig. 1.28 Camshaft housing drilling point – 1.6 (Sec 32)

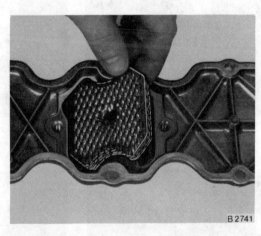

Fig. 1.29 Camshaft housing filter – 1.6, 1.8 and 2.0 (Sec 32)

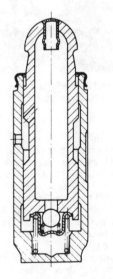

Fig. 1.30 Sectional view of hydraulic valve lifter (Sec 32)

33 Engine – reassembly, general

1 To ensure maximum life with minimum trouble from a rebuilt engine, not only must everything be correctly assembled, but everything must be spotlessly clean, all the oilways must be clear, locking washers and spring washers must always be fitted where indicated and all bearing and other working surfaces must be thoroughly lubricated during assembly.

2 Before assembly begins renew any bolts or studs, the threads of which are in any way damaged, and whenever possible use new spring washers.

3 Apart from your normal tools, a supply of clean rag, an oil can filled with engine oil (an empty plastic detergent bottle thoroughly cleaned and washed out, will do just as well), a new supply of assorted spring washers, a set of new gaskets, and a torque wrench, should be collected together.

34 Engine – complete reassembly

Crankshaft and main bearings

1 Ensure that the crankcase and crankshaft are thoroughly clean and that all oilways are clear. If possible blow the drillings out with compressed air, and then inject clean engine oil through them to ensure they are clear.

34.5A Centre main bearing shell showing thrust flanges

34.5B Main bearing shell locating notch

34.8A Lowering the crankshaft into position

34.8B Crankshaft rear oil seal

34.9A Fitting main bearing cap

34.9B Tightening main bearing cap bolt

34.10A Fitting rear main bearing cap

34.10B Injecting RTV sealer into rear main bearing cap grooves

34.12 Checking the crankshaft endfloat using feeler gauge method

2   Wipe the shell seats in the crankcase and bearing caps clean and then fit the upper halves of the main bearing shells into their seats.
3   Note that there is a tab on the back of each bearing which engages with a groove in the shell seating (in both crankcase and bearing cap).
4   Wipe away all traces of protective grease on the new shells.
5   The central bearing shell also takes up the crankshaft endfloat. Note that the half-shells fitted to the cylinder block all have oil duct holes (photos).
6   When the shells are fully located in the crankcase and bearing caps, lubricate them with clean engine oil.
7   Fill the lips of a new crankshaft oil seal with grease and fit it to the end of the crankshaft.
8   Carefully install the crankshaft into position in the crankcase (photos).
9   Lubricate the crankshaft main bearing journals and then refit the

centre and intermediate main bearing caps. Tighten the retaining bolts to the specified torque wrench setting (photos).
10 Clean the grooves of the rear main bearing cap free from old sealant, then coat the inner surfaces of the cap with sealant to GM spec 15 04 200/8 983 368. (This sealant is available in 200 ml tubes from GM parts departments.) Fill the side grooves of the bearing cap with RTV jointing compound, then after fitting the bearing cap and tightening its securing bolts, inject further RTV jointing compound into the side grooves until it is certain that they are full. Wipe clean any excess jointing compound (photo).
11 Fit the front main bearing cap but before fitting the retaining bolts, smear them with sealant, and then tighten to the specified torque wrench setting. Check that the bearing cap is exactly flush with the end face of the crankcase as it is tightened.
12 Now rotate the crankshaft and check that it turns freely, and shows

Fig. 1.31 Applying sealant to main bearing cap inner surfaces (Sec 34)

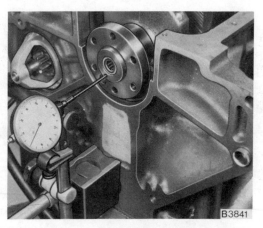

Fig. 1.32 Checking crankshaft endfloat using a dial gauge (Sec 34)

no signs of binding or tight spots. Check that the crankshaft endfloat is within the limits specified. Alternative centre bearing shells are available if necessary to adjust the endfloat. The endfloat can be checked using a dial gauge or with feeler blades inserted between the flange of the centre bearing shell and the machined surface of the crankshaft. Before measuring, make sure that the crankshaft has been forced fully towards one end of the crankcase to give the widest gap at the measuring location (photo).

Piston rings

13 Check that the piston ring grooves are thoroughly clear. Always move the rings into position from the top of the piston.

14 The easiest method of fitting piston rings is to use feeler gauges (or similar) around the top of the piston and move the rings into position over the feelers. This sequence is a reversal of the removal procedure detailed earlier in this Chapter.

15 Follow the manufacturer's instructions carefully when fitting rings to ensure that they are correctly fitted. Several variations of compression and oil control rings are available and it is of the utmost importance that they be located correctly in their grooves.

16 When the rings are in position, check that the compression rings are free to expand and contract in their grooves. Certain types of multi-segment oil control rings are a light interference fit in their grooves and this may not therefore apply to them. When all the rings are in position on the pistons move them around to bring each ring gap to be some 180° away from the gap on the adjacent ring(s). When the oil control ring consists of two rails and a spacer, offset the upper rail gap 25 to 50 mm (1 to 2 in) to the left of the spacer gap; offset the lower rail gap a similar distance to the right.

Piston/connecting rods

17 As previously described, removing and refitting pistons on the connecting rod is a job for your dealer or specialist repairer. Press equipment and a means of accurately heating the connecting rod will be required for removal and insertion of the gudgeon pin.

18 Commence reassembly by laying the piston/connecting rod assemblies out in their correct order, complete with bearing shells, ready for refitting into their respective bores in the cylinder block.

19 Wipe out the bores and oil them. Oil the piston rings liberally.

20 Fit a piston ring compressor to the first assembly to be installed.

21 Insert the rod and piston into the top of the bore so that the base of the compressor stands on the block. Check that the rod markings are towards the side of the engine as noted before dismantling. This is very important as the piston crowns do not have front directional marks.

22 Apply the wooden handle of a hammer to the piston crown and tap the assembly into the bore. The compressor will be left standing on top of the block.

23 Guide the big-end of the connecting rod near to the crankpin. Fit and oil the bearing shells, then fit the cap and bolts (photos).

Oil pump

24 Before refitting the oil pump, steps must be taken to protect the seal lips from damage or turning back on the shoulder at the front end of the crankshaft. To do this, grease the seal lips and then bind tape around the crankshaft to form a gentle taper. Locate a new gasket (photos).

25 Refit the oil pump and unwind and remove the tape.

26 Tighten the bolts to the specified torque.

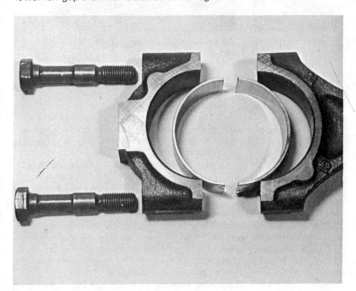

34.23A Connecting rod big-end components

34.23B Fitting a big-end cap

34.23C Tightening a big-end cap bolt

34.24A Crankshaft step taped

34.24B Fitting oil pump and gasket

34.27A Oil pick-up pipe connecting flange

34.27B Oil pick-up pipe support bracket

34.28 Fitting the sump and gasket

34.29 Fitting Woodruff key to crankshaft

34.30 Flywheel correctly located

34.32 Tightening a flywheel bolt

27 Refit the oil pick-up pipe and strainer (photos).

28 Refit the sump (Section 10) (photo).

29 Fit the Woodruff key to the front end of the crankshaft and then stand the engine on the sump (photo).

Flywheel

30 Offer the flywheel to the crankshaft rear mounting flange, align the bolt holes which are offset, so that the flywheel can only be fitted in one position (photo).

31 Apply thread locking compound to the bolt threads and screw in the bolts.

32 Jam the starter ring gear teeth and tighten the bolts to the specified torque (photo).

Cylinder head and camshaft housing

33 Ensure that all valves and springs are clean and free from carbon deposits and that the ports and valve guides in the cylinder head have no carbon dust or valve grinding paste left in them.

34 Starting at one end of the cylinder head, fit the valve components as follows.

35 Insert the appropriate valve into its guide, making sure that the valve stem is well lubricated. The valves must be installed into the seats into which they have been ground, which, in the case of the original valves, will mean that their original sequence of fitting is retained (photo).

36 If working on an inlet valve, fit the spring seat. If working on an exhaust valve, fit the valve rotator (photos).

37 Hold the valve in position, and gently push the valve stem oil seal over the valve stem and onto the valve guide, using finger pressure only, until the bead on the seal slips into the groove in the guide. Do not push the seal beyond the groove, or the sealing properties will be lost. Note that the oil seals for 1.6 and 1.8 engines have been modified. Fig. 1.33 shows the old and new types. New type seals can be fitted to old (pre-modification) engines.

38 Place the valve spring in position over the valve.

39 Place the cap over the spring, with the recessed part inside the coil of the spring (photo).

40 Place the end of the spring compressor over the cap and valve stem and with the screw head of the compressor over the valve head, screw up the clamp until the spring is compressed past the groove in the valve stem. Then put a little grease round the groove.

41 Place the two halves of the split collets into the groove with the narrow ends pointing towards the spring. The grease will hold them in the groove (photo).

42 Release the clamp slowly and carefully, making sure that the collets are not dislodged from the groove. When the clamp is fully released the top edges of the collets should be in line with each other. Give the top of each spring a smart tap with a soft-faced mallet when assembly is complete to ensure that the collets are properly settled.

43 Lubricate the hydraulic valve lifters (valve lash adjuster) and insert them into their bores in the cylinder head (photo). If new hydraulic lifters are being used, initially immerse each one in a container of clean engine oil and compress it (by hand) several times to charge it.

44 Fit the rockers and the thrust pads, also new spark plugs of the specified type (photos).

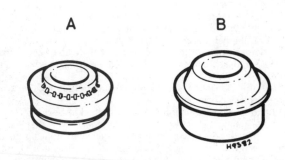

Fig. 1.33 Valve stem oil seal types (Sec 34)

A   Early type seal   *B   Late type seal*

34.35 Fitting a valve to the cylinder head

34.36A Exhaust valve rotator (A) and inlet valve spring seat (B)

34.36B Valve components
A   Exhaust   B   Inlet

34.39 Fitting a valve spring cap

34.41 Fitting valve split collets

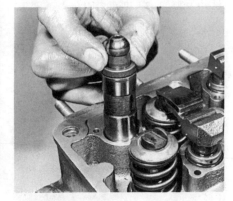

34.43 Fitting a hydraulic valve lifter to cylinder head

34.44A Fitting a thrust pad

34.44B Fitting a rocker

45 Fit the thermostat into its seat, use a new sealing ring and fit the thermostat housing cover. Screw in the bolts (photo).

46 On 1.3 models, fit the timing belt cover backplate to the front end of the camshaft cover (photo).

47 Lubricate the camshaft bearings and carefully insert the camshaft into its housing (photo).

48 Fit the retaining plate and fixing screws and then check the camshaft endfloat (photos).

49 Fit a new seal into the seal retainer (if not already done), then hold the camshaft still with an open-ended spanner while the sprocket and its bolt are fitted and the bolt tightened to the specified torque (photo).

50 Thoroughly clean the mating faces of the cylinder head and block.

51 Locate a new cylinder head gasket on the block so that the word OBEN can be read from above (photo).

52 Locate the cylinder head on the block so that the positioning dowels engage in their holes (photo).

53 Apply jointing compound to the mating flanges of the cylinder head and the camshaft housing and refit the camshaft housing to the cylinder head (camshaft sprocket marks in alignment) (photo).

54 Screw in the cylinder head bolts, and tighten them in the sequence shown in Fig. 1.3. The bolts must be tightened in the five stages given in the Specifications, and described in detail in Section 8.

55 Fit the coolant pump as described in Chapter 2, but leave the bolts finger tight pending adjustment of the timing belt (photo).

56 Bolt on the belt cover backplate (photo).

57 Fit the belt sprocket to the front end of the crankshaft so that the raised key on the sprocket will engage in the pulley slot when it is fitted (photo).

58 Refit the crankshaft sprocket bolt and tighten to the specified torque (see Specifications).

59 Fit and tension the timing belt as described in Section 5.

60 Fit the timing belt cover. On early models, note that the upper screw can only be screwed in after the camshaft housing cover has been fitted using a new gasket (photos).

61 Using new gaskets, bolt on the inlet and exhaust manifolds. Do not forget the lifting lugs (photos).

62 Fit the hot air shroud to the exhaust manifold (1.3 and 1.6) (photo).

63 Fit the ancillary components by reference to the appropriate

34.45 Tightening a thermostat housing bolt

34.46 Timing belt cover backplate (1.3)

34.47 Inserting the camshaft

34.48A Camshaft retaining plate (arrowed)

34.48B Checking camshaft endfloat

34.49 Tightening camshaft sprocket bolt

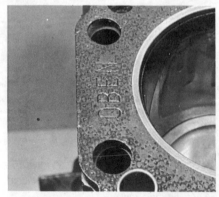
34.51 Cylinder head gasket top marking

34.52 Lowering cylinder head onto block

34.53 Fitting camshaft housing

34.54 Tightening a cylinder head bolt

34.55 Fitting coolant pump

34.56 Fitting timing belt cover backplate

34.57 Crankshaft sprocket

34.60A Fitting camshaft housing cover

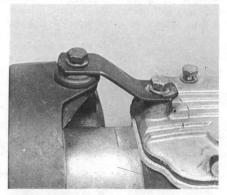

34.60B Timing belt cover connecting link to camshaft housing cover

34.61A Engine lifting lug location on inlet manifold stud

34.61B Engine lifting lug location on exhaust manifold stud

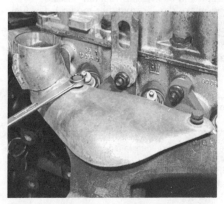

34.62 Exhaust manifold hot air collecting shield

Chapters, but do not fit the alternator or drivebelt until the engine is installed otherwise access to the right-hand rear mounting will be restricted. Do not fit the starter motor until the engine is installed.
64 On 1.8 engines, reconnect the fuel injection system (Chapter 3).

35 Engine – refitting (manual transmission still in the vehicle)

1 If the clutch has been disturbed, the driven plate (friction disc) must be centralised before the engine can be coupled to the transmission, otherwise the input shaft will not pass through the hub to the plate.
2 To do this, locate the driven plate against the flywheel so that the greater projecting hub of the plate is away from the flywheel.
3 Bolt on the cover, aligning the marks made before dismantling, but only screw in the bolts finger tight.
4 An alignment tool will now be required to pass through the hub of the driven plate and to engage in the bearing in the end of the crankshaft in order to align the plate. A stepped rod, or one of the clutch alignment tools available at motor stores, should be used to do this.
5 When the plate is aligned, tighten the cover bolts to the specified torque and withdraw the tool.
6 Lower the engine into the engine compartment at an angle so that it can be coupled to the flywheel housing.
7 Screw in the upper connecting bolts.
8 Refit the clutch cover plate.
9 With the weight of engine and transmission now taken on the hoist, remove the jack which has been supporting the transmission.
10 Fit the alternator and its mounting bracket.
11 Reconnect the right rear engine mounting.
12 Reconnect the right front engine mounting and the two left-hand engine mountings.
13 Remove the hoist.
14 Refit the crankshaft pulley and where applicable (1.6 and 1.8 models) refit the torsional damper. Tighten the securing bolt(s) to the specified torque wrench setting whilst holding the crankshaft from rotating by jamming the starter ring gear with a large screwdriver inserted through the starter motor aperture.
15 Refit the starter motor and the alternator.
16 Reconnect the input shaft to the clutch driven plate (friction disc) and the flywheel by reversing the withdrawal operations described in Section 18, paragraphs 9 to 13.
17 Reconnect the exhaust downpipe to the manifold and the exhaust rear section coupling.
18 Lower the front end of the vehicle.
19 Reconnect the supply and return fuel hoses.
20 Fit the drivebelt and tension it as described in Chapter 2.
21 Reconnect the electrical leads to the terminals indicated in Section 18, paragraph 8.
22 Reconnect the carburettor controls. On fuel injection models, reconnect and refit wiring plugs and components and other items mentioned in Section 18, paragraph 6.
23 Refit the radiator.
24 Reconnect the coolant and heater hoses.
25 Reconnect the distributor and brake servo vacuum hoses.
26 Fit the air cleaner and intake duct (carburettor models). On fuel injection models reconnect the air intake duct.
27 Refit the bonnet.
28 Fill the cooling system (Chapter 2).
29 Fill the engine and transmission with oil.
30 Connect the battery.

36 Engine/manual transmission – reconnection before refitting

1 If the clutch has been disturbed, centralise the driven plate as described in Section 35.
2 Offer the transmission to the engine without allowing its weight to hang upon the input shaft while the latter is engaged in the hub of the driven plate.
3 Locate the bellhousing flange on the dowels and then insert and tighten the connecting bolts.

4 Refit the clutch cover plate.
5 Refit the starter motor.

37 Engine – refitting (complete with manual transmission)

1 With the front end of the vehicle raised and safely supported on stands, position the engine/transmission on the floor under the engine compartment (photo).
2 Hoist the assembly upwards and turn it slightly until the right-hand driveshaft can be engaged in the transmission final drive side gear.
3 Connect the engine front mountings.
4 Connect the engine rear mountings.
5 Leave all mounting bolts and nuts finger tight until the weight of the power unit is lowered onto the mountings. This will allow the unit to take up its correct alignment. This is provided for by means of the elongated holes in the left-hand front mounting bracket.
6 Connect the transmission earth strap.
7 Reconnect the left-hand driveshaft, the suspension control arm and anti-roll bar by reversing the removal operations.
8 Refer to Chapter 10 for details of control arm support bolt fitting which is very important.
9 Refit the roadwheel. The tightening of the driveshaft nut can wait until the vehicle is lowered onto its roadwheels.
10 Remove the engine lifting hoist.
11 With the weight of the engine now on its mountings, tighten all mounting nuts and bolts to the specified torque.
12 Check that all suspension, hub and steering nuts and bolts have been tightened to the specified torque.
13 Refit the roadwheels and lower the vehicle to the floor.
14 Reconnect the speedometer cable to the transmission.
15 Reconnect the reverse lamp switch wires to the transmission.
16 Reconnect the clutch operating cable.
17 Reconnect the gearchange rod.
18 Check the clutch cable adjustment (Chapter 5) and the gearchange linkage adjustment (Chapter 6).
19 Reconnect the fuel hoses.
20 Reconnect the electrical leads to all the components listed in Section 18, paragraph 8.
21 Reconnect the controls to the carburettor. On fuel injection engines reconnect all the items mentioned in Section 16, paragraph 6 and refit the system components (Chapter 3).
22 Connect the vacuum hoses to the brake servo and the distributor.
23 Reconnect the heater and radiator coolant hoses.
24 Refit the air cleaner and pre-heater ducting (carburettor models). On fuel injection models reconnect the air intake ducting.
25 Refit the bonnet.
26 Fill the engine with oil and coolant.
27 Refill or top up the transmission.
28 Reconnect the battery.

37.1 Engine/transmission ready for installation

38 Engine – refitting (automatic transmission still in the vehicle)

1 Using a hoist, lower the engine into its compartment and engage it on the transmission locating dowels.
2 Connect the engine mountings.
3 Fit and tighten the bellhousing to engine bolts.
4 Remove the hoist and transmission jack.
5 Align the white spot on the driveplate with the coloured spot on the torque converter and screw in **new** bolts. Tighten the bolts to the specified torque while preventing the torque converter from rotating by jamming the starter ring gear.
6 Fit the torque converter cover plate.
7 Bolt on the starter motor.
8 Reconnect the kickdown cable.
9 Carry out the operations described in Section 35, paragraphs 17 to 30.
10 Refit the crankshaft pulley and the torsional damper (1.6 and 1.8 models), see Section 35, paragraph 14.
11 Adjust the kickdown cable as described in Chapter 6.

39 Engine/automatic transmission – reconnection before refitting

1 Check that the torque converter is fully inserted into the bellhousing (see Chapter 6).
2 Offer the transmission to the engine so that the white spot on the driveplate is aligned with the coloured spot on the torque converter.
3 Screw in the bellhousing bolts.
4 Screw in **new** driveplate-to-torque converter connecting bolts and while jamming the starter ring gear, tighten the bolts to the specified torque.
5 Bolt on the torque converter cover plate.
6 Fit the starter motor.

40 Engine – refitting (complete with automatic transmission)

1 Position the engine/transmission on the floor under the engine compartment.
2 Hoist the assembly into position, twisting it in order to be able to engage the right-hand driveshaft in the transmission side gear.
3 Connect the mountings, but leave the mounting nuts and bolts finger tight until the weight of the power unit is lowered onto the mountings. This will allow the unit to take up its correct alignment. This is provided for by means of the elongated holes in the left-hand front mounting bracket.
4 Connect the transmission earth strap.
5 Reconnect the left-hand driveshaft, the suspension lower arm and the anti-roll bar by reversing the removal operations (refer to Chapter 10).
6 Lock the driveshafts into the transmission side gears by applying a drift to the weld bead on the inboard joint and striking it hard to engage the driveshaft circlip in its groove.
7 Reconnect the exhaust downpipe to the manifold, also at its spring-loaded balljoint coupling.

8 Tighten the driveshaft to hub nuts to the specified torque preventing the hub from rotating by locking it as described at dismantling.
9 Fit the nut lock or split pin.
10 Fit the roadwheel.
11 Reconnect the oil cooler fluid lines.
12 Refit the fluid level dipstick and filler tube to the transmission.
13 Reconnect the speedometer drive cable.
14 Reconnect the speed selector lever.
15 Reconnect the kickdown cable.
16 Reconnect the fuel hoses to the fuel pump.
17 Reconnect the electrical leads to all accessories and components.
18 Connect the carburettor controls. On fuel injection models, reconnect all the items mentioned in Section 18, paragraph 6.
19 Reconnect the brake vacuum hose.
20 Reconnect the heater and radiator coolant hoses.
21 Refit the air cleaner and pre-heater duct.
22 Refit the bonnet.
23 Reconnect the battery.
24 Fill the cooling system (Chapter 2).
25 Fill the engine and transmission with oil.
26 Check the adjustment of the kickdown cable and the speed selector control linkage (refer to Chapter 6).

41 Engine – initial start-up after overhaul

1 Make sure the battery is fully charged and that all lubricants, coolant and fuel are replenished.
2 If the fuel system has been dismantled it will require several revolutions of the engine on the starter motor to pump the petrol up to the carburettor.
3 As soon as the engine fires and runs, keep it going at a fast tickover only (no faster), and bring it up to the normal working temperature. Expect some initial noise from the hydraulic valve lifters until they are properly pressurized with oil.
4 As the engine warms up there will be odd smells and some smoke from parts getting hot and burning off oil deposits. The signs to look for are leaks of water or oil which will be obvious if serious. Check also the exhaust pipe and manifold connections, as these do not always 'find' their exact gastight position until the warmth and vibration have acted on them, and it is almost certain that they will need tightening further. This should be done, of course, with the engine stopped.
5 When normal running temperature has been reached adjust the engine idling speed, as described in Chapter 3, and check the ignition timing as described in Chapter 4. With the engine stopped, also carry out the final stage of cylinder head bolt tightening, if applicable (see Specifications and Section 8).
6 Stop the engine and wait a few minutes to see if any lubricant or coolant is dripping out when the engine is stationary.
7 Road test the car to check that the timing is correct and that the engine is giving the necessary smoothless and power. Do not race the engine – if new bearings and/or pistons have been fitted it should be treated as a new engine and run in at a reduced speed for the first 500 miles (800 km). Some valve clatter is to be expected until the hydraulic valve lifters fill with oil.
8 On vehicles equipped with automatic transmission, pay particular attention to checking the fluid level as described in Chapter 6.

42 Fault diagnosis – engine

Symptom	Reason(s)
Engine fails to turn when starter control operated	
No current at starter motor	Flat or defective battery
	Loose battery leads
	Defective starter solenoid or switch or broken wiring
	Engine earth strap disconnected
Current at starter motor	Jammed starter motor drive pinion
	Defective starter motor

Symptom	Reason(s)
Engine turns but will not start	
No spark at spark plug	Ignition leads or distributor cap damp or wet
	Ignition leads to spark plugs loose
	Shorted or disconnected low tension leads
	Dirty, incorrectly set, or pitted contact breaker points (1.3*)
	Faulty condenser (1.3)*
	Defective ignition switch
	Ignition leads connected wrong way round
	Faulty coil
	Contact breaker point spring earthed or broken (1.3)*
No fuel at carburettor float chamber or at jets	No petrol in petrol tank
	Vapour lock in fuel line (in hot conditions or at high altitude)
	Blocked float chamber needle valve
	Fuel pump filter blocked
	Choked or blocked carburettor jets
	Faulty fuel pump
Engine stalls and will not restart	
Excess of petrol in cylinder or carburettor flooding	Too much choke allowing too rich a mixture or wet plugs
	Float damaged or leaking or needle not seating
	Float level incorrectly adjusted
No spark at spark plug	Ignition failure – sudden
	Ignition failure – misfiring precedes total stoppage
	Ignition failure – in severe rain or after traversing water splash
No fuel at jets	No petrol in petrol tank
	Petrol tank breather choked
	Sudden obstruction in carburettor
	Water in fuel system
	Defective fuel pump
Engine misfires or idles unevenly	
Intermittent spark at spark plug	Ignition leads loose
	Battery leads loose on terminals
	Battery earth strap loose on body attachment point
	Engine earth lead loose
	Low tension leads on coil loose
	Low tension lead to distributor loose
	Dirty or incorrectly gapped plugs
	Dirty, incorrectly set, or pitted contact breaker points (1.3)*
	Tracking across inside of distributor cover
	Ignition too retarded
	Faulty coil
Fuel shortage at engine	Mixture too weak
	Air leak in carburettor
	Air leak at inlet manifold to cylinder head, or inlet manifold to carburettor
	Defective fuel pump
Lack of power	
Mechanical wear (poor compression)	Burnt out valves
	Sticking or leaking valves
	Weak or broken valve springs
	Worn valve guides or stems
	Worn pistons and piston rings
Fuel/air mixture leaking from cylinder (poor compression)	Burnt out valves
	Sticking or leaking valves
	Worn valve guides and stems
	Weak or broken valve springs
	Blown cylinder head gasket (accompanied by increase in noise)
	Worn pistons and piston rings
	Worn or scored cylinder bores
Incorrect adjustments	Ignition timing wrongly set
	Contact breaker points incorrectly gapped (1.3)*
	Incorrectly set spark plugs
	Carburation too rich or too weak

Symptom	Reason(s)
Carburation and ignition faults	Dirty contact breaker points (1.3)* Fuel filter blocked Air cleaner blocked Distributor automatic advance and retard mechanisms not functioning correctly Faulty fuel pump giving top end fuel starvation
Excessive oil consumption Oil being burnt	Excessively worn valve stems and valve guides Worn piston rings Worn pistons and cylinder bores Excessive piston ring gap allowing blow-by Piston oil return holes choked
Oil being lost due to leaks	Leaking oil filter gasket Leaking camshaft cover gasket Leaking sump gasket Loose sump plug
Unusual noises from engine Excessive clearances due to mechanical wear	Worn valve gear (noisy tapping from cylinder head)** Worn big-end bearing (regular heavy knocking) Worn main bearings (rumbling and vibration) Worn crankshaft (knocking, rumbling and vibration) Faulty hydraulic valve lifter
Pinking on acceleration	Fuel octane rating too low Ignition timing over-advanced Carbon build-up in cylinder head Ignition timing incorrect Mixture too weak Overheating

* *Models up to 1982*
** *It is normal for a considerable amount of noise to come from hydraulic valve lifters on initial start-up after overhaul. This should only continue until the valve lifters are properly pressurized with oil. Additionally, on a high-mileage engine, there may be some initial noise if the engine has not been started for a period of time*

Chapter 2 Cooling and heating systems

For modifications, and information applicable to later models, see Supplement at end of manual

Contents

Specifications

System .... Pressurised, 'no-loss', with remote expansion tank. Coolant pump driven by toothed timing belt

Coolant type/specification .... Ethylene glycol based antifreeze (Duckhams Universal Antifreeze and Summer Coolant)

Coolant capacity

	Manual transmission	Automatic transmission
1.3	6.3 litres (11.1 pints)	7.1 litres (12.5 pints)
1.6	7.9 litres (13.9 pints)	7.7 litres (13.6 pints)
1.8	7.6 litres (13.4 pints)	7.4 litres (13.0 pints)

Thermostat

Opening temperature:
1.3	91°C (196°F)
1.6 and 1.8	92°C (198°F)

Fully open temperature:
1.3	103°C (217°F)
1.6 and 1.8	107°C (225°F)

Expansion tank cap

Colour .... Blue or yellow

Opening pressure:
Blue	1.20 to 1.35 bar (17.4 to 19.6 lbf/in²)
Yellow	1.02 to 1.15 bar (14.8 to 16.7 lbf/in²)

Fan thermoswitch (all models)

Switches on at	97°C (207°F)
Switches off at	93°C (199°F)

Torque wrench settings

	Nm	lbf ft
Coolant pump bolts:		
1.3	8	6
1.6 and 1.8	25	18
Thermostat housing bolts:		
1.3	10	7
1.6 and 1.8	15	11
Temperature sender in manifold	10	7
Temperature sender in thermostat housing	8	6

1 General description

Engine cooling is achieved by a conventional pump-assisted system in which the coolant is pressurised. The system consists of a radiator, an engine-driven pump, an electrical fan, a thermostat and connecting hoses. Hoses also conduct coolant to and from a heat exchanger mounted in the car to provide heat for the ventilation and heating system.

The system works in the following way. Cold coolant from one side of the radiator, which is mounted at the front of the engine compartment, is directed to the inlet side of the coolant pump where it is then forced round the cooling passages in the engine cylinder block and the cylinder head. The coolant, now hot, is returned to the other side of the radiator where it flows across the radiator and cools to repeat the cycle.

Air flows through the radiator to cool the coolant as a result of the car's forward motion. However, if the coolant temperature exceeds a given figure, a temperature switch in the radiator switches on an electrical fan to assist and increase the airflow through the radiator. In this way the fan is only driven when it is really needed, with a consequent reduction in noise and energy consumption.

To enable the engine to warm up quickly when starting from cold, the thermostat located in the cylinder head outlet prevents coolant flowing to the radiator until the temperature has risen sufficiently. Instead, the outflow from the cylinder head is redirected around the engine. When hot, the thermostat opens to send the coolant to the radiator.

An expansion/header tank is incorporated in the system to accommodate coolant expansion. The system is topped-up through a filler cap on this tank.

2 Routine maintenance – cooling system

1   Check the coolant level in the expansion tank at the specified intervals. If the coolant level drops below the KALT mark on the expansion tank, remove the cap from the tank (photos), and top up with coolant, which should be an antifreeze mixture made up in the same proportions as the original coolant. If the engine is hot, cover the cap with a cloth and **take care** to avoid scalding by steam or coolant escaping from the pressurised system.
2   If topping-up is required on anything but the rarest occasion, suspect a leak in the system, or a blowing cylinder head gasket, and rectify.
3   Renew the coolant at the specified intervals, and check the antifreeze strength at the beginning of each winter.
4   Periodically check the cooling system hoses and connections for condition and security. Renew if necessary.

3 Cooling system – draining

Note: *Take care to protect the hands from escaping steam when removing the expansion tank filler cap if the system is hot.*
1   Before draining the system park the car on level ground, remove the filler cap on the expansion tank and move the heater control to full heat. If the coolant is less than two years old it should be collected for re-use.
2   Position a clean container such as a basin under the radiator bottom hose and loosen a hose clip. If the hose joint has not been disturbed for some time it will be necessary to manipulate the hose to break the joint and allow the coolant to flow into the container.
3   On completion of the draining remove the container to a safe place and cover it to prevent contamination of the coolant if it is to be reused.
4   As no cylinder block drain plug is fitted and the radiator bottom hose may be situated halfway up the radiator, the system will not drain fully. Care should be taken when refilling to maintain antifreeze strength.

4 Cooling system – flushing

1   If effective draining or renewing the coolant has been neglected, then in time the cooling system will gradually lose efficiency as the radiator becomes choked with rust, scale deposits and other sediment from the system. This is one of the main reasons why old cars suffer so

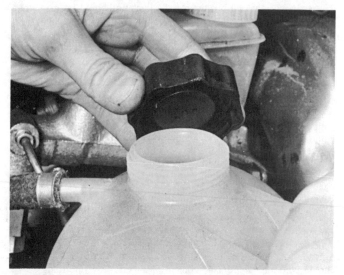

2.1A Expansion tank filler cap removal – take care if coolant is hot

2.1B Topping up the coolant expansion tank

much from overheating compared with newer cars. To maintain cooling system efficiency it is necessary to flush the system clean. First drain the system as explained in the previous Section and then remove the thermostat as explained in Section 8. Temporarily refit the thermostat housing and reconnect the hose. Disconnect the radiator top hose at the radiator and cover the engine with a sheet of plastic to prevent it from getting wet during the flushing process.
2   Using a garden hose, direct a flow of clean water through the radiator to wash the system out. Continue flushing until rust-free water emerges. If the contamination is particularly bad disconnect the radiator bottom hose and, with suitable connectors, feed the flushing water in at the bottom of the radiator to flush it in reverse. This should dislodge deposits which were not moved by conventional flushing. Repeat the procedure on the engine block. Where any doubt exists about the cleanliness of the radiator after reverse flushing it, it should be removed as explained in Section 7 so that it can be flushed and agitated at the same time. After reverse flushing, carry out a normal flow flush before refitting the thermostat and reconnecting the system hoses.
3   In extreme cases the use of a proprietary de-scaling compound such as Holts Radflush or Holts Speedflush may be necessary. If such a compound is used, adhere to the maker's instructions and satisfy yourself that no damage will be caused to the engine or cooling system components.

4   As the system will not drain fully, flushing should be performed every time the coolant is renewed. This will minimise impurities remaining in the system.

5   Antifreeze mixture

1   In these cars it is important to use an antifreeze mixture in the system all the year round. The mixture should be made up from clean, preferably soft, tap water (or rain water) and a good quality antifreeze liquid containing corrosion inhibitor. The proportions of water to antifreeze will depend on the degree of protection required.
2   25% of antifreeze should be regarded as the minimum proportion required to maintain good anti-corrosion characteristics and to protect against freezing down to −10°C (+14°F).
3   For absolute protection, use a 50% mixture.
4   Before filling with fresh antifreeze, drain and flush the system as described in Sections 3 and 4 and check that all the hoses are in good condition and that the clips are all tight. Antifreeze has a searching action and will leak more rapidly than plain water.
5   Refill the system as described in Section 6. All future topping-up should be done using mixed coolant of the correct proportions.
6   The antifreeze should be renewed every two years as the corrosion inhibitor will then be of little use. Don't attempt to use engine antifreeze in the windscreen wash system; it will attack the car's paintwork and will smear the windscreen. Finally remember that antifreeze is poisonous and must be handled with due care.
7   In climates where antifreeze is not required, use a corrosion inhibitor in the cooling system water, never use plain water.

6   Cooling system – filling

If renewing the coolant, the system should always be flushed (Section 4).
1   Before attempting to fill the cooling system make sure that all the hoses and hose clips are in good condition and that the clips are tight. These vehicles must have antifreeze mixture in the system all the year round, to prevent corrosion of light alloys with which the coolant comes into contact as well as preventing the system from freezing in winter.
2   Check that the heater control is in the full heat position and then remove the filler cap from the expansion tank. To release air from the system as it is being filled, on 1.3 engines, partially unscrew the temperature sender from the inlet manifold. On the larger engine variants, release the bleed screw on the thermostat housing. If a bleed screw is not fitted to the thermostat housing, the system is self-bleeding.
3   Fill the system slowly (by pouring coolant into the expansion tank) to prevent air locks forming.
4   If renewing the antifreeze, start by pouring a couple of pints of water into the system, followed by the correct quantity of antifreeze. Refer to the Specifications for the entire system capacity and add half that amount of antifreeze (to give a 50% antifreeze/water mixture). Top up with more water.

5   Close the bleed screw, or refit the temperature sender (if applicable) when coolant, free of air, emerges. Fill to 10 mm (0.4 in) above the level marked KALT (ie COLD) on the expansion tank. Repeated squeezing of the large coolant hoses will induce surging of the mixture in the system which will help to dislodge any air bubbles. Refit the expansion tank filler cap tightly and mop up any spilt fluid.
6   Run the engine at a fast tickover until the cooling fan motor engages and, particularly if the system has been disturbed in any way, examine carefully for leaks. Stop the engine and allow it to cool before topping-up the level in the expansion tank as necessary. Remember that the system must be cold before an accurate level is indicated in the expansion tank.

7   Radiator – removal, inspection and refitting

1   The radiator can be removed complete with the electrically-driven cooling fan if there is no need to disturb the fan. If the fan must be removed, refer to Section 11.
2   Drain the system as described in Section 3, and disconnect and remove the battery.
3   Detach the radiator top and bottom hoses, and also the small diameter vent hose between the top of the radiator and the expansion tank (photo). On automatic transmission models it will also be necessary to disconnect the fluid cooler hoses from the radiator and suitably plug them to avoid loss of automatic transmission fluid.
4   Disconnect the electric wiring from the thermal switch in the radiator at the lower right-hand side. Disconnect the fan motor leads at the connector near the front of the battery.
5   Remove the two clips which secure the radiator located at the top left and right corners of the radiator. Pull the top of the radiator back to free it from the top mountings and then lift it out of the bottom mountings and clear of the car (photos).
6   With the radiator assembly removed it is easier to examine for leaks which will show up as corroded or stained areas. If a leak is found it is advisable to contact a specialist repairer or renew the complete assembly. In an emergency, if a leak is detected with the radiator *in situ*, then a radiator sealant such as Holts Radweld may be used.
7   Clean out the inside of the radiator by flushing as described in Section 4 and also clean the matrix, removing all the dead flies and bugs which reduce the radiator's efficiency. Take this opportunity to inspect the hoses and clips, making sure that all are fit for further use.
8   Refitting the radiator is the reverse of the removal procedure. Check that the rubber mountings are in good condition and ensure that the bottom location pegs fit correctly on installation. Refer to Section 6 for refilling the system. On automatic transmission models check and top-up the transmission fluid level as necessary.

8   Thermostat – removal, testing and refitting

1   Typical symptoms of thermostat malfunction are either a slow warm-up of the engine, anything in excess of 7 to 8 minutes, or an overheating engine as betrayed by high gauge readings, pinking, running-on or boiling of coolant.

7.3 Radiator top hose

7.5A Radiator clip

7.5B Removing the radiator

8.4A Removing the thermostat housing (1.3)

8.4B Extracting the thermostat and seal (1.3)

8.5 Opening temperature is marked on thermostat

8.6A Fitting a new thermostat seal

8.6B Fitting the thermostat to the cylinder head (1.3)

8.8 Thermostat housing and cover (1.6)

2   Before removing the thermostat the system will have to be at least partially drained as described in Section 3.

1.3 models

3   After draining the coolant, undo the securing bolts and remove the timing belt cover. Disconnect the radiator upper hose at its connection on the engine, which is the thermostat housing.

4   Undo the two securing bolts and remove the housing to reveal the thermostat in the cylinder head. Remove the thermostat, noting how it fits in the recesses in the aperture (photos).

5   The thermostat can be tested easily for correct functioning if this should be in doubt. Boil a pan of water and suspend the thermostat on a piece of cord. Lower the thermostat into the hot water and it should be seen to open on immersion. Remove the thermostat from the water and it should be seen to close. This is only a simple functional test but it will identify a failed thermostat. With a thermometer you can check the correct opening temperature, see Specifications, but the full open temperature will be difficult to check as it is above the boiling point of water. When renewing this component make sure that the replacement item is the correct one for your car as thermostats are made for a wide range of different models and conditions (photo).

6   Refitting the thermostat is the reverse procedure to removal, but fit a new rubber seal to the thermostat and install it to locate in the two recesses noted during removal (photos).

7   Tighten the thermostat housing bolts to the specified torque, and don't forget to top up the cooling system.

1.6 and 1.8 models

8   The procedure for removing, testing and refitting of the thermostat on these models is basically the same as that given for the 1.3 model. However, the thermostat is located in a housing which is located externally to the toothed belt cover allowing easier access (photo).

9   On carburettor models, remove the air cleaner unit for improved access to the thermostat housing cover. Drain the engine coolant and then unbolt the thermostat housing cover.

10   Remove the thermostat and test it if necessary as described in paragraph 5.

11   When refitting the thermostat, always use a new cover seal.

12   If the thermostat housing is to be removed, first remove the camshaft toothed belt and the belt rear cover from the engine (see Chapter 1).

13   Disconnect all hoses from the thermostat housing, noting their position for subsequent reconnection (if still attached).

14   Remove the two bolts securing the thermostat housing and lift off the housing. Extract the sealing ring.

15   Refitting is a reversal of the removal procedure. Use a new sealing ring and tighten the thermostat housing bolts to the specified torque.

16   Refill the cooling system (Section 6).

9   Coolant pump – removal and refitting

1   Drain the cooling system as described in Section 3.

2   Slacken the alternator mounting nuts and bolts, swing the alternator in towards the engine and remove the drivebelt.

3   Undo the securing bolts and remove the toothed belt cover. Turn the crankshaft to align the timing mark on the camshaft sprocket with the mark at the top of the housing behind the sprocket, and at the same time align the notch in the rim of the crankshaft pulley with the timing pointer.

4   Slacken the three bolts which hold the pump in the engine block. The pump shaft is eccentric in the pump body so that, by rotating the pump body, the tension in the toothed timing belt can be released. Turn the body of the pump inwards to slacken the toothed belt and slip the belt off the pump pulley. Make sure that the crankshaft and the camshaft are not turned while the belt is removed as, apart from losing the valve timing, the valves or pistons could be damaged. Unbolt and remove the timing belt cover backplate. Withdraw the coolant pump from the engine block (photos).

5   Although the pump can be dismantled and reassembled, a press and several special tools are necessary and it is considered that the

9.4A Removing the coolant pump

9.4B Coolant pump showing drive sprocket

9.6A Coolant pump O-ring seal

9.6B Coolant pump correctly fitted with rotational stops arrowed

work is outside the scope of the home mechanic. For this reason a defective pump should be renewed.

6 Before fitting the coolant pump, clean its mounting in the engine block and fit a new O-ring seal to the pump body. Install the pump in the block and fit the three retaining bolts and washers, but only hand tighten them at this stage (photos). The cut-out in the pump flange must be positioned as shown to act as the toothed belt adjustment limit stop when the pump is rotated to tension the timing belt. Refit the belt cover backplate.

7 Fit the toothed belt to the pump pulley and refer to Chapter 1 for the procedure for tensioning the belt. Tighten the three bolts securing the pump to the specified torque.

8 Refit the toothed belt cover and then fit the drivebelt to the crankshaft and alternator pulleys. Refer to Section 10 for the procedure for tensioning the belt and tighten the alternator mounting bolts.

9 Refill the cooling system as described in Section 6. Finally run the engine up to its normal operating temperature and check for leaks.

10 Drivebelt – removal, refitting and tensioning

1 This belt drives the alternator, taking its power from the crankshaft pulley.

2 Correct tensioning of the drivebelt will ensure that it has a long and useful life. Beware, however, of overtightening as this can cause excessive wear in the alternator.

3 A regular inspection of the belt should be made and if it is found to be overstretched, worn, frayed or cracked it should be renewed before it breaks in service. To insure against such an event arising it is a good idea to carry a spare belt, of the correct type, in the car at all times.

4 To remove an old belt, loosen the alternator mounting bolts and nuts just sufficiently to allow the unit to be pivoted in towards the engine. This will release all tension from the belt which can now be slipped off the respective pulleys. Fit a new belt after checking that it is of the correct type and take up the slack in the belt by swinging the alternator away from the engine and lightly tightening the bolts just to hold it in that position. Note that on models fitted with power steering, it will first be necessary to remove the power steering pump drivebelt. Refer to Chapter 8, Section 14. Don't forget to refit it after the alternator drivebelt has been refitted.

5 Although special tools are available for measuring the belt tension, a good approximation can be achieved if the belt is tensioned so that there is 13 mm (0.5 in) of free movement at the mid-point position on the longest run of belt between pulleys. With the alternator bolts just holding the unit firm, lever the alternator away from the engine using a wooden lever at the mounting bracket end until the correct tension in the belt is reached and then tighten the alternator bolts. On no account apply any loads at the free end of the alternator as serious damage can be caused internally.

6 When a new belt has been fitted it will probably stretch slightly to start with and the tension should be rechecked, and if necessary adjusted, after about 5 minutes running.

Fig. 2.1 Coolant pump mounting bolts – arrowed (Sec 9)

11 Radiator electric cooling fan – removal and refitting

1 Disconnect the battery negative terminal.
2 Disconnect the fan motor leads at the connecting plug.
3 Unbolt the fan/shroud assembly from the radiator and withdraw it upwards (photo).

Fig. 2.2 Cooling fan shroud securing bolts – arrowed (Sec 11)

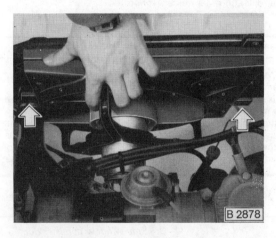

Fig. 2.3 Withdrawing the cooling fan/shroud assembly (Sec 11)

Fig. 2.4 Cooling fan motor mounting nuts – arrowed (Sec 11)

4 To separate the fan motor from the shroud, unscrew the three nuts.
5 Further dismantling of the assembly depends on the extent of the problem. If the motor is defective it would be better to have it overhauled by a specialist as spare parts for it may be difficult to get hold of. The only other course of action would be to renew the complete motor and this may be cheaper and quicker in the long run.
6 Reassembly, if the unit was dismantled, and refitting to the car are the reverse of the dismantling and removal sequences. On completion run the engine up to normal operating temperature and check the fan for correct functioning.

12 Cooling fan thermal switch – removal and refitting

1 The cooling fan is controlled by a thermal switch which is located in the right-hand rear face of the radiator at the bottom corner. If the fan fails to work when it should, the circuit can be tested by connecting together the two electrical leads serving the switch and turning the ignition on. If the fan now works then the switch is at fault and needs changing.
2 To remove the switch, first drain the coolant from the system as described in Section 3, and then disconnect the battery earth lead.
3 Disconnect the electrical wires from the switch and unscrew it from the radiator (photo).

11.3 Radiator/fan shroud assembly. Two securing bolts are arrowed

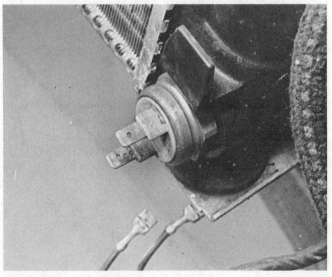

12.3 Radiator thermostat switch

13.1 Coolant temperature sender (1.3)

14.5 Air outlet grille (Saloon model)

15.9 Heater blower motor

4   Refitting is the reverse of the removal procedure, but smear a little sealant on the switch threads before installing it. Refill the system and run the engine up to its normal operating temperature to check the fan for correct functioning, and to check for leaks.

13 Coolant temperature sender – removal and refitting

1   The sender unit is screwed into the inlet manifold on 1.3 models (photo). On other models, the sender is located on the thermostat housing.
2   Before removing the sender unit drain sufficient coolant from the system to avoid spillage, as described in Section 3, and then disconnect the battery earth lead.
3   Disconnect the electrical wire from the sender unit terminal and unscrew the unit from its location.
4   Refitting is the reverse of the removal procedure. Use sealant on the sender unit threads. Refill the system as described in Section 6 and run the engine to check the functioning of the sender unit, and to check for leaks.

14 Heater – description

1   The heater system depends upon fresh air being drawn into the grille at the base of the windscreen and passed through a matrix which is heated from the engine cooling system.
2   Temperature regulation is controlled by mixing cold intake air with warm air, using flap valves both for this function and for the direction of air to the interior, windscreen or side air outlets.
3   An electric booster fan is mounted within the engine compartment to supplement the normal ram effect provided when the vehicle is in forward motion.
4   An independent fresh air ventilation system provides a supply of unheated fresh air at the nozzles on the instrument panel.
5   Stale air is exhausted from the vehicle interior through the slots just to the rear of the rear side windows on Saloon models, or from vents at the rear pillar on other models (photo).

15 Heater components – removal and refitting

Control unit
1   Remove the panel from the bottom of the facia.
2   Prise off the four retaining clips and remove the cover from the heater matrix housing.
3   Extract the self-tapping screws and remove the switch plate from the facia panel. As the switch plate is withdrawn, disconnect the plugs from the rear of the switches. On RHD cars the facia switch panel is retained by four screws. The two bottom screws are in the same

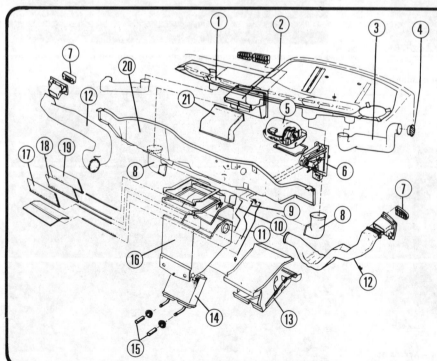

Fig. 2.5 Exploded view of heater (Sec 15)

1   Facia padding
2   Fresh air duct
3   Side window demister duct
4   Side window demister nozzle
5   Blower motor
6   Control unit
7   Heater side vent
8   Windscreen demister hose
9   Control rod (air distributor valve)
10 Control rod (air mix)
11 Control rod (upper distributor valve)
12 Heater vent hose
13 Matrix housing
14 Matrix
15 Coolant flow and return hoses
16 Air distribution housing
17 Upper distributor valve
18 Air mix flap
19 Lower distributor valve
20 Bulkhead
21 Centre duct

positions as those on LHD cars shown in Fig. 2.8. Where a centre console is fitted, this must first be removed or displaced to gain access to the screws. The other two securing screws are located in the heated rear window switch recess and in the choke control recess. These screws are visible in photos 21.3 and 44.26 of Chapter 12.

4 Note the position of the heater control rods in their clamps and clips. Use quick-drying paint if necessary to mark the rods, then disconnect them from the heater housing and from the operating arms of the flap valves in the air distribution housing (Fig. 2.10).

5 Extract the two self-tapping screws which secure the heater control assembly and remove it (Fig. 2.11).

6 Refitting is a reversal of removal, but reconnect the control rods in the following sequence:

   (a) Short rod to upper heat distribution valve arm
   (b) Intermediate rod to lower heat distribution valve arm
   (c) Long rod to air mix flap

Blower motor

7 Open the bonnet and prop it open.

8 Remove the water deflector (if fitted) from the opening on the top

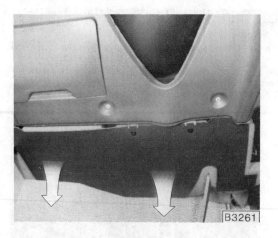

Fig. 2.6 Facia panel removal (arrowed) for control unit access (Sec 15)

Fig. 2.7 Heater matrix lower cover removal (Sec 15)

Retaining clips arrowed

Fig. 2.8 Facia switch plate removal (left-hand drive shown) (Sec 15)

Clips and screws arrowed

Fig. 2.9 Switch lead connecting plugs – arrowed (Sec 15)

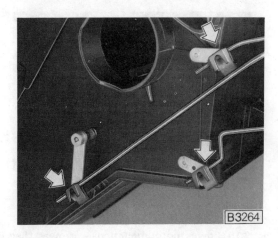

Fig. 2.10 Control rods and levers – arrowed (Sec 15)

of the engine compartment rear bulkhead (Fig. 2.12).

9 Disconnect the wiring harness from the blower motor at the multi-pin plug (photo).

10 Prise off the clips which retain the cover over the motor and remove it.

11 Unscrew the two motor mounting screws and lift the motor from its location (Fig. 2.15).

12 Refitting is a reversal of removal.

Heater matrix

13 Clamp the heater hoses close to the engine compartment rear bulkhead. Self-locking grips will serve for this purpose.

14 Disconnect the heater hoses from the matrix pipe stubs.

15 Plug the pipe stubs to prevent coolant spillage during removal of the matrix.

16 Extract the two screws and remove the centre console.

17 Remove the lower left panel from under the facia, then remove the

Fig. 2.11 Control unit fixing screws – arrowed (Sec 15)

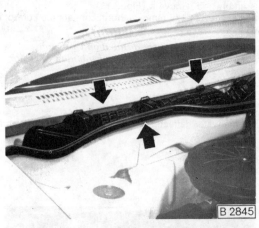

Fig. 2.12 Removing the water deflector (Sec 15)
Securing clips/screws arrowed

Fig. 2.13 Blower motor wiring harness plug (Sec 15)
Disconnect as arrowed

Fig. 2.14 Removing the blower motor cover clips (Sec 15)

Fig. 2.15 Blower motor mountings – arrowed (Sec 15)

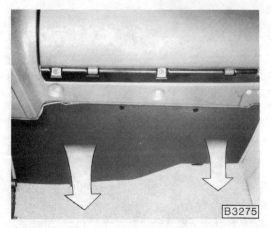

Fig. 2.16 Removal of lower right panel from facia – arrowed (Sec 15)

right-hand one (refer to Chapter 11).

18 Prise off the four retaining clips and remove the cover from the base of the matrix housing (photo).

19 Extract the four screws and one nut which hold the flanges of the air distribution chamber and the matrix housing together (Fig. 2.17).

20 Disconnect the control rod for the air mix flap valve.

21 Release the air mix control rod on the right-hand side.

22 Extract the matrix mounting screws and withdraw the matrix from the heater housing. In order to reach the upper mounting screws, move the flap valve (A) to a vertical position (Fig. 2.18). As the matrix is withdrawn, ease the pipe stubs and their sealing grommets through the bulkhead. Be prepared for some coolant spillage.

23 If the matrix is blocked, try reverse flushing as described for the radiator in Section 4. If this fails, try a radiator cleansing agent, but use it strictly in accordance with the manufacturer's instructions.

24 If the matrix is leaking, have it professionally repaired by a radiator repairer, or purchase a new one. Temporary repairs are not worth the trouble if the unit has to be removed again after a short period of service.

25 Refitting is a reversal of removal.

26 Top up the cooling system. On 1.3 engines, bleed the system as described in Section 6.

Air distribution housing

27 Remove the heater matrix as described in paragraphs 13 to 22.

28 Extract the screws and remove the glove compartment (Fig. 2.20).

15.18 Heater blower cover

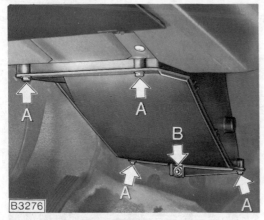

Fig. 2.17 Connection of matrix housing to air distribution chamber (Sec 15)

A   Self-tapping screws   B   Nut

Fig. 2.18 Matrix mounting screws shown with flap valve (A) in vertical position (Sec 15)

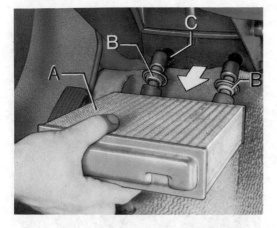

Fig. 2.19 Withdrawing heater matrix (Sec 15)

A   Matrix   B   Grommet   C   Bulkhead

Fig. 2.20 Glove compartment screws – arrowed (Sec 15)

29 Extract the securing screws from the switch plate. Pull the plate forwards until the switch plugs can be disconnected and the assembly removed.

30 Extract the two mounting screws and remove the heater control lever assembly.

31 Extract the two screws which retain the centre fresh air nozzle housing and then pull the housing down and out of the facia panel.

32 Where applicable, disconnect the leads for the radio and clock (Fig. 2.22).

33 Pull off the air distribution ducts A and B for the heater side vents, also the hose from the air distribution housing X (Fig. 2.23).

34 Release but do not remove the two screws A and B (Fig. 2.24) and pull the instrument panel slightly away from the bulkhead.

35 Disconnect the air distribution housing at the top from the bulkhead, and at the base from the facia panel (Fig. 2.25).

36 Remove the air distribution housing (Fig. 2.26).

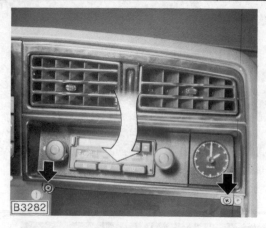

Fig. 2.21 Removal of centre fresh air nozzle housing (Sec 15)

Securing screws arrowed

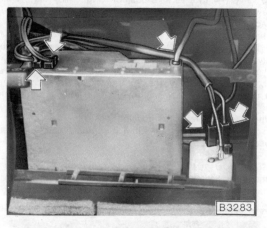

Fig. 2.22 Radio and clock mounting plugs – arrowed (sec 15)

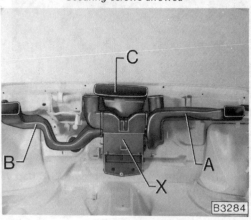

Fig. 2.23 Air distribution housing and ducts (Sec 15)

A   Heater side vent   C   Centre (windscreen) vent
B   Heater side vent   X   Housing

Fig. 2.24 Instrument panel fixing screws A and B (Sec 15)

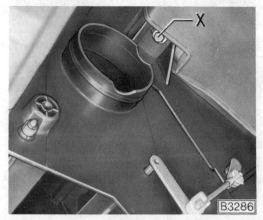

Fig. 2.25 One of the air distribution housing-to-bulkhead fixing screws (X) (Sec 15)

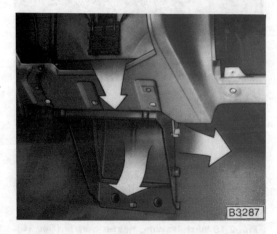

Fig. 2.26 Removing the air distribution housing (Sec 15)

37 Refitting is a reversal of removal, but make sure that the foam sealing strip is in good condition (Fig. 2.27). Reconnect the control rods as described in paragaph 6.

38 Remember to top up the cooling system and if necessary bleed it.

Fig. 2.27 Air distribution housing flange seal – arrowed (Sec 15)

16 Vents and grilles – removal and refitting

Door window demister nozzle

1 Carefully remove the nozzle by prising it from the facia panel padding with a screwdriver.

Side heater vent

2 Remove the swivelling insert by tilting it downwards and carefully depressing one side of it to disengage the locating pivot lug.

3 According to which side the vent is being removed from, either remove the glove compartment or the lighting switch and strip.

4 Extract the two self-tapping screws and pull the vent housing from the facia panel.

Centre fresh air nozzle

5 The swivelling vent is removed in exactly the same way as described for the side vent in paragraph 2.

Stale air exhaust grille

6 Carefully lever off the grille from its fixing grommets.

General

7 Refitting of all components is a reversal of removal, but apply sealing compound around the fixing grommets when engaging the grille lugs in order to make a good weatherproof seal.

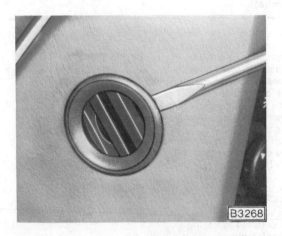

Fig. 2.28 Side (door) window demister nozzle removal (Sec 16)

Fig. 2.29 Removing side vent swivelling insert (Sec 16)

Fig. 2.30 Side vent housing fixing screws – arrowed (Sec 16)

Fig. 2.31 Removing centre fresh air nozzle (Sec 16)

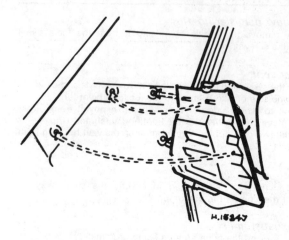

Fig. 2.32 Stale air outlet grille fixings (Saloon) (Sec 16)   Fig. 2.33 Stale air outlet grille (Hatchback) (Sec 16)

17 Fault diagnosis – cooling and heating systems

Symptom	Reason(s)
Overheating	Insufficient coolant in system
	Electric cooling fan inoperative
	Radiator blocked either internally or externally
	Kinked or collapsed hose causing coolant flow restriction
	Thermostat not working properly
	Engine out of tune
	Ignition timing retarded or auto advance malfunction
	Cylinder head gasket blown
	Engine not yet run-in
	Exhaust system partially blocked
	Engine oil level too low
	Brakes binding
Engine running too cool	Faulty, incorrect or missing thermostat
Loss of coolant	Loose hose clips
	Hoses perished or leaking
	Radiator leaking
	Filler/pressure cap defective
	Blown cylinder head gasket
	Cracked cylinder block or head
Heater gives insufficient output	Engine overcooled (see above)
	Heater matrix blocked
	Heater controls maladjusted or broken

Chapter 3 Fuel and exhaust systems

For modifications, and information applicable to later models, see Supplement at end of manual

Contents

Specifications

Part A: Carburettor systems
General
System type .... Rear-mounted fuel tank, mechanically-operated fuel pump, dual barrel carburettor and temperature-controlled air cleaner
Fuel tank capacity .... 61 litres (13.4 gals)
Fuel octane rating .... 98 RON (minimum) – 4-star (see also Section 26)

Fuel pump
Operation .... Mechanical from camshaft
Pressure .... 0.25 to 0.36 bar (3.6 to 5.2 lbf/in²)

Air cleaner
Application:
  1.3 and 1.6 .... Champion W103
  1.8 carburettor .... Champion U512

GM Varajet II carburettor
Throttle valve diameter:
  Stage 1 .... 35.0 mm
  Stage 2 .... 46.0 mm
Venturi diameter .... 28.0 mm
Main jet:
  1.3 201
  1.6 204
Partial load needle 1.51
Float weight 5.6g
Float setting (top surface to flange) .... 4.5 to 6.5 mm
Automatic choke valve gaps (see text):
  A (pull-down) .... 2.8 to 3.4 mm
  B (fast idle) .... 2.3 to 2.8 mm
  C (full throttle) .... 9.5 to 10.5 mm
Manual choke valve gap .... 2.8 to 3.4 mm
Accelerator pump plunger adjustment .... 7.8 to 8.2 mm
Air valve lever free play at rod .... 0.1 to 0.3 mm

Pierburg 2E3 carburettor – 1.3

	Primary	Secondary
Venturi diameter	20 mm	24 mm
Main jet	X97.5	X112.5
Air correction jet	X80	X100
Emulsion tube code number	88	60
Partial load enrichment orifice	0.5 mm	–
Pre-atomizer diameter	8 mm	7 mm
Mixture outlet orifice	2.5 mm	3.0 mm
Idle fuel jet	37.5	–
Idle air jet	130	–

Fuel enrichment jet	–	105 to 125
Float needle valve diameter	1.5 mm	–
Float level	28 to 30 mm	–
Pull-down unit code	55	
Pull-down unit code	59	
Throttle valve fast idle gap:		
Manual transmission	0.8 to 0.9 mm	–
Automatic transmission	1.1 to 1.2 mm	–
Choke valve gap:		
Manual transmission	1.7 to 2.1 mm	
Automatic transmission	2.1 to 2.5 mm	
Accelerator pump delivery (cc per stroke):		
Manual transmission	0.38 to 0.62	–
Automatic transmission	0.18 to 0.42	–

Pierburg 2E3 carburettor – 1.6

	Primary	Secondary
Venturi diameter	20	24
Main jet	X95	X105
Air correction jet	X110	X80
Emulsion tube code number	88	51
Partial load enrichment orifice	0.55	–
Pre-atomizer diameter	8 mm	7 mm
Mixture outlet orifice	2.5 mm	3.0 mm
Idle fuel jet	42.5	–
Idle air jet	132.5	–
Fuel enrichment jet	–	85 to 105
Float needle valve diameter	1.5 mm	–
Float level	28 to 30 mm	–
Throttle valve fast idle gap:		
Manual transmission	0.8 to 0.9 mm	–
Automatic transmission	1.1 to 1.2 mm	–
Choke valve gap:		
Manual transmission	1.7 to 2.1 mm	
Automatic transmission	2.1 to 2.5 mm	
Accelerator pump delivery (cc per stroke):		
Manual transmission	0.38 to 0.62	–
Automatic transmission	0.18 to 0.42	–

Adjustment data

	Manual transmission	Automatic transmission
Idle speed	900 to 950 rpm	800 to 850 rpm
Fast idle speed:		
Varajet II:		
1.3 with automatic choke	2150 to 2250 rpm	2550 to 2650 rpm
1.3 with manual choke	2500 rpm	2600 rpm
1.6	2050 to 2150 rpm	2250 to 2350 rpm
Pierburg 2E3	2100 to 2500 rpm	2400 to 2800 rpm
Exhaust gas CO content at idle	1.0 to 1.5%	1.0 to 1.5%

Torque wrench settings

	Nm	lbf ft
Fuel pump nuts:		
1.3	20	15
1.6	15	11
Carburettor mounting nuts:		
1.3	20	15
1.6	15	11

Part B: Fuel injection systems

General

System type	Rear-mounted fuel tank, Bosch LE Jetronic injection system
Fuel tank capacity	61 litre (13.4 gals)
Fuel octane rating	98 RON (minimum) – 4-star (see also Section 26)

Air cleaner

Champion U511

Fuel pump

Type	Electric
Pressure	2.5 bar (36 lbf/in²)

Fuel filter

Champion L201

Adjustment data

Idle speed:	
Manual transmission	900 to 950 rpm
Automatic transmission	800 to 850 rpm
Exhaust gas CO content at idle	0.2 to 0.5%

Torque wrench setting

	Nm	lbf ft
Fuel injectors	32	24

1 General description

The fuel system on 1.3 and 1.6 models comprises a rear-mounted fuel tank, a mechanically-operated fuel pump, a downdraught twin (dual) barrel carburettor and a temperature-controlled air cleaner.

On 1.8 models a fuel injection system is fitted, a description of which is given in Section 20.

Warning: Fuel hazards

Petrol offers multiple hazards – fire, explosion and toxicity. Do not smoke when working on the fuel system, or allow naked flames nearby. Ensure adequate ventilation if fuel vapour is likely to be produced. Refer to 'Safety first' at the beginning of the manual for more details.

2 Routine maintenance – fuel and exhaust systems

Carry out the following procedures at the intervals given in the Routine Maintenance section at the beginning of the Manual

1 Check all fuel lines and hoses for damage and security, including those located on the underbody.

2 Check the throttle pedal operation and the throttle cable for correct adjustment.

3 Renew the air filter element as described in Section 3.

4 On carburettor engines, clean the pump filter (where applicable), referring to Section 5 for details.

5 On fuel injection models renew the filter unit, referring to Section 25 for details.

6 Check the idle speed and mixture adjustment, referring to Section 10, 15 or 22 as applicable.

7 Examine the exhaust system for security, damage and any signs of leaks. Repair as necessary.

3 Air cleaner – description and testing

1 The air cleaner on all models provides clean air for combustion, excluding airborne dust and dirt which could damage the engine, carburettor or fuel injection system.

2 On carburettor models, a thermostatically-controlled air cleaner is used to regulate the temperature of the air entering the carburettor, according to ambient temperatures and engine load. The air cleaner has two sources of supply, through the normal intake spout (cold air) or from a hot air box mounted on the exhaust manifold (hot air).

3 The airflow through the air cleaner is controlled by a flap valve in the air cleaner spout, which covers or exposes the hot or cold air ports according to temperature and manifold vacuum.

4 A vacuum motor operates the flap valve, and holds it fully open when the temperature in the air cleaner is below a predetermined level. As the air intake temperature rises, the vacuum motor opens or closes the flap valve dependent entirely on manifold vacuum. Thus, during light or constant throttle applications, the flap valve will remain open, supplying the carburettor with hot air, and will close under heavy throttle applications, so that only cold air enters the carburettor.

5 As the temperature in the air cleaner rises still further, the vacuum motor closes the flap valve, therefore allowing only cold air to enter the carburettor under all operating conditions.

6 The vacuum motor is operated by vacuum created in the inlet manifold, and is controlled by a temperature-sensing unit located inside the air cleaner.

7 Should the operation of the temperature-regulating components be suspect, their operation can be tested as follows.

8 Remove the air cleaner as described in the following Section.

9 Apply warm air to the hot air intake port from an external source, such as a hair dryer. At the same time apply vacuum (suction by mouth) to the vacuum hose. Observe the operation of the flap valve, with reference to the previous operating description, as the heat source and suction are applied and removed.

10 If the flap valve fails to respond as described, make sure that the vacuum hoses and connections are sound, and if so, a fault in one of the temperature regulating components is indicated. On 1.6 models, it is possible to renew the temperature-sensing unit after prising off the retaining plate, and also the vacuum motor and intake spout assembly after prising the spout out of the air cleaner body (photos). On 1.3 models, none of the parts are available separately, and a complete air cleaner must be obtained. In all cases, consult with a dealer concerning parts availability before disturbing any of the components.

4 Air cleaner – servicing, removal and refitting

Servicing
Carburettor models

1 To remove the air cleaner element, remove the air cleaner cover. This is secured by a centre nut or bolt, or by three screws (photos). Additionally, release the spring clips around the edge of the cover or, if spring clips are not fitted, carefully prise around the lower edge of the cover with your fingers to release the retaining lugs.

2 With the cover removed, lift out the element (photo).

3 Wipe inside the air cleaner, being careful not to introduce dirt into the carburettor throat. It is preferable to remove the air cleaner completely. Remember to clean the inside of the air cleaner cover.

4 Fit the new element, then refit and secure the cover. Observe any cover-to-body alignment lugs or slots (photos).

Fuel injection models

5 The air cleaner on these models is contained within the airflow sensor housing.

6 Release the locking clip, and disconnect the plug from the airflow sensor (photos). Disconnect the air trunking.

7 Release the spring clips, and lift off the air cleaner cover with airflow sensor attached. The element will probably come away with the cover (photos). Do not drop or jar the airflow sensor.

8 Fit a new element to the cover, engaging the element seal in the cover recess (photo). Refit and secure the cover, then reconnect the airflow sensor plug. Refit the air trunking.

Removal and refitting
Carburettor models

9 Remove the centre retaining nut or bolt or the three screws from the air cleaner cover.

10 Lift the air cleaner off the carburettor, disengaging the hot air pick-up from the manifold shroud, together with the breather and vacuum hoses (photos).

3.10A Air cleaner temperature sensing unit vacuum hose connections (A) and retaining plate (B) (1.6)

3.10B Removing the intake spout from the air cleaner body (1.6)

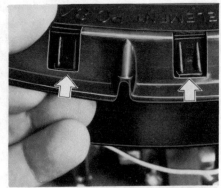

Fig. 3.1 Air cleaner cover securing lugs (arrowed) – 1.3 (Sec 4)

4.1A Air cleaner cover centre bolt and spring clips (1.6)

4.1B Air cleaner cover retaining screws (1.3)

4.2 Air cleaner element renewal

4.4A Air cleaner cover alignment mark (1.3)

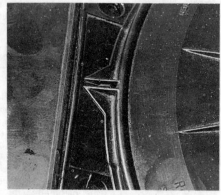

4.4B Air cleaner cover alignment slot (1.6)

4.6A Releasing the airflow sensor plug locking clip

4.6B Disconnecting the airflow sensor plug

4.7A Air cleaner cover spring clip

4.7B Removing the air cleaner cover, element and airflow sensor

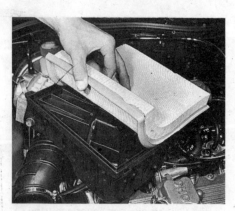

4.8 Fitting a new element to the air cleaner cover

4.10A Disconnect the breather hose at the air cleaner...

4.10B ...and the vacuum hose (arrowed) at the carburettor

5.1 Fuel pump (1.3)

5.5 Fuel pump cover, filter and seal

5.11 Fuel pump hoses

11 Refit by reversing the removal operations, making sure that the gasket or sealing ring is in place on the carburettor.

Fuel injection models
12 Remove the air cleaner element as previously described, then undo the retaining screws, disconnect the air intake tube and remove the housing.
13 Refit by reversing the removal operations.

5 Fuel pump – description, maintenance, testing, removal and refitting

Carburettor models
1 The fuel pump is mounted on the camshaft housing and actuated by a pushrod from an eccentric cam on the camshaft (photo).
2 The mounting location of the pump differs slightly between the 1.3 and 1.6 engines.
3 The fuel pump is of the disposable semi-sealed type; no repairs are possible.
4 At the specified intervals (see *Routine Maintenance*) the filter screen within the pump should be cleaned. To do this, extract the cover retaining screw.
5 Withdraw the cover, turn it over and remove the rubber sealing ring and filter screen (photo).
6 Wipe out the cover and wash the filter screen in clean fuel if it is clogged or partially choked with dirt. Renew the screen at the specified intervals.
7 Locate the filter screen in the cover and fit the sealing ring. Fit the cover to the pump and insert the screw. Do not overtighten the screw.
8 In the event of lack of fuel at the carburettor (and there is known to be fuel in the tank) test the pump in the following way.
9 Disconnect the LT lead which connects the distributor to the ignition coil. This will prevent the engine from firing.
10 Turn the ignition key to operate the starter motor through several revolutions and observe the fuel being ejected from the open end of the fuel hose. It should come out in well-defined spurts, if not, the pump is faulty and must be removed for renewal.
11 To remove the pump, disconnect and plug the fuel hoses. Unscrew and remove the pump mounting bolts and withdraw the pump from the camshaft housing (photo).
12 Refitting is a reversal of removal, but use new flange joint gaskets.

Fuel injection models
13 The fuel pump is of the electrically-operated type, and can be removed as described in Section 25.

6 Fuel tank sender unit – removal and refitting

Warning: *Take adequate fire precautions during this procedure.*

1 Disconnect the battery negative lead. Siphon the fuel from the tank into a clean metal container which can be sealed.

2 Disconnect the leads from the sender unit terminals. On later models also disconnect the fuel line to the pump (photo). Clamp the hose to prevent fuel leakage.

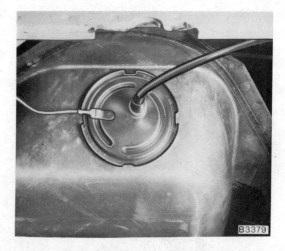

Fig. 3.3 Fuel tank sender unit – 1.3 and 1.6 (Sec 6)

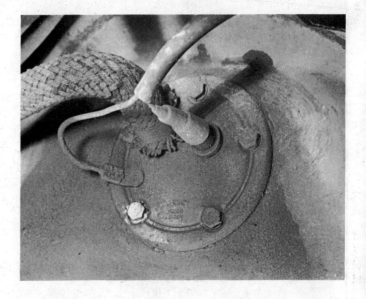

6.2 Fuel tank sender unit – 1.8 with sender unit retained by bolts

3 To remove the sender unit, either engage a flat piece of steel as a lever between two of the raised tabs on the sender unit and turn it anti-clockwise to release it, or undo the retaining bolts (as applicable).

4 Remove the unit carefully to avoid bending the float arm.

5 Take out the sealing ring.

6 Refit by reversing the removal operations, but make sure that the sealing ring is in good condition and seats correctly.

7 Fuel tank – removal and refitting

Warning: *Take adequate fire precautions during this procedure.*

1 Disconnect the battery and then siphon the fuel from the tank into a clean metal container which can be sealed.

2 Measure the exposed part of the threads on the short handbrake cable at the equaliser for ease of resetting, then disconnect the cable.

3 Release the exhaust system at the mounting adjacent to the rear axle to provide greater flexibility.

4 Disconnect the longer handbrake cable from the pullrod.

5 Bend the bracket under the fuel tank upwards and to the rear.

6 Disconnect and clamp the fuel outlet hose from the fuel tank (photo). Note that on fuel injection models, this is connected to the sender unit (photo 6.2).

7 Disconnect the leads from the sender unit terminals.

8 Release the clips and disconnect the filler and short vent hoses from the tank (photos).

9 Support the weight of the fuel tank on a jack with a block of wood as an insulator.

10 Release the tank mounting straps (photo) and then lower the tank sufficiently to be able to disconnect the long vent hose and fuel feed hose (where applicable) from it.

11 Remove the fuel tank from the vehicle.

12 If the tank contains sediment or water, it may be cleaned out using two or three rinses with paraffin. Shake vigorously using several changes of paraffin, but before doing so remove the sender unit (see Section 6). Allow the tank to drain thoroughly.

13 If removal of the tank was carried out in order to mend a leak, have it repaired professionally; radiator repairers will usually do this. *On no account attempt to weld or solder a fuel tank yourself.* To remove all trace of vapour requires several hours of steaming out.

14 Refitting the fuel tank is a reversal of removal, but observe the following points:

   (a) Use new hose clips

   (b) Make sure that the rubber buffers are in position on the left-hand mounting strap (Fig. 3.7)

   (c) Check the handbrake adjustment, see Chapter 9

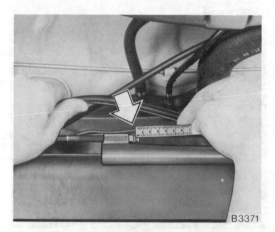

Fig. 3.4 Measuring handbrake cable thread length – arrowed (Sec 7)

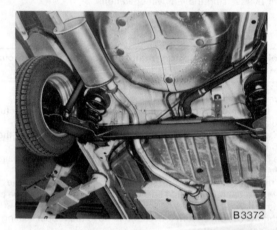

Fig. 3.5 Exhaust system route under fuel tank, but over axle beam (Sec 7)

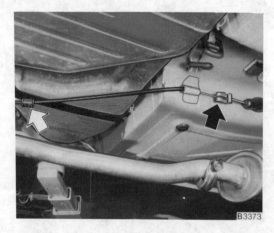

Fig. 3.6 Handbrake cable connection to pullrod – arrowed (Sec 7)

Fig. 3.7 Rubber buffers for left-hand mounting strap on fuel tank – arrowed (Sec 7)

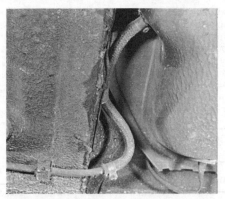

7.6 Fuel tank outlet hose (carburettor models)

7.8A Fuel tank filler/vent hose connections

7.8B Filler/vent hose routing under rear wing

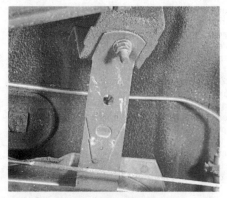

7.10 Fuel tank mounting strap

8.1A Fuel tank vent chamber – early type

8.1B Fuel tank vent chamber – later type

8 Fuel tank vent chamber – description, removal and refitting

1   The vent line from the fuel tank incorporates a vent chamber. This chamber acts as an expansion tank for any increase in the volume of fuel which may occur due to a rise in temperature (photos).

2   The chamber incorporates three individual cells which are interconnected by holes.

3   When filling the fuel tank, it is worth remembering the significance of the following if the tank capacity is to be fully utilized.

4   When fuel reaches the end of the tank vent pipe, the fuel dispensing pump on the garage forecourt will cut off. This indicates that the tank is 95% full. More fuel may be added slowly for a further 30 seconds. After this period, no more fuel should be added, otherwise there will be no space left to allow for fuel expansion, and fuel could be lost through the vent pipe under conditions of rising temperature.

5   The vent chamber also acts as a housing for the fuel cut-off valve. This valve is designed to prevent fuel from escaping from the tank through the vent chamber should the vehicle turn over after an accident.

6   To remove the vent chamber, remove the clips and pull the hoses from it.

7   The hose clips should be levered off with a screwdriver and then discarded as they cannot be used again. Purchase new clips of a suitable type.

8   To check the functioning of the valve, invert the chamber. Pour some fuel into nozzle A and check that fuel is not seen to leak from nozzle B (Fig. 3.8).

9   Refitting is a reversal of removal. Make sure that the hoses are correctly connected and use new hose clips.

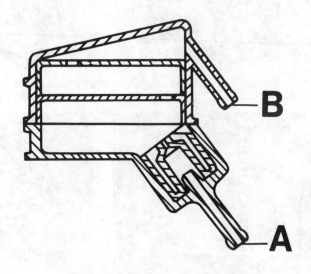

Fig. 3.8 Fuel tank vent chamber (Sec 8)

A   Vent line from tank   B   To atmosphere

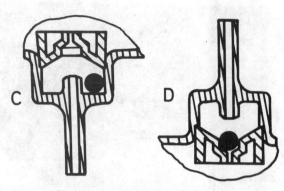

Fig. 3.9 Fuel cut-off valve (Sec 8)

C   *Vehicle in normal attitude*   D   *Vehicle overturned*

9 Carburettor (GM Varajet) – description

1 The GM Varajet II carburettor is of dual barrel downdraught design (photos).
2 On all 1.6 models, and on 1.3 models built before August 1982, an automatic electrically-heated choke is fitted.
3 As from engine numbers 0832150 (manual) and 0858780 (automatic), 1.3 models are fitted with a manual choke Varajet carburettor.
4 The carburettors are very similar except for the choke (cold start) arrangement.
5 On later versions of the 1.3 automatic choke carburettor, a damping valve was introduced in order to overcome a tendency to misfire during hard acceleration between 2700 and 3500 rpm. This valve (Part No

96009298) may be fitted to earlier model carburettors.
6 Enrichment and compensation systems are incorporated to provide optimum performance under all operating and load conditions, and a mechanically-operated accelerator pump is fitted.
7 The new 1.3 manual choke carburettor has a weakening (choke pull-down) feature in which the choke valve plate is opened according to intake vacuum immediately after starting, to prevent over-rich mixtures during the warming-up period.

10 Carburettor (GM Varajet) – idle speed and mixture adjustment

1 The carburettor throttle speed screw and mixture adjusting screws are set during production and are fitted with tamperproof caps (photos).
2 An additional mixture adjusting screw (bypass) is provided. This is not fitted with a tamperproof cap as it is the means by which the engine idle speed is adjusted.
3 Before carrying out any adjustments to the carburettor, make sure that the engine is at normal operating temperature, with the ignition settings (timing and spark plug gaps) correct, that the choke is fully open and that the throttle cable is adjusted correctly.
4 Connect a tachometer to the engine in accordance with the maker's instructions.
5 If the idle speed is outside the specified tolerance (see Specifications), turn the additional mixture (bypass) screw as necessary. This will not alter the CO content of the exhaust gas to any extent.
6 If the carburettor has been subjected to major overhaul or the renewal of internal components, the speed and mixture must be reset in the following way.
7 Connect a tachometer and an exhaust gas analyser in accordance with the manufacturer's instructions. Connect a vacuum gauge to the distributor vacuum take-off point.

9.1A View of GM Varajet carburettor – float chamber side

9.1B View of GM Varajet carburettor – vacuum capsule side

9.1C View of GM Varajet carburettor – automatic choke side

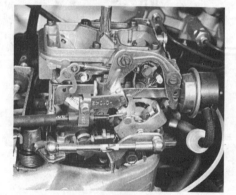

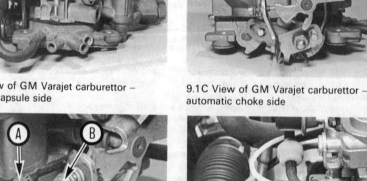

9.1D View of GM Varajet carburettor – manual choke type

10.1A GM Varajet carburettor showing throttle speed (A) and fast idle (B) adjustment screws

10.1B GM Varajet carburettor showing additional mixture screw (bypass) (C) and main mixture screw (D) locations, also the coolant and vacuum hose connections at the rear of the carburettor

8   Remove the tamperproof caps. Satisfy yourself that you are not breaking any local or national laws by so doing.

9   With the engine at normal operating temperature, check the CO content of the exhaust gas. If it is outside the permitted tolerance, turn the main mixture adjusting screw as necessary to correct it.

10 Reduce the idle speed to 600 rpm to check the vacuum reading. If the reading is outside the range 0 to 20 mbar, break off the tamperproof cap from the throttle speed screw and adjust to obtain a reading of 10 mbar. Restore the correct idle speed by means of the additional mixture (bypass) screw.

11 When the adjustments are correct, fit new tamperproof caps to the screws. These are blue in colour and are obtainable from your Vauxhall/Opel dealer.

11 Carburettor (GM Varajet) – in-vehicle adjustments

Automatic choke type carburettor
Fast idle speed

1   First make sure that the engine idle speed is correct as described in the preceding Section.

2   Remove the air cleaner and then plug the end of the vacuum hose which normally connects with the vacuum capsule in the air cleaner.

3   Switch off the ignition.

4   Slightly open the throttle valve plate so that the fast idle screw can be positioned on the second highest step of the cam (Fig. 3.10).

5   Without touching the accelerator, start the engine. The engine speed should be as specified. If it is not, turn the fast idle screw as necessary (photo 10.1A).

Choke valve flap pull-down setting (gap A)

6   In order to be able to carry out this adjustment, a suitable vacuum pump must be available. It is possible to create sufficient vacuum using a modified hand pump or by making a connection with a rubber hose or plastic tube between the choke vacuum unit of the carburettor and the inlet manifold of another vehicle (engine running).

7   Remove the air cleaner.

8   Position the fast idle screw on the uppermost step of the cam. Check that the choke valve plate is fully closed. This may not be the case if the choke cover is still warm, in which case use a rubber band to close it (Fig. 3.11).

9   Apply vacuum to the choke vacuum unit as described in paragraph 6.

10 Refer to Fig. 3.12. Measure the gap A between the edge of the choke valve plate and the wall of the carburettor. Measure at the flatter side of the valve plate. A twist drill or similar should be used as a gauge. The gap should be as specified.

11 If necessary, turn the screw B to bring the gap to the specified clearance. If the gap was found to be too small, it will probably be necessary to bend the pullrod slightly to provide sufficient clearance for movement of the adjustment screw.

Fig. 3.10 Carburettor fast idle screw (arrowed) set on second highest cam step (2) (Sec 11)

Fig. 3.11 Using a rubber band to close the choke valve plate (Sec 11)

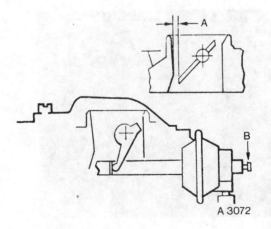

Fig. 3.12 Checking valve plate-to-carburettor gap (Sec 11)

A   See Specifications   *B   Adjustment screw on vacuum unit*

12 On completion of adjustment, lock the adjustment screw with a drop of suitable sealant.

13 Now check the play between the baffle flap lever and the pullrod with the vacuum source still connected so that the pullrod is in the fully extended position (Fig. 3.13). The clearance A must be as shown. Where necessary, bend the end of the pullrod to bring the clearance within tolerance.

Choke valve flap fast idle setting (gap B)

14 Close the choke valve with a rubber band (see Fig. 3.11).

15 Open the throttle and position the fast idle screw on the second highest step of the fast idle cam. Release the throttle and check that the screw stays on the step.

16 Open the choke valve slightly and release it in order to let it find its correct position. Check the choke valve gap B by the same method as when checking the pull-down gap.

17 If adjustment is necessary, remove the carburettor and take off the choke cover. Bend the rod which connects the fast idle cam to the choke valve lever until the gap is correct.

18 If adjustment has been necessary, recheck the pull-down gap afer refitting the carburettor.

Choke valve flap full throttle setting (gap C)

19 Close the choke valve with a rubber band. Open the throttle fully and hold it open while measuring the choke valve gap.

20 If adjustment is necessary, bend that part of the linkage shown in Fig. 3.14. Bend the tag to the right to increase the gap, to the left to decrease it.

Automatic choke cover

21 The pointer on the choke housing cover should be set in the central position. If there is any tendency to stall or hesitate during warm-up, it is permissible to turn the cover through one or two divisions towards R (rich).

22 When starting the engine from cold, it should take between two and three minutes for the choke valve plate to reach the fully open position. If a longer time is required, renew the choke cover and check the valve plate for free movement.

Accelerator pump

23 With the air cleaner removed, check that, with the engine at normal operating temperature, the throttle valve plate lever is in the idle position. Stop the engine.

24 With the fingers, open the throttle valve plate smoothly to the full throttle position, at the same time observing the fuel being ejected from the accelerator pump nozzle. The fuel stream must be continuous without interruption over the complete pump stroke. If it is not, the pump must be dismantled and worn seals renewed.

25 Using a screwdriver, depress the accelerator pump pushrod to its stop and then measure the clearance between the end of the lever and the rod (Fig. 3.15). This should be within the specified limits. If it is not, bend the pump lever.

Float level

26 Remove the carburettor cover.

27 Using moderate finger pressure, hold the fuel inlet needle valve closed by applying pressure to the float arms and pivot clip.

28 The top surface of the float should be the specified distance below the carburettor top flange (Fig. 3.16).

29 Where necessary, bend the arms of the float equally at the points indicated (Fig. 3.17).

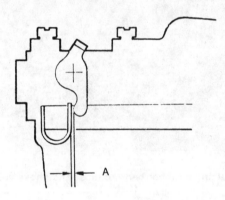

Fig. 3.13 Baffle flap-to-pullrod clearance (Sec 11)

A = 0.1 to 0.3 mm (0.004 to 0.012 in)

Fig. 3.14 Varajet carburettor adjustment: bend tag G to adjust the choke valve gap (Sec 11)

Fig. 3.15 Accelerator lever-to-rod setting (Sec 11)

A = 7.8 to 8.2 mm (0.31 to 0.32 in)

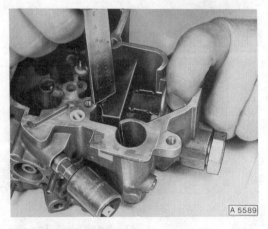

Fig. 3.16 Measuring float setting (Sec 11)

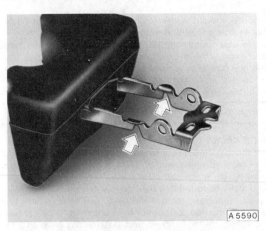

Fig. 3.17 Float level adjustment (Sec 11)

Bend at points arrowed

Fig. 3.18 Varajet manual choke cable adjustment (Sec 11)

1   Spring retaining clip
2   Inner cable clamp
3   Outer cable clamp

Fig. 3.19 Varajet carburettor damping valve (arrowed) may be fitted to later models (Sec 9)

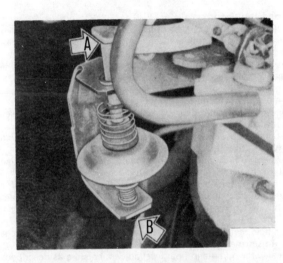

Fig. 3.20 Varajet carburettor throttle damper (Sec 11)

A   Damper pin   B   Locknut

Manual choke type carburettor

Choke valve flap pull-down

30 Remove the air cleaner.

31 Pull the choke control until the mark on the cam is aligned with the centre of the fast idle screw.

32 An outside vacuum source must now be applied to the carburettor vacuum unit. To do this, either use a hand-operated suction pump, or connect a tube to the inlet manifold of another vehicle which has its engine idling.

33 Check the gap between the edge of the choke valve plate and the carburettor throat wall. The gap should be measured with a twist drill of suitable diameter (see Specifications).

34 Where adjustment is required, turn the adjusting screw (see Fig. 3.12). Should it be found that the gap is too small for correction, bend the rod end fitting.

Fast idle speed

35 With the engine at normal operating temperature, stop the engine and remove the air cleaner.

36 Plug the end of the small bore hose which was disconnected from the air cleaner and runs to the carburettor.

37 Pull the choke control cable until the mark on the cam is aligned with the centre of the fast idle screw.

38 Hold the choke valve plate fully open using the fingers or a rubber band.

39 Start the engine and check that the fast idle speed is as given in the Specifications. The vehicle tachometer can be used for this, but if one is not fitted, then a suitable instrument will have to be temporarily connected in accordance with the manufacturer's instructions.

40 If adjustment is required then the fast idle screw should be turned in or out as necessary (photo 10.1A).

Choke cable adjustment

41 Incorrect setting of the choke cable can prevent full opening of the primary barrel flap, isolating the secondary barrel, resulting in lack of performance once the vehicle has reached normal operating temperature.

42 Adjust the choke cable as follows:

43 Release the clamp screws on the inner and outer choke cables.

44 Push the choke control arm to the fully off position, when the control arm should be engaged with the spring metal retaining clip.

45 Position the outer cable comfortably in its clamp and tighten the retaining screw.

46 Now tighten the clamp screw on the inner cable.

47 Check the operation of the choke for full and free movement, and that it returns to the fully off position in contact with the spring metal retaining clip (Fig. 3.18).

Manual and automatic choke type carburettors

Throttle linkage damper – automatic transmission models

48 Automatic transmission models may be equipped with a throttle linkage damper, the purpose of which is to stop the throttle snapping shut suddenly when the pedal is released.

49 Correct adjustment of the damper is carried out as follows. Release the damper locknut and unscrew the damper until the damper pin is only just touching the throttle lever. From this position, screw the damper back in between 3 and 4 complete turns, then secure with the locknut (Fig. 3.20).

**Fig. 3.21 Varajet carburettor part load regulator screw –
arrowed (Sec 11)**

Part load regulator screw

50 Conditions such as jerking or hesitation at light throttle openings, or excessive fuel consumption despite moderate driving habits, may be due to incorrect adjustment of the part load regulator screw.
51 It is emphasised that this adjustment should not be attempted until all other possible causes of the problems mentioned have been investigated.
52 Remove the carburettor from the vehicle.
53 Prise out the metal plug covering the part load regulator screw (adjacent to the fuel inlet union) (Fig. 3.21).
54 If stalling or hesitation is the reason for adjustment – ie the mixture is too weak – turn the screw one-quarter turn anti-clockwise.
55 If excessive fuel consumption is the problem – ie the mixture is too rich – turn the screw one-quarter turn clockwise.
56 Refit the carburettor and test drive the vehicle to see if any improvement has occurred. If necessary a further adjustment can be made, but **do not** deviate from the original setting by more than half a turn of the screw.
57 Fit a new metal plug on completion, where this is required by law.
Other adjustments
58 Accelerator pump and float level adjustments are as described for the automatic choke carburettor earlier in this Section.

12 Carburettor (GM Varajet) – removal and refitting

1 Remove the air cleaner as described in Section 4. Disconnect the battery.
2 Disconnect the fuel hose from the carburettor and plug the hose.
3 Disconnect the electrical lead from the automatic choke, or disconnect the manual choke cable.
4 Disconnect the throttle control linkage at the balljoint. Disconnect

the distributor vacuum hose, also the one to the air cleaner (see photo 10.1B).
5 Clamp the coolant hoses to the rear of the throttle body, these being the warm-up feed and return hoses.
6 Unscrew and remove the four mounting nuts from the carburettor flange and remove the carburettor from the manifold.
7 Refitting is a reversal of removal. Use new flange gaskets.

13 Carburettor (GM Varajet) – overhaul

Automatic choke type
1 It is rare for the carburettor to require complete dismantling: indeed, normally where this is required then it would probably be more economical to renew the complete unit.
2 It will usually be found that the first few operations described in the following paragraphs to remove the cover will be sufficient to enable cleaning of the jets and carburettor float chamber to be carried out.
3 With the carburettor removed and external dirt cleaned away, pull off the vacuum hose from the choke vacuum unit.
4 Extract the three screws from the automatic choke retaining ring and withdraw the assembly.
5 Extract the split pin and disconnect the accelerator pump rod from the lever (Fig. 3.24).
6 Unscrew the fuel inlet nozzle and extract the gauze filter from inside it (photo).
7 Extract the retaining clip and disconnect the choke connecting rod from the cam (Fig. 3.25).
8 Extract the three short and four long carburettor cover retaining bolts (photo).
9 Remove the cover, making sure that, as it is withdrawn, the gasket remains behind on the flange of the float chamber. Remember that the accelerator pump plunger is under spring tension.
10 Remove the accelerator pump plunger and spring and carefully peel off the cover gasket (photo). Remove the pump suction valve spring retainer (Fig. 3.27).
11 Pull or twist out the vacuum piston spring and needle of the carburettor first stage. Take care not to bend the retaining bracket or partial load needle (Figs. 3.28 and 3.29).
12 If necessary, the partial load plunger may be withdrawn by gripping its rod with a pair of pliers.
13 Remove the packing piece, float and needle from the float chamber. Empty the fuel from the chamber (photo).
14 Note their location and unscrew the jets (Figs. 3.31 and 3.32).
15 Extract the four retaining screws and remove the throttle valve plate block (Fig. 3.33).
16 Further dismantling is not recommended.
17 Clean all components and renew any that are worn or damaged. If the throttle valve plate spindle is worn then the complete throttle block must be renewed. Clean jets and passages with air pressure only; never probe with wire or their calibration will be ruined.
18 Obtain a repair kit which will contain all the necessary renewable items, including gaskets.
19 Reassembly is a reversal of dismantling, but observe the following points.

13.6 Fuel inlet union and gauze

13.8 Varajet carburettor top cover

13.10 Removing the accelerator pump plunger and spring

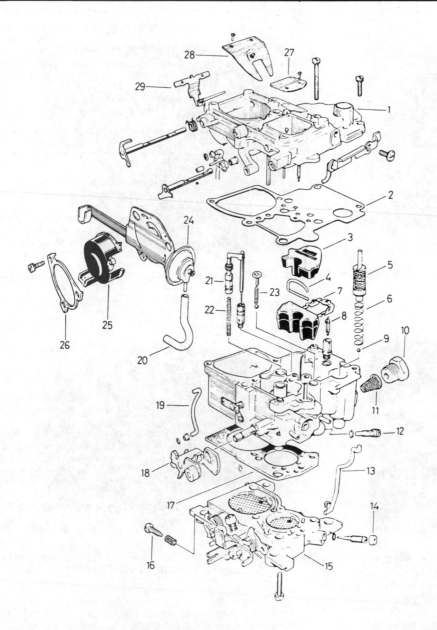

Fig. 3.22 Exploded view of the GM
Varajet carburettor (Sec 13)

1   Cover
2   Gasket
3   Packing piece
4   Float pin
5   Accelerator pump plunger
6   Spring
7   Float
8   Fuel inlet needle valve
9   Check ball (accelerator pump)
10 Fuel filter union
11 Fuel filter
12 Bypass screw
13 Link rod
14 Mixture screw
15 Throttle valve block
16 Fast idle screw and spring
17 Gasket
18 Fast idle cam
19 Fast idle link rod
20 Vacuum hose
21 Part load needle valve and piston
22 Spring
23 Suction valve and check ball
24 Choke vacuum unit
25 Choke housing cover
26 Cover retainer
27 Choke valve plate (primary barrel)
28 Baffle flap (secondary barrel)
29 Full load needle valve

Fig. 3.23 Automatic choke mounting bracket – GM Varajet
(Sec 13)

Fig. 3.24 Accelerator pump rod-to-lever connection
(arrowed) – GM Varajet (Sec 13)

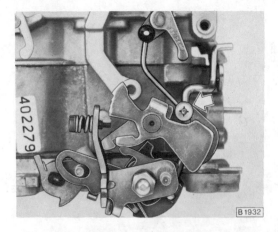

Fig. 3.25 Choke rod-to-cam connection – GM Varajet (Sec 13)

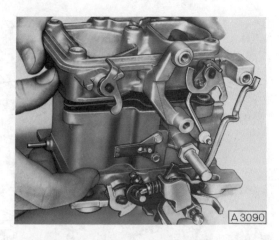

Fig. 3.26 Removing the carburettor cover – GM Varajet (Sec 13)

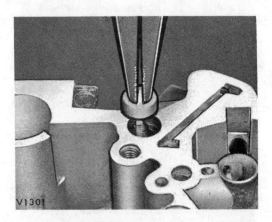

Fig. 3.27 Removing the pump suction valve spring retainer – GM Varajet (Sec 13)

Fig. 3.28 Removing the vacuum piston, spring and needle (arrowed) – GM Varajet (Sec 13)

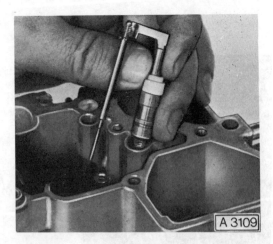

Fig. 3.29 Part load needle valve withdrawal – GM Varajet (Sec 13)

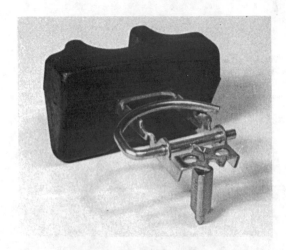

13.13 Float and fuel inlet valve removed

Fig. 3.30 Packing piece and float removal – GM Varajet
(Sec 13)

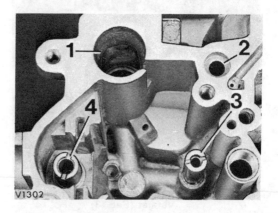

Fig. 3.31 Jet and bore locations – GM Varajet (Sec 13)

1   Accelerator pump bore   3   Main jet
2   Vacuum valve spring drilling   4   Fuel inlet valve seat

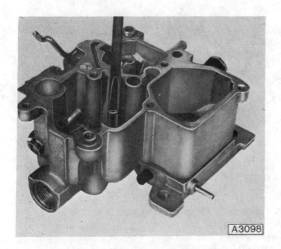

Fig. 3.32 Removing a jet from the GM Varajet carburettor
(Sec 13)

Fig. 3.33 Throttle block securing screws (arrowed) – GM
Varajet (Sec 13)

Fig. 3.34 Removing the throttle block – GM Varajet (Sec 13)

20 When assembling the accelerator pump, ensure that the check ball is correctly located (Fig. 3.35).

21 Check that the needle valve spring is correctly located (Fig. 3.36).

22 When installing the cover to the carburettor body, take care that the accelerator pump plunger does not become wedged.

23 Make sure that the breather screen is in position.

24 Check that the bi-metallic spring of the automatic choke engages positively with the choke valve plate spindle arm (Fig. 3.37).

25 Check the operation of the throttle valve plate lever. Remember that the secondary valve plate does not open until the primary valve plate has opened by two-thirds of its travel. The secondary throttle valve plate will not open until the choke valve plate is fully open after the engine has reached operating temperature.

26 Carry out those checks and adjustments described in Section 11 which can be done with the carburettor on the bench.

27 When the carburettor has been refitted to the engine, adjust the idle speed and the fuel/air mixture (CO content of exhaust gas) as described in Section 10. Also carry out the remainder of the adjustments described in Section 11.

Manual choke type

28 The operations are very similar to those described in the preceding paragraphs, but ignore all reference to automatic choke components.

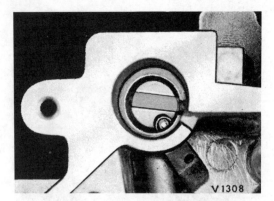

Fig. 3.35 Location of accelerator pump check ball – GM Varajet (Sec 13)

Fig. 3.36 Fuel inlet valve with spring (arrowed) – GM Varajet (Sec 13)

Fig. 3.37 Automatic choke housing – GM Varajet (Sec 13)

1 Bi-metallic spring   2 Choke spindle lever

14 Carburettor (Pierburg 2E3) – description

1   The Pierburg 2E3 carburettor is a dual barrel downdraught instrument with automatic choke. It is fitted to vehicles with the 1.6 engine and the 1.3 engine made from 1985 (photos).
2   The automatic choke is of the usual strangler type, controlled by a bi-metallic spring; the choke cover is heated electrically and by coolant, ensuring a rapid response to changing engine and ambient temperature. Over-choking is avoided by the eccentric mounting of the choke valve plate, by a vacuum pull-down system and by a mechanical linkage with the throttle mechanism.
3   With the engine at operating temperature, idling mixture is supplied via a bypass system. Although an idle cut-off valve is shown in some of the illustrations, no such valve was found on the carburettor examined. Unusually, idle speed adjustment takes place at the throttle stop screw.

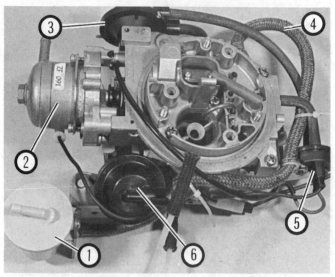

14.1A Top view of Pierburg carburettor

1 Vapour separator
2 Choke cover
3 Choke pull-down unit
4 Fuel hose
5 Vacuum switch
6 Secondary throttle vacuum unit

4   Opening of the throttle valves is sequential. The primary throttle valve is opened mechanically; the secondary throttle valve is opened by vacuum developed in both venturis, but is prevented from so doing until the primary valve is at least half open. For safety reasons both throttle valves are closed mechanically.
5   Efficient operation under all speed and load conditions is ensured by a part load enrichment valve and by primary and secondary transition systems. An accelerator pump provides extra fuel needed for rapid acceleration.

14.1B Pierburg carburettor – showing side view choke cover

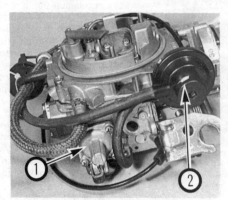

14.1C Pierburg carburettor – side view showing accelerator pump (1) and choke pull-down unit (2)

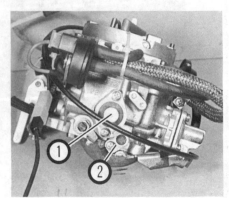

14.1D Pierburg carburettor – side view showing part load enrichment valve (1) and accelerator pump cam (2)

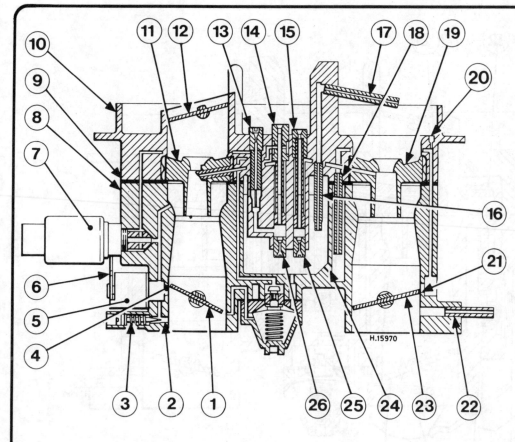

Fig. 3.38 Sectional view of the Pierburg 2E3 carburettor (Sec 14)

1 Primary throttle valve
2 Idle mixture outlet
3 Idle mixture adjustment screw
4 Transition louvre
5 Not on Cavalier
6 Not on Cavalier
7 Not on Cavalier
8 Carburettor body
9 Gasket
10 Carburettor cover
11 Primary pre-atomizer
12 Choke valve
13 Idle fuel and air jet
14 Primary air correction jet and emulsion tube
15 Secondary air correction jet and emulsion tube
16 Riser tube (secondary full load enrichment)
17 Discharge beak (secondary full load enrichment)
18 Riser tube (secondary transition)
19 Secondary pre-atomizer
20 Secondary transition vent
21 Secondary transition louvre
22 Choke pull-down vacuum take-off
23 Secondary throttle valve
24 Secondary transition jet
25 Secondary main jet
26 Primary main jet

H.15970

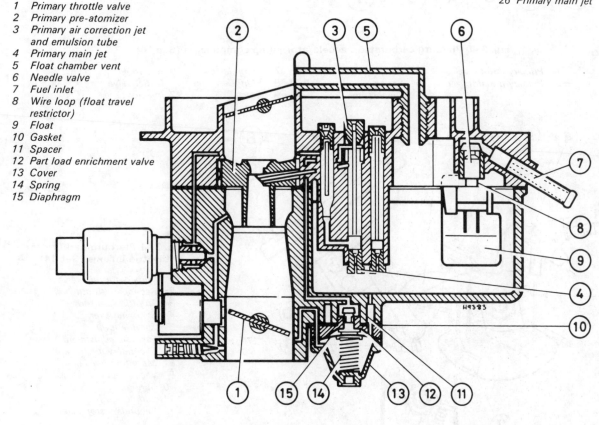

1 Primary throttle valve
2 Primary pre-atomizer
3 Primary air correction jet and emulsion tube
4 Primary main jet
5 Float chamber vent
6 Needle valve
7 Fuel inlet
8 Wire loop (float travel restrictor)
9 Float
10 Gasket
11 Spacer
12 Part load enrichment valve
13 Cover
14 Spring
15 Diaphragm

H9383

Fig. 3.39 Pierburg carburettor: float chamber and part load enrichment (Sec 14)

92

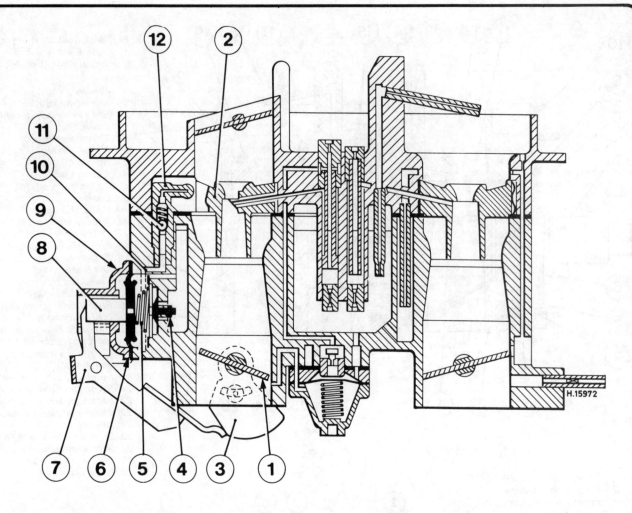

Fig. 3.40 Pierburg carburettor: accelerator pump components (Sec 14)

1	Primary throttle valve	4	Pump intake valve	7	Pump lever	10	Return jet
2	Primary pre-atomizer	5	Spring	8	Plunger	11	Outlet valve
3	Cam	6	Diaphragm	9	Cover	12	Injector tube

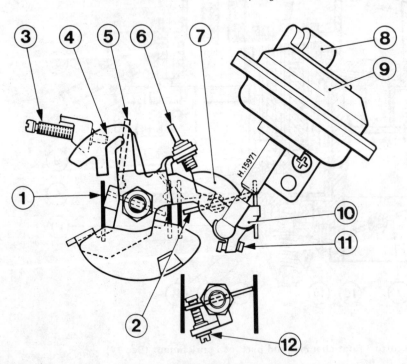

Fig. 3.41 Pierburg carburettor throttle linkage (Sec 14)

1 Primary throttle valve
2 Secondary throttle valve
3 Throttle stop screw
4 Segment lever
5 Throttle lever
6 Fast idle adjustment screw
7 Secondary interlock lever
8 Mounting bracket
9 Vacuum unit
10 Spring
11 Fork lever
12 Secondary stop screw

15 Carburettor (Pierburg 2E3) – idle speed and mixture adjustment

1 The engine must be at normal operating temperature (but the radiator fan must not be working) and all other factors which may affect the idle speed (spark plug condition and gaps, ignition timing, valve clearances) must be correct. The air cleaner element must be clean and the hot air pick-up system must be operating correctly. Electrical loads (lights, heated rear window etc) must be switched off.
2 Connect a tachometer and an exhaust gas analyser to the engine in accordance with their makers' instructions. If an exhaust gas analyser is not available, a proprietary mixture indicating device may be used instead.
3 Start the engine and allow it to idle. If the idle speed is outside the specified limits, adjust by means of the throttle stop screw (photo).
4 When the idle speed is correct, check the CO level in the exhaust gas. If it is outside the specified limits, adjust by means of the idle mixture adjustment screw. In production the screw is covered by a tamperproof plug; satisfy yourself that you are not breaking any local or national laws before removing the plug (photo).
5 With the idle mixture correct, readjust the idle speed if necessary.
6 When both speed and mixture are correct, stop the engine and disconnect the test equipment. Fit a new tamperproof plug to the idle mixture adjustment screw where this is required by law.

16 Carburettor (Pierburg 2E3) – in-vehicle adjustments

The checks and adjustments described below are not normally necessary and should only be made if the adjustments described in Section 15 fail to provide a satisfactory performance from the carburettor. These checks and adjustments may also be necessary after dismantling and overhaul of the carburettor.
Fast idle speed
1 The engine must be at operating temperature and the idle speed

and mixture must be correctly adjusted. Remove the air cleaner to improve access.
2 Position the fast idle adjustment screw on the second highest step of the fast idle cam. Connect a tachometer to the engine. Make sure that the choke plate is fully open.
3 Start the engine without touching the throttle pedal and compare the engine speed with that given in Specifications. If adjustment is necessary, remove the tamperproof cap from the head of the fast idle screw by crushing it with pliers and adjust by means of the screw (photo).
4 When adjustment is correct, stop the engine and disconnect the tachometer. Fit a new tamperproof cap where this is required by law.
Choke pull-down
5 Remove the air cleaner.
6 Remove the choke cover by removing the three screws and the securing ring. There is no need to disconnect the coolant hoses, just move the cover aside. Notice how the loop in the end of the bi-metallic spring engages in the choke drive lever (photo).
7 Move the choke drive lever to close the choke valve completely. Position the fast idle screw on the highest step of the cam.
8 Apply vacuum to the choke pull-down unit (at the hose nearest the carburettor body) using a modified bicycle pump or similar item. Apply light pressure to the choke drive lever in a clockwise direction (as if to close the choke valve) and check the choke valve gap by inserting a gauge rod or twist drill of the specified size (photo).
9 If adjustment is necessary, turn the adjusting screw on the side of the choke housing (photo).
10 Refit the choke cover, making sure that the spring loop engages in the choke drive lever. Align the notches in the choke cover and choke housing when tightening the screws (photo).
Vacuum units – checking for leaks
11 If a vacuum source incorporating a gauge is available, apply approx 300 mbar (9 inHg) to the choke pull-down unit at the hose nearest the carburettor body. Close off the vacuum source and check that the vacuum is held. If there is a leak, rectify or renew the leaking component.
12 Similarly check the secondary throttle vacuum unit.

15.3 Throttle stop screw (arrowed) on Pierburg carburettor

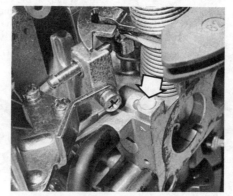
15.4 Idle mixture adjustment screw is under tamperproof plug (arrowed) – carburettor removed for clarity

16.3 Fast idle adjustment screw (arrowed) – carburettor removed for clarity

16.6 Choke drive lever (A) engages loop (B)

16.8 Checking the choke pull-down gap with a twist drill. Apply vacuum to hose arrowed

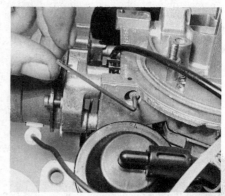
16.9 Choke pull-down adjusting screw

16.10 Choke cover alignment marks (arrowed)

17.8 Removing the Pierburg carburettor

18.4 Removing fuel strainer from inlet pipes

13 If a suitable vacuum source is not available, testing of suspect vacuum units must be by substitution of a known good item.

17 Carburettor (Pierburg 2E3) – removal and refitting

1 Remove the air cleaner, as described in Section 4.
2 Disconnect the battery earth lead.
3 Disconnect and plug the coolant hoses from the automatic choke, noting which hose goes to which connection. Be prepared for some coolant spillage.
4 Disconnect and plug the fuel return hose from the top of the vapour separator and the fuel supply hose from the side of the vapour separator. Be prepared for some fuel spillage.
5 Disconnect the throttle cable outer by pulling it out of its bracket. Unhook the inner cable from the throttle operating plate.
6 Disconnect the distributor vacuum hose at the distributor.
7 Disconnect the carburettor electrical supply at the wiring harness connector near the bulkhead.
8 Remove the three nuts from the top of the carburettor and lift the carburettor off its studs (photo).
9 Refit in the reverse order to removal. Use a new carburettor-to-manifold gasket if the old one was damaged. If much coolant was lost, check the coolant level after the engine has been run and top up if necessary.

18 Carburettor (Pierburg 2E3) – overhaul

1 With the carburettor removed from the vehicle, drain the fuel from the float chamber and vapour separator. Clean the outside of the carburettor.
2 Remove the hoses and wires from the carburettor, making identifying marks or notes to avoid confusion on reassembly.
3 Access to the jets and float chamber is obtained by removing the top half of the carburettor, which is secured by five screws. Blow through the jets and drillings with compressed air, or air from a foot pump – do not probe them with wire. If it is wished to remove the jets, unscrew them carefully with well-fitting tools.
4 Remove the fuel strainer from the inlet pipe by hooking it out with a small screwdriver, or by snaring it with a long thin screw. Renew the strainer (photo).
5 Clean any foreign matter from the float chamber. Renew the inlet needle valve and seat if wear is evident, or if a high mileage has been covered. Renew the float if it is punctured or otherwise damaged.
6 No procedure has been specified for float level adjustment; in any case the tolerance allowed is so wide that precision setting is clearly unnecessary. Simply check that the inlet needle valve is closed completely before the float reaches the top of its stroke.
7 Renew the diaphragms in the part load enrichment valve and in the accelerator pump. If additional pump or valve parts are supplied in the overhaul kit, renew these parts also.
8 Further dismantling is not recommended. Pay particular attention to the throttle opening mechanism if it is decided to dismantle it; the interlocking arrangement is important.

9 Reassemble in the reverse order to dismantling. Use new gaskets and seals throughout, lubricate linkages with a smear of molybdenum-based grease.
10 Before refitting the carburettor, carry out the checks and adjustments described in the following Section.

19 Carburettor (Pierburg 2E3) – adjustments with carburettor removed

Fast idle cam position

1 The choke pull-down adjustment previously described (Section 16) must be correct.
2 If not already done, remove the choke cover.
3 Open the throttle, then close the choke valve by light finger pressure on the choke drive lever. Release the throttle.
4 Check that the fast idle adjustment screw is resting on the second highest step of the fast idle cam, in the position shown in Fig. 3.42. If not, first check that the choke return spring is correctly positioned, then adjust by bending the lever 2 (Fig. 3.42).
5 Refit and secure the choke cover, observing the alignment marks.

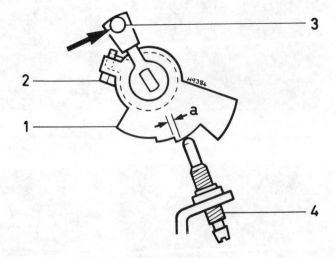

Fig. 3.42 Pierburg carburettor: fast idle cam adjustment (Sec 19)

1   Fast idle cam
2   Adjustment lever

3   Choke drive lever (press in direction arrowed)
4   Fast idle adjustment screw

a = 0.2 to 0.8 mm (0.008 to 0.031 in)

Throttle valve fast idle gap

6 Position the fast idle adjustment screw on the highest step of the fast idle cam.

7 Use a gauge rod or twist drill of the specified diameter to measure the opening of the primary throttle screw. Adjust if necessary at the fast idle adjustment screw. (This is a preliminary adjustment; final adjustment of the fast idle speed should take place with the engine running.)

Accelerator pump delivery

8 It will be necessary to feed the float chamber with fuel from a small reservoir during this test. Take all necessary fire precautions when dealing with fuel and fuel vapour.

9 Position the primary barrel over an accurate measuring glass. Fully open and close the throttle ten times, taking approximately one second for each opening and pausing for three seconds after each return stroke. Make sure that the fast idle cam is not restricting throttle travel at either end.

10 Measure the quantity of fuel delivered and divide by ten to obtain the quantity per stroke. Compare the quantity per stroke with the specified value.

11 If adjustment is necessary, release the clamp screw and turn the cam plate in the desired direction (photo). Tighten the clamp screw and recheck the pump delivery.

19.11 Accelerator pump delivery adjustment (+ to increase, − to decrease)

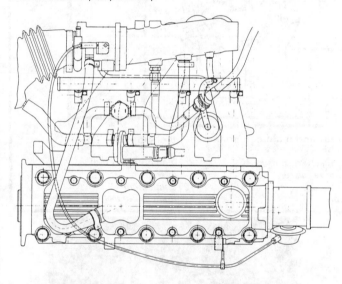

Fig. 3.43 Plan view of the LE Jetronic fuel injection system showing the hose connections – 1.8 engine (Sec 20)

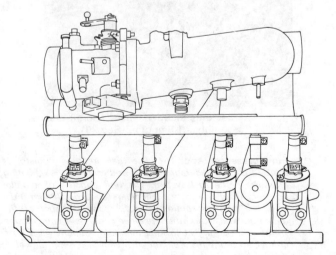

Fig. 3.44 Plan view of the LE Jetronic fuel injection system, showing the throttle valve housing and injector layout – 1.8 engine (Sec 20)

20 Fuel injection system – description

1 A Bosch LE Jetronic fuel injection system is fitted to 1.8 models.

2 By means of electronic control, the fuel injection system supplies the precise amount of fuel for optimum engine performance, with minimum exhaust emission levels. This is achieved by continuously monitoring the engine using various sensors, whose data is input to an electronic control unit in the form of electrical signals. Based on this constantly-changing data, the control unit determines the fuel necessary to suit all engine speed and load conditions, which is then injected directly into the inlet manifold.

3 The main components of the system are:

(a) **Control unit.** *The signals delivered by the various sensors are processed in the control unit, and from these signals, the appropriate control impulses for the fuel injectors are generated. Additional circuitry within the control unit operates an overrun fuel cut-off to reduce fuel consumption, and a cold start booster for cold starting fuel enrichment.*

(b) **Control relay.** *This comprises an electronic timing element and a switch relay, which cuts off the fuel supply immediately after the engine stops.*

(c) **Airflow sensor.** *The amount of air drawn in by the engine is measured by the airflow sensor to determine the engine load condition. This is achieved by using a flap valve attached to a spindle, which is free to pivot within the airflow sensor bore, and is deflected by the passage of intake air. Attached to the flap valve spindle is a potentiometer, which transforms the angular position of the flap valve into a voltage, which is then sent to the control unit. Airflow passing through the sensor is one of the main variables used by the control unit to determine the precise fuel requirement for the engine at any given time.*

(d) **Fuel injectors.** *Each fuel injector consists of a solenoid-operated needle valve, which opens under commands from the control unit. Fuel from the fuel distribution pipe is then delivered through the injector nozzle into the inlet manifold. All four fuel injectors operate simultaneously; once for each turn of the crankshaft, regardless of inlet valve position. Therefore, each injector will operate once with the inlet valve closed, and once with it open, for each cycle of the engine. The fuel injectors always open at the same time relative to crankshaft position, but the length of time in which they stay open, eg the injector duration, is governed by other variables, and is determined by the control unit. For a given volume of air passing through the airflow sensor, the control unit can enrich the air/fuel mixture ratio by increasing the injector duration, or weaken it by decreasing the duration.*

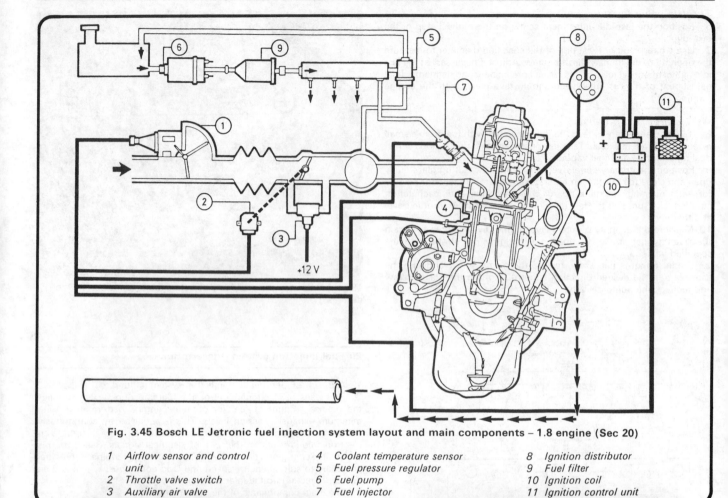

Fig. 3.45 Bosch LE Jetronic fuel injection system layout and main components – 1.8 engine (Sec 20)

1 Airflow sensor and control unit	4 Coolant temperature sensor	8 Ignition distributor
2 Throttle valve switch	5 Fuel pressure regulator	9 Fuel filter
3 Auxiliary air valve	6 Fuel pump	10 Ignition coil
	7 Fuel injector	11 Ignition control unit

Fig. 3.46 Control unit fitted with the LE Jetronic fuel injection system – 1.8 engine (Sec 20)

Fig. 3.47 LE Jetronic airflow sensor and air cleaner assembly – 1.8 engine (Sec 20)

(e) **Fuel pump.** *The fuel pump is an electric self-priming roller cell unit, located at the rear of the car. Fuel from the tank is delivered by the pump, at a predetermined pressure, through the fuel filter to the fuel distribution pipe. From the fuel distribution pipe, the fuel is supplied to the four fuel injectors – the excess being returned to the fuel tank via the fuel pressure regulator. A greater volume of fuel is circulated through the system than will be needed, even under the most extreme operating conditions, and this continual flow ensures that a low fuel temperature is maintained. This reduces the possibility of vapour lock, and ensures good hot starting characteristics.*

(f) **Fuel pressure regulator.** *The fuel pressure regulator is fitted to the fuel distribution pipe, and controls the operating pressure in the fuel system. The unit consists of a metal housing, divided into two chambers by a diaphragm. Fuel from the fuel distribution pipe fills one chamber of the regulator, whilst the other chamber contains a compression spring, and is subject to inlet manifold vacuum via a hose connected to the manifold, downstream of the throttle valve. A valve attached to the diaphragm opens a fuel return port in the fuel chamber of the regulator as the diaphragm deflects. When the fuel pressure in the regulator exceeds a certain value, the diaphragm is deflected, and fuel returns to the tank*

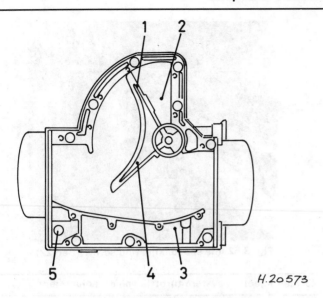

Fig. 3.48 Internal view of the airflow sensor and flap valve assembly – 1.8 engine (Sec 20)

1 Flap valve damper
2 Damping chamber
3 Bypass channel
4 Flap valve
5 Idle mixture adjusting screw

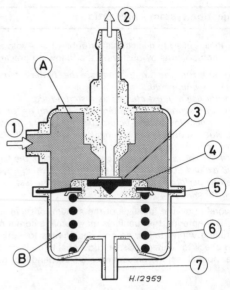

Fig. 3.49 Sectional view of the fuel pressure regulator – 1.8 engine (Sec 20)

1 Fuel inlet connection
2 Fuel return connection
3 Valve plate
4 Valve holder
5 Diaphragm
6 Compression spring
7 Vacuum connection
A Fuel chamber
B Vacuum chamber

through the now-open return port. This also occurs when the port is opened by the deflection of the diaphragm under the influence of manifold vacuum. Therefore, as manifold vacuum increases, the regulated fuel pressure is reduced in direct proportion.

(g) **Throttle valve switch.** The throttle valve switch is attached to the throttle spindle on the throttle valve housing. As the throttle spindle turns in response to movement of the accelerator pedal, contacts within the switch are closed at the two extremes of shaft movement. One contact closes in the idle position, and one in the full-throttle position. These signals are then processed by the control unit to determine throttle valve position.

(h) **Auxiliary air valve.** This device comprises a large-bore air channel, connected by hoses to the throttle housing and inlet manifold, and allowing intake air to bypass the throttle valve. In the centre of the air channel is a blocking plate attached to a bi-metal strip. When the engine is cold, the blocking plate is withdrawn from the air channel, allowing air to pass through the valve. As the engine warms up, a current is supplied to the valve, heating the bi-metal strip and causing the blocking plate to begin closing the air channel until, as engine temperature increases, the channel is closed completely. The additional air passing through the valve is measured by the airflow sensor, which compensates by increasing the injector duration to provide additional fuel. Therefore, the engine receives a greater air/fuel mixture during cold driveaway and warm-up conditions.

(i) **Temperature sensors.** Information on engine (coolant) temperature and intake air temperatures are measured by sensors, one located in the coolant jacket, and the other in the intake air stream. The sensors consist of resistors whose resistance decreases as temperature increases. The change in electrical resistance of the sensors is measured by the control unit, and th. information is used to modify injector duration accordingly.

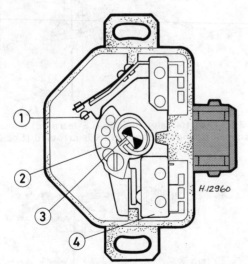

Fig. 3.50 Throttle valve switch internal components – 1.8 engine (Sec 20)

1 Full-throttle contact
2 Contact cam
3 Throttle spindle
4 Idle contact

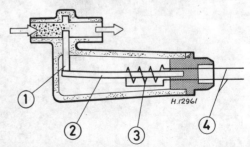

Fig. 3.51 Sectional view of the auxiliary air valve – 1.8 engine (Sec 20)

1 Blocking plate
2 Bi-metal strip
3 Electric heating element
4 Electrical connection

21 Fuel injection system – precautions

1   The fuel injection system is normally trouble-free. Avoid damage to the electrical components by observing the following precautions:

  (a) *Do not run the engine unless the battery terminals are securely connected*
  (b) *Do not use a boost charger as a starting aid*
  (c) *Do not disconnect the battery with the engine running*
  (d) *Disconnect the battery before using a battery charger*
  (e) *Do not disconnect or reconnect the control unit plug, or any other engine harness plugs, with the ignition switched on*
  (f) *Remove the control unit in conditions where the temperature will exceed 80°C (176°F) – eg in a paint-drying oven*
  (g)) *Before performing a cylinder compression test, unplug the control relay*

2   When working on the fuel side of the system, observe scrupulous cleanliness. Dirt entering the fuel lines may damage components.
3   When tracing wiring faults, do not 'flash' wires to earth, or use a test lamp to check for voltage. Use a good quality multi-meter.
4   Observe normal safety precautions when handling fuel – see Section 1.

22 Fuel injection system – idle speed and mixture adjustment

Note: *Before carrying out the following adjustments, ensure that the ignition system is in good order, the air cleaner element is clean, and that the engine itself is in good mechanical condition*

1   With the engine at normal operating temperature, connect an accurate tachometer in accordance with its manufacturer's instructions.
2   Allow the engine to idle, and compare the idle speed with that given in the Specifications. If adjustment is necessary, slacken the locknut and turn the idle speed adjusting screw until the specified speed is obtained. The adjusting screw is situated on the rear of the throttle valve housing (Fig. 3.52). Tighten the locknut on completion.
3   To check the mixture (CO level), connect an exhaust gas analyser or other proprietary mixture analysis device in accordance with its manufacturer's instructions. With the engine idling at the specified speed, read the CO level and compare it with that specified.
4   If adjustment is necessary, remove the tamperproof cap from the mixture adjusting screw on the airflow sensor (photo). Turn the screw clockwise to enrich the mixture, and anti-clockwise to weaken it.
5   On completion, re-adjust the idle speed if necessary.
6   Failure to bring the CO level within the specified range indicates a fault in the injection system, or a well-worn engine.

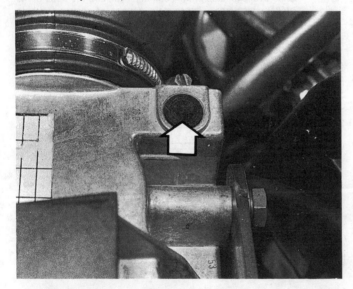

22.4 Tamperproof cap (arrowed) covering mixture adjusting screw

Fig. 3.52 Idle speed adjusting screw (Sec 22)

23 Fuel injection system throttle valve – adjustment

1   Make sure that the throttle valve plate is closed. Refer to Fig. 3.53 or 3.54 as appropriate.
2   Unscrew both the throttle valve stop screw and locknut until they are clear of their cam, then screw the screw in again, until it just contacts the cam. Now give it a further quarter of a turn, and tighten its locknut.
3   On manual transmission models, release the locknuts on the connecting rod and adjust its length by rotating it so that dimension X is as shown in Fig. 3.53.

24 Fuel injection system throttle valve switch – adjustment

1   Release the switch mounting screws (photo) and rotate the switch in an anti-clockwise direction until resistance is felt. Tighten the screws.
2   Have an assistant open the throttle valve slightly by depressing the accelerator pedal. A click should be heard from the switch. A click should also be heard when the pedal is released.

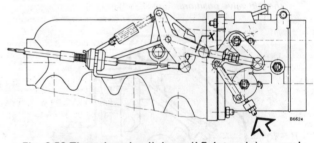

Fig. 3.53 Throttle valve linkage (LE Jetronic) manual transmission models. Stop screw is arrowed (Sec 23)
X = 0.5 mm (0.02 in)

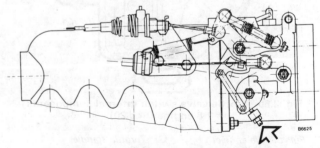

Fig. 3.54 Throttle valve linkage (LE Jetronic) automatic transmission models. Stop screw is arrowed (Sec 23)

25 Fuel injection system components – removal and refitting

1   It is not possible to repair the main components of the fuel injection system. In the event of a fault occurring, it is best to have the fault isolated by your Vauxhall/Opel dealer or a fuel system specialist as special equipment will be necessary. However, once the problem has been diagnosed, there is no reason why the defective component cannot be renewed by carrying out the following instructions.

Throttle valve housing

2   Disconnect the distributor vacuum hose from the throttle housing (photo).
3   Disconnect the crankcase ventilation hose (photo).
4   Disconnect the coolant (preheat) hoses from the housing connection (photo). Clamp the hoses to be prevent the loss of coolant. If the engine is still warm when this work is being carried out then the system pressure must be released before disconnecting the hoses. Do this by gently unscrewing the expansion bottle cap.
5   Release the securing clips and disconnect the flexible ducting which connects the throttle valve housing with the airflow sensor (photo).
6   Disconnect the wiring plug from the throttle valve switch.
7   If removing the throttle housing on its own, separate the throttle linkage by disengaging at the balljoint, then undo the retaining nuts and withdraw the throttle housing from the inlet manifold.
8   If removing the throttle housing together with the inlet manifold, the following must also be detached.
9   Disconnect the brake servo hose and the auxiliary air hose from the manifold (photo).
10 Disconnect and plug the fuel hoses from the distribution tube pipe stubs. Note that the hose with the white band is located nearer the alternator. Do not connect these hoses incorrectly (photo).
11 Release the wiring harness by disconnecting all the plugs and the earth connections (photos). These include:

   (a) Airflow sensor plug
   (b) Coolant temperature sensor
   (c) Fuel injectors
   (d) Throttle valve switch
   (e) Auxiliary air valve
   (f) Cam cover earth screw

12 Disconnect the throttle cable from the throttle valve housing. The ball coupling on the end of the cable is retained by a wire clip. The outer cable end fitting is retained in its bracket by an E-clip locating in a groove in the end fitting. This arrangement provides the adjustment for tensioning the cable (photos).
13 Unscrew the inlet manifold fixing nuts. The lower ones are difficult to reach, but present no problems to remove if a small socket or ring spanner is used.
14 Lift the throttle housing and manifold as a complete unit and remove. Peel off the flange gasket; renew it on reassembly (photos).
15 Refitting is a reversal of removal, but note the wiring harness connections. Number 4 fuel injector is nearest the flywheel housing.

Throttle valve switch

16 Disconnect the three-pin wiring plug (photo).
17 Unscrew the two mounting screws and pull the switch from the throttle valve spindle.
18 Refitting is a reversal of removal, but adjust the switch as described in Section 24.

Fuel pump

19 The fuel pump is located at the rear of the fuel tank on the right-hand side (photo). Before removing the pump or associated components, detach the battery earth lead.
20 Clamp the fuel hoses on either side of the pump to prevent loss of fuel when they are disconnected. Self-locking grips are useful for this. Disconnect the hoses.
21 Unscrew the pump mounting clamp bolts and withdraw the pump from its flexible insulator. Disconnect the electrical plug as the pump is withdrawn (photos).
22 Alternatively, the pump can be removed complete with filter and damper diaphragm unit if the mounting strap nuts are unscrewed and the assembly removed from its flexible mountings.

24.1 Release the throttle valve switch mounting screws

25.2 Disconnect the distributor vacuum hose from the throttle valve housing

25.3 Disconnect the crankcase ventilation hose from the throttle housing

25.4 Disconnect the throttle housing coolant hoses. The other hose is on the underside

25.5 Separate the duct from the throttle housing

25.9 Disconnect the brake servo hose (A) and the auxiliary air hose (B)

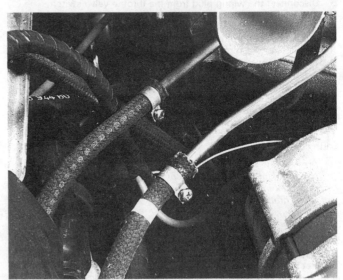

25.10 Fuel hoses in engine compartment

25.11A Air sensor plug lead detachment

25.11B Coolant temperature switch plug location

25.11C Fuel injector wiring plug detachment

25.11D Auxiliary air valve and wiring plug

25.11E Cam cover earthing point

25.12A Removing the throttle valve housing and inlet manifold

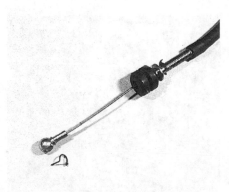

25.12B Throttle control cable at engine end

25.14A Throttle valve housing showing control linkage

25.14B Throttle valve housing and inlet manifold removed

25.14C Throttle valve housing showing operation of throttle valves

25.16 Throttle valve switch and plug

25.19 Fuel pump location

25.21A Fuel pump mounting bolt

Fuel filter

23 The fuel filter is adjacent to the fuel pump (photo).

24 Clamp the fuel hoses to prevent loss of fuel when they are disconnected. Self-locking grips are useful for this. Disconnect the hoses and remove the filter.

25 Refitting is a reversal of removal. Observe the AUS (out) marking on the filter showing the direction of fuel flow. If required, the damper diaphragm unit mounted on the common bracket between the filter and pump units can be removed in a similar manner (photos).

Fuel injectors

26 Make sure that the engine is cool to eliminate the danger of fuel igniting. Do not smoke, and guard against external sources of ignition (eg pilot lights).

27 Release the hose clamps and pull the fuel distribution pipe from the hoses of the injectors (photo). Catch as much fuel as possible.

28 Disconnect the wiring plug.

29 Unscrew the retaining bolts and withdraw the injector from its holder, taking care not to damage the needle valve (photo).

30 Refitting is a reversal of removal, but renew the sealing rings if there is any doubt about their condition.

Airflow sensor

31 The airflow sensor is located between the air cleaner and the throttle valve housing.

32 Pull the wiring harness plug from the airflow sensor. Release the securing band and remove the rubber trunking (photo).

33 Release the toggle locks and remove the airflow sensor with the upper part of the air cleaner housing.

34 Unbolt the airflow sensor from the air cleaner housing (photo).

35 Check the airflow sensor flap valve for free movement, without any jerkiness.

25.21B Fuel pump and damper diaphragm unit mounting bolt

25.23 Fuel filter showing mounting and hose connections

25.25A Fuel filter and damper diaphragm unit location

25.25B Fuel filter directional marking

25.27 Slackening a fuel distribution pipe hose clamp

25.29 Fuel injector removal

25.32 Disconnecting the airflow sensor rubber trunking

25.34 Airflow sensor securing bolts (arrowed)

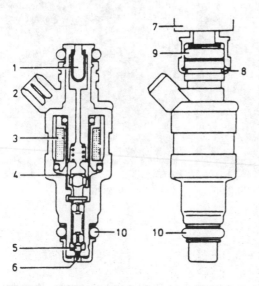

Fig. 3.56 Airflow sensor removal – LE Jetronic (Sec 25)

B 6605

Fig. 3.55 Sectional view of a fuel injector (Sec 25)

1	Strainer	6	Pintle
2	Electrical connection	7	Distributor line
3	Solenoid coil	8	Fuse holder
4	Solenoid plunger	9	Upper seal ring
5	Nozzle needle	10	Lower seal ring

Control unit (LE Jetronic system)
36 The control unit is located at the side of the front footwell.
37 Remove the trim panel from the side of the front footwell on the passenger side (photos).
38 Pull the wiring plug from the control unit by pressing aside the retaining spring.
39 Extract the three screws and remove the control unit.

25.37A Footwell side trim panel removal gives access to the ...

25.37B ... control unit (LE Jetronic)

25.46 Disconnecting the auxiliary air valve wiring plug

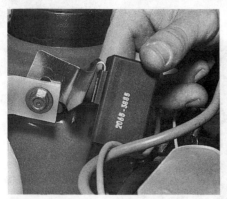

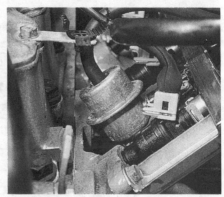

25.51A Unscrew the control relay mounting bolt ...

25.51B ... and disconnect the wiring plug

25.53 Pressure regulator

Coolant temperature sensor

40 This sensor, located next to the alternator, is an additional sensor fitted to vehicles equipped with a fuel injection system (Fig. 3.57).
41 Partially drain the cooling system, about 3 litre (5 pints) should be sufficient.
42 Disconnect the electrical lead and unscrew the sensor.
43 Refitting is a reversal of removal.
44 Top up and bleed the cooling system as described in Chapter 2.

Auxiliary air valve

45 This valve is located on the side of the camshaft housing.
46 Pull the connecting plug from the valve (photo).
47 Disconnect the hoses. Unscrew the two mounting bolts and remove the valve.
48 A check can be made on the serviceability of the valve by observing the blocking plate. With the valve cold, the plate should be open; with the valve hot (by connection to a 12V battery) the plate should be closed.
49 Refitting is a reversal of removal.

Control relay

50 The relay is located on the front suspension strut turret (photo).
51 Unscrew the mounting bolt, disconnect the wiring plug and remove the relay (photo).
52 Refitting is a reversal of removal.

Fuel pressure regulator

53 The fuel pressure regulator is located between injectors 3 and 4 (photo).
54 Clamp the fuel hoses to prevent loss of fuel. Self-locking grips are useful for this.
55 Disconnect the fuel hoses and the vacuum hose from the pressure regulator.
56 Refitting is a reversal of removal.

26 Unleaded high octane petrol

1 All ohc engines used in the Vauxhall Cavalier have been manufactured with valve seats of a material which enables the use of high octane unleaded fuel, providing the following changes are made.

2 Using unleaded petrol can cause high speed knock which cannot be heard, but can lead to engine damage; the ignition timing **must** be retarded by 5° (see Chapter 4).
output and efficiency when run on 98 RON (4-star) fuel. For adjustment details, refer to Chapter 4.

27 Throttle control cable – adjustment and renewal

1 The throttle control is of cable-operated type, with a pendant foot pedal.

Fig. 3.57 Coolant temperature sensor (Sec 25)

2 There are two points of adjustment. A screw is located on the pedal arm to control the fully released position of the pedal stop, and a clip is located on a threaded section of the outer cable at the bracket on the intake manifold (photos).
3 Adjust the cable so that when the accelerator pedal is released, there is just the slightest amount of slackness in the cable at the throttle valve housing (fuel injection models) or the carburettor end.
4 With the air cleaner removed, check that when the pedal is fully depressed, the throttle valve plate is fully open. Adjust the E-clip in its groove and the pedal stop screw to achieve the desired results.
5 To renew the cable, slacken off all adjustment by removing the E-clip from the groove in the end fitting. Release the inner cable from the slot in the pedal arm.
6 Pull the clip from the cable ball end fitting and withdraw the cable through the bulkhead (photo).
7 Refit by reversing the removal operations.

28 Choke cable – removal and refitting

1 Disconnect the battery earth lead.
2 Tap out the small pin which secures the choke control knob to the cable end fitting. Unscrew and remove the knob.

27.2A Throttle pedal stop screw

27.2B Throttle cable bracket and clip at carburettor

27.6 Throttle link balljoint with retaining clip released

3   Undo the retaining ring or nut which secures the choke control to the facia. Push the control into the facia and disconnect the warning light switch (when fitted).
4   Remove the air cleaner.
5   Disconnect the choke inner and outer cable from the carburettor.

28.5 Choke cable connections at carburettor
A   Inner cable clamp   B   Outer cable clamp

On some carburettors the inner cable is secured by a grub screw which must be undone with an Allen key (photo).
6   Release the bulkhead grommet and remove the cable.
7   Refit in the reverse order to removal. Adjust the positions of the inner and outer cables as described in Section 11.

29 Manifolds – removal and refitting

1   The inlet and exhaust manifolds are on opposite sides of the cylinder head.

Inlet manifold (1.3 and 1.6)
2   Before the inlet manifold can be removed, the cooling system must be drained and the coolant hoses disconnected from it.
3   On 1.3 models, disconnect the lead from the coolant temperature sender switch.
4   Disconnect the brake vacuum hose.
5   The manifold may be removed complete with carburettor or independently.
6   To remove the carburettor first, refer to Section 12 or 17 (as applicable).
7   To remove the manifold complete with carburettor, refer to the appropriate carburettor removal Section and disconnect the associated items from the carburettor, but leave the carburettor-to-manifold retaining nuts.
8   Unscrew the manifold nuts and lift the assembly from the cylinder head (photo).
9   Remove and discard the flange gasket.
10 Refitting is a reversal of removal. Use a new flange gasket. Refill and bleed the cooling system on completion.

Inlet manifold (1.8)
11 Removal and refitting of the throttle valve housing, which takes the place of the inlet manifold on engines with fuel injection, is covered in Section 25.

Exhaust manifold
12 Unbolt the heat shield (warm air collector) from the manifold.
13 Disconnect the manifold from the downpipes by removing the nuts at the connecting flange (photo).
14 Unscrew and remove the exhaust manifold nuts and lift the manifold from the cylinder head (photo).
15 Remove the flange gaskets.

29.8 Inlet manifold removal (complete with carburettor)

29.13 Exhaust downpipe flanges at manifold

29.14 Removing the exhaust manifold

16 Refitting is a reversal of removal. Use new gaskets. Should a gas leak occur at the downpipe flange on the exhaust manifold, two gaskets may be used to remedy the leak.

30 Exhaust system – removal and refitting

1 The exhaust system comprises a dual downpipe, a front silencer and a rear expansion box with a tailpipe.

2 The exhaust system fitted at the factory, and any Vauxhall replacement system, is of heavy duty aluminised construction. Under normal operating conditions this should be found to last a considerable time before removal is necessary.

3 Holts Flexiwrap and Holts Gun Gum exhaust repair systems can be used for effective repairs to exhaust pipes and silencer boxes, including ends and bends. Holts Flexiwrap is an MOT approved permanent exhaust repair.

4 The system fitted in production is of three-piece construction. Sections may therefore be renewed individually if necessary.

5 If the complete system is to be renewed, position the vehicle over an inspection pit. If this is not possible, jack the vehicle up as high as possible and secure it on axle stands.

6 When renewing the complete system, cutting through the connecting pipes will probably make removal in sections easier than attempting to dismantle corroded joints.

7 If only one section is to be renewed, and this section is to be cut to remove it, make quite sure than an adequate overlap of the original pipe is left to fit the new section. Failure to do this will prevent a gastight joint being achieved.

8 The exhaust system is flexibly mounted. Remove any mounting components which are deformed or have deteriorated. Always renew clamps (photos).

9 When connecting a new section of pipe, expansion box or silencer, remove burrs from the socket joints and apply a little grease before connecting. Fit the clamps only finger tight at first until the alignment of the system has been checked and adjusted.

10 Make sure that no component of the system is likely to touch adjacent parts of the bodyframe or suspension when deflected within the full extent of movement of its flexible mounting.

11 Application of some graphite grease to the contact surfaces of the spring-loaded ball coupling before bolting up will prevent it seizing due to rust (photo).

30.8A Exhaust system coupling joint and mounting

30.8B Alternative type of exhaust flexible mounting

30.8C Exhaust flexible mounting

30.11 Exhaust spring-loaded ball coupling

31 Fault diagnosis – fuel system

Unsatisfactory engine performance and excessive fuel consumption are not necessarily the fault of the fuel system. In fact they more commonly occur as a result of ignition and timing faults. Before acting on the following it is necessary to check the ignition system first. Even though a fault may lie in the fuel system it will be difficult to trace unless the ignition is correct. The faults below, therefore, assume that this has been attended to first (where appropriate).

Part A: Carburettor engines

Symptom	Reason(s)
Smell of petrol when engine is stopped	Leaking fuel lines or unions Leaking fuel tank
Smell of petrol when engine is idling	Leaking fuel line unions beween pump and carburettor Overflow of fuel from float chamber due to wrong level setting, ineffective needle valve or punctured float
Excessive fuel consumption for reasons not covered by leaks or float chamber faults	Worn jets Over-rich setting Sticking mechanism Dirty air cleaner element Sticking air cleaner thermostatic mechanism
Difficult starting, uneven running, lack of power, cutting out	One or more jets blocked or restricted Float chamber fuel level too low or needle valve sticking Fuel pump not delivering sufficient fuel Faulty solenoid fuel shut-off valve (if fitted) Induction leak
Difficult starting when cold	Choke control or automatic choke maladjusted Automatic choke not cocked before starting
Difficult starting when hot	Automatic choke malfunction Accelerator pedal pumped before starting Vapour lock (especially in hot weather or at high altitude)
Engine does not respond properly to throttle	Faulty accelerator pump Blocked jet(s) Slack in accelerator cable
Engine idle speed drops when hot	Defective temperature compensator Overheated fuel pump

Part B: Fuel injection engines

Symptom	Reason(s)
Difficult starting from cold	Fuel pump fault Blocked fuel line or filter Supplementary air device faulty Temperature sensor faulty Vacuum system leak
Difficult starting when hot	Air filter blocked Faulty fuel pump Vacuum system leak
Excessive fuel consumption	Excessive fuel pressure Temperature sensor faulty Airflow sensor faulty Vacuum system leak
Uneven idling	Air leak in intake system Incorrect mixture setting Throttle switch in need of adjustment Loose electronic control unit connector Leaky injector(s)
Idle speed adjustment difficult (too high)	Auxiliary air device not closing

Chapter 4 Ignition system

For modifications, and information applicable to later models, see Supplement at end of manual

Contents

Specifications

Part A: Mechanical breaker type ignition

General
Type	Battery, coil and camshaft driven distributor having mechanical contact breaker points
Application	1.3 up to 1982
Firing order	1-3-4-2 (No 1 at timing belt end of engine)

Type	Bosch
Rotational direction of rotor	Anti-clockwise (viewed from cap)
Contact breaker points gap	0.4 mm (0.016 in)
Dwell angle	47 to 53°
Timing	10° BTDC (crankshaft pulley notch and oil pump housing pulley pointer in alignment)

Spark plugs
Type	Champion RN7YCC or RN7YC
RN7YCC	0.8 mm (0.032 in)
RN7YC	0.7 mm (0.028 in)

HT leads
Application:
1.3 litre models	Champion CLS 11
1.6 and 1.8 litre carburettor models	Champion CLS 4
1.8 litre injection models	Champion CLS 12

Ignition coil
Type:
Delco-Remy	12 VDR 502 (3474200)
Bosch	KW 12 (0221 119 023)
Primary winding resistance	1.2 to 1.6 ohm
Voltage	12 000 to 14 000 V

Torque wrench settings
	Nm	lb ft
Spark plugs	20	15
Distributor clamp nuts	22	16

Part B: Breakerless type ignition

General
Type and application	Bosch (Hall effect) or AC Delco electronic
Firing order	1-3-4-2 (No 1 at timing belt end of engine)

Distributor

Type	
Rotational direction of rotor	Bosch Anti-clockwise (viewed from cap)
Centrifugal advance*:	**Commences** **Maximum**
1.3	0 to 3° at 1000 rpm 22 to 28° at 4200 rpm
1.6	0 to 6° at 1200 rpm 17 to 23° at 3000 rpm
1.8	0 to 2° at 1000 rpm 15 to 21° at 4000 rpm
Vacuum advance*:	**Commences** **Maximum**
1.3	76 to 140 mmHg 6 to 10° at 65 mmHg
1.6 and 1.8	83 to 135 mmHg 11.5 to 17.5° at 188 to 195 mmHg
Timing	10° BTDC (crankshaft pulley notch and oil pump housing pulley pointer in alignment)

Information not available for all models

Spark plugs

Type	Champion RN7YCC or RN7YC
Electrode gap:	
RN7YCC	0.8 mm (0.032 in)
RN7YC	0.7 mm (0.028 in)

Ignition coil

	Bosch KW 12V	Delco-Remy
Type		
Code	1227 020 009	3 474 221
Primary winding resistance (ohm)	0.6 to 0.9	0.3 to 0.6
Voltage	16 000 to 20 000 V	16 000 to 18 000V

Torque wrench settings

	Nm	lbf ft
Spark plugs	20	15
Distributor clamp nuts	22	16

PART A: MECHANICAL BREAKER TYPE IGNITION

1 General description

In order that the engine can run correctly it is necessary for an electrical spark to ignite the fuel/air mixture in the combustion chamber at exactly the right moment in relation to engine speed and load. The ignition system is based on feeding low tension voltage from the battery to the coil where it is converted to high tension voltage. The high tension voltage is powerful enough to jump the spark plug gap in the cylinders many times a second under high compression, providing that the system is in good condition and that all adjustments are correct.

The ignition system is divided into two circuits, low tension and high tension.

The low tension circuit (sometimes known as the primary) consists of the battery, lead to the ignition switch, lead from the ignition switch to the low tension or primary coil windings, and the lead from the low tension coil windings to the contact breaker points and condenser in the distributor.

The high tension circuit consists of the high tension or secondary coil winding, the heavy ignition lead from the centre of the coil to the centre of the distributor cap, the rotor arm, and the spark plug leads and spark plugs.

The system functions in the following manner. Low tension voltage is changed in the coil into high tension voltage by the opening and closing of the contact breaker points in the low tension circuit. High tension voltage is then fed via the carbon brush in the centre of the distributor cap to the rotor arm of the distributor cap, and each time it comes in line with one of the four metal segments in the cap, which are connected to the spark plug leads, the opening and closing of the contact breaker points causes the high tension voltage to build up, jump the gap from the rotor arm to the appropriate metal segment and so via the spark plug lead to the spark plug, where it finally jumps the spark plug gap before going to earth.

The ignition is advanced and retarded automatically, to ensure that the spark occurs at just the right instant for the particular load at the prevailing engine speed.

The ignition advance is controlled both mechanically and by a vacuum-operated system. The mechanical governor comprises two weights, which move out from the distributor shaft as the engine speed rises due to centrifugal force. As they move outwards they rotate the cam relative to the distributor shaft, and so advance the spark. The weights are held in position by two light springs and it is the tension of the springs which is largely responsible for correct spark advancement.

The vacuum control consists of a diaphragm, one side of which is connected via a small bore tube to the carburettor, and the other side to the contact breaker plate. Depression in the inlet manifold and carburettor, which varies with engine speed and throttle opening, causes the diaphragm to move, so moving the contact breaker plate, and advancing or retarding the spark (photo).

A resistance wire in the low tension feed to the coil keeps the coil voltage down to 6V during normal running. This wire is bypassed when the starter motor is operating, to compensate for reduced battery voltage.

1.8 Distributor vacuum pipe at carburettor end

2 Routine maintenance – ignition system

The following routine maintenance procedures must be carried out at the specified intervals at the start of this manual

1 Remove the spark plugs and thoroughly clean away all traces of carbon. Examine the porcelain insulator round the central electrode

inside the plug. If damaged, renew the plug. Reset the gap between the electrodes. Renew the spark plugs at the specified intervals, irrespective of condition.

2   Remove the distributor cap, rotor arm, cover and bearing plates, and put one or two drops of engine oil into the centre of the cam recess where appropriate. Smear the surfaces of the cam itself with petroleum jelly. Do not over-lubricate as any excess could get onto the contact point surfaces and cause ignition difficulties.

3   Examine the contact point surfaces. If there is a build-up of deposits on one face and a pit in the other it will be impossible to set the gap correctly and they should be renewed. Set the gap dwell angle when the contact surfaces are in order. Renew the contact breaker points at the specified intervals, irrespective of condition.

4   Examine all leads and terminals for signs of broken or cracked insulation. Also check all terminal connections for slackness or signs of fracturing of some strands of wire. Partly broken wire should be renewed. The HT leads are particularly important as any insulation faults will cause the high voltage to 'jump' to the nearest earth and this will prevent a spark at the plug. Check that no HT leads are loose or in a position where the insulation could wear due to rubbing against part of the engine.

3   Distributor contact breaker points – gap and dwell angle adjustment

1   Prise the distributor cap weatherproof cover apart (if fitted) and remove it (photo).

2   Unclip the distributor cap and lift the cap clear.

3   Wipe the inside and outside of the cap clean with a dry cloth. Scrape away any small deposits from the four studs and inspect the cover for cracks or surface deterioration. Check the brush in the centre of the cap, it should protrude about 6 mm (0.25 in). Renew the cap if cracked or if any of the HT studs are corroded, worn away or cracked (photo).

4   Lift the distributor rotor arm from the central shaft and wipe the metal tip clean (photo).

5   Remove the plastic cover which protects the contact breaker and prevents condensation from settling on the mechanism and reducing its effectiveness. Do not remove the upper bearing plate (photo).

6   Now that the contact breaker points are exposed, gently prise the contacts apart and examine the condition of their faces. If they are rough, pitted or dirty, it will be necessary to remove them for new points to be fitted.

7   Presuming the points are satisfactory, or they have been cleaned or replaced, measure the gap between the points by turning the engine until the contact breaker arm is on the peak of one of the four cam lobes. Refer to the Specifications for the size of the feeler gauge to use when measuring the gap. Take care not to contaminate the point faces with oil (photo).

8   If the points are too close or too far apart, slacken the contact breaker mounting screw. Move the stationary point until the correct gap has been achieved and then secure by tightening the setscrew in the breaker set mounting plate.

9   Check the gap once again to ensure the adjustment was not disturbed when the setscrew was tightened.

10 Refit the plastic cover, then the rotor arm and finally the distributor cap with its plastic cover.

11 On modern engines, setting the contact breaker gap in the distributor using feeler gauges must be regarded as a basic adjustment only. For optimum engine performance, the dwell angle must be checked. The dwell angle is the number of degrees through which the distributor cam turns during the period between the instants of closure and opening of the contact breaker points. Checking the dwell angle not only gives a more accurate setting of the contact breaker gap but also evens out any variations in the gap which could be caused by wear in the distributor shaft or its bushes, or difference in height of any of the cam peaks.

12 The angle should be checked with a dwell meter connected in accordance with the maker's instructions. Refer to the Specifications for the correct dwell angle. If the dwell angle is too large, increase the points gap, if too small, reduce the points gap.

13 The dwell angle should always be adjusted before checking and adjusting the ignition timing.

3.1 Removing the distributor cap cover

3.3 Interior of distributor cap

3.4 Removing the rotor arm

3.5 Removing distributor plastic cover

3.7 Checking the contact breaker gap

4 Distributor contact breaker points – removal and refitting

1   If the contact breaker points are burned, pitted or badly worn, they must be removed and renewed.
2   Remove the distributor cover, the cap, rotor arm, and contact breaker mechanism cover.
3   Remove the rotor shaft upper bearing plate (photos).
4   Pull off the LT spade connector, then remove the setscrew which retains the contact breaker mechanism and lift out the breaker assembly.
5   Lift off the moving contact arm and spring followed by the fixed contact plate.
6   It is possible to reface the contact points using a fine carborundum stone or emery paper. However, if the points show signs of burning or pitting, it is strongly recommended that they are replaced with a new set. Clean the faces of new points with methylated spirit before fitting.
7   Refitting of the points follows the reverse sequence to removal.
8   Adjust the points gap and dwell angle as described in Section 3.

5 Condenser – removal, testing and refitting

1   The purpose of the condenser (sometimed known as the capacitor) is to ensure that when the contact breaker points open there is no sparking across them which would waste voltage and cause wear.
2   On the Bosch distributor the condenser is mounted on the outside of the distributor body. If it develops a short-circuit it will cause ignition failure as the points will be prevented from interrupting the low tension circuit (photo).
3   If the engine becomes very difficult to start, or begins to miss after several miles running, and the breaker points show signs of excessive burning, then the condition of the condenser must be suspect. A further test can be made by separating the points by hand with the ignition switched on. If this is accompanied by a strong blue flash it is indicative that the condenser has failed in the open circuit mode.
4   Without special equipment the only sure way to diagnose

condenser trouble is to replace a suspected unit with a new one and note if there is any improvement.
5   To remove the condenser from the distributor take off the distributor cap, rotor arm and cover.
6   Remove the bearing plates, then pull off the contact points LT lead from the spade terminal located inside the distributor casing.
7   Remove the LT lead connecting the coil to the distributor, from the ignition coil.
8   Undo and remove the screw securing the condenser and LT lead assembly to the distributor case. Note that the condenser is supplied complete with the LT lead to the coil and the LT spade tag and mounting grommet.
9   Refitting of the condenser follows the reverse procedure to removal.

6 Distributor – removal and refitting

1   Disconnect the battery earth terminal.
2   Remove the distributor cap and place it aside and out of the way.
3   If the cap and leads are to be dismantled then number the leads by putting tags on them to avoid mixing them up on reassembly.
4   Remove the spark plugs and check that the transmission is in neutral. This will enable the engine to be turned over by hand without resistance from compression.
5   Rotate the crankshaft by means of the pulley bolt until No 1 piston can be felt to be rising on its compression stroke (finger over spark plug hole). Continue turning until the notch in the crankshaft pulley is aligned with the pointer on the belt cover (photo). The cut-out in the top of the distributor shaft should now be aligned with the mark on the rim of the distributor housing.
6   Once the engine has been set in this position ensure that the engine is not disturbed from this position whilst the distributor is removed. This will make the installation task easier.
7   Detach the LT lead from the coil.
8   Disconnect the vacuum advance tube from the distributor.
9   Unscrew and remove the distributor clamp plate. Withdraw the distributor from the engine (photo).

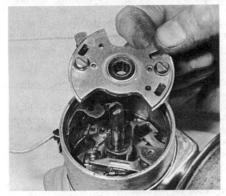

4.3A Rotor shaft upper bearing plate

4.3B Contact breaker/baseplate assembly

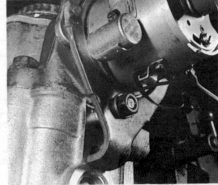

5.2 Distributor condenser and clamp plate

6.5 Ignition timing mark

6.9 Releasing distributor clamp

Fig. 4.1 Rotor alignment mark on distributor rim (Sec 6)

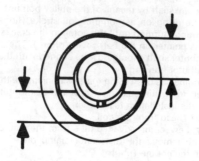

Fig. 4.2 Offset drive slots in camshaft (Sec 6)

10 Refitting the distributor is a direct reversal of the removal sequence. Check that the engine has not been disturbed from any position set before removal. If the engine was turned over for any reason reset it to the position given in paragraph 5.

11 Fit a new O-ring seal to the distributor flange and then align the cut-out in the distributor shaft with the mark on the rim of the distributor body. Check that the distributor drive dog is in the correct relative position to engage in the camshaft drive slots, and push the distributor into position (photos).

12 Turn the distributor body as necessary to align the distributor shaft cut-out with the mark on the rim of the distributor body again.

13 Screw in and tighten the distributor clamp bolt.

14 Reconnect the LT lead to the coil and the vacuum tube to the

vacuum unit. Refit the cap, leads, plugs and battery earth terminal to complete.

15 Check the timing using a stroboscope as described in Section 8.

7 Distributor – dismantling, inspection and reassembly

1 Before dismantling the distributor, check on the availability of parts which may be necessary. If the distributor has seen a lot of service then the chances are that it is generally worn and should be renewed.

2 If the distributor is to be dismantled, the work should be carried out on a clean workbench where the respective components can be laid out in order as they are removed.

3 If it has not already been removed, disconnect the distributor cap and cover, together with the leads (see Section 3). Withdraw the rotor arm and damp proof cover.

4 Remove the contact breaker set as described in Section 4.

5 Remove the condenser as described in Section 5.

6 Prise the circlip from the vacuum control rod-to-timing plate spindle (photo).

7 Unscrew the vacuum control unit retaining screws and remove the unit, unhooking the control rod (photos).

8 Unscrew and lift out the baseplate (photos).

9 The centrifugal weights and springs can now be inspected and removed if required, but take note of the respective spring and weight positions (photo).

10 To withdraw the spindle, the drivegear or drive dog must be removed. Use a small punch and drive out the retaining pin and then extract the spindle upwards.

11 Clean all parts in an oil and grease solvent and wipe/blow dry ready for inspection.

12 Inspect all components for obvious signs of excessive wear or damage. Check the spindle play and drivegear teeth or drive dog faces for wear. Renew any parts which are defective or suspect.

13 Prior to reassembly smear all sliding parts and the centrifugal weight springs with a small amount of medium grease.

14 Slide the spindle into position and relocate the drivegear or dog. Drive a new retaining pin into position to secure the gear or dog.

15 Reassemble the centrifugal weights and springs, ensuring that they are securely located.

16 Refit the contact plates and tighten screws to secure.

17 Refit the vacuum control unit, relocating the control rod and tightening the screws to secure. Relocate the circlip to retain the rod on the plate spindle. Apply a little grease to the plate spindle.

18 Refit the condenser as described in Section 5.

19 Refit the contact breaker set as described in Section 4 and readjust the contact gap in accordance with Section 3.

20 Lubricate the sliding parts of the contact breaker base plate assembly with some clean oil and smear a small amount of high melting-point grease onto the cam surface.

21 Check the spindle for freedom of rotation and the contact points for correct operation. Support the gear and apply finger pressure to the rotor arm in the reverse direction to that in which it operates. It should spring back freely to its static position.

22 The distributor is now ready for refitting.

6.11A Fitting distributor O-ring seal

6.11B Fitting distributor

7.6 Extract vacuum rod circlip

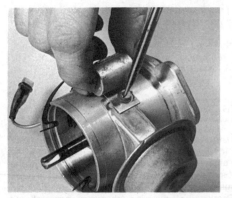

7.7A Condenser/vacuum unit fixing screw

7.7B Unhooking vacuum unit control rod

7.8A Releasing baseplate/clip fixing screw

7.8B Removing baseplate

7.9 Centrifugal weights and springs

8 Ignition timing – adjustment

Full-leaded petrol

1 It is necessary to time the ignition when it has been upset due to overhauling or dismantling. Also, if maladjustments have affected the engine performance it is very desirable, although not always essential, to reset the timing starting from scratch. In the following procedures it is assumed that the intention is to obtain standard performance from the standard engine which is in reasonable condition. It is also assumed that the recommended fuel octane rating is used.

2 Set the transmission to neutral and remove all four spark plugs.

3 Place a thumb over No 1 cylinder spark plug hole and rotate the engine clockwise by means of the crankshaft pulley bolt until pressure is felt building up in No 1 cylinder. This indicates that the No 1 cylinder piston is approaching top dead centre (tdc) on the firing stroke.

4 Continue to rotate the crankshaft until the notch in the pulley is directly opposite the timing cover mark or the pointer as appropriate.

5 In this position, the timing is set at the specified BTDC number of degrees **not** TDC.

6 Slacken the distributor clamp bolt or nut and rotate the distributor body until the contact breaker points are just opening and then tighten the clamp bolt or nut.

7 Difficulty is sometimes experienced in determining exactly when the contact breaker points open. This can be ascertained most accurately by connecting a 12V bulb in parallel with the contact breaker points (one lead to earth and the other from the distributor low tension terminal). Switch on the ignition and turn the distributor body until the bulb lights up, indicating that the points have just opened.

8 If it was found impossible to align the rotor arm correctly the distributor cam assembly has been incorrectly fitted on the driveshaft. To rectify this, it will be necessary to partially dismantle the distributor and check the position of the cam assembly on the centrifugal advance mechanism; it may be 180° out of position.

9 As a final check on the ignition timing the best method is to use a strobe lamp.

10 Put a spot of white paint on the notch in the crankshaft pulley and the timing mark or the pointer and connect the strobe light into the No 1 cylinder HT circuit following the maker's instructions.

11 Run the engine at idling speed and point the strobe lamp at the timing marks. At idling speed the white paint marks should appear to be immediately opposite each other; open the throttle slightly and check that as the engine revolutions rise the spot on the crankshaft will move away from the pointer. This indicates the centrifugal advance mechanism is operating correctly.

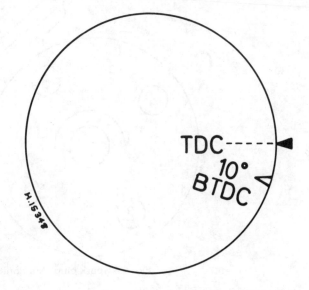

Fig. 4.3 TDC and 10° BTDC ignition timing (Sec 8)

12 If the timing marks do not line up under the strobe light, slightly slacken the distributor clamp bolt and carefully turn the distributor in its location to bring the marks into line and retighten the clamp bolt.

High octane unleaded petrol

13 The engines used in Vauxhall Cavalier models are designed to run on unleaded high octane petrol, but on carburettor variants the manufacturers state that the ignition should be retarded by up to 5° if detonation (pinking or knock) is experienced.

14 The crankshaft pulley only has one timing mark (10° BTDC), so it will be necessary to make additional marks to accurately retard the ignition.

15 Turn the engine by means of the crankshaft pulley bolt, or by engaging top gear and pulling the car forward, until No 1 piston is at TDC on the firing stroke. This can be felt by removing No 1 spark plug and feeling for compression with your fingers as the engine is turned. The precise TDC point will have to be determined using a blunt probe (such as a knitting needle) inserted through No 1 spark plug hole.

16 Make a mark on the crankshaft pulley in alignment with the timing mark, or pointer, on the engine.

17 The original pulley mark indicates 10° BTDC, and the new mark TDC; 5° ignition retardation, therefore, is central between the two.

18 Make a new timing mark on the crankshaft pulley, and adjust the ignition timing as described in paragraphs 11 and 12, but align the new (5°) mark.

19 It should be noted that the recommendation is to retard the ignition by up to 5° if detonation occurs; some experimentation may be worthwhile to achieve satisfactory running.

9 Spark plugs and HT leads – general

1   The correct functioning of the spark plugs is vital for the correct running and efficiency of the engine. It is essential that the plugs fitted are appropriate for the engine, and the suitable type is specified at the beginning of this chapter. If this type is used and the engine is in good condition, the spark plugs should not need attention between scheduled replacement intervals. Spark plug cleaning is rarely necessary and should not be attempted unless specialised equipment is available as damage can easily be caused to the firing ends.

2   At the intervals specified in *Routine Maintenance*, the plugs should be removed, cleaned and re-gapped.

3   To remove the plugs, first open the bonnet and pull the HT leads

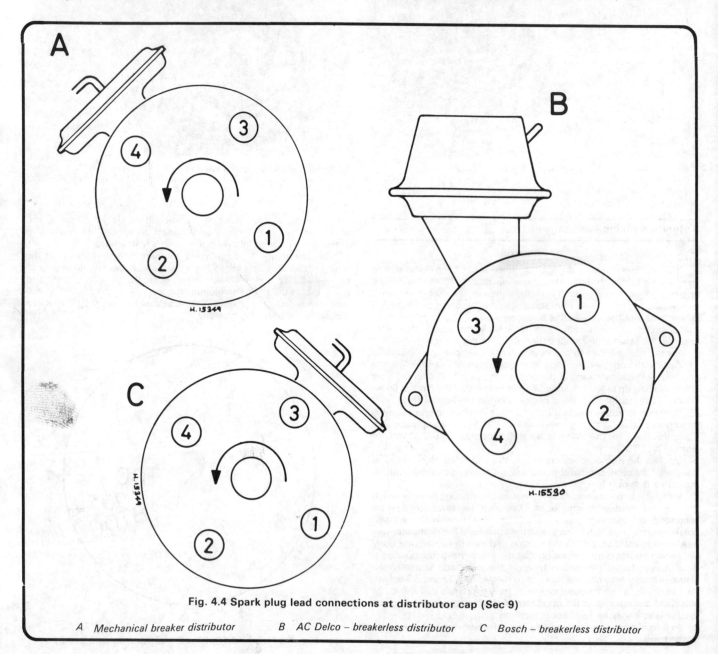

Fig. 4.4 Spark plug lead connections at distributor cap (Sec 9)

A Mechanical breaker distributor   B AC Delco – breakerless distributor   C Bosch – breakerless distributor

from them. Grip the rubber end fitting, not the lead, otherwise the lead connection may be fractured. Then remove the heat shields from the plugs. These will be a very tight fit, and pulling with pliers or levering with a screwdriver will be required to remove them. Be extremely careful as it is easy to break a plug.

4 Brush out any accumulated dirt or grit from the spark plug recess in the cylinder head otherwise it may drop into the combustion chamber when the plug is removed.

5 Unscrew the spark plugs with a deep socket or a box spanner. Do not allow the tool to tilt otherwise the ceramic insulator may be cracked or broken.

6 Examination of the spark plugs will give a good indication of the condition of the engine.

7 If the insulator nose of the spark plug is clean and white, with no deposits, this is indicative of a weak mixture, or too hot a plug (a hot plug transfers heat away from the electrode slowly, a cold plug transfers heat away quickly).

8 If the insulator nose is covered with light tan to greyish brown deposits, then the mixture is correct and it is likely that the engine is in good condition.

9 The spark plug gap is of considerable importance, as, if it is too large or too small, the size of the spark and its efficiency will be seriously impaired. For the best results the spark plug gap should be set in accordance with the Specifications at the beginning of this Chapter.

10 To set it, measure the gap with a feeler gauge, and then bend open, or close, the outer electrode until the correct gap is achieved. The centre electrode should never be bent as this may crack the insulation and cause plug failure if nothing worse.

11 Special spark plug electrode gap adjusting tools are available from most motor accessory stores.

12 Screw each plug in by hand. This will make sure that there is no chance of cross threading.

13 Tighten up to the specified torque. If a torque wrench is not available, just nip up each plug. **It is better to slightly undertighten rather than overdo it and strip the threads from the light alloy cylinder head.**

14 When reconnecting the spark plug leads, make sure that they are refitted in their correct order, 1-3-4-2; No 1 cylinder being at the timing belt end of the engine.

15 The plug leads require no routine attention other than being kept clean and wiped over regularly. At intervals of 6000 miles (10 000 km), however, pull each lead off the plug in turn and remove it from the distributor. Water can seep down into the joints giving rise to a white corrosive deposit which must be carefully removed from the end of each cable.

10 Coil – general

1 The coil is an auto-transformer and has two sets of windings wound around a core of soft iron wires. The resistance of the primary winding is given in Specifications at the beginning of this Chapter (photo).

2 If the coil is suspect then the resistance may be checked by an auto-electrician and if faulty it may readily be renewed after undoing the mounting bolts.

11 TDC sensor

1 As briefly mentioned in Chapter 1, a facility for connecting a TDC sensor to the crankcase is incorporated on this engine.

2 A brass sleeve is located in the crankcase to accept the sensor which in turn monitors the position of the two pins which are fitted to the crankshaft counterweights (photo).

3 Without a suitable ignition tester it is unlikely that this device will be of use to the home mechanic, only to garages or service stations.

4 No 1 piston is at TDC when the notch in the crankshaft pulley is 10° past the timing pointer, the pulley having been turned in the normal direction of crankshaft rotation.

12 Ignition switch – removal and refitting

1 Disconnect the battery.

10.1 The AC Delco coil

2 Extract the screws and remove the lower shroud from the upper end of the steering column.

3 Extract the two small securing screws and withdraw the ignition switch from the end of the steering column lock housing (photos).

13 Fault diagnosis – mechanical breaker ignition system

1 By far the majority of breakdown and running troubles are caused by faults in the ignition system either in the low tension or high tension circuits.

2 There are two main symptoms indicating faults. Either the engine will not start or fire, or the engine is difficult to start and misfires. If it is a regular misfire, (ie the engine is running on only two or three cylinders), the fault is almost sure to be in the secondary or high tension circuit. If the misfiring is intermittent the fault could be in either the high or low tension circuits. If the car stops suddenly, or will not start at all, it is likely that the fault is in the low tension circuit. Loss of power and overheating, apart from faulty carburation settings, are normally due to faults in the distributor or to incorrect ignition timing.

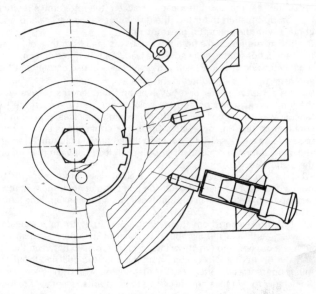

Fig. 4.5 TDC sensor and crankshaft pins (Sec 11)

11.2 TDC sensor pins in crankshaft

12.3A Extracting ignition switch fixing screws

12.3B Ignition switch removal from steering lock

Engine fails to start

3   If the engine fails to start and the car was running normally when it was last used, first check that there is fuel in the petrol tank, If the engine turns over normally on the starter motor and the battery is evidently well charged, then the fault may be in either the high or low tension circuits. First check the HT circuit.

4   One of the commonest reasons for bad starting is wet or damp spark plug leads and distributor. Remove the distributor cap. If condensation is visible internally dry the cap with a rag and also wipe over the leads. Refit the cap. If the engine fails to start due to either damp HT leads or distributor cap, a moisture dispersant, such as Holts Wet Start, can be very effective. To prevent the problem recurring, Holts Damp Start can be used to provide a sealing coat, so excluding any further moisture from the ignition system. In extreme difficulty, Holts Cold Start will help to start a car when only a very poor spark occurs.

5   If the engine still fails to start, check that voltage is reaching the plugs by disconnecting each plug lead in turn at the spark plug end, and holding the end of the cable with rubber or an insulated tool about 6 mm (0.25 in) away from the cylinder block. Spin the engine on the starter motor. **Note** *Do not operate the starter system with the plug leads disconnected in any other way to that described, or damage to system components may result.*

6   Sparking between the end of the cable and the block should be fairly strong with a regular blue spark. If voltage is reaching the plugs, then remove them and clean and regap them. The engine should now start.

7   If there is no spark at the plug leads, take off the HT lead from the centre of the distributor cap and hold it to the block as before. Spin the engine on the starter once more. A rapid succession of blue sparks between the end of the lead and the block indicates that the coil is in order and that the distributor cap is cracked, the rotor arm is faulty or the carbon brush in the top of the distributor cap is not making good contact with the spring on the rotor arm.

8   If there are no sparks from the end of the lead from the coil, check the connections at the coil end of the lead. If it is in order start checking the low tension circuit. Possibly, the points are in bad condition. Clean and reset them as described in this Chapter, Section 3.

9   Use a 12V voltmeter or a 12V bulb and two lengths of wire. With the ignition switched on and the points open, test between the low tension wire to the coil and earth. No reading indicates a break in the supply from the ignition switch. Check the connections at the switch to see if any are loose. Refit them and the engine should run. A reading shows a faulty coil or condenser, or broken lead between the coil and the distributor.

10   Take the condenser wire off the points assembly and with the points open test between the moving point and earth. If there is now a reading then the fault is in the condenser. Fit a new one and the fault is cleared.

11   With no reading from the moving point to earth, take a reading between earth and the distributor terminal of the coil A reading here shows a broken wire which will need to be replaced between the coil and the distributor. No reading confirms that the coil has failed and must be renewed, after which the engine will run once more. Remember to refit the condenser wire to the points assembly. For these tests it is sufficient to separate the points with a piece of dry paper while testing with the points open.

Engine misfires

12   If the engine misfires regularly, run it at a fast idling speed. Pull off each of the plug caps in turn and listen to the note of the engine. Hold the plug cap in a dry cloth or with a rubber glove as additional protection against a shock from the HT supply.

13   No difference in engine running will be noticed when the lead from the defective circuit is removed. Removing the lead from one of the good cylinders will accentuate the misfire.

14   Remove the plug lead from the plug which is not firing and hold it about 6 mm (0.25 in) away from the block. Restart the engine. If the sparking is fairly strong and regular, the fault must lie in the spark plug.

15   The plug may be loose, the insulation may be cracked, or the points may have burnt away giving too wide a gap for the spark to jump. Worse still, one of the points may have broken off. Either renew the plug, or clean it, reset the gap, and then test it.

16   If there is no spark at the end of the plug lead, or if it is weak and intermittent, check the ignition lead from the distributor to the plug. If the insulation is cracked or perished, renew the lead. Check the connections at the distributor cap.

17   If there is still no spark, examine the distributor cap carefully for tracking. This can be recognised by a very thin black line running between two or more electrodes, or between an electrode and some other part of the distributor. These lines are paths which now conduct electricity across the cap thus letting it run to earth. The only answer is a new distributor cap.

18   Apart from the ignition timing being incorrect, other causes of misfiring have already been dealt with under the Section dealing with the failure of the engine to start. To recap, these are that:

   (a)   The coil may be faulty giving an intermittent misfire
   (b)   There may be a damaged wire or loose connection in the low tension circuit
   (c)   The condenser may be faulty
   (d)   There may be a mechanical fault in the distributor (broken driving spindle or contact breaker spring)

19   If the ignition timing is too far retarded, ti should be noted that the engine will tend to overheat, and there will be a quite noticeable drop in power. If the engine is overheating and the power is down, and the ignition timing is correct, then the carburettor should be checked, as it is likely that this is where the fault lies.

20   If the ballast resistor wire is broken or disconnected, the engine will fire when the starter motor is operating but will refuse to run. Renewal of the resistor wire will cure the problem. Do not bypass the resistor wire with ordinary wire, or overheating of the coil will occur.

PART B: BREAKERLESS TYPE IGNITION

14 General description

1   One of two makes of electronic ignition system are fitted. On 1.3 versions (after September 82) an AC Delco system is fitted, while on 1.6 and 1.8 models a Bosch (Hall effect) system is used. Both systems are similar in that they require virtually no maintenance or adjustment.

2 The main components consist of a control unit, an ignition coil and a camshaft-driven distributor.

3 In view of the high voltage used in this system, care must be used when handling wiring or components with the ignition switched on. This is particularly important to anyone equipped with a cardiac pacemaker.

4 Instead of the reluctor and pick-up on the AC Delco induction system, the Hall effect system incorporates a permanent magnet, a detector/amplifier, and four vanes. When a vane is masking the detector/amplifier no voltage is induced in the detector, and under these conditions the control unit passes current through the low tension windings of the coil.

5 Rotation of the distributor will uncover the detector and cause it to be influenced by the magnetic field of the permanent magnet. The Hall effect induces a small voltage in the detector plate which is then amplified and triggers the control unit to interrupt the low tension current in the coil.

6 The control unit in the Hall effect system incorporates a circuit which switches off the low tension circuit if the time between consecutive signals exceeds 1.5 seconds. The coil and internal circuits are therefore protected if the ignition is left switched on inadvertently.

7 It is not recommended that this type of distributor is dismantled beyond the limits of the operations described in the following Sections.

8 Ballast resistors are no longer used in conjuction with breakerless ignition systems, but it is possible that old stocks of wiring harness which incorporated a ballast resistor wire may be encountered. In this case, the wire is inoperative and should be ignored.

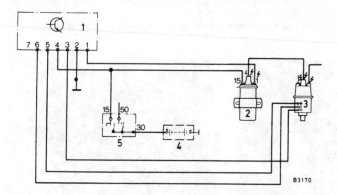

Fig. 4.6 Bosch electronic ignition layout (Sec 14)

1 Control unit	4 Battery
2 Ignition coil	5 Ignition switch
3 Distributor	

15 Breakerless ignition system (all models) – precautions

1 Besides the usual precautions against personal electric shocks, the following points should be observed to avoid damage to the breakerless (electronic) ignition system components:

(a) If measuring the resistance of the coil windings, do so only with the ignition switched off

(b) Do not connect an ohmmeter, or any other self-powered equipment, to the distributor Hall sensor

(c) Do not use a rapid charger, or any power source in excess of 16 volts, as a starting aid

(d) Do not fit any other type of ignition coil

(e) Do not connect any suppression capacitors or test lamps to coil terminal 1

(f) Do not earth coil terminal 1, even as an anti-theft measure, nor connect the battery positive terminal to it

(g) Always earth the coil HT lead if it is necessary to disable the ignition system (eg for a compression test); alternatively unplug the control unit connector. If the system is energised without the HT side earthed, insulation damage may result

2 Note also that some types of tachometers will give erratic readings – usually a multiple or sub-multiple of the actual engine speed – with this type of ignition system. This does not indicate a fault in the ignition system.

16 Routine maintenance – breakerless ignition system

1 Proceed as described in paragraphs 1 and 4 in Section 2 of this Chapter, but observe the precautions given in Section 15.

2 Although the breakerless distributor is otherwise maintenance-free, if removed at any time, clean and check the distributor cap and rotor arm, and inspect for signs of excessive wear or damage. Renew as necessary.

17 Distributor – removal and refitting

1.3 models

1 Remove the spark plugs (Section 9).

2 Undo the distributor cap retaining screws, lift off the cap and place it to one side.

3 With the transmission in gear and the handbrake released, pull the car forwards, until, with a finger over the plug hole, compression can be felt in No 1 cylinder (the cylinder nearest the crankshaft pulley). Continue moving the car forwards until the notch on the crankshaft pulley is aligned with the timing pointer (photo). (On automatic transmission models, turn the engine by means of a spanner on the

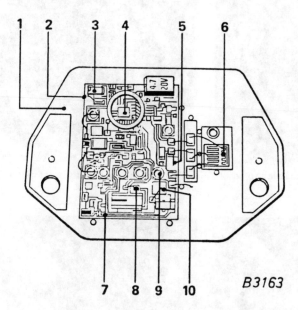

Fig. 4.7 Bosch electronic ignition control unit (Sec 14)

1 Metal base	6 Transistor output stage
2 Thick film board	7 Conductors
3 Capacitor chip	8 Diode chip
4 Dwell angle control	9 Contact points for connecting wires
5 Precision resistor (current measuring)	10 Zener diode chip

crankshaft bolt.) If the distributor cap is temporarily placed in position, the distributor rotor should be pointing towards the No 1 spark plug lead segment in the cap.

4   Disconnect the distributor wiring connector at the ignition coil (photo), and detach the vacuum advance pipe from the distributor vacuum unit.

5   Undo the distributor clamp retaining nut (or bolt), lift off the clamp plate, and withdraw the distributor from the camshaft housing (photo).

6   Before refitting the distributor, check that the engine has not been inadvertently turned whilst the distributor was removed; if it has, return it to the original position as described in paragraph 3.

7   Position the distributor so that the rotor contact is in line with the arrow or notch in the distributor body (photo). In this position, the offset lug on the distributor drive coupling will be in the correct

position to engage the similarly-offset slot in the end of the camshaft (photos).

8   Check that the O-ring seal is in place on the distributor body, then insert the distributor into its camshaft housing location. With the rotor contact and arrow on the distributor body still in line, refit and secure the distributor clamp.

9   Refit the distributor cap, spark plugs and leads, wiring plug and vacuum pipe.

10 Refer to Section 19 and adjust the ignition timing.

1.6 and 1.8 models

11 The procedure is similar to that just described for 1.3 models, with the following differences.

12 The wiring connector must be unplugged from the distributor, not

17.3 Crankshaft pulley timing notch (arrowed) aligned with pointer

17.4 Disconnecting the distributor wiring connector at the ignition coil

17.5 Removing the distributor from the camshaft housing

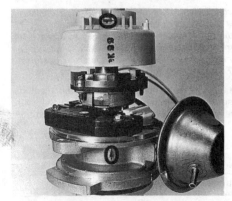

17.7A Distributor rotor contact, and arrow on distributor body (circled) in alignment ...

17.7B ... causing the drive coupling to be aligned like this ...

17.7C ... to engage the offset slot in the camshaft

17.12 Unplugging the distributor LT connector (1.6/1.8)

17.13 Removing the distributor cap (1.6/1.8)

17.14 Removing the flash shield to expose the No 1 cylinder reference mark (arrowed) (1.6/1.8)

17.15 Removing the distributor upper securing nut (1.6/1.8)

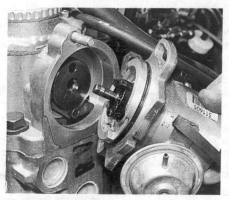

17.16 Removing the distributor – note peg-and-hole drive (1.6/1.8)

Fig. 4.8 Distributor clamp nut (arrowed) – 1.3 models (Sec 17)

from the coil (photo).

13 The distributor cap is secured by two spring clips, not by screws (photo).

14 There is a mark on the edge of the distributor body to indicate the rotor contact position for No 1 cylinder firing, but the rotor and flash shield must be removed to expose it (photo). The rotor can then be refitted to confirm the alignment.

15 The distributor is secured by two nuts, not by a clamp plate (photo).

16 The distributor drive is by means of an offset peg and hole, not by a slot and dogs (photo).

18 Distributor – dismantling, inspection and reassembly

1.3 models

1 Remove the distributor from the engine, as described in the previous Section.

2 Undo the two retaining screws and lift off the rotor.

3 Disconnect the two electrical plugs, one at each end, from the ignition module (photo).

4 Undo the two module retaining screws (photo), and withdraw the unit from the distributor.

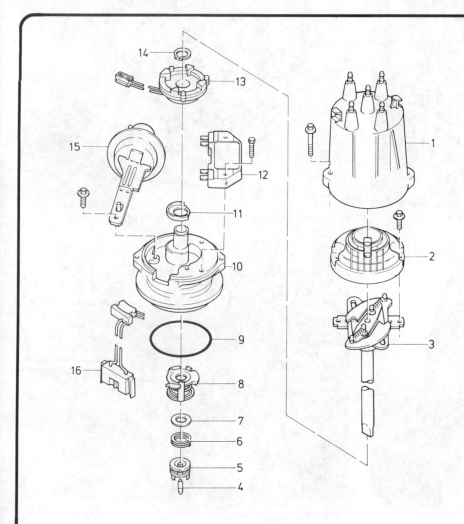

Fig. 4.9 Exploded view of AC Delco breakerless type distributor as fitted to the 1.3 models (Sec 18)

1 Distributor cap
2 Rotor
3 Shaft
4 Pin
5 Drive dog
6 Spring
7 Washer
8 Spring
9 O-ring
10 Body
11 Seal
12 Module (pick-up)
13 Induction sensor (reluctor)
14 Circlip
15 Vacuum unit
16 Plug to coil

5 Undo the two vacuum unit retaining screws (photo), disengage the operating rod and remove the vacuum unit.

6 Due to its design and construction, this is the limit of dismantling possible on this distributor. It is possible to renew the rotor, vacuum unit, ignition module and distributor cap separately, but if inspection shows any of the components remaining on the distributor to be in need of attention, the complete distributor assembly must be renewed.

7 Check the distributor cap for corrosion of the segments, and for signs of tracking, indicated by a thin black line between the segments. Make sure that the carbon brush in the centre of the cap moves freely, and stands proud of its holder. Renew the cap if necessary.

8 If the metal portion of the rotor is badly burnt or loose, renew the rotor. If slightly burnt it may be cleaned with a fine file.

9 Suck on the end of the vacuum unit outlet, and check that the operating rod moves in as the suction is applied. Release the suction, and check that the rod returns to its original position. If this is not the case, renew the vacuum unit.

10 Inspect the distributor body and shaft assembly for excessive side movement of the shaft in its bushes. Check that the advance weights are free to move on their pivot posts, and that they return under the action of the springs. Check the security of all the components on the distributor shaft, and finally check for wear of the lug on the drive coupling.

11 Reassembly of the distributor is the reverse sequence to dismantling, but apply a few drops of engine oil to the advance weight pivot posts before refitting the rotor. If a new ignition module is being fitted, the new module will be supplied with a small quantity of silicone grease. This should be applied between the module and its housing, to improve heat dissipation.

12 Refit the distributor as described in Section 17, after reassembly.

1.6 and 1.8 models

13 Remove the distributor as described in Section 17.

14 Pull off the rotor arm, and unclip the flash shield.

15 Although the top bearing plate can be removed after undoing its retaining screws, this is of academic interest, since no spare parts are available, neither are there any items requiring adjustment.

16 The vacuum unit can be renewed separately if required. Remove it by undoing the two retaining screws and unhooking the operating arm from the baseplate (photos). Note that the screws are not of equal length; the longer screw also secures one of the distributor cap clips.

17 Test the vacuum unit, as described in paragraph 9.

18 Inspect the distributor cap and rotor, as described in paragraphs 7 and 8.

19 Reassemble the distributor in the reverse order to that followed when dismantling. Make sure that the vacuum unit operating arm is correctly engaged with the peg on the baseplate; several attempts may be needed to reconnect it.

20 Refit the distributor as described in Section 17, after reassembly.

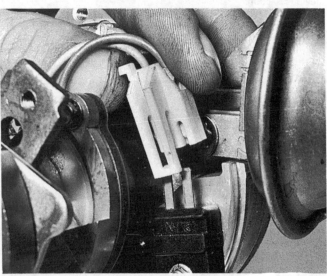

18.3 Disconnecting an electrical plug from the ignition module

18.4 Ignition module securing screws (arrowed)

18.5 Vacuum unit retaining screws (arrowed)

18.16A Removing a vacuum unit retaining screw (1.6/1.8)

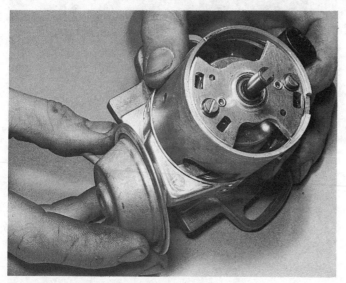

18.16B Removing the vacuum unit (1.6/1.8)

19 Ignition timing – adjustment

Full-leaded petrol

1 Static timing cannot be checked with the breakerless ignition system. However, if the distributor is correctly refitted (Section 17), the timing should be accurate enough to start the engine and permit it to run.

2 Dynamic timing, using a stroboscopic timing light, is carried out as described in Section 8, paragraphs 10, 11 and 12. Note, however, that the distributor is secured by two nuts instead of a clamp bolt. When making timing checks/adjustments, observe the precautions outlined in Section 15.

3 Dwell angle checking and adjustment is not necessary with breakerless distributors.

High octane unleaded petrol

4 The engines used in Cavalier models are designed to run on high octane unleaded petrol, but the manufacturers recommend that the ignition timing is adjusted in accordance with the following guidelines.

Carburettor engines

5 If detonation ('pinking' or 'knock') occurs, the timing should be retarded by up to 5° (see Section 8, paragraphs 13 to 19).

Fuel injection engines

6 When using high octane unleaded petrol, the timing **must** be retarded by 5°, as such fuel can cause inaudible high speed knock, which can lead to engine damage. The procedure is given in Section 8, paragraphs 14 to 18.

20 Coil – general

1 The coil is an auto-transformer, having two sets of windings wound around a core of soft iron wires or laminations. It is located on the left-hand inner wing.

2 If the coil is suspect, the surest test is by substitution of a known good unit. If suitable equipment is available, the winding resistances can be checked. The primary winding resistance is given in the Specifications; secondary resistance is not specified, but is typically in the range 4000 to 12 000 ohms.

3 To remove the coil, disconnect its LT and HT leads, and remove the securing bolts. On 1.6 and 1.8 models, also unplug the ignition module (photos).

4 The cylindrical type of coil can be removed from its clamp by slackening the clamp screw and nut (photo).

5 Some coils have a safety plug; in the event of overheating, the plug

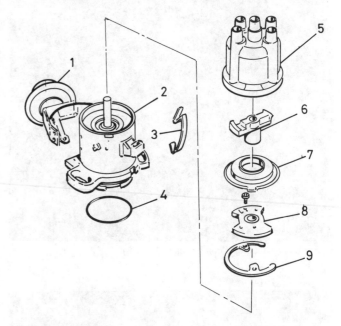

Fig. 4.10 Exploded view of the Bosch breakerless type distributor, as fitted to 1.6 and 1.8 models (Sec 18)

1 Vacuum unit	6 Rotor
2 Body	7 Flash shield
3 Cap retaining clip	8 Top bearing plate
4 O-ring	9 Abutment ring
5 Distributor cap	

will come out, and oil or other insulating material will be discharged. Should this happen, renew the coil and the ignition module.

6 The different types of coil used with the different ignition systems are not interchangeable.

7 When refitting the coil, note that the LT connectors are of different size and shape, thus preventing incorrect refitting.

21 Ignition module – removal and refitting

1 On 1.3 models, the ignition module is located in the distributor. See Section 18 for details.

2 On 1.6 and 1.8 models, the module is located on the coil mounting plate. To gain access, first remove the coil, as described in Section 20.

3 With the coil removed from its bracket, the module can be unbolted from the mounting plate (photo).

4 If a new module is being fitted, it should be supplied with a small quantity of silicone grease, which must be applied to the mounting plate to improve heat dissipation (photo). Similar heat sink compounds can also be obtained from shops selling radio and electronic components.

5 Refit the ignition module in the reverse order to removal. Make sure that the locating pins engage with the holes in the mounting plate.

22 Spark plugs and HT leads – general

Refer to Section 9.

23 Ignition switch – removal and refitting

Refer to Section 12.

20.3A Disconnecting a coil LT lead (1.6/1.8)

20.3B Ignition module wiring plug (1.6/1.8)

20.3C Removing a coil securing bolt

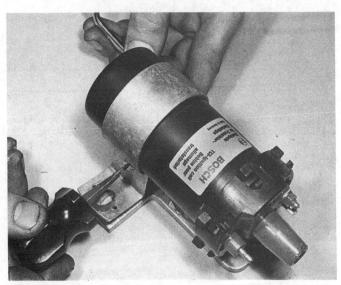

20.4 Undoing the coil clamp screw and nut

21.3 Unbolting the ignition module (1.6/1.8)

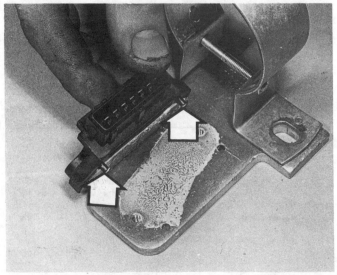

21.4 Ignition module and mounting plate – note locating pins (arrowed), and heat sink compound on baseplate (1.6/1.8)

24 Fault diagnosis – breakerless ignition system

Symptom	Reason(s)
Starter turns but engine will not start	Plug under cap of coil displaced with loss of sealing compound*
	Wires from ignition switch to control unit (terminal 2 or 4) disconnected or loose
	Wire from ignition switch to coil terminal (15) also terminal (1) to control unit plug and earth wire terminal (2) disconnected or loose
Engine runs but misfires	Faulty HT leads or spark plug
	Faulty ignition coil
	Incorrect ignition timing
	Faulty control unit

*Should this be observed, renew both the coil and the control unit, but only with units of specified type

It is possible for a complete ignition failure to occur when the vehicle is in close proximity to certain types of VHF equipment. This is only likely to happen if the system incorporates an early type (grey and black) control unit. With later type control units, this cannot occur. The later units are coloured all black

Chapter 5 Clutch

Contents

Specifications

General

Type	Single dry plate with diaphragm spring. Cable actuation
Adjustment	By nut on cable at release lever
Release bearing	Sealed ball-bearing
Driven plate diameter:	
1.3	190.5 mm (7.5 in)
1.6	203.2 mm (8.0 in)
1.8	215.9 mm (8.5 in)

Torque wrench settings

	Nm	lbf ft
Clutch cover bolts	15	11
Release fork to lever bolt	35	26
Flywheel housing cover plate bolts	7	5
Flywheel housing-to-engine bolts	75	55
Transmission end cover bolts	22	16
End cover screw plug (F10, F10.4, F16.4)	50	37
End cover screw plug (F10.5, F16.5)	30	22

1 General description

All models covered by this manual are fitted with a single plate diaphragm spring clutch which is enclosed in a pressed steel cover bolted to the flywheel. The gearbox input shaft projects through the clutch and is located at its forward end in a needle roller spigot bearing within the centre of the crankshaft.

The clutch driven plate is located between the flywheel and the clutch pressure plate and it can slide on splines on the gearbox input shaft. When the clutch is engaged, the diaphragm spring forces the pressure plate to grip the driven plate against the flywheel and drive is transmitted from the crankshaft, through the driven plate, to the gearbox input shaft. On disengaging the clutch the pressure plate is lifted to release the driven plate with the result that the drive to the gearbox is disconnected.

The clutch is operated by a foot pedal suspended under the facia and a cable connected to the clutch release lever mounted on the clutch bellhousing. Depressing the pedal causes the release lever to move the thrust bearing against the release fingers of the diaphragm spring in the pressure plate assembly. The spring is sandwiched between two rings which act as fulcrums. As the centre of the spring is moved in, the periphery moves out to lift the pressure plate and disengage the clutch. The reverse takes place when the pedal is released.

As wear takes place on the driven plate with usage, the foot pedal will rise progressively relative to its original position. Periodic adjustment is not required.

An unusual feature of the design of this particular clutch is that the driven plate, release bearing and seal can be renewed without having to remove either the engine or the transmission from the car.

2 Clutch – adjustment

1   The clutch is normally self-adjusting, but if the cable or driven plate are renewed, the following initial adjustment will be required.

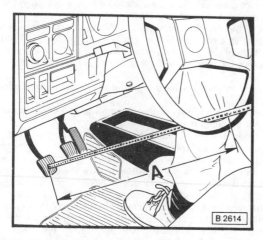

Fig. 5.1 Clutch pedal released measurement (A) (Sec 2)

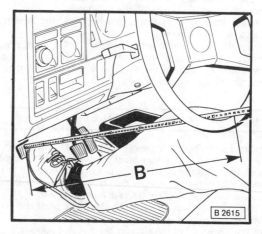

Fig. 5.2 Clutch pedal depressed measurement (B) (Sec 2)

2   Take a measurement from the edge of the steering wheel to the centre of the clutch pedal and then take another measurement with the pedal fully depressed. These measurements can be taken using a suitable strip of wood or metal as the important figure is the difference between the two measurements, ie the movement (stroke) of the pedal itself. This should be 138 mm (5.4 in) and if this is not the case, the nut on the threaded end of the cable where it fits into the clutch release lever must be adjusted to obtain the correct pedal movement. Before adjusting the nut, remove the spring clip, and refit it after the adjustment has been made. Recheck the pedal movement on completion (Fig. 5.1 and 5.2).

3   After some period in use, it will not be possible to adjust the cable in this fashion and it will be an indication that the driven plate is due for renewal. Note that when correctly adjusted, the clutch pedal will be slightly higher than the brake pedal and it is incorrect for the two pedals to be in alignment. If they are aligned the clutch cable needs adjusting. Note also that there should be no play in the clutch pedal of these vehicles.

3   Clutch cable – removal and refitting

1   The most obvious reason for having to renew the clutch cable is breakage, but it may also be necessary if the pedal action is stiff or jerky.

2   Before disturbing the installation, take a measurement of the length of the threaded end of the cable fitting protruding through the

Fig. 5.3 Clutch operating cable clip – arrowed (Sec 3)

Fig. 5.4 Cable attachment at clutch pedal – arrowed (Sec 3)

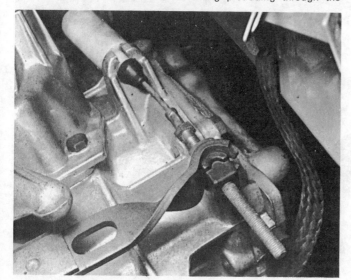

3.3 Clutch operating cable at release lever

adjusting nut at the release lever end. This will enable you to preset the new cable and so simplify its installation.

3   Remove the spring clip from the cable (Fig. 5.3), slacken the adjusting nut and disconnect the cable from the release lever. The cable assembly can now be extracted from the lug on the bellhousing case (photo).

4   Working inside the car, unhook the return spring from the clutch foot pedal and disconnect the cable from the pedal lever (Fig. 5.4).

5   The cable assembly can now be withdrawn into the engine compartment by pulling it through the bulkhead.

6   If a headlamp washer system is installed, then the fluid reservoir will have to be moved aside.

7   Refitting the clutch cable is the reverse of the removal procedure. Position the cable adjusting nut initially so that the same amount of thread protrudes through the nut as noted during removal, then adjust the clutch as described in Section 2.

4   Clutch pedal – removal and refitting

1   Remove the cardboard trim panel from under the instrument panel.

2   Refer to the previous Section and disconnect the clutch cable from the release lever and the clutch pedal, but there is no need to remove the assembly from the lug on the bellhousing case or withdraw the assembly from the car. Release the pedal return spring.

3   Remove the wire locking clip from the pedal pivot retaining nut, then remove the nut and washer.

4   Push the pivot out of the support bracket and remove the clutch pedal and the return spring.

5   Refitting is the reverse of the removal procedure. Before inserting the pedal pivot, lightly smear the bearing surface with a molybdenum disulphide grease. Refit the cable as described in the previous Section and adjust if necessary.

5   Clutch unit – removal, inspection and refitting (leaving engine/transmission in the vehicle)

Removal

1   A good feature of these models is that of being able to renew the clutch pressure plate, the driven plate, the release bearing, the release pivot bushes and the clutch seal without having to remove either the engine or the transmission.

2   Although the maker's procedure requires the use of special tools, these are not essential and the work can be carried out using the tools normally available to the home mechanic.

3   Some of the operations are best carried out by working under the front of the vehicle, so apply the handbrake fully, jack up the front of the vehicle and support securely on axle stands. Unbolt and remove the flywheel housing cover plate from the base of the clutch bellhousing.

4   Unscrew and remove the plug from the transmission casing end cover (photos).

5   Extract the circlip, now esposed, from the end of the input shaft using a pair of circlip pliers (photo).

6   Underneath the circlip is a socket-headed (12-point) screw, which will require a 12-point splined key to extract it. Motor accessory tool shops usually stock this type of key. Remove the screw (photos).

7   The shaft can now be slid out of engagement with the splined hub of the clutch driven plate. To do this, the makers provide a special tool, but an effective substitute is to remove one of the four bolts which secure the gearchange mechanism cover to the top of the transmission case. Screw the bolt into the end of the input shaft and use the bolt to pull the shaft out to its stop. Refit the bolt to the cover on the transmission case (photos). On some 5-speed transmission units, it is not unknown for the input shaft to be very tight, in which event it may prove difficult to withdraw it without using the special tool or a puller of some sort. In extreme cases, a slide hammer will have to be attached to the end of the shaft to enable it to be withdrawn.

8   Before the clutch can be removed the pressure plate must be compressed against the tension of the diaphragm spring, otherwise the clutch assembly will be too thick to pass through the space between the flywheel and the edge of the bellhousing when withdrawing it.

9   The vehicle makers can supply three special clamps (KM526) for this job, but substitutes can be made up from strips of metal. The clamps should be U-shaped and conform to the following dimensions.

Thickness of metal strip 3.0 mm (0.12 in)
Distance between U legs 15.0 mm (0.59 in) (photos)

10 Bevel the edges of the clamps to make it easier to fit them. Have an assistant depress the clutch pedal fully and then fit each clamp

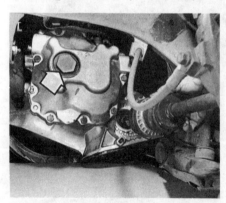

5.4A Threaded plug in 4-speed transmission end cover – arrowed

5.4B Unscrewing threaded plug (4-speed transmission)

5.5 Extracting the input shaft circlip

5.6A Splinded key for removing 12-point socket-head screws

5.6B Removing the input shaft screw

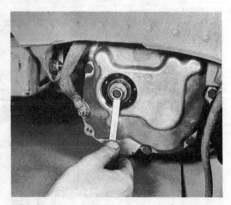

5.7A Screwing bolt into input shaft

5.7B Withdrawing input shaft to stop

5.9A Retaining clip for clutch removal

5.9B Retaining clip viewed from pressure plate side

5.9C Retaining clip viewed from clutch cover side

5.12 Unscrewing clutch cover bolts

5.14 Removing clutch with retaining clips fitted

securely over the edge of the clutch cover/plate assembly engaging them in the apertures spaced around the rim of the clutch cover. Turn the crankshaft by means of the pulley bolt to bring each clip location into view.

11 Once the clips have been fitted, release the clutch pedal.

12 Progressively loosen and remove each of the six bolts which hold the clutch cover to the flywheel (photo).

13 Although positioning dowels are not used to locate the clutch cover to the flywheel, the coloured spot on the flywheel should be in alignment with the notch in the rim of the clutch cover.

14 Withdraw the clutch assembly downwards and out of the bellhousing. The pressure plate can be compressed in a vice in order to be able to remove the clips (photo).

Fig. 5.5 Removing clutch assembly (Sec 5)

Inspection

15 In the normal course of events, clutch dismantling and reassembly involves simply fitting a new clutch pressure plate, driven plate and release bearing. Under no circumstances should the diaphragm spring clutch unit be dismantled. If a fault develops in the pressure plate assembly, a new or exchange replacement unit must be fitted.

16 Do not attempt to reline a driven plate yourself, it is just not worth it, but obtain a new component. The necessity for renewing the plate will be apparent if the lining material has worn down to the rivets or the linings are oil stained. If the latter, rectify the faulty engine or transmission oil seal which must be the cause. The driven plate may also have broken torsion springs or worn hub splines.

17 If a new clutch is being fitted, it is false economy not to renew the release bearing at the same time (see Section 7). This will preclude having to replace it at a later date.

18 Check the machined faces of the flywheel and the pressure plate. If either is badly grooved it should be machined until smooth, or replaced with a new item. If the pressure plate is cracked or split it must be renewed.

Refitting

19 Some clutch assemblies are supplied already compressed with the retaining clips fitted. If this is not the case, the pressure plate should be compressed evenly in a vice; using protectors to prevent damage to the machined face of the plate. Alternatively, use a heavy bolt and nut with two metal strips having a hole drilled in them to do the job. Fit the clips.

20 Apply a smear of molybdenum disulphide grease to the splines of the driven plate hub and then offer the plate to the flywheel so that the greater projecting side of it is away from the flywheel. Hold the plate against the flywheel while the clutch pressure plate assembly (compressed) is offered into position.

21 Push the input shaft through the hub of the driven plate and engage its end in the pilot bearing in the end of the crankshaft. Note that it is not permissible to use hammer blows to assist in refitting the input shaft.

22 If the input shaft cannot be pushed home by hand, steady pressure

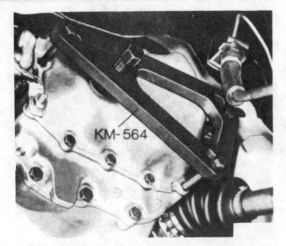

Fig. 5.6 Transmission input shaft fitting tool KM-564 in use (Sec 5)

should be exerted by means of a screw or hydraulic device. The special tool KM-564, shown in Fig. 5.6 is produced expressly for the purpose, but it should be possible to improvise something similar at home. If the shaft is hammered home, transmission damage may result.

23 Bolt the clutch cover to the flywheel and tighten them to the specified torque.

24 Have your assistant depress the clutch pedal and then remove the temporary clips.

25 To the end of the input shaft, screw in the recessed screw and fit a new circlip.

26 On four-speed transmissions only, apply sealant or PTFE tape to the threads of the plug and screw it into the transmission end cover. Tighten to the specified torque. The plug should not project more than 4.0 mm (0.16 in) from the face of the end cover when correctly fitted (photo).

27 Check the clutch adjustment (Section 2).

28 Fit the cover plate to the flywheel housing.

29 Lower the front of the vehicle.

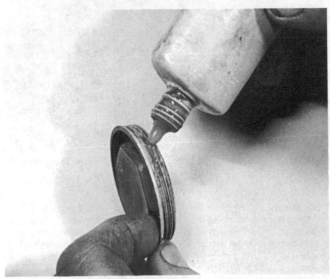

5.26 Applying sealant to end cover plug (4-speed gearbox)

6 Clutch unit – removal, inspection and refitting (engine or transmission, or engine/transmission removed)

1 Having obtained access to the clutch by removing the engine on its own, the transmission on its own or the combined engine/transmission as described in Chapter 1, unbolt the clutch cover from the flywheel and remove it, together with the driven plate.

2 Inspect the components and renew as necessary as described in the preceding Section.

3 To refit the clutch, offer the driven plate to the flywheel so that the more projecting side of the hub is furthest from the flywheel.

4 Locate the clutch cover so that the notch in the cover rim is aligned with the coloured spot on the flywheel.

5 Screw in the clutch cover bolts progressively, but only finger tight.

6 The driven plate must now be centralised. To do this insert a clutch alignment tool through the splined hub of the driven plate and engage the end of the tool in the pilot bearing in the end of the crankshaft flange. This will have the effect of sliding the driven plate sideways and so centralising it so that the transmission inut shaft will pass through it without obstruction (photo).

7 Clutch alignment tools can be purchased from motor accessory stores or one can be made up from a length of dowelling or rod using tape wound around it to match the diameter of the splined hole in the hub of the driven plate.

8 Once the alignment tool is an easy sliding fit in the hub, tighten the clutch cover bolts to the specified torque. Remove the tool.

9 Reconnect and refit the engine and transmission as described in Chapter 1.

6.6 Using a clutch alignment tool (typical)

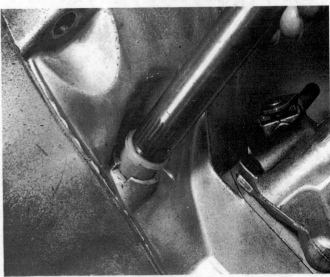

7.3A Withdrawing release lever shaft

7.3B Release lever shaft bushes

7.3C Clutch release bearing

7.4 Fitting new oil seal to release bearing guide

7 Clutch release bearing, lever, bushes and seal – removal and refitting

1 Wear of the clutch release bearing is indicated by a squealing noise when the clutch pedal is depressed with the engine running.
2 To gain access to the release bearing it is necessary first to remove the clutch unit as described in Section 5 or 6.
3 After removing the clutch unit, undo the clamp bolt securing the release fork to the release lever pivot shaft. Disconnect the clutch cable from the release lever, see Section 3 for details if necessary, and then pull the release lever pivot shaft up and out of the housing and remove the release fork. Unscrew the three bolts securing the release bearing guide to the casing and remove the guide. Prise the old seal out of the release bearing guide location. If required, the bushes supporting the release lever pivot can be drifted out of the case using a suitable drift (photos).
4 Refitting is the reverse of the removal procedure but the following points should be noted:

(a) After fitting a new seal to the release bearing guide fill the space between the lips of the seal with a good quality general purpose grease (photo).
(b) When fitting the new O-ring seal to the casing at the release bearing guide location do not use any grease or oil as this seal should be fitted dry.
(c) Lightly smear the release bearing guide surface on which the bearing slides with molybdenum disulphide grease and tighten the securing bolts to the specified torque
(d) If being renewed, drift the new release lever bushes into their housings, ensure that their locating tongues are engaged in the slots in the case, and coat the inner surfaces of the bushes with molybdenum disulphide grease.
(e) Fit the release bearing and the release fork together and tighten the release fork clamp bolt to the specified torque
(f) Refit the clutch as described in Section 5 or 6
(g) Check the adjustment as described in Section 2.

8 Fault diagnosis

Symptom	Reason(s)
Judder when taking up drive	Loose engine or gearbox mountings Badly worn friction linings or contaminated with oil Worn splines on gearbox input shaft or driven plate hub Worn input shaft needle bearing in flywheel (before engine No 14089444)
*Clutch spin (failure to disengage) so that gears cannot be meshed	Incorrect release bearing to pressure plate clearance Rust on splines (may occur after vehicle standing idle for long periods) Damaged or misaligned pressure plate assembly Cable stretched or broken
Clutch slip (increase in engine speed does not result in increase in vehicle road speed – particularly on gradients)	Incorrect release bearing-to-pressure plate finger clearance Friction linings worn out or oil contaminated
Noise evident on depressing clutch pedal	Dry, worn or damaged release bearing Incorrect pedal adjustment Weak or broken pedal return spring Excessive play between driven plate hub splines and input shaft splines
Noise evident as clutch pedal released	Distorted drive plate Broken or weak driven plate cushion coil springs Incorrect pedal adjustment Weak or broken clutch pedal return spring Distorted or worn input shaft Release bearing loose on retainer hub

* This condition may also be due to the driven plate being rusted to the flywheel or pressure plate. It is possible to free it by applying the handbrake, depressing the clutch, engaging top gear and operating the starter motor. If really badly corroded, then the engine will not turn over, but in the majority of cases the driven plate will free. Once the engine starts, rev it up and slip the clutch several times to clear the rust deposits

Chapter 6 Manual and automatic transmissions

For modifications, and information applicable to later models, see Supplement at end of manual

Contents

Specifications

Part A: Manual transmission

Type .... Four or five forward speeds (all with synchromesh) and reverse. Unit transversely mounted at front of car

Designation
1.3 up to 1982 .... F10 (4-speed)
1.3 from 1983 .... F10.4 (4-speed) or F10.5 (5-speed)
1.6 and 1.8 .... F16 (4-speed), F16.4 (4-speed) or F16.5 (5-speed)

Gear ratios (typical)

	F10	F10.4W/5W	F16	F16.4W/5W	F16.5C
1st	3.64:1	3.55:1	3.55:1	3.42:1	3.42:1
2nd	2.21:1	1.96:1	2.16:1	1.95:1	2.16:1
3rd	1.43:1	1.30:1	1.37:1	1.28:1	1.48:1
4th	0.97:1	0.89:1	0.97:1	0.89:1	1.12:1
5th (when applicable)	–	0.71:1	–	0.71:1	0.89:1
Reverse	3.18:1	3.18:1	3.33:1	3.33:1	3.33:1
Final drive	4.18:1	4.29:1	3.74:1	3.74:1	3.94:1
Speedometer drive	2:1	2:1	2:1	2:1	2:1

Suffix W indicates standard ratios, suffix C indicates sports ratios

Oil type/specification .... Gear oil, viscosity SAE 80EP, or GM gear oil 90 188 629 (Duckhams Hypoid 80, or Hypoid 75W/90S)

Oil capacity
F10 and F10.4 .... 1.7 litres (3.0 pints) approx
F10.5 .... 1.8 litres (3.2 pints) approx
F16 and F16.4 .... 2.0 litres (3.5 pints) approx
F16.5 .... 2.1 litres (3.7 pints) approx

Torque wrench settings

	Nm	lbf ft
Flywheel housing-to-engine bolts	75	55
End cover bolts	22	16
Selector cover bolts	15	11
End cover screw plug (F10, F10.4, F16, F16.4)	50	37
End cover screw plug (F10.5, F16.5)	30	22
Differential cover plate bolts	30	22
Crownwheel bolts	85	63
Exhaust bracket to transmission casing	60	44
Mounting bracket bolts to transmission	30	22
Mounting bolts to bodyframe	40	29
Reverse lamp switch	20	15
5th gear selector fork pivot socket screws	22	16
5th gear pawl socket screws	9	6

Part B: Automatic transmission

Type .... General Motors Hydromatic Torque converter (fluid coupling) with chain drive to gear trains. Three forward and one reverse gear

Designation .... 125 THM

Speed ratios
1st 2.84:1
2nd 1.60:1
3rd 1.00:1
Reverse 2.07:1
Final drive 3.33:1

Fluid type/specification
.... Dexron II type ATF (Duckhams D-matic)

Fluid capacity
Dry converter and casing .... 9.0 litres (15.8 pints) approx
At service fluid change .... 7.0 litres (12.3 pints) approx

Torque wrench settings

	Nm	lbf ft
Fluid pan bolts	16	12
Fluid cooling hose connections to transmission	38	28
Torque converter housing-to-engine bolts	75	55
Torque converter-to-driveplate bolts:		
1.3	65	48
Other models	60	44
Fluid cooling hose to cooler	22	16
Mounting bracket bolts to transmission	22	16
Mounting bolts to bodyframe	40	30

PART A: MANUAL TRANSMISSION

1 General description

The manual transmission is of four or five-speed type (depending upon model) combined in one housing with the differential and final drive.

The transmission unit transmits power through open driveshafts to the front roadwheels. Gear selection is by means of a floor-mounted lever and a remote control rod.

Procedures described for F10 series transmissions apply equally to F10, F10.4 and F10.5 types.

2 Routine maintenance – manual transmission

1 Routine maintenance is restricted to checking the oil level; draining and refilling with fresh lubricant is not specified.

2 However, if the lubricant must be drained for any reason, most of it can be removed if the pressed steel cover plate is unbolted and pulled away from the differential.

3 The level plug is located close to the driveshaft inboard joint on the right-hand side of the car on F16 transmissions, and on the left-hand side of the car on F10 transmissions (Fig. 6.1).

4 The oil level should be maintained at the bottom of the level plug opening. If topping-up is required, remove the breather from the transmission casing and pour it into the breather plug hole (photo). *On no account attempt to top up by pouring oil into the level plug hole.*

2.4 Topping-up the manual transmission oil

5 Use only the correct grade of oil specified (see *Recommended Lubricants* at the start of the manual). When topping-up, do not intermix SAE 80 mineral types with a semi-synthetic oil type. If the oil type in the gearbox is not known it is advisable to drain and renew the transmission oil.

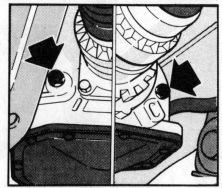

Fig. 6.1 Transmission oil level plugs (arrowed) seen from below (Sec 2)

F16 Left-hand illustration   F10 Right-hand illustration

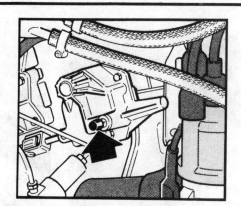

Fig. 6.2 Transmission breather/filler plug (arrowed) (Sec 2)

3 Gearchange lever – removal and refitting

Early models

1 Set the gearchange lever in neutral then release the rubber boot at the base and slide it up the lever.
2 If a central console is fitted, it may be necessary to remove it for access, depending on type (see Chapter 11).
3 Extract the circlip from its groove in the housing.
4 Press the gearchange lever to the left-hand side and withdraw it.
5 If essential, the gearchange lever housing complete with insulator can be removed from the underside of the floor. Renew the complete assembly.
6 If the boot is to be renewed, the knob can be pulled off if it is first heated in very hot water.
7 Refitting is a reversal of removal, but observe the following points:

   (a) Apply grease to the pivot ball and socket
   (b) Note that the tab on the underside of the boot is towards the front of the vehicle
   (c) When fitting the gear lever knob, align it with the stop on reverse gear sleeve

Later models

8 Proceed as described in paragraphs 1 and 2 above.
9 Undo the four selector unit-to-floor securing bolts and lift the lever assembly clear (photo).
10 To remove the selector housing unit, prise free the C-clip, extract the pin and withdraw the housing unit from the lever bottom end (photos).
11 The selector lever ball rubber can be removed by prising it free from the groove in the ball (photo).
12 The gear lever knob and rubber boot are removed in the manner described for earlier models (paragraph 6).
13 Removal and dismantling of the gearchange gate unit is possible as required, but take a note of the fitting orientation of any components removed to assist when reassembling.

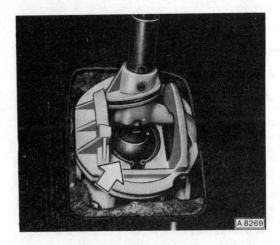

Fig. 6.3 Gearchange lever circlip (arrowed) on early models (Sec 3)

14 Refit in the reverse order of removal, observing the following points:

   (a) Lubricate the pivot ball and socket with grease
   (b) Ensure that the gear lever knob is correctly aligned and all gearchange control components are correctly orientated before refitting
   (c) When refitted, ensure that the alignment markings on the side of the selector housing and gate change unit align when the lever is in neutral (photo)

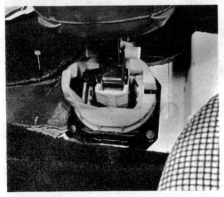

3.9 Later type gear lever-to-floor mounting

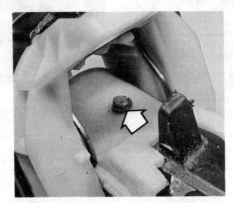

3.10A Remove the C-clip (arrowed) from the pin groove ...

3.10B ... withdraw the pin ...

3.10C ... and separate the lever from the housing (later models)

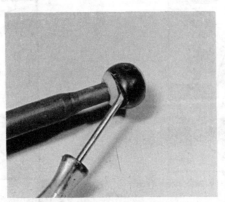

3.11 Rubber insulator removal from the selector lever ball (later models)

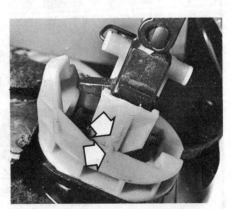

3.14 Alignment marks for neutral on lever and housing – arrowed (later models)

Fig. 6.4 Gearchange lever alignment tab (arrowed) on early models (Sec 3)

Fig. 6.5 Gearchange lever knob alignment with reverse gear sleeve on early models – arrowed (Sec 3)

4 Gearchange lever reverse selector cable – removal and refitting

1   The reverse blocker mechanism, which is released by lifting the collar on the gear lever when engaging reverse gear, is operated by a cable which runs inside the gear lever. If the cable breaks it may be renewed as follows, but check first that the necessary parts are available.

2   Remove the gear lever, as described in Section 3.

3   Pull the knob from the gear lever, first heating the knob in boiling water. Even after heating, it is likely that the knob will be destroyed during removal. Extract the spring from below the knob.

4   Remove the two grub screws from the top of the gear lever. The top screw has a recessed hexagonal head and is undone with an Allen key; the lower screw has a slotted head and is undone with a small screwdriver (photo).

5   Drive out the roll pins which secure the plastic coupling and shift finger to the gear lever. It is likely that the coupling will be destroyed during removal. Remove the cable and its end fitting (photo).

6   Refit in the reverse order to removal, using new roll pins and (where necessary) a new plastic coupling and gear lever knob. No adjustment procedure is described, so the position in which the cable is clamped by the grub screws will have to be determined by trial and error.

5 Gearchange linkage – removal and refitting

1   Working at the transmission, slacken the pinch-bolt at the gearchange rod coupling (Fig. 6.6).

Fig. 6.6 Gearchange rod coupling pinch-bolt – arrowed (Sec 5)

2   Remove the screws which hold the gearchange rod protective housing and detach the rubber cover at the end of the housing (Fig. 6.7 and 6.8).

3   Separate the base of the gearchange lever from the eye in the gearchange rod and then withdraw the linkage assembly from the vehicle.

4   Withdraw the bellows and boot from the protective housing (photo).

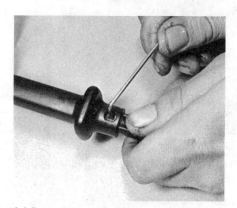

4.4 Removing a grub screw from the gearlever (early models)

4.5 Drive out the roll pins

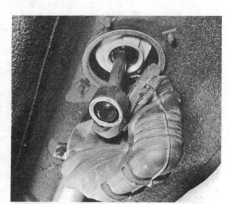

5.4 Protective boot at base of gear lever

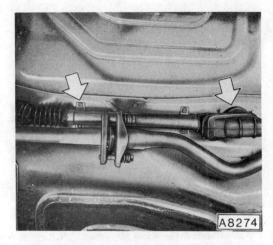

Fig. 6.7 Gearchange rod protective housing and boot –
arrowed (Sec 5)

Fig. 6.8 Removing gearchange rod protective covering
(Sec 5)

Fig. 6.9 Removing gearchange rod intermediate lever roll
pin (Sec 5)

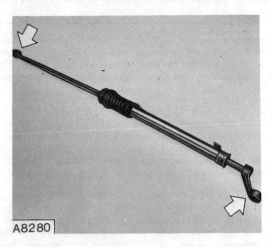

Fig. 6.10 Intermediate lever to clamp alignment – arrowed
(Sec 5)

5   The assembly may be further dismantled to renew worn
components by driving out the retaining pin from the intermediate
lever and control rod (Fig. 6.9).
6   Tap the rod out of the lever.
7   The universal joint may be dismantled by grinding off the rivet
heads.
8   Use a rod to remove the bushes from the protective housing.
9   Commence reassembly by filling the protective housing sleeve
bush grooves with grease and inserting the bushes into the housing.
10 Special pins with circlips are available to replace the original rivets
when reassembling the universal joints.
11 Connect the intermediate lever to the control rod using a new pin,
but make sure that it is aligned with the clamp as shown (Fig. 6.10).
12 Fit the bellows and boot to the protective housing and apply
silicone grease liberally inside the boot.
13 Slide the gearchange rod into the housing and fit to the floorpan.
14 Adjust the linkage as described in the next Section.

6   Gearchange linkage – adjustment

1   Set the gearchange hand control lever in neutral.
2   If fitted, remove the centre console (see Chapter 11).
3   Slacken the pinch-bolt on the gearchange rod coupling (Fig.
6.11).
4   Prise out the small blanking plug from the transmission cover.
5   Looking towards the front of the vehicle, grip the gearchange rod

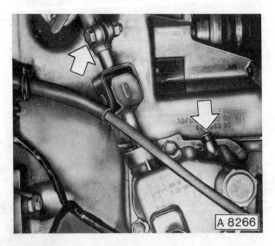

Fig. 6.11 Transmission adjuster hole and clamp pinch-bolt –
arrowed (Sec 6)

and twist it in an anti-clockwise direction until a 4.5 mm (0.18 in)
diameter twist drill can be inserted into the hole left by removal of the
plug. Insert the drill until it fully enters the hole in the selector lever as
shown (photo).

6.5 Setting gearchange rod (casing removed for clarity)

7.2 Reverse lamp switch leads

7.7 Transmission earth strap

6   The help of an assistant will now be required to withdraw the gearchange lever boot upwards and to move the lever across the neutral gate until it is aligned with the 1st/2nd (centre) point of the gate, up against the reverse stop (Fig. 6.12).
7   Without moving the set position of the gearchange lever, tighten the rod coupling pinch-bolt.
8   Withdraw the twist drill and refit the plug. To prevent oil leakage when the vehicle is operating, it is vital that this plug seals perfectly, if not, renew it.
9   Refit the gear lever boot and the centre console.

Fig. 6.12 Gearchange lever alignment during adjustment – arrowed (Sec 6)

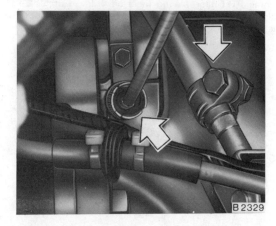

Fig. 6.13 Speedometer cable and gearchange rod connection to transmission – arrowed (Sec 7)

7   Transmission – removal and refitting

Removal
1   Disconnect the clutch operating cable from the release lever.
2   Disconnect the leads from the reverse lamp switch (photo).
3   Disconnect the gearchange rod by removing the bolt from the coupling clamp.
4   Disconnect the speedometer drive cable from the transmission casing by unscrewing the knurled ring or unbolting the retainer plate according to type.
5   Raise the front of the vehicle and support it securely on axle stands.
6   Remove the left-hand front roadwheel.
7   Disconnect the earth strap which runs between the transmission and the bodyframe (photo).
8   Remove the long exhaust pipe bracket from the transmission (if applicable).
9   Disconnect the anti-roll bar from the left-hand suspension lower control arm.
10   Unbolt the suspension control arm support, as described in Chapter 10. With the suspension arm and support suspended by the stub axle carrier balljoint, swivel the assembly to one side out of the way.
11   Release the driveshaft from the transmission using a suitable tool as described in Chapter 7. Anticipate some loss of oil as the driveshafts are released. Withdraw the left-hand driveshaft from the transmission by pulling it towards you.
12   Unscrew the plug from the transmission end cover.
13   Extract the retaining circlip now exposed (photo).
14   A screw will now be observed which has a splined recess in its head. A twelve-sided splined key will be required to unscrew it. Accessory shops can usually supply a socket adaptor for this purpose,

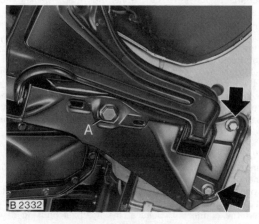

Fig. 6.14 Suspension control arm support retaining bolts – arrowed (1.3 and some 1.6 – see Chapter 10) (Sec 7)

A   Centre bolt at positioning sleeve

7.13 Input shaft circlip

7.14 Extracting input shaft 12-point socket-head screw

7.18 Transmission left-rear mounting bracket

7.33A Applying PTFE tape to end plug threads

7.33B End cover plug installed

otherwise an Allen key may do the job (photo).

15 Unscrew and remove the screw.

16 As described in more detail in Chapter 5, the input shaft can be slid out of engagement with the clutch driven plate and to do this, the makers provide a speical tool. To overcome this problem, borrow one of the four bolts which secure the gearchange selector cover to the top of the transmission casing. Screw the bolt into the end of the input shaft and pull the shaft out of engagement with the clutch driven plate using a pair of self-locking pliers. Don't forget to refit the bolt to the gearchange selector cover.

17 Take the weight of the engine on a hoist or jack. Place a jack, preferably of trolley type, under the transmission.

18 Disconnect the left rear mounting bracket from both the transmission case and the flexible mount (photo).

19 Disconnect the left-hand front mounting bracket from the transmission case and the flexible mount.

20 Clear controls, cables and electrical leads away from the transmission casing.

21 Remove the transmission bellhousing-to-engine connecting bolts.

22 Unbolt and remove the cover plate from the lower part of the flywheel housing. This is the cover that faces towards the timing belt end of the engine.

23 Lower the transmission. The right-hand driveshaft will drop out, be ready to support it. Remove the transmission from under the vehicle.

24 Clean away external dirt. If overhaul is to be carried out, place the unit securely on a bench or other firm working surface.

Refitting

25 Manoeuvre the transmission under the vehicle and raise it on a jack to connect with the engine. If the clutch has been dismantled then the driven plate must have been centralised as described in Chapter 5. As the transmission is raised, engage the right-hand driveshaft with it.

26 Insert the connecting bolts at the flywheel housing flange and tighten to the specified torque. Refit the flywheel cover plate.

27 Refit the front engine mountings followed by the rear ones.

28 Reconnect the driveshafts to the transmission case and secure their locking rings by applying a heavy drift to the driveshaft joint weld bead

and then giving the drift a sharp blow with a hammer (refer to Chapter 7).

29 Refit the suspension control arm and support as described in Chapter 10.

30 Ensure that the control arm support bolts are cleaned of old thread sealant. Apply new sealant before tightening to the specified torque (Chapter 10).

31 Reconnect the anti-roll bar to the control arm. Do not overtighten the connecting bolt or nut, but only enough to maintain the dimension (A) as shown (Fig. 6.15).

32 Push the input shaft into engagement with the clutch driven plate splined hub. Screw in the splined socket-headed screw and fit the retaining circlip.

33 Fit the screw plug to the transmission end cover. It is essential that this plug makes a leakproof joint so apply sealant to the threads or wind some PTFE tape around them on 4-speed units. On 5-speed transmissions, the plug is of different design and does not require this treatment (photos).

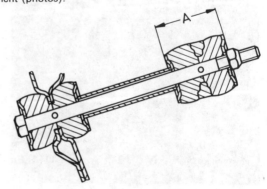

Fig. 6.15 Anti-roll bar end fitting diagram (Sec 7)

A = 38.0 mm (1.5 in)

34 Reconnect the earth strap.
35 Refit the roadwheel.
36 Reconnect the reverse lamp switch leads, the clutch and speedometer cables.
37 Reconnect and adjust the gearchange control rod (Sections 5 and 6).
38 Lower the vehicle to the floor.
39 Fill the transmission with the correct grade and quantity of oil.

8 Transmission (type F10 and F10.4) – dismantling into major assemblies

Gearbox
1 With the transmission removed from the vehicle, clean away external dirt using paraffin and a stiff brush, or a water-soluble solvent.
2 Unbolt and remove the selector cover from the transmission casing (photo).
3 Unbolt the retaining plate and withdraw the speedometer driven gear.
4 Unscrew and remove the reversing lamp switch and allow the oil to drain out (photo).
5 Using a screwdriver as a lever, engage 2nd gear by moving the selector fork nearest the end cover (Fig. 6.16).
6 Unscrew and remove the end cover bolts and nuts.
7 Withdraw the main casing from the end cover and geartrains (photo).
8 Prise out the detent plugs from the end cover and extract the springs and detent plungers (photos).
9 Drive out the roll pins which secure the selector forks to the selector rods.
10 Move the synchro sleeve back to the neutral position and then withdraw 3rd/4th and reverse selector forks and their rods from the end cover.

Fig. 6.16 Engaging 2nd gear (Sec 8)

Move selector fork in direction of arrow

11 Extract the circlips which retain the mainshaft and input shaft geartrains. Extract the swarf collecting magnet (photos).
12 Remove the geartrain assemblies and the 1st/2nd selector fork and rod simultaneously (photo).
13 Extract the selector rod interlock pins from the end cover.
14 Remove the reverse idler shaft from the end cover. To do this, grip the shaft in the jaws of a vice fitted with soft metal protectors and using a brass drift, gently tap the cover off the shaft. Take care not to lose the locking ball (photo).

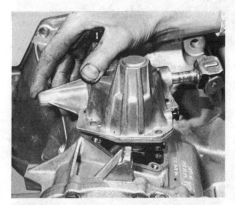

8.2B Removing selector cover

8.4 Removing reverse lamp switch

8.7 Withdrawing transmission main casing

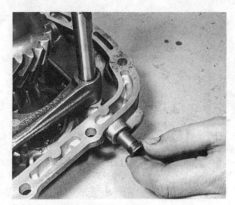

8.8A Removing a detent plug

8.8B Withdrawing a detent plunger and spring

8.11A Mainshaft securing circlip

8.11B Swarf collecting magnet

8.12 Removing geartrains from end cover

Differential

15 Unbolt and remove the pressed steel cover from the transmission casing.

16 Mark the position of the bearing adjuster ring in relation to the transmission casing. Unbolt the ring lockplate (photos).

17 Unscrew the bearing adjuster ring. A piece of flat steel bar will act as a suitable wrench (photo).

18 Withdraw the differential/crownwheel assembly (photo).

19 Depending upon the need for further dismantling due to leaking oil seals or worn bearings, proceed in the following way.

20 Renew the oil seals and bearings in the adjuster ring and transmission casing using a piece of tubing to remove the old components and to install the new (photos).

21 Using a suitable puller remove the tapered roller bearings from the differential.

22 Unbolt the crownwheel and tap it from its register using a brass drift. If the crownwheel or pinion gear are to be renewed, they must always be renewed as a matched pair.

23 Split the speedometer drivegear and discard it (Fig. 6.23).

24 Extract the circlips from the differential pinion shaft (Fig. 6.24).

25 Use a drift to remove the pinion shaft from the differential case.

26 Screw the differential pinions and side gears out of the differential case. Remove the spring discs.

8.14 Reverse idler shaft and locking ball

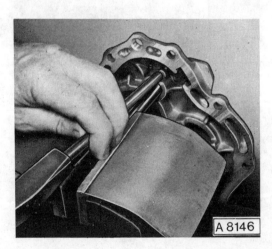

Fig. 6.17 Tapping end cover from reverse idler shaft (Sec 8)

8.16A Marking position of differential bearing adjuster ring

8.16B Bearing ring alignment marks (arrowed)

8.16C Unbolting bearing adjuster ring lockplate

8.17 Unscrewing bearing adjuster ring

8.18 Removing differential drive

8.20A Fitting bearing adjuster ring oil seal

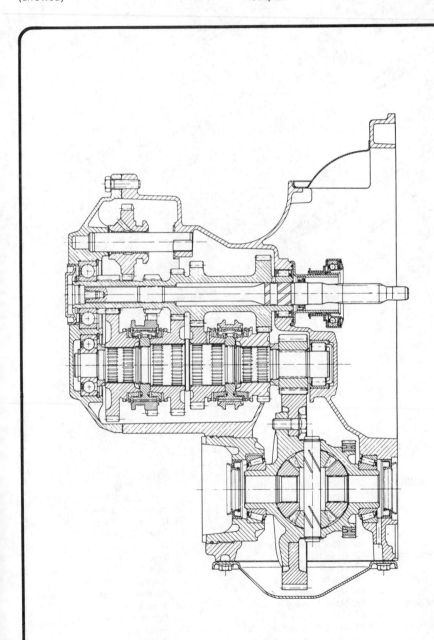

Fig. 6.18 Sectional view of type F.10.4 manual transmission (Sec 8)

8.20B Fitting driveshaft oil seal

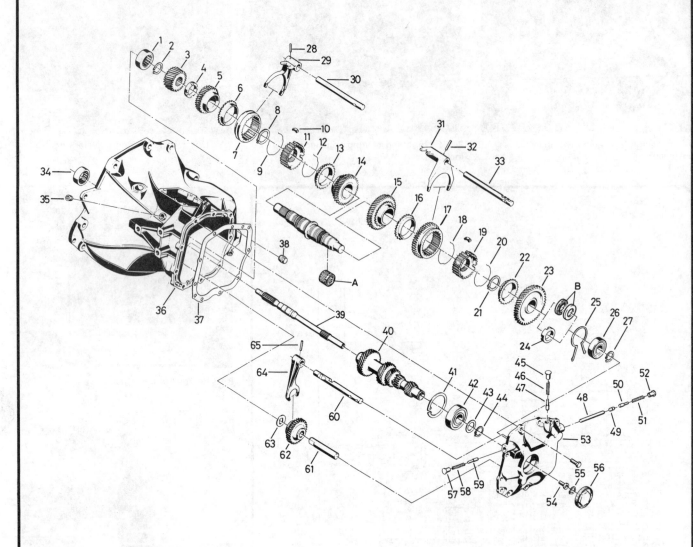

Fig. 6.19 Exploded view of type F10.4 manual transmission (Sec 8)

1 Mainshaft roller bearing (in casing)	18 Synchro spring	35 Plug	51 Detent spring
2 Circlip	19 Synchro-hub (1st/2nd)	36 Transmission casing	52 Detent plug
3 Pinion drivegear	20 Synchro spring	37 Gasket	53 End cover
4 Spacer	21 Circlip	38 Plug	54 Input shaft screw
5 4th gear	22 Baulk ring	39 Input shaft	55 Circlip
6 Baulk ring	23 1st gear	40 Input geartrain	56 Threaded plug
7 Synchro sleeve (3rd/4th)	24 Spacer	41 Input geartrain retaining circlip	57 Detent plug
8 Circlip	25 Mainshaft securing circlip	42 Bearing	58 Detent spring
9 Synchro spring	26 Bearing	43 Thrust washer	59 Detent plunger
10 Sliding key	27 Circlip	44 Circlip	60 Reverse selector rod
11 Synchro-hub (3rd/4th)	28 Roll pin	45 Detent plug	61 Reverse idler shaft
12 Synchro spring	29 3rd/4th selector fork	46 Detent spring	62 Reverse idler gear
13 Baulk ring	30 Selector rod	47 Detent plunger	63 Thrust washer
14 3rd gear	31 1st/2nd selector fork	48 Long interlock plunger	64 Reverse selector fork
15 2nd gear	32 Roll pin	49 Short interlock plunger	65 Roll pin
16 Baulk ring	33 Selector rod	50 Detent plunger	
17 1st/2nd synchro sleeve with reverse gear	34 Needle bearing (in transmission casing)	A Needle bearing on later models	
		B Bearing replaces spacer (24) on later models	

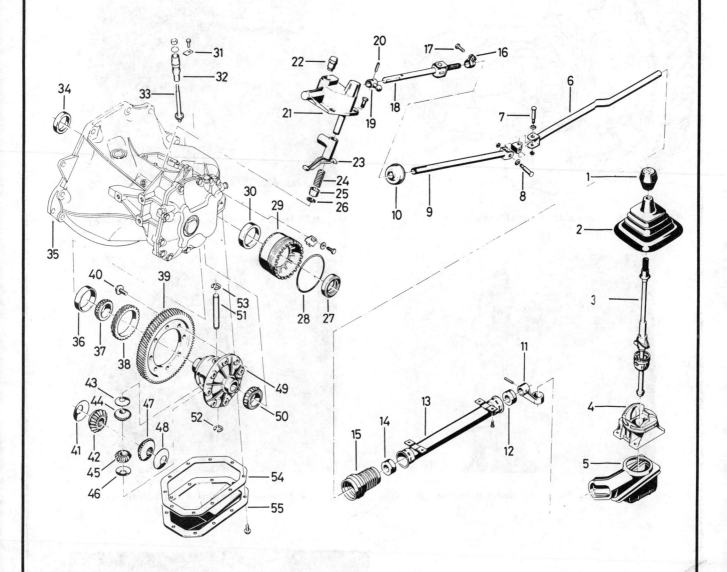

Fig. 6.20 Type F10.4 differential and selector components (Sec 8)

1 Gear lever knob	15 Bellows
2 Boot	16 Coupling
3 Gearchange lever	17 Pinch-bolt
4 Gear lever socket housing	18 Gearchange rod
5 Boot	19 Selector finger
6 Remote control rod	20 Roll pin
7 Joint pin	21 Selector housing
8 Joint pin	22 Vent plug
9 Remote control rod	23 Selector lever
10 Cap	24 Spring
11 Gearchange rod intermediate	25 Guide pin spring retainer
lever	26 Circlip
12 Bush	27 Oil seal
13 Protective housing	28 O-ring
14 Bush	

29 Bearing adjuster ring	42 Side gear
30 Bearing track	43 Spring disc
31 Speedo driven gear	44 Pinion gear
lockplate	45 Pinion gear
32 Speedo driven gear guide	46 Spring disc
33 Speedo driven gear	47 Side gear
34 Oil seal	48 Spring disc
35 Transmission casing	49 Differential case
36 Bearing track	50 Tapered roller bearing
37 Tapered roller bearing	51 Pinion shaft
38 Speedo drivegear	52 Circlip
39 Crownwheel	53 Circlip
40 Crownwheel bolt	54 Gasket
41 Spring disc	55 Pressed steel cover

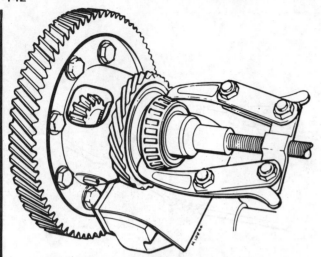

Fig. 6.21 Removing a differential bearing (Sec 8)

Fig. 6.22 Unscrewing crownwheel bolts (Sec 8)

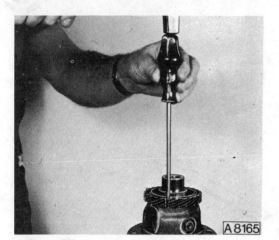

Fig. 6.23 Splitting the speedometer drivegear (Sec 8)

Fig. 6.24 Removing the pinion shaft circlips (Sec 8)

Fig. 6.25 Removing differential pinions and gears (Sec 8)

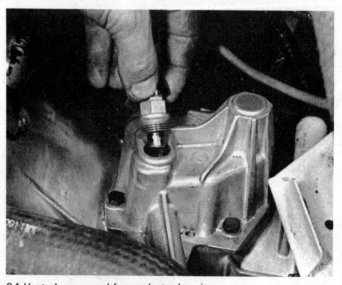

9.1 Vent plug removal from selector housing

9.2A Interior of selector cover

9.2B Circlip removal from selector guide pin

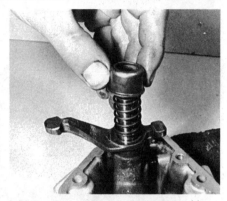

9.3A Retainer removal from selector guide pin

9.3B Selector lever removal

9.4 Selector lever roll pin removal

10.4A Speedometer driven gear O-ring

10.4B Speedometer driven gear end seal

10.6 Transmission case needle bearing

11.2 Extracting input shaft bearing retaining circlip

9 Selector housing cover (type F10 and F10.4) – overhaul

1   Unscrew and remove the vent plug (photo).
2   Remove the circlip from the top of the guide pin (photos).
3   Take off the retainer, coil spring and intermediate selector lever (photos).
4   Drive out the retaining pin to release the selector finger from the rod and withdraw both components from the cover (photo).
5   If the flexible joint on the selector rod is worn, grind off the rivet to dismantle it and to fit new components. A pin and circlip are supplied as replacements.
6   Renew the oil in the selector cover.

10 Transmission case (type F10 and F10.4) – overhaul

1   Inspect the case for cracks, especially around the bolt holes.

2   Mop out any oil and swarf.
3   Prise out the speedometer driven gear and its guide.
4   Always renew the O-ring and oil seal before refitting (photos).
5   Within the bellhousing, check the needle bearing for wear. If it requires renewal, remove the clutch release mechanism as described in Chapter 5.
6   Remove and install the needle bearing using a suitable drift (photo).
7   Inspect the mainshaft supporting roller bearing in the transmission case and, if worn, remove it using a puller or a bolt, nut and distance piece.

11 Input shaft (type F10 and F10.4) – overhaul

1   Support the end of the geartrain and tap or press the shaft from it.
2   Extract the circlip which secures the bearing to the end of the shaft. Take off the washer (photo).

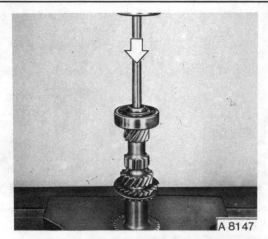

Fig. 6.26 Pressing gear train from input shaft (Sec 11)

3 Using a piece of tubing, drive the geartrain out of the bearing.

4 If any of the gears are damaged, the geartrain complete will have to be renewed. This will mean that the matching gears on the mainshaft will also have to be renewed.

5 Reassembly is a reversal of dismantling, but note that the sealed side of the bearing is away from the gear.

6 Remember to locate the geartrain securing circlip ready for installation in its transmission casing groove.

12 Mainshaft (type F10 and F10.4) – overhaul

A hydraulic press, or suitable heavy-duty puller, may be required to carry out the following procedure.

Note: *Before pressing the shaft out of the gear, synchro, etc, ensure that the lower face of the component is firmly supported. Similarly, if a puller is being used, ensure that the claws of the puller are securely located on the main body of the component, **not** solely on the gear teeth. In extreme cases, removal of stubborn components may be aided by gentle heating, bearing in mind that it is not recommended to heat any component above 100°C (212°F)*

1 Extract the retaining circlip from the bearing at the end of the shaft (photo).

2 Support the 1st gear and drive the shaft out of the bearing and gear. Note the spacer washer between the bearing and gears (photos). On some later models there is a radial needle bearing fitted instead of the spacer, in which case remove this bearing and also the gear bearing.

3 Support 2nd gear and then extract the circlip which secures the 1st/2nd synchro (photo).

4 Take the synchro baulk ring from the shaft (photo).

5 Fit a pulley or a press plate below 2nd gear.

6 Pull or press the shaft out of 2nd gear and 1st/2nd synchro unit.

7 Separate 2nd gear from the synchro unit and recover 2nd gear baulk ring.

8 Now turn your attention to the opposite end of the mainshaft. Extract the circlip which secures the pinion drivegear to the shaft (photo).

9 Remove the pinion gear (photo).

10 Remove the spacer washer (photo).

11 Remove 4th gear (photo).

12 Remove the baulk ring (photo).

13 Extract the circlip which secures the 3rd/4th synchro unit to the mainshaft (photo).

14 Remove 3rd/4th synchro unit (photo).

15 Remove the next baulk ring (photo).

16 Remove 3rd gear (photo).

17 With the mainshaft completely dismantled, examine the gears for chipped or worn teeth and the shaft for deformation of splines.

18 Renew all circlips. Ensure that any replacement parts obtained are correct by comparing them with the original component. This is par-

12.1 Extracting mainshaft bearing circlip

12.2A Mainshaft bearing removal

12.2B Spacer removal from 1st gear face. Note: Needle bearing on some models

12.2C 1st gear removal

12.3 Circlip removal from 1st/2nd synchro

12.4 Removing 1st/2nd baulk ring

12.8 Extracting circlip from pinion drivegear

12.9 Removing pinion gear

12.10 Spacer removal from 4th gear face

12.11 4th gear removal

12.12 Baulk ring removal from 4th gear

12.13 Circlip removal from 3rd/4th synchro

12.14 Removing 3rd/4th synchro

12.15 Baulk ring removal from 3rd gear

12.16 3rd gear removal

ticularly important when renewing any of the following components which were modified in April 1986.

a   The synchro cones of the first gear are larger in diameter: being 58 mm (2.28 in) instead of the previous 51 mm (2.01 in). The shift fork and yoke were modified to suit and are not inter-changeable with the earlier types

b   Grooved ball-bearings are changed from the open type to the closed type

c   The F10.4 type transmission has two modifications to 1st gear. The gear now runs on a needle bearing with a split type bear-ing cage, and additionally a radial needle bearing is fitted in place of the spacer. Refer to the insets in Fig. 6.19

19   If there has been a history of noisy gear changing or if the synchromesh could be easily beaten during changes, renew the synchro unit complete or overhaul as described in the next Section.

20   With all parts clean and oiled, reassemble in the following sequence. Where necessary, components should be pressed onto the shaft using a suitably-sized tubular spacer which bears on the main body of the component and not on the gear teeth.

21   Fit 3rd gear to the pinion gear end of the mainshaft.

22   Place the baulk ring on the cone of 3rd gear.

23   Fit the 3rd/4th synchro unit, applying pressure to the hub (photo). Preheating the synchro unit to 100°C (212°F) is recommended.

24   Secure the synchro unit with a new circlip.

25   Fit the baulk ring and 4th gear.

26   Fit the spacer washer and the pinion gear. Preheating of both these components to 100°C (212°F) is recommended.

27   Secure the pinion gear with a new circlip.

28   Working at the other end of the mainshaft, fit 2nd gear (photo).

29   Fit the baulk ring to the cone of 2nd gear (photo).

30   Preheat 1st/2nd synchro unit to 100°C (212°F), then press it into the shaft with the reverse gear teeth nearer 2nd gear (photo).

12.23 Using a tube to press on 3rd/4th synchro unit

12.28 Fitting 2nd gear

12.29 Fitting 2nd gear baulk ring

12.30 Fitting 1st/2nd synchro unit – note orientation of reverse teeth

12.33 Spacer washer grooves (arrowed) face 1st gear

13.6A Synchro-hub and sleeve

13.6B Fitting a synchro sliding key

13.6C Fitting a synchro spring

31 Secure the synchro unit with a new circlip.

32 Fit 1st gear baulk ring and 1st gear.

33 Preheat the spacer washer to 100°C (212°F), then press it onto the shaft; grooves towards 1st gear (photo).

34 Locate a new long-eared circlip ready for installation in its transmission casing groove.

35 Fit the bearing and secure it with a new circlip.

13 Synchroniser units – overhaul

1 Components of 1st/2nd and 3rd/4th synchro units are interchangeable.

2 It is not good practice, however, to mix parts which have been in use for a high mileage and which have run-in together.

3 If either the hub or sleeve show signs of wear in their teeth, the individual part may be renewed, but general wear is best rectified by complete renewal of the unit.

4 To dismantle, push the sleeve of the hub, taking care not to allow the sliding keys to fly out.

5 Extract the circular springs and keys.

6 Reassembly is a reversal of dismantling. Make sure that the hooked ends of the springs engage in the same sliding key but run in opposite directions in relation to each other (photos).

7 To check the baulk rings for wear, twist them onto the gear cones. The ring should 'stick' to the cone and show a definite clearance between the ring and the gear shoulder. If these conditions are not met, renew the baulk rings.

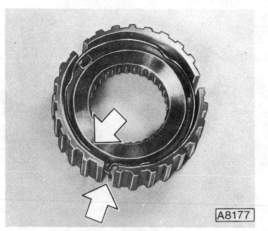

Fig. 6.27 Synchro spring locations – arrowed (Sec 13)

14 Transmission (type F10 and F10.4) – reassembly

1 Liberally oil the differential components.
2 Install the side gears and pinions, the spring discs and the pinion shaft into the differential case.
3 Fit new retaining circlips.
4 If the speedometer drivegear was removed, warm the new gear in hot water (80°C/176°F) and tap it onto the differential case with a piece of tubing until it snaps into position. Make sure that the lugs on the gear are aligned with the cut-outs in the differential case.
5 Warm the crownwheel to 80°C (176°F) and locate it on the differential case. Use new bolts and tighten them to the specified torque.
6 Fit the tapered roller bearings to the differential case (if removed at dismantling).

7 If not already done, fit the bearing outer tracks to the transmission casing.
8 Fit new driveshaft seals into the transmission casing (if not already done) and fill the lips with grease.
9 Lower the differential into the transmission casing.
10 Fit a new O-ring and oil seal to the bearing adjuster ring. Apply grease to the seal lips and to the screw threads (photos).
11 Screw the adjuster ring into the transmission casing, hand tight at this stage (photo).
12 Adjust the bearing in one of the following ways, depending upon whether the original bearings have been refitted or new ones installed.
13 **Original bearing:** Simply screw in the adjuster ring until the alignment marks made before dismantling are opposite to each other. Should any axial play exist, the ring may be further adjusted to give a turning torque of between 5.3 and 8.9 lbf in as described for new bearings in the following paragraph.
14 **New bearings:** The bearing preload must be adjusted by means of the adjuster ring so that a torque of 13.3 to 15.9 lbf in is required to keep the crownwheel and bearings turning slowly. Unless a special torsion or friction gauge is available, push a tapered softwood rod into the splined side gear and then wrap a cord round it and attach it to a spring balance. Provided the cord leaves the rod at a point about 1.0 in from the centre point of its cross section, the torque will be fairly accurate. Adjust the ring until the turning torque is within the specified range.
15 Fit the adjuster ring lockplate without moving the position of the ring. The lockplate bolt hole is elongated to make this possible.
16 Use a new gasket and bolt the pressed steel cover to the transmission casing (photo).
17 Fit the reverse idler shaft to the transmission end cover, making sure that the locking ball is in position.
18 Pin the 1st/2nd selector fork to its rod, but leave the pin projecting by approximately 2.0 mm (0.08 in).
19 Hold the mainshaft, input shaft and reverse gear trains meshed together, with the 1st/2nd selector fork and rod engaged in the groove of 1st/2nd synchro.
20 Locate the assembly into the end cover. The help of an assistant

14.10A Bearing adjuster O-ring

14.10B Filling oil seal lips with grease

14.11 Fitting bearing adjuster

14.16 Fitting pressed steel cover and gasket

14.20A Fitting short interlock plunger

14.20B Fitting long interlock plunger

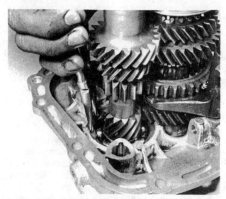

14.21A Engaging input shaft circlip to transmission casing

14.21B Reverse idler thrust washer

14.22A Fitting 3rd/4th selector fork and rod

14.22B Fitting reverse selector rod and fork

14.23A Pinning 1st/2nd selector fork to rod

14.23B Pinning reverse selector fork to rod

14.26 Fitting transmission case gasket

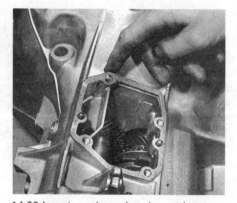

14.29 Locating selector housing gasket

will facilitate the work. Fit the selector rod interlock plunger (photos).
21 Fit the circlips which retain the mainshaft and input shaft assemblies to the transmission casing. Make sure that they engage positively in their grooves. Fit the thrust washer to the reverse idler gear, also the swarf collecting magnet (photos).
22 Check that the sleeve on 1st/2nd synchro is in neutral then fit the 3rd/4th and reverse selector forks and rods (photos).
23 Pin the forks to the rods (photos).
24 Refit the detent plungers and springs. If the sealing plugs are not a really tight fit, oversize ones should be obtained and driven in.
25 Using a screwdriver, move the sleeve of the appropriate synchro unit to engage 2nd gear.
26 Stick a new gasket, with grease, to the transmission casing and then insert the geartrains with end cover into the casing until the fixing bolts and nuts can be screwed in to the specified torque (photo).
27 Fit the speedometer driven gear and bolt on its retainer plate.
28 Screw in the reversing lamp switch to the specified torque.

29 Set the transmission in neutral and stick a new selector housing gasket in position (photo).
30 Bolt on the selector housing, tightening the bolts to the specified torque.
31 The transmission can be filled with oil now, provided it is held in the in-vehicle attitude, otherwise wait until it has been refitted to the vehicle.

15 Transmission (type F10.5) – description

1 The F10.5 transmission is fitted to 1.3 engine models from 1983 on as an optional fitting.
2 The transmission design is the same as that of the F10.4 described previously, but with the addition of a 5th gear housed in the end cover.

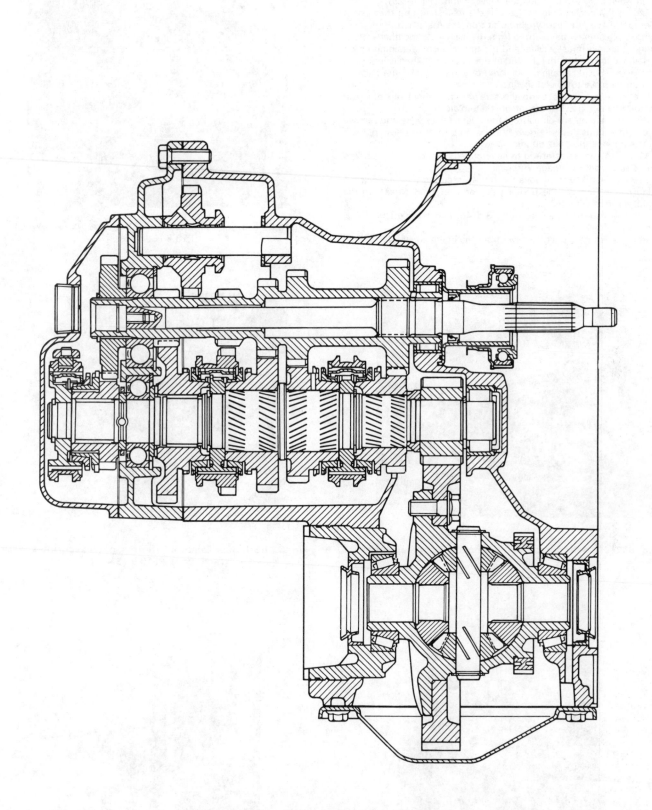

Fig. 6.28 Sectional view of F10.5 transmission (Sec 15)

3 Additional operations involved in dismantling and reassembling this type of transmission are described below.
4 Modifications applicable to the F10.5 gearbox are described in Section 12.

16 Transmission (type F10.5) – dismantling and reassembly

1 With the transmission removed from the vehicle, remove the end cover and separate the transmission casing from the intermediate plate.

2   Move 5th gear synchro unit by hand to its engaged position, then use an Allen key to unbolt 5th gear selector fork (Fig. 6.29).

3   Extract the circlip from the end of the mainshaft and then use a puller to remove 5th gear synchro unit from the mainshaft.

4   5th gear can now be removed from the mainshaft, together with its bearing, the split thrust washer and the thrust washer retaining ring.

5   Remove the circlip from the end of the input shaft, then lever or pull off 5th gear. If using a puller, take care not to damage the input shaft – use a thrust piece to spread the load.

6   Use an Allen key to undo the screws which hold the 5th gear selector interlock pawl to the intermediate plate (Fig. 6.31).

7   Prise out the detent plugs from the intermediate plate and remove the detent springs and plungers. Make a note to obtain new plugs if you damage the old ones during removal.

8   Move 5th gear selector rod to its engaged position, and push 2nd gear selector fork to engage 2nd gear.

9   Use an Allen key to remove the screws securing the interlock pin bridge piece. Remove the bridge piece and return the gears to the neutral position (Fig. 6.32).

10 Drive out the roll pins securing 3rd/4th and reverse shift forks. Remove the forks and their rods.

11 Pull the 5th gear selector driver from the intermediate plate.

Fig. 6.29 5th gear selector fork Allen screws (arrowed) – F10.5 (Sec 16)

Fig. 6.30 5th gear components removed from mainshaft – F10.5 (Sec 16)

Fig. 6.31 5th gear selector interlock pawl securing screws (arrowed) – F10.5 (Sec 16)

Fig. 6.32 Interlock pin bridge piece screws (arrowed) – F10.5 (Sec 16)

Fig. 6.33 Removing 5th gear selector driver – F10.5 (Sec 16)

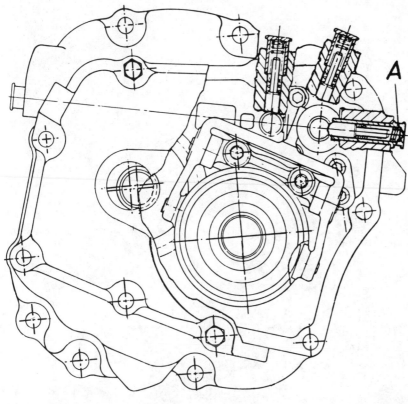

Fig. 6.34 3rd/4th detent plug (A) is longer
than the rest – F10.5 (Sec 16)

12 Remove the circlips retaining the mainshaft and input shaft to the
intermediate plate. The geartrains can now be removed, together with
the reverse idler gear, 1st/2nd shift fork and shift rod.

13 Further dismantling and overhaul can now proceed as described
for the F10.4 transmission in Section 8. Note that both 1st and 5th
gears on the F10.5 transmission mainshaft have split needle bearings.

14 Reassembly is a reversal of the dismantling procedure, but note the
following points:

(a) Use new screws to secure the interlock pin bridge piece and the
     5th gear selector interlock pawl. The proper screws are
     pre-coated with thread locking compound and must be
     renewed whenever they have been loosened.
(b) Note that the longer detent plug serves 3rd/4th gears (Fig.
     6.34).
(c) Heat 5th synchro unit to 100°C (212°F) before fitting it to the
     mainshaft
(d) There is no need to use sealant on the end cover plug threads

17 Transmission (type F16 and F16.4) – dismantling and overhaul

1 The operations are very similar to those described in earlier
Sections for the type F10 transmission, but if the mainshaft is being
overhauled then the modified design of the mainshaft must be noted
together with the additional components. These include:

(a) Radial needle bearing against 1st gear
(b) Needle roller bearings for 1st, 2nd, 3rd and 4th gears
(c) Semi-circular thrust washers between 2nd and 3rd gears
     complete with washer retaining ring
(d) 3rd/4th synchro retaining circlip
(e) Composite mainshaft with pinion gear
(f) Roller bearing, semi-circular thrust washers and washer
     retaining ring next to pinion gear

2 If either the crownwheel or pinion (part of mainshaft) is being
renewed then the pair must be renewed as a matching set.

3 All the synchromesh sleeves are interchangeable.

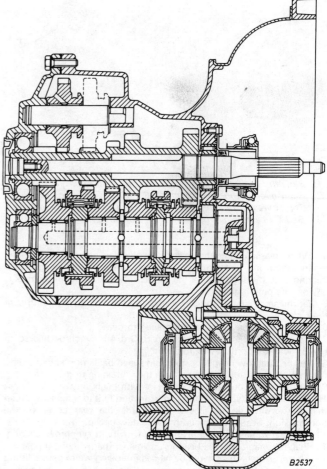

Fig. 6.35 Sectional view of the type F16.4 manual
transmission (Sec 17)

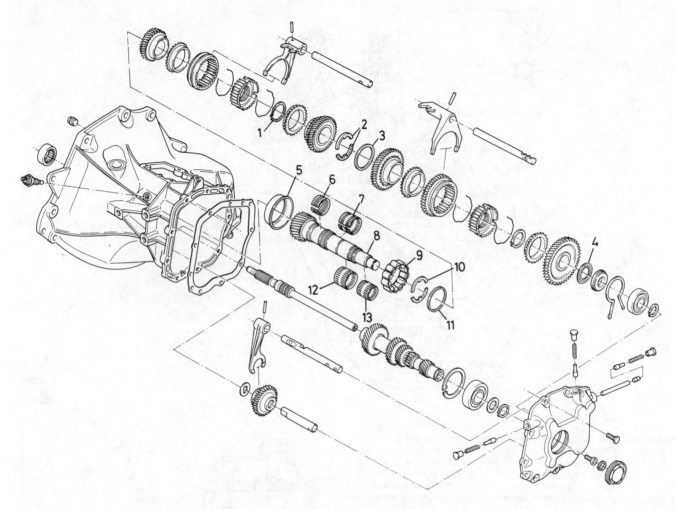

**Fig. 6.36 Exploded view of F16.4 manual transmission
(Sec 17)**

Key as for 6.19 except for additional parts annotated

1	*3rd/4th synchro circlip*	5	*Bearing outer track*
2	*Semi-circular thrust washers*	6	*4th gear needle bearing*
3	*Thrust washer retaining ring*	7	*3rd gear dual row needle*
4	*Radial needle bearing*		*bearing*

8	*Mainshaft with pinion gear*	12	*2nd gear dual row needle*
9	*Roller cage*		*bearing*
10	*Semi-circular thrust washers*	13	*1st gear dual row needle*
11	*Thrust washer retaining ring*		*bearing*

4   When reassembling the mainshaft, oil each component liberally when fitting and observe the following points. First slide the roller bearing onto the shaft so that the smaller diameter of the inner track is against the pinion gear.

5   Fit the semi-circular thrust washers and slip the retaining ring over them.

6   Follow with the needle bearing and 4th gear.

7   Continue with 4th gear baulk ring, 3rd/4th synchro (heated in boiling water) and the synchro circlip.

8   Fit the dual row needle bearing, 3rd speed baulk ring and gear and the semi-circular thrust washers with their retaining ring.

9   Fit the needle bearing and 2nd gear with baulk ring.

10   Heat 1st/2nd synchro in boiling water and fit it to the mainshaft so that the groove in its sleeve is towards the rear cover of the transmission. Secure the synchro with a new circlip.

11   Fit the next needle bearing and 1st gear with its synchro baulk ring.

12   Place the radial needle bearing up against the face of 1st gear.

13   Fit the spacer. This should be heated in boiling water before fitting and the larger diameter of the spacer will be next to the axial needle bearing.

14   Fit the ball-bearing so that the ball positioning cage is towards the end of the shaft. Fit a new circlip.

18   Transmission (type F16.5) – dismantling

Note: *The operations in paragraphs 6 and 7 should have been carried out during transmission removal, but are added here to provide a complete procedure.*

1   With the transmission removed from the vehicle, clean away external dirt using paraffin or a water soluble solvent and a stiff brush.

2   Unbolt the cover plate from the final drive housing and allow the lubricant to drain.

3   Unbolt and remove the cover plate from the flywheel housing.

4   Unbolt and remove the selector housing and peel off the flange gasket.

5   Unbolt and remove the end cover with gasket.

6   Extract the circlip from the end of the input shaft now exposed. This circlip is located deep in the shaft recess and a pair of long-nosed pliers will be needed to extract it.

7   Unscrew and remove the splined type screw from the shaft recess. It is possible to use a close fitting Allen key to do the job.

8   Unbolt and remove the transmission main casing from the intermediate plate.

9   Using an Allen key, unbolt the 5th gear selector fork. It will faciliate removal of the socket-headed screws if 5th gear synchro unit is first

18.11A Extracting circlip from end of input shaft

18.11B Levering off input shaft 5th gear

18.13A Prising out a detent plug

18.13B Tool made up to extract longer 3rd/4th detent plug

18.13C Slide hammer attached to detent plug extracting tool

moved by hand to its engaged position.

10 Extract the circlip from the end of the mainshaft and then using a two-legged puller, draw 5th gear and 5th gear synchro unit from the mainshaft. Locate the puller claws under 5th gear.

11 Extract the circlip from the end of the input shaft and withdraw (large) 5th gear from the shaft. Two tyre levers placed under the gear will remove it quite easily (photos).

12 Using an Allen key, unscrew the socket-headed screws which hold the 5th gear selector interlock pawl to the intermediate plate.

13 Using a forked lever, or slide hammer with suitable attachment, withdraw the detent plugs from the edge of the intermediate plate. Be prepared to catch the coil springs which will be ejected. Pull out the detent plungers (photos).

14 If you have damaged the detent caps during removal, they should be renewed.

15 Move 5th gear selector to its engaged position.

16 Push 2nd gear selector fork to engage the gear.

17 Again using the Allen key unscrew the socket-headed screws and remove the interlock pin bridge piece.

18 Return all gears to neutral.

19 Drive out the securing roll pin and remove the selector shaft and fork for 3rd/4th gears. Remove reverse selector in a similar way.

20 Withdraw the interlock rod from the intermediate plate.

21 Pull the 5th gear selector driver from the intermediate plate.

22 Drive out the roll pin and remove the 1st/2nd selector rod and fork.

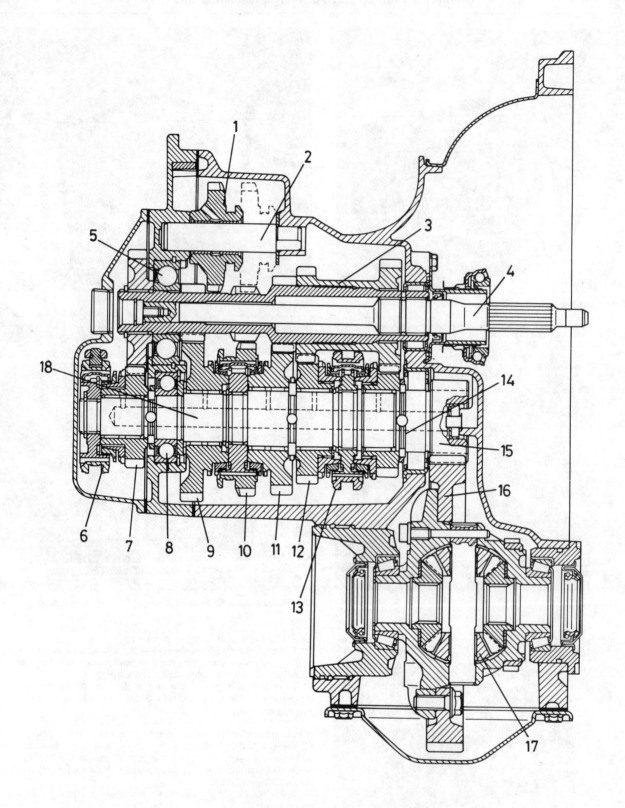

Fig. 6.37 Sectional view of the type F16.5 manual transmission (Sec 18)

1	Reverse idler gear	5	Ball-bearing
2	Reverse idler shaft	6	5th speed synchro unit
3	Input gear cluster	7	5th gear
4	Input shaft (removable from gear cluster)	8	Ball-bearing
		9	1st gear

10	1st/2nd synchro unit with reverse
11	2nd gear
12	3rd gear
13	3rd/4th synchro unit

14	Roller bearing
15	Pinion gear
16	Crownwheel
17	Differential
18	Mainshaft

23 Squeeze together the ends of the large circlip which hold the mainshaft bearing into the intermediate plate. A piece of thin rod should be made up to form a retaining clip to keep the circlip contracted (photo).
24 Now expand the legs of the circlip which holds the input shaft bearing in the intermediate plate.
25 With the help of an assistant, withdraw the geartrains complete with reverse idler gear. The shafts and bearings may require a little gentle tapping with a plastic-faced hammer to eject them from the intermediate plate. Note the washer on the reverse idler.

Input shaft and gear cluster
26 Examine the gear teeth for wear. If evident then the cluster must be renewed (photo).
27 The bearings may be renewed using a suitable puller.
28 The shaft may be tapped from the gear cluster using a plastic faced hammer.

Mainshaft
29 Place the claws of a two-legged puller under the 1st gear and draw the gear and shaft ball-bearings from the mainshaft (photo).
30 Extract the circlip, remove the plain thrust washer and then the needle type thrust washer.
31 Remove 1st gear baulk ring.
32 Remove the split type needle roller bearing.
33 Extract the circlip.
34 Take off the plain thrust washer.
35 Place the claws of a puller under 2nd gear and withdraw 1st/2nd synchro unit (with reverse), the baulk ring and 2nd gear all together from the mainshaft. Note that the reverse gear teeth on the synchro sleeve are towards the pinion gear on the end of the shaft.
36 Remove the semi-circular thrust washers and their retaining ring.
37 Remove 3rd gear.
38 Remove 3rd gear baulk ring.
39 Take off the split type needle roller bearing.
40 Extract the circlip which retains the 3rd/4th synchro unit.

41 Take off the thrust washer.
42 Place the claws of a puller behind 4th gear and draw off 3rd/4th synchro unit, 4th gear baulk ring and 4th gear all together from the mainshaft.
43 Take off the split type needle roller bearing.
44 Remove the semi-circular thrust washers with their retaining ring.
45 Remove the roller race from the shaft. The pinion gear cannot be removed.

Synchroniser units
46 Refer to Section 13.

Transmission case
47 Refer to Section 10 (photo).

Selector housing cover
48 Refer to Section 9.

Differential and final drive
49 The operations for removal, refitting and adjustment are as described in Sections 8 and 14.

19 Transmission (type F16.5) – reassembly

1 Apply thick grease to retain the rollers in their cage, and fit the bearing assembly up against the mainshaft pinion gear.
2 Locate the semi-circular thrust washers so that their keys engage in the holes in the shaft and then fit the retaining ring (photos).
3 Fit the split type needle roller bearing (photo).
4 Fit 4th gear (photo).
5 Fit 4th gear baulk ring (photo).
6 Fit 3rd/4th synchro unit so that the thin groove in the sleeve is furthest from the shaft pinion. Drive the synchro-hub down the shaft

18.23 Circlip retaining clip

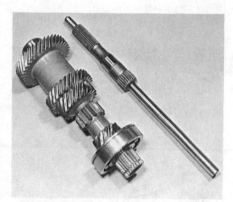
18.26 Input shaft and gear cluster

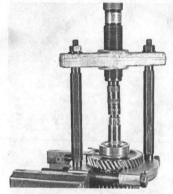
18.29 Removing mainshaft 1st gear and bearing

18.47 Transmission case bearing

19.2A Mainshaft pinion bearing semi-circular thrust washers

19.2B Mainshaft thrust washers with retaining ring

19.3 Split type needle roller bearing (4th gear)

19.4 Fitting 4th gear

19.5 4th speed baulk ring fitted

19.6 Fitting 3rd/4th speed synchro unit

19.7 Fitting thrust washer

19.8 Fitting circlip

19.9 Fitting 3rd speed baulk ring

19.10 Fitting needle roller bearing (3rd gear). Note thin groove in synchro sleeve (see para 6)

19.11 Fitting 3rd gear

using a bearing puller or by applying a length of tubing to the synchro-hub (photo).

7   Fit the thrust washer (photo).

8   Fit the circlip (photo).

9   Fit 3rd gear baulk ring (photo).

10   Fit the split type needle roller bearing (photo).

11   Fit 3rd gear (photo).

12   Fit the semi-circular thrust washers and their retaining ring. Fit the needle roller bearing (photos).

13   Fit 2nd gear (photo).

14   Fit 2nd gear baulk ring (photo).

15   Fit 1st/2nd synchro unit so that the reverse gear teeth on its sleeve are towards the shaft pinion gear. Draw or tap the assembly down the shaft (photo).

16   Fit the plain thrust washer (photo).

17   Fit the circlip (photo).

18   Fit the 1st gear baulk ring (photo).

19   Fit the split type needle roller bearing, followed by 1st gear (photos).

20   Fit the needle roller type thrust washer (photo).

21   Fit the plain thrust washer so that the step is positioned as shown (photo). This is essential to allow for clearance when the mainshaft bearing circlip is contracted ready for geartrain installation into the intermediate plate. Drop the large mainshaft bearing circlip onto the shaft (photo).

22   Fit the ball-bearing to the mainshaft so that the sealed side is visible when fitted (photo).

23   Locate the mainshaft bearing circlip in the step of the thrust washer, squeeze the legs of the circlip together and fit a retainer as previously described (Section 18, paragraph 23).

24   Expand the input shaft circlip (photo).

25   With the help of an assistant, mesh the input and mainshaft

19.12A Semi-circular thrust washers

19.12B Thrust washer retaining ring

19.12C Needle roller bearing (2nd gear)

19.13 Fitting 2nd gear

19.14 Fitting 2nd gear baulk ring

19.15 Fitting 1st/2nd synchro unit

19.16 Plain thrust washer against 3rd/4th synchro hub

19.17 Circlip fitted

19.18 1st gear baulk ring fitted

19.19A Split type needle roller bearing (1st gear)

19.19B Fitting 1st gear

19.20 Needle type thrust washer against 1st gear

19.21A Plain thrust washer showing step in rim

19.21B Mainshaft bearing large circlip

19.22 Mainshaft ball-bearing

19.24 Expanding input shaft circlip

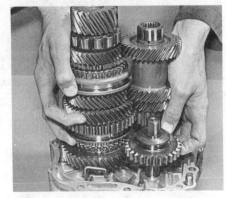

19.25 Installing geartrains to intermediate plate

19.27A 1st/2nd selector rod and fork

19.27B Selector fork roll pin

19.28 Reverse selector rod and fork

19.30A 5th speed selector dog and 3rd/4th fork being offered into position

geartrains together with the reverse idler gear held in position with the fingers (selector fork groove towards mainshaft pinion gear) (photo).

26 Install the geartrains with reverse gear into the intermediate plate. Release the input shaft bearing circlip and remove the mainshaft bearing circlip retaining clip.

27 Refit the 1st/2nd selector rod and fork. Drive in the roll pin which retains the fork to the rod (photos).

28 Fit reverse selector rod and fork and drive in a new roll pin (photo).

29 Fit 5th speed selector driver into the intermediate plate.

30 Locate 5th speed selector dog and 3rd/4th selector fork and insert the selector rod through them (photos).

31 Fix 3rd/4th selector fork to its rod with a new roll pin (photo).

32 Insert the interlock rod into the hole in the intermediate plate.

33 Fit the interlock pin bridge piece. The screws will only be able to be screwed in if 2nd gear and then 5th gear driver are moved to the

engaged position (photos).

34 Engage the 5th gear interlock pawl in the cut out of the driver and then bolt the pawl to the intermediate plate (photo).

35 Insert the detent plungers and their coil springs in their holes in the intermediate plate (photos).

36 Tap in the plugs noting that the one for 3/4th selector is longer than the other three (photo).

37 Locate the thrust washer (which has the centre hole with flat sides) on the reverse idler shaft. Retain it with thick grease (photo).

38 Fit the magnet (clean) into its slot in the intermediate plate (photo).

39 Place a new gasket on the transmission casing flange and lower the geartrains with intermediate plate into the casing (photo).

40 Mesh the pinion and crownwheel teeth as the geartrains are lowered (photo).

19.30B Inserting 5th dog and 3rd/4th selector rod

19.31 Fork roll pin

19.32 Interlock rod

19.33A Interlock pin bridge piece

19.33B Bridge piece fixing screws

19.34A 5th gear interlock pawl

19.34B Tightening a pawl screw

19.35A Inserting detent components into intermediate plate

19.35B Detent identification

19.35C Reverse detent

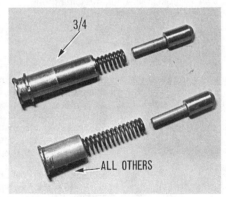

19.36 Detent components

19.37 Reverse thrust washer

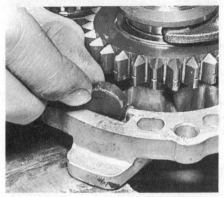
19.38 Swarf collecting magnet

19.39 Lowering geartrains into casing

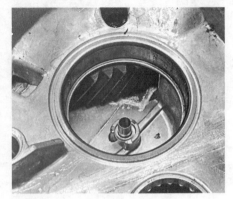
19.40 Crownwheel teeth

19.42 Fitting input shaft

19.43A Fitting 5th gear onto input shaft

19.43B Fitting 5th gear circlip

19.44A Semi-circular thrust washers

19.44B Thrust washers and retaining ring

19.45 5th speed split type needle roller bearing

41 Screw in the securing bolts.
42 If the input shaft was removed, now is the time to refit it into the input shaft gear cluster (photo).
43 Fit the 5th gear to the end of the input shaft. Secure it with the circlip (photos).
44 To the end of the mainshaft fit the semi-circular thrust washers and retaining ring (photos).
45 Fit the split type needle roller bearing to the mainshaft (photo).
46 Fit 5th gear to the mainshaft (photo).
47 Fit 5th gear baulk ring (photo).
48 Fit 5th gear synchro unit so that the side where the movable keys are visible is towards 5th gear (photo).
49 Fit the retaining circlip (photo).
50 Move 5th gear to its engaged position and fit the selector

fork/pivot assembly. Tighten the socket-headed screws (photo).
51 Fit the screw and the circlip to the end of the input shaft. The circlip is located in a groove deep in the recess in the end of the shaft and a pair of long-nosed pliers will be required to reach it (photos).
52 Using a new gasket bolt on the end cover (photos).
53 Screw the threaded plug (if removed) into the end cover (photo).
54 Using a new gasket, locate the selector cover so that the selector fingers engage in the dogs (gears in neutral). Insert and tighten the fixing bolts (photo).
55 Bolt on the final drive cover plate.
56 Bolt on the flywheel housing cover plate (photo).
57 Check the selection of all gears is smooth and positive (photo).
58 Fill the transmission with lubricant after it has been refitted to the vehicle.

19.46 Fitting 5th gear to mainshaft

19.47 Fitting 5th gear baulk ring

19.48 Fitting 5th gear synchro unit

19.49 Fitting mainshaft circlip

19.50 Tightening a 5th speed selector fork pivot screw

19.51A Fitting splined screw to input shaft recess

19.51B Fitting circlip to input shaft recess

19.52A Fitting end cover

19.52B Tightening end cover bolt

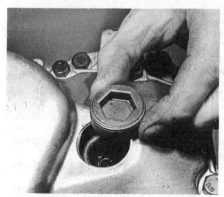

19.53 Screwing in end cover screw plug

19.54 Fitting selector cover

19.56 Flywheel housing cover plate

20 Fault diagnosis – manual transmission

Symptom	Reason(s)
Weak or ineffective synchromesh	Synchro baulk rings worn, split or damaged
	Synchromesh units worn, or damaged
Jumps out of gear	Gearchange mechanism worn
	Synchromesh units badly worn
	Selector fork badly worn
Excessive noise	Incorrect grade of oil in gearbox or oil level too low
	Gear teeth excessively worn or damaged
	Intermediate gear thrust washers worn allowing excessive end play
	Worn bearings
Difficulty in engaging gears	Clutch pedal adjustment incorrect
Noise when cornering	Wheel bearing or driveshaft fault
	Differential fault

Note: *It is sometimes difficult to decide whether it is worthwile removing and dismantling the gearbox for a fault which may be nothing more than a minor irritant. Gearboxes which howl, or where the synchromesh can be 'beaten' by a quick gearchange, may continue to perform for a long time in this state. A worn gearbox usually needs a complete rebuild to eliminate noise because the various gears, if re-aligned on new bearings, will continue to howl when different wearing surfaces are presented to each other. The decision to overhaul therefore, must be considered with regard to time and money available, relative to the degree of noise or malfunction that the driver has to suffer.*

19.57 Gear selector gate legend

PART B: AUTOMATIC TRANSMISSION

21 General description

The automatic transmission is of General Motors design and manufacture and is optionally available on most models. The unit provides three forward speeds and reverse with a 'kickdown' facility. As with manual transmission, the differential and final drive are built into the transmission casing.

The main components are a torque converter (fluid coupling), which transmits power to the gear trains through a chain drive, and a hydraulic circuit which regulates the selection of gears, clutches and brakes according to speed and engine load. Due to the close tolerances to which the unit operates, cleanliness is absolutely essential whenever fluid is being added or any component removed. Entry of grit or dirt into the transmission will cause a malfunction of the valves and possible damage to the internal components.

The automatic transmission is a complex piece of equipment and the home mechanic should limit himself to undertaking the operations

described in the following Sections. More extensive operations should be left to your dealer or automatic transmission specialist.

22 Routine maintenance – automatic transmission

Checking and topping-up the fluid level

1 The importance of maintaining the correct fluid level in the automatic transmission cannot be over emphasised.

2 The level may be checked cold or hot.

3 To check cold, have the vehicle standing on a level floor with the engine running and P selected. Withdraw the dipstick, wipe it clean with a fluff-free cloth, replace it and withdraw it for the second time. Read the fluid level on the side of the dipstick marked with +20°C, it should be up to the MAX mark (Fig. 6.39).

4 To check the fluid level hot, the vehicle must have just covered a road operating distance of at least 10 miles (15 km). Check the fluid level in a similar way to that just described, but read off the level on the side marked +94°C, it should be between the MIN and MAX marks.

5 Carry out the foregoing checks when the engine has been idling for one minute, but not more than three minutes, otherwise an incorrect reading will be obtained.

6 Top up as necessary through the dipstick guide tube. Make sure that the fluid is absolutely clean and of the specified type. Do not fill above the MAX mark (Fig. 6.40).

7 With the transmission cold, a fluid level 5.0 mm below the MAX mark will indicate the need for the addition of 0.25 litre of fluid.

Transmission fluid renewal

8 At the intervals specified in Routine Maintenance the transmission fluid must be renewed. Do this more frequently if the vehicle is used under particularly arduous operating conditions or for towing a trailer.

9 Allow the transmission to cool down before draining, as the fluid can be very hot indeed.

10 Remove all the fluid pan screws except one which should be unscrewed through several turns.

11 Release the fluid pan from its gasket and as the end of the pan tilts downwards, catch the fluid in a suitable container.

12 Remove the remaining screw and the pan. Peel off the joint gasket or sealant bead.

13 Pull the filter mesh from its securing clips then clean it in fuel and allow it to dry.

14 Renew the O-ring seal exposed by removal of the filter and then refit the filter securely.

15 Bolt on the fluid pan using a new gasket. On some transmissions, a gasket is not used. Instead, a bead of silicone rubber (instant gasket) is

used. In this case, apply a bead of sealant about 5.0 mm (0.2 in) thick to clean surfaces. The fluid pan which is fitted with a gasket can be identified by the strengthening ribs on the pan flanges. The pan for use with silicone sealant has plain flanges.

16 Fill the transmission with the specified quantity of fluid and then check the level as described for the COLD process earlier in this Section.

17 Discoloration of the fluid noticed when changing the fluid will probably be due to overheating.

18 The quantity of fluid required to raise the level on the dipstick from MIN to MAX is 0.5 litre.

23 Kickdown cable – renewal and adjustment

1   Remove the air cleaner from the carburettor.

2   Disconnect the kickdown cable from the adjuster mechanism A (Fig. 6.41) by first relieving the spring pressure and then pulling out the securing pin – hook a piece of wire through the hole in the pin to pull it out if necessary.

3   Prise the cupped end fitting B from the ball-stud on the lever.

4   Working at the transmission end of the cable, remove the locking bolt from the sleeve (Fig. 6.42) and pull the sleeve upwards.

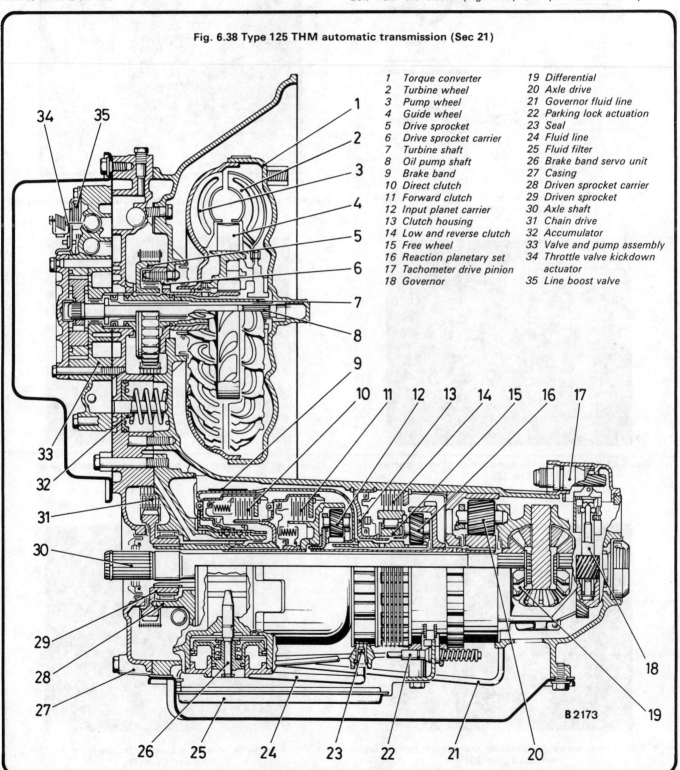

Fig. 6.38 Type 125 THM automatic transmission (Sec 21)

1	Torque converter	19	Differential
2	Turbine wheel	20	Axle drive
3	Pump wheel	21	Governor fluid line
4	Guide wheel	22	Parking lock actuation
5	Drive sprocket	23	Seal
6	Drive sprocket carrier	24	Fluid line
7	Turbine shaft	25	Fluid filter
8	Oil pump shaft	26	Brake band servo unit
9	Brake band	27	Casing
10	Direct clutch	28	Driven sprocket carrier
11	Forward clutch	29	Driven sprocket
12	Input planet carrier	30	Axle shaft
13	Clutch housing	31	Chain drive
14	Low and reverse clutch	32	Accumulator
15	Free wheel	33	Valve and pump assembly
16	Reaction planetary set	34	Throttle valve kickdown
17	Tachometer drive pinion		actuator
18	Governor	35	Line boost valve

B 2173

Disconnect the inner cable from the transmission.

5   Release the cable adjusting mechanism from its support bracket by depressing the lugs (Fig. 6.43).

6   Refit the cable by first connecting at the transmission, keeping the cable tight, and refitting the sleeve. The cable must be routed between the brake pipes at the master cylinder. The cable will not operate smoothly if routed under the brake pipes.

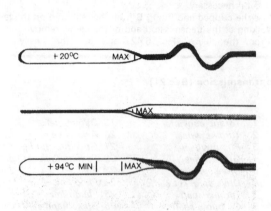

Fig. 6.39 Dipstick fluid level markings – automatic transmission (Sec 22)

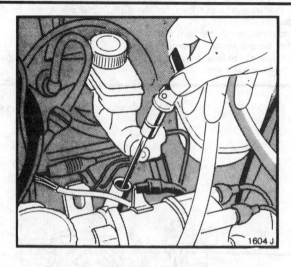

Fig. 6.40 Dipstick guide/filler tube – automatic transmission (Sec 22)

Fig. 6.41 Kickdown cable connection at carburettor (Sec 23)

A   Cable adjuster   B   Ball cap end fitting

Fig. 6.42 Kickdown cable connection at transmission – arrowed (Sec 23)

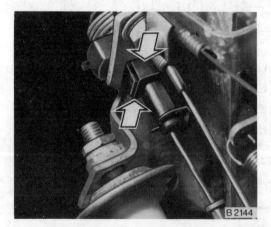

Fig. 6.43 Kickdown cable adjusting mechanism release lug – arrowed (Sec 23)

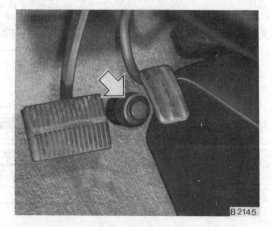

Fig. 6.44 Kickdown switch under accelerator pedal – arrowed (Sec 23)

7 Push the cable adjusting mechanism into its support bracket, ensuring that the lugs locate correctly.
8 Reconnect the cable to the carburettor.
9 The cable must now be adjusted as follows. First depress the accelerator pedal until it just contacts the kickdown switch (Fig. 6.44). Check that in this position the throttle valve plate is fully open. If not adjust the throttle cable at the carburettor. Now release the accelerator pedal, and check that there is no free play in the cable at this idle position. If the cable is slack, adjustment can be made using the adjuster on the pedal mechanism.
10 Slowly depress the accelerator until the kickdown switch has been actuated. The kickdown cable adjustment mechanism will automatically set itself – operation of the ratchet should confirm this. Adjustment will now remain automatically in this position.
11 Release the accelerator pedal, and refit the air cleaner to the carburettor.

24 Speed selector control cable – removal, refitting and adjustment

1 From the centre console extract the four retaining screws, lift the selector lever cover, turn it and remove it; disconnecting the lamp electrical lead as it is withdrawn.
2 Extract the two console securing screws, set the selector lever in P and remove the console.
3 Working at the transmission, release the selector cable by pulling off the retaining clip (A) and then unscrewing the cable from the support (B) (Fig. 6.47).
4 Working inside the vehicle, disconnect the cable from the selector hand control lever.
5 Release the cable from the clamp (A), loosen and remove sleeve (B) (Fig. 6.48).

Fig. 6.45 Selector lever cover screws – arrowed (Sec 24)

Fig. 6.46 Centre console screws – arrowed (Sec 24)

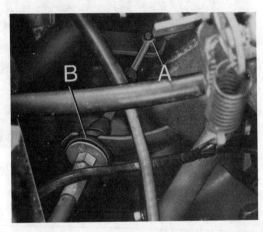

Fig. 6.47 Selector cable retaining clip (A) and support (B) (Sec 24)

Fig. 6.48 Selector cable attachment at hand control lever (Sec 24)

A Clamp   B Sleeve

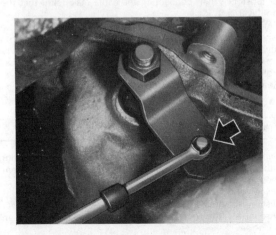

Fig. 6.49 Selector cable connection at transmission – arrowed (Sec 24)

Fig. 6.50 Selector cable support bracket and bolts. (A) also serves as torque converter housing-to-engine bolt (Sec 24)

Fig. 6.51 Torque converter housing-to-engine bolts – arrowed (Sec 25)

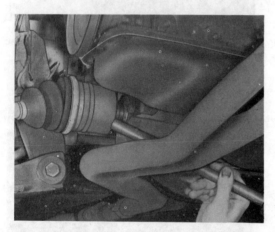

Fig. 6.52 Release right-hand driveshaft with a drift (Sec 25)

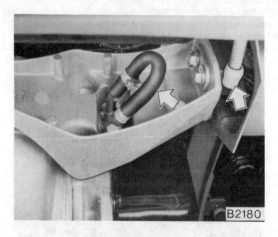

Fig. 6.53 Fluid cooler line disconnection at transmission – arrowed (Sec 25)

6   Withdraw the cable assembly by pulling it into the engine compartment.

7   Fitting a new cable is a reversal of the removal operations, but observe the following points: Check that the cable grommet at the bulkhead makes a good seal. Set the cable in its sleeve so that it is not under tension. When connecting the cable make sure that the hand control lever is in P.

8   With the help of an assistant check that with the hand control lever in each position, the lever on the transmission can be felt to be positively positioned in its correct detent and not under any tension. Where this is not the case, adjust the cable at (A) adjacent to the hand control lever (Fig. 6.48).

9   Refit the centre console and selector lever cover.

25 Transmission – removal and refitting

1   Removal of the automatic transmission together with the engine is described in Chapter 1. To remove the transmission independently, proceed in the following way.

2   Disconnect and remove the battery.

3   Disconnect the earth strap from the transmission.

4   Disconnect the kickdown cable from the carburettor and the transmission.

5   Disconnect the selector cable from the lever on the tranmission.

6   Extract the retaining clip and pull the lever from the transmission.

7   Unscrew the selector cable support bracket, there is no need to disconnect the cable from the bracket.

8   Unscrew and remove the bolts which connect the torque converter housing to the engine (Fig. 6.51).

9   Remove the remaining bolt and lift away the starter motor and tie it up with a piece of wire. There is no need to disconnect the electrical leads.

10   Disconnect the speedometer cable from the transmission.

11   Remove the fluid dipstick.

12   Raise the front of the car sufficiently high so that the transmission will pass out under the front end when removing it.

13   Remove the front left-hand roadwheel.

14   Attach a suitable hoist to the engine or support it on a jack.

15   Disconnect the left rear transmission to bodymember mounting.

16   Disconnect the anti-roll bar from the left-hand suspension lower arm.

17   Disconnect the left-hand lower suspension control arm support from the bodyframe as described in Chapter 10.

18   Disconnect the left-hand driveshaft from the transmission as described in Chapter 7.

19   Release the right-hand driveshaft from the transmission as described in Chapter 7.

20   Disconnect the oil cooler lines at the transmission end and plug the hoses (Fig. 6.53).

21   Unbolt and remove the torque converter cover plate. (Fig. 6.54).

22   Unscrew the driveplate-to-torque converter connecting bolts. Jam the starter ring gear while releasing each bolt. The driveplate will have to be rotated to bring each bolt head to an accessible position. Do this by turning the crankshaft pulley or torsional damper bolt. New bolts must be fitted on reassembly.

23   Unbolt and remove the left-hand front mounting (Fig. 6.56).

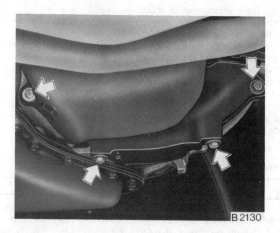

Fig. 6.54 Torque converter cover plate bolts – arrowed
(Sec 25)

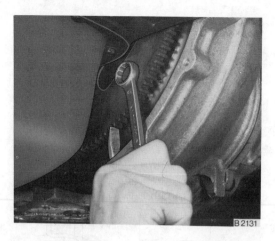

Fig. 6.55 Unscrewing a torque converter-to-engine
driveplate connecting bolt (Sec 25)

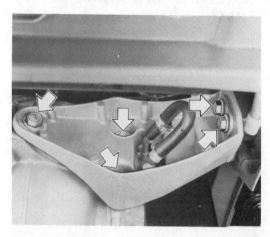

Fig. 6.56 Left-hand front mounting bolts – arrowed (Sec 25)

Fig. 6.57 Exhaust bracket-to-transmission bolts – arrowed
(Sec 25)

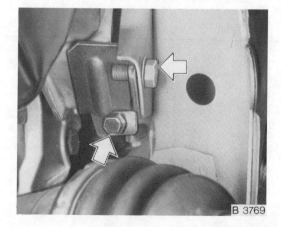

Fig. 6.58 Left-hand rear mounting bracket bolts – arrowed
(Sec 25)

Fig. 6.59 Transmission bolts at engine mounting bracket –
arrowed (Sec 25)

24 Unbolt the exhaust bracket from the transmission and swing the bracket upwards (Fig. 6.57).
25 Pull out the dipstick guide/filler tube. Be prepared for some loss of fluid.
26 Support the transmission on a jack, preferably of trolley type.
27 Working under the vehicle, disconnect the left-hand rear mounting bracket from the bodyframe member, also the two bolts from the engine mounting bracket (Figs. 6.58 and 6.59).

28 Pull the transmission from the engine to clear the positioning dowels and then lower the transmission jack. Withdraw the transmission from under the front of the vehicle.
29 Refitting is a reversal of removal, but observe the following points.
30 Before offering the transmission to the engine, check that the torque converter is fully meshed with the oil pump. To do this, measure (A) as shown in the diagram. This should be between 9.00 and 10.00 mm (0.35 and 0.39 in). If it is not, turn the converter at the same time

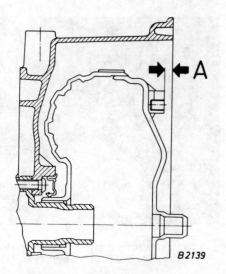

Fig. 6.60 Torque converter installation diagram (Sec 25)

A = 9.0 to 10.0 mm (0.35 to 0.39 in)

applying hand pressure (Fig. 6.60).
31 Apply a smear of molybdenum disulphide grease to the torque converter pilot spigot.
32 When bolting the torque converter to the driveplate, align the white spot on the plate with the coloured spot on the torque converter.
33 When connecting the kickdown cable, first attach it to the transmission. Adjust as described in Section 23.
34 Fill the transmission as described in Section 22.
35 Check all nuts and bolts have been tightened to the specified torque and that thread locking compound has been applied to the threads (clean) of the suspension control arm support bolts.

26 Fault diagnosis – automatic transmission

As has been mentioned elsewhere in this Chapter, no service repair work should be considered by anyone without the specialist knowledge and equipment required to undertake this work. This is also relevant to fault diagnosis. If a fault is evident, carry out the various adjustments previously described, and if the fault still exists consult the local garage or specialist.

Before removing the automatic transmission for repair, make sure that the repairer does not require to perform diagnostic tests with the transmission installed.

Chapter 7 Driveshafts

Contents

Specifications

Type .... Open tubular with homokinetic joint at each end

Driveshaft joint grease specification .... GM grease 19 41 521 (Duckhams LBM 10)

Torque wrench settings

	Nm	lbf ft
Driveshaft to hub carrier:		
Stage 1	100	74
Slacken then Stage 2	20	15
Stage 3*	Tighten further through 90°	Tighten further through 90°
Suspension lower arm bolts:		
Smaller bolts	110	81
Large centre bolts	130	96
Roadwheel bolts	90	66

Turn nut back if necessary to align split pin hole. Do not tighten to align

1 Description and maintenance

The driveshafts are of open type, having a homokinetic joint at each end. The right-hand shaft is longer than the left-hand one.

Maintenance consists of regularly inspecting the bellows for splits or damage. Renew if evident (Section 3).

2 Driveshaft – removal and refitting

1 Raise the front of the vehicle and support it securely.
2 Remove the front roadwheel.
3 Extract the split pin from the castellated nut or nut lock at the end of the driveshaft. Unscrew the nut. This nut is very tight and will require the use of a long knuckle bar to release it. To prevent the driveshaft turning, have an assistant apply the brake pedal or bolt a bar to two of the wheel bolt holes as shown (Fig. 7.1). There is no need to remove the brake caliper.
4 Disconnect the anti-roll bar from the suspension lower control arm.
5 Disconnect the suspension lower control arm support from the bodyframe side-member (Chapter 10) and, with it suspended by its balljoint, swivel the control arm aside.

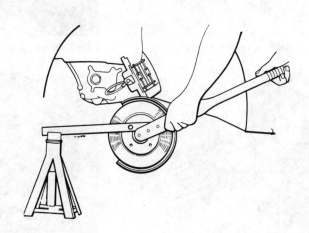

Fig. 7.1 Releasing a driveshaft nut (Sec 2)

6 A tool will now be required for insertion between the transmission casing and the inner driveshaft joint. In the absence of the official tool a flat steel bar with a good chamfer on one end will serve as a substitute. Drive the tool into the gap between the joint and casing to release the shaft snap-ring from the differential. Be prepared for some loss of oil and plug the hole (even with a piece of rag) ro prevent loss of oil and entry of dirt (photos).

7 It should now be possible to push the driveshaft out of the hub using finger pressure. If it is not, use a hub puller (photo).

8 When removing the left-hand driveshaft, it may be found difficult to engage a suitable tool to release it from the transmission. In this case, apply a long steel rod to the edge of the joint and drive it out.

9 On models produced after October 1982, shafts are fitted to 1.6, 1.8 and 2.0 models with automatic transmission which incorporate a modified inboard joint. This type of joint does not incorporate a stop to restrict the sliding travel within the joint. *Great care must therefore be taken when removing or handling this type of driveshaft not to pull on the shaft, or the joint members will become separated and the complete shaft ruined.*

10 On 1.6, 1.8 and 2.0 models with manual transmission, the longer right-hand driveshaft has a two-part weight fitted to act as a torsional vibration damper. If this is removed for any reason, it is important that it is refitted so that the distance between the inner end of the outer joint bellows and the outer face of the weight is 260 mm (10.24 in).

11 Do not move the vehicle on its wheels with one or both driveshafts removed from their hubs. If this precaution is not observed, the front wheel bearings may be damaged.

12 The driveshaft-to-hub nut should be renewed every time it is disturbed.

13 Before refitting a driveshaft, make sure that the contact surfaces of the shaft joint and hub bearing are absolutely clean (Fig. 7.3). Apply some grease to the shaft splines and insert into the hub carrier. Screw on the shaft nut finger tight. Fit a new snap-ring to the inboard end of the driveshaft (photo).

14 Insert the inboard end of the driveshaft into the transmission as far as it will go (photo).

15 Now apply a screwdriver to the weld bead of the inboard joint, **not** the metal cover, and drive the driveshaft into the differential until the

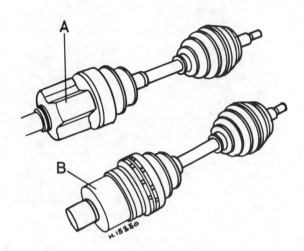

Fig. 7.2 Driveshaft inboard joint comparison on automatic transmission models (Sec 2)

A From 1983   B Earlier models

retaining snap-ring engages positively. Pull on the driveshaft to check the engagement (photo).

16 Reconnect the suspension arm and the anti-roll bar as described in Chapter 10 and tighten all nuts and bolts to the specified torque.

17 Tighten the new driveshaft/hub nut to the specified torque in stages (see Specifications).

18 Fit the nut lock (where installed) and insert a new split pin. Bend over the ends of the pin.

19 Fit the roadwheel and lower the vehicle to the ground.

20 Top up the transmission oil (see Chapter 6).

2.6A Suitable driveshaft releasing tool

2.6B Releasing a driveshaft from the differential

2.7 Driveshaft released from hub carrier

2.13 Driveshaft inboard joint snap-ring (arrowed)

2.14 Inserting driveshaft into transmission

2.15 Securing driveshaft joint to transmission

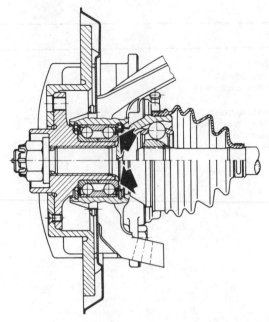

Fig. 7.3 Sectional view of front hub (Sec 2)

Clean the surfaces indicated

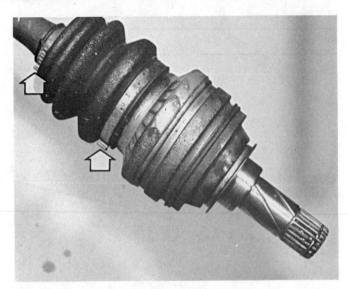

3.2 Driveshaft inboard joint showing bellows clips (arrowed)

3 Driveshaft joint – bellows renewal

1 With the driveshaft removed from the vehicle as described in the preceding Section, remove the retaining band and slide the bellows from the joint.

2 Expand the retaining circlip and remove the joint from the splines of the driveshaft (photo).

3 Slide the defective bellows from the driveshaft.

4 Clean away the old grease from the joint and repack liberally with the specified grease. If excessively worn or damaged, a driveshaft joint must be renewed as a unit (see Section 4).

5 Slide the new bellows onto the shaft so that the smaller diameter opening is located in the groove on the driveshaft.

6 Refit the joint so that the retaining circlip engages in its groove, then slide the bellows over the joint and squeeze them to expel as much air as possible.

7 Fit new bellows retaining bands. There are many suitable types of band available, but those used as original equipment will require the use of special pliers to tighten them.

4 Driveshaft joint – renewal

1 A worn driveshaft joint cannot be overhauled, only renewed as a complete assembly. Remove the driveshaft (Section 2).

2 Release the securing band and slide the bellows off the worn joint.

3 Expand the circlip which secures the joint to the driveshaft (Fig. 7.4).

4 Using a plastic-faced hammer, tap the joint from the driveshaft (Fig. 7.5).

5 Tap on the new joint until the securing circlip engages in its groove.

6 Repack the joint with the specified grease.

7 Refit the bellows as described in the preceding Section.

8 Fit the driveshaft to the vehicle.

Fig. 7.4 Driveshaft joint retaining circlip – arrowed (Sec 4)

Fig. 7.5 Tapping joint from driveshaft (Sec 4)

5   Fault diagnosis – driveshafts

Symptom	Reason(s)
Vibration	Driveshaft bent
	Worn universal joints
	Out-of-balance roadwheels
'Clonk' on taking up drive or on overrun	Worn universal joints
	Worn splines on shaft, hub carrier or differential side gears
	Loose driveshaft nut
	Loose roadwheel bolts

Chapter 8 Steering

Contents

Specifications

Type .... Rack and pinion with a safety column. Power steering on certain models

Manual steering gear

Ratio:
   1.3 manual gearbox models 22.0:1
   All other models 24.5:1
Pinion identification:
   1.3 manual gearbox models .... Plain
   All other models .... One groove
Number of rack teeth:
   1.3 manual gearbox models 28
   All other models 32
Grease specification:
   Internal components .... GM grease 18 48 588 (Duckhams Adgear 00)
   Pinion ball-bearing .... GM grease 19 46 254

Power steering gear

Ratio 18.0:1
Fluid type .... Dexron II type ATF (Duckhams D-Matic)

Turning circle (between kerbs) .... 10.1 m (33.1 ft)

Wheel alignment

Camber (non adjustable):
   Laden* .... −1°15' to +0°15'
   Maximum deviation side to side .... 1°
Castor (non-adjustable):
   Laden* .... 0 to +2°
   Maximum deviation side to side .... 1°
Toe:
   Laden*:
     Up to 1985 .... 0.5 to 2.5 mm toe-out
     From 1985 .... 1.0 mm toe-out to 1.0 mm toe-in

Laden indicates a vehicle containing two front seat occupants and a half-filled fuel tank

Torque wrench settings

	Nm	lbf ft
Adjustment screw locknut	60	44
Column spindle coupling clamp bolt	22	16
Pinion-to-coupling clamp bolt	22	16
Steering wheel nut	25	18
Steering gear unit mounting nuts	15	11
Pinion attachment bolt	40	30
Column-to-dash panel bolts	22	16
Damper bolts to steering gear housing	22	16
Tie-rod to steering gear	110	81
Tie-rod balljoint nut	60	44
Tie-rod clamp pinch-bolt	20	15

Torque wrench settings (continued)

Power steering items:

	Nm	lbf ft
Flow and return pipes to steering gear (special retaining bolt)	37	27
High pressure hose union nut	42	31
Pump pressure lines union nut (to connectors)	28	21
Fluid reservoir bracket bolts	7	5
Support-to-cylinder block bolts	40	30
Oil pump bolts	15	11
Support tightening screw	40	30
Tightening piece to support bolts	15	11
Tightening piece bolt locknut	40	30

1 General description

The steering gear is of rack-and-pinion type, movement being transmitted to the front wheels through tie-rods which are connected to the rack through a sliding sleeve.

The steering column consists of an outer column which incorpo-

rates a deformable section, and a shaft connected to a flexible coupling at its lower end.

As from 1983, power steering gear is fitted as standard to all 1.8 CD models and is available as an option on other models.

With this type of steering gear, a rotary slide valve design is employed which gives exceptionally precise steering with good 'feel' and operational safety.

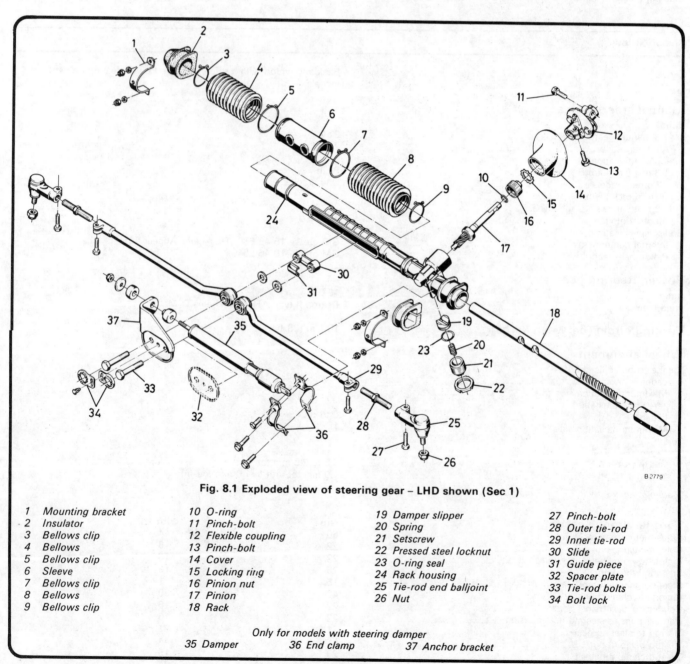

Fig. 8.1 Exploded view of steering gear – LHD shown (Sec 1)

1 Mounting bracket	10 O-ring	19 Damper slipper	27 Pinch-bolt
2 Insulator	11 Pinch-bolt	20 Spring	28 Outer tie-rod
3 Bellows clip	12 Flexible coupling	21 Setscrew	29 Inner tie-rod
4 Bellows	13 Pinch-bolt	22 Pressed steel locknut	30 Slide
5 Bellows clip	14 Cover	23 O-ring seal	31 Guide piece
6 Sleeve	15 Locking ring	24 Rack housing	32 Spacer plate
7 Bellows clip	16 Pinion nut	25 Tie-rod end balljoint	33 Tie-rod bolts
8 Bellows	17 Pinion	26 Nut	34 Bolt lock
9 Bellows clip	18 Rack		

Only for models with steering damper

35 Damper   36 End clamp   37 Anchor bracket

B 2779

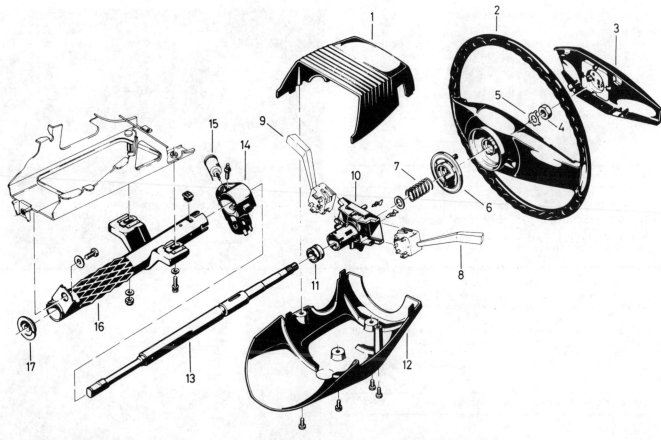

Fig. 8.2 Exploded view of steering column and associated components (Sec 1)

1	Upper shroud	6	Cam assembly
2	Steering wheel	7	Spring
3	Horn push	8	Headlamp switch
4	Steering wheel nut	9	Wiper switch
5	Lockplate	10	Switch housing

11	Upper bearing	15	Ignition switch
12	Lower shroud	16	Column tube
13	Steering shaft	17	Centralising plastic disc
14	Steering lock/ignition switch housing		

2 Routine maintenance – steering

1   At regular intervals inspect the flexible bellows on the steering rack housing, and the tie-rod end balljoint gaiters, for splits or damage. Renew as necessary as described in later Sections of this Chapter.

2   Check the tie-rod end balljoints for wear. This is best done by having an assistant move the steering wheel from side to side through an arc of travel of about 20° while the balljoint connection to the steering arm on the front hub carrier is observed. Any loss of movement or shake in the balljoint will indicate wear and a new tie-rod end will have to be fitted (see Section 3).

3   On models with power steering, check the fluid level in the reservoir, using the dipstick built into the reservoir cap (photo). With the engine at operating temperature, the level should be up to the 'FULL' mark. With the engine cold, the level must not fall below the 'ADD' mark. Top up if necessary, with clean fluid of the specified type.

4   Check the condition and tension of the power steering pump drivebelt, as described in Section 14.

5   Have the front wheel toe setting checked at the specified intervals, or sooner if abnormal tyre wear is experienced (Section 12).

3 Tie-rod end – removal and refitting

1   Raise the front of the car and remove the roadwheel.

2   Slacken the tie-rod end balljoint nut, release the ball-pin using a balljoint separator tool, and remove the nut (photo). Extract the balljoint from the steering arm.

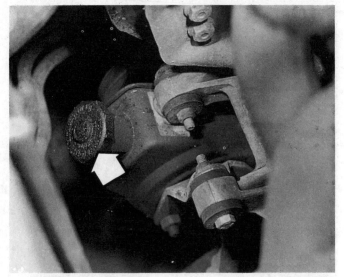

2.3 Power steering pump showing reservoir cap/dipstick (arrowed)

Fig. 8.3 Tie-rod balljoint identification – arrowed (Sec 3)

3   Slacken the clamp bolt which secures the tie-rod end to the outer tie-rod. Mark the position of the tie-rod end on the outer tie-rod with paint or tape, then unscrew the tie-rod end.

4   Note that the tie-rod ends are handed. The right-hand end is marked with an 'R'; the left-hand end has no marking.

5   Screw the new tie-rod end onto the tie-rod to approximately the same position as was occupied by the old one. Secure it with the clamp bolt.

6   Connect the tie-rod end to the steering arm, and secure it with a new self-locking nut, tightened to the specified torque.

7   Refit the roadwheel, and lower the car to the ground.

8   Check and adjust the front wheel alignment (toe setting), as described in Section 12.

---

4   Steering gear – removal and refitting

Manual steering

1   Remove the air cleaner.

2   If a headlamp washer system is fitted, release the fluid reservoir and move it to one side.

3   Disconnect the battery earth lead.

4   Working at the centre of the steering rack housing, remove both tie-rod bolts and remove the bolt locks and the spacer plate (photo).

5   On models fitted with a steering damper, detach the damper brackets from the steering gear housing and remove the damper.

6   Pull off the cardboard panel from under the facia panel to give access to the steering column shaft flexible coupling.

7   Set the steering wheel and front roadwheels in the straight-ahead position.

8   Unscrew the two pinch-bolts on the flexible coupling at the base of the steering column shaft (photo).

3.2 Typical balljoint extractor

4.4 Tie-rod connection to steering rack

4.8 Flexible coupling upper pinch-bolt (arrowed)

4.10 Steering rack showing mounting clamp (arrowed)

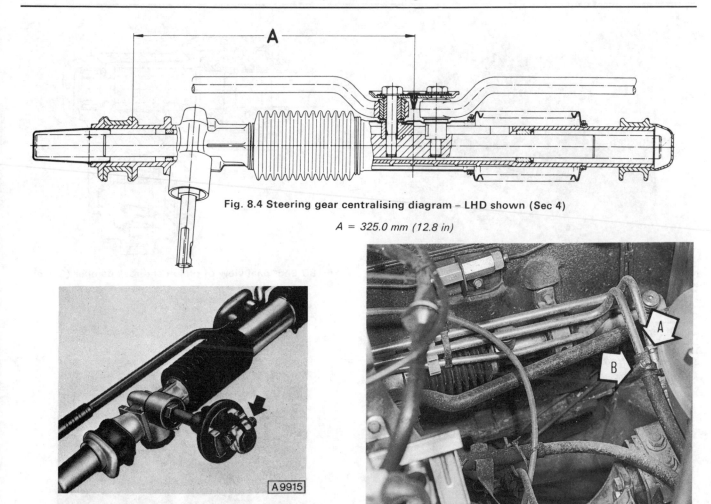

Fig. 8.4 Steering gear centralising diagram – LHD shown (Sec 4)

A = 325.0 mm (12.8 in)

Fig. 8.5 Flexible coupling upper pinch-bolt alignment when steering centralised – arrowed (LHD shown) (Sec 4)

4.20 Power steering pressure pipe union (A) and return hose clip (B)

9 Slide the flexible coupling upwards off the pinion.

10 Unbolt the steering gear mounting clamps and withdraw the rack-and-pinion housing through the front right-hand wheel arch (photo).

11 Refitting is a reversal of removal, but before connecting the flexible coupling to the pinion, the steering must be centred in the following way.

12 Jack up the front of the car and turn the pinion on the steering gear until the distance between the centre of the spacer plate and the rib on the mounting is as shown (Fig. 8.4).

13 Set the steering wheel in its straight-ahead position.

14 Where a steering damper is fitted, bolt it to the steering gear housing and tighten the bolts to the specified torque wrench setting.

15 Push the flexible coupling down and connect it with the pinion, then tighten the coupling bolt to its specified torque setting.

16 The upper clamp should now be lying so that the pinch-bolt is parallel with the steering housing. If it is not, this will indicate that the pinion is out of phase with the rack, and the components will have to be repositioned in relation to each other as described in Section 6.

17 Check that the concave end of the mounting bracket is pointing downward when the steering gear is installed.

18 If the pinion sealing cap has been disturbed, make sure that its notch is engaged with the rib on the steering gear housing.

Power steering

19 The operations are similar to those just described for the manual steering gear, except that the flow (pressure) and return pipes must be disconnected prior to removal.

20 Undo the pressure pipe union and slacken the return hose clip, then separate the pipe and hose unions (photo).

21 Allow the fluid to drain from the open pipe and hose unions, then cover the unions with small plastic bags or tape to prevent dirt ingress.

22 When refitting the steering gear, centralise it by counting the number of turns from lock to lock while turning the pinion shaft. Then set the steering by turning the pinion shaft from the full lock position through half the number of turns counted.

23 Fit the flexible coupling to the pinion shaft (steering still centralised) so that the upper pinch-bolt lies horizontally and on top of the pinion shaft.

24 Reconnect the pipe and hose unions, then fill and bleed the system as described in Section 13.

5 Steering rack bellows – renewal

1 To renew faulty bellows, the steering gear must first be removed from the vehicle as described in the preceding Section.

2 Remove the mounting bracket and its rubber insulator from the housing. If working on power steering, undo the banjo unions and remove the fluid pipes.

3 Remove the bellows clamp wires and pull the bellows from the housing. If both bellows are to be renewed, the complete bellows/sleeve assembly may be slid from the housing.

4 Refitting is a reversal of removal, but observe the following essential requirements.

5 The concave end of the mounting bracket bolt hole flange must be pointing down when the steering gear is installed.

6 If the pinion sealing cap has been removed, make sure that its notch is engaged with the rib on the steering gear housing (Fig. 8.6).

7 On power steering gear, refit the banjo unions using new sealing washers.

Fig. 8.6 Rack housing mounting bracket and pinion sealing cap correctly installed – arrowed (LHD shown) (Sec 5)

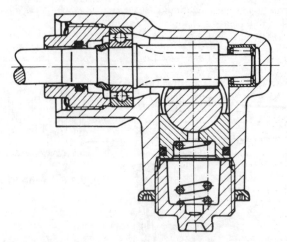

Fig. 8.7 Sectional view of pinion and rack damper (Sec 6)

6   Steering gear – overhaul

Manual steering

1   Remove the steering gear from the vehicle as previously described.
2   Clean away external dirt.
3   Remove the bellows and housing sleeve.
4   Remove the slide and guide piece from the rack.
5   Release the pressed steel locknut from the rack adjuster setscrew.
6   Unscrew and remove the setscrew and extract the coil spring, seal and damper slipper.
7   Extract the locking ring from around the pinion nut, unscrew the nut and extract the seal.
8   Withdraw the rack and the pinion.
9   Push out the cap from the end of the housing using a long rod (Fig. 8.9).
10   Further dismantling is not possible. If the rack bushes or pinion needle bearing are worn, renew the housing complete. The pinion can only be renewed complete with the ball-bearing.
11   Clean away old lubricant and apply the specified grease to internal components. Insert 50g (1³/₄ oz) of the grease between the rack bushes in the inside of the housing.
12   Insert the rack into the housing and locate it so that its end furthest from the pinion is set as shown (Fig. 8.10).
13   Now insert the pinion so that when its gear is finally meshed with the rack teeth, the cut-out on the pinion shaft is at right-angles to the rack and located, as shown away from A in Fig. 8.10.

Fig. 8.8 Extracting steering pinion locking ring – LHD shown (Sec 6)

Fig. 8.9 Driving out rack housing cap – arrowed (LHD shown) (Sec 6)

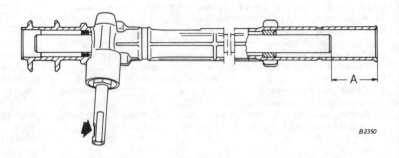

Fig. 8.10 Pinion shaft cut-out set furthest away from longer tubular section of rack housing – LHD shown (Sec 6)

14 Apply specified grease to the pinion ball-bearing and screw in the pinion nut to the specified torque. Fit a new nut retaining ring, driving it home with a piece of tubing.

15 The steering gear must now be adjusted. To do this, make up two distance pieces to the dimensions shown in Fig. 8.11. Using the tie-rod eye attaching bolts, bolt the slide, guide piece and distance pieces to the rack (Fig. 8.12).

16 Insert the rack damper slipper and coil spring into their hole and screw in the setscrew until some resistance is felt.

17 Unscrew the setscrew between $1/8$ and $1/4$ of a turn and check that the rack will move freely throughout its complete travel.

18 Without disturbing the setting of the setscrew, fit the pressed steel locknut and tighten to the specified torque.

19 Tap a new end cap into the housing, fit the bellows and remove the temporary distance pieces and tie-rod eye bolts from the rack.

20 Fit the mountings and the pinion cap seal as described in Section 5, paragraphs 5 and 6.

21 Check the centering of the steering gear as described in Section 4, paragraphs 12 to 16. If the pinion-to-rack tooth engagement is incorrect, the pinion will have to be withdrawn and moved as necessary to correct the setting.

22 Once the gear has been installed in the vehicle, carry out a test drive on a route having curves and corners. The gear should exhibit a well-defined self-centering action after steering lock has been applied. If it does not, the rack damper has been over-adjusted and should be reset.

Power steering

23 Overhaul of the power steering gear is not recommended. Any fault or wear should be overcome by renewal of the assembly.

---

7 Steering damper – removal and refitting

1 Certain models are equipped with a steering damper which is fitted between the rack and the rack housing.

2 First unbolt the damper from the rack bracket at the centre of the steering assembly and then unclamp it from the rack housing. Remove the damper.

3 Refitting is a reversal of removal, but tighten the spindle nut only sufficiently to maintain the length (A) of exposed threads as shown in Fig. 8.14.

4 The clamp should be set as shown in Fig. 8.15, before tightening all bolts to the specified torque.

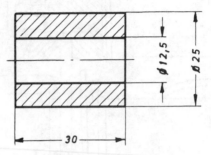

Fig. 8.11 Distance piece dimensional diagram (Sec 6)

Dimensions in mm

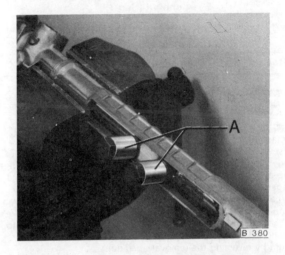

Fig. 8.12 Adjustment distance pieces (A) bolted to steering rack – LHD shown (Sec 6)

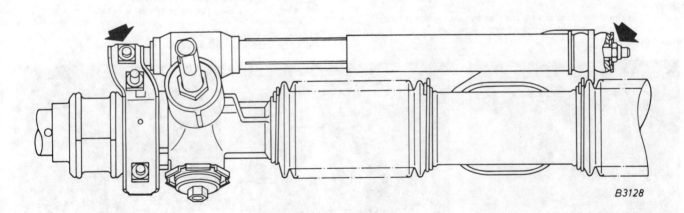

Fig. 8.13 Steering damper fixing bolts – arrowed (LHD shown) (Sec 7)

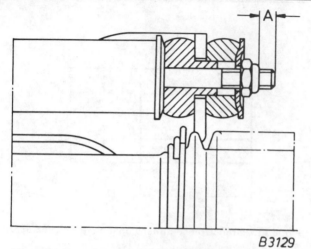

Fig. 8.14 Steering damper mounting nut setting – LHD shown (Sec 7)

A = 6.0 mm (0.24 in)

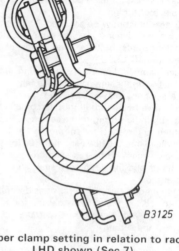

Fig. 8.15 Damper clamp setting in relation to rack housing – LHD shown (Sec 7)

8 Steering wheel – removal and refitting

1 Disconnect the battery negative lead.
2 Prise out the horn button from the centre of the steering wheel and detach the wiring connections (photo).
3 Set the steering wheel in the straight-ahead position and unscrew the retaining nut.
4 Use a puller to remove the steering wheel, tapped holes are provided for puller anchor bolts in the wheel hub. Do not attempt to thump the wheel off or the safety type steering column may be damaged (photo).
5 When necessary, the horn contact ring may be renewed by unclipping it from the wheel hub. When fitting the new ring, make sure that the direction indicator switch cancelling segment is to the left-hand side.
6 Refit by reversing the removal operations.
7 Check that the steering wheel is correctly aligned before tightening its retaining nut to the specified torque.

9 Steering column – removal and refitting

1 Disconnect the battery earth lead. Extract the four screws and remove both halves of the steering column shroud.
2 Unclip the direction indicator and wiper switches by depressing the upper and lower locking tabs and sliding the switches from their grooves.
3 Pull out the wiring harness for the steering and ignition locks.
4 Set the steering wheel and the front roadwheels in the straight-ahead position.

5 Unscrew and remove the upper pinch-bolt from the steering flexible coupling.
6 Unscrew and remove the bolt that secures the base of the column to the bulkhead.
7 The bolts must now be extracted from the column upper mounting bracket. The left-hand bolt is of shear-head type and must be centre-punched, drilled out (using an $1/8$ inch bit) and a bolt extractor used to remove it. A self-locking nut is used on the right-hand side.
8 Withdraw the column assembly into the vehicle interior and then remove it from the vehicle. Handle the column carefully, avoid knocks or impact of any kind. Remove the steering wheel (Section 8).
9 If a new column assembly is being installed, a plastic washer is located on the base of the shaft as an aid to centering the shaft in the column tube.
10 Centre the steering gear as described in Section 4, paragraphs 12 to 16.
11 Engage the plastic washer for centering the shaft in the column tube.
12 Offer the column into position and connect the coupling as described in Section 4, paragraphs 13 to 15.
13 Loosely connect the upper mounting using a new shear bolt.
14 Loosely screw in the column lower fixing bolt and the coupling pinch-bolt.
15 Tighten the lower fixing bolt to its specified torque. Tighten the shear-head bolt until its head breaks off.
16 Pull up on the steering shaft until contact is made with the shaft bearing stop. Tighten the coupling pinch-bolt.
17 Remove the temporary plastic centering washer.
18 Refit the wiring harness and column switches, also the column upper shrouds (photo).
19 Refit the steering wheel and reconnect the battery.

8.2 Horn button removed

8.4 Removing steering wheel

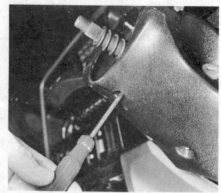

9.18 Steering column shroud screw

Fig. 8.16 Steering column switch locking tabs – arrowed
(LHD shown) (Sec 9)

10 Steering column – overhaul

Note: *The steering column may be dismantled and reassembled either with the column fitted in the car or removed, the procedures being similar. That described here is for column fitted.*

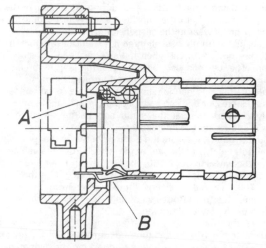

Fig. 8.18 Sectional view of steering column switch
housing (Sec 10)

A Thrust washer   B Contact springs

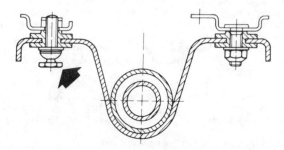

Fig. 8.17 Steering column upper bracket mounting bolts.
Shear-head bolt arrowed (Sec 9)

1 With the assembly removed from the vehicle as previously described, withdraw the steering wheel from the steering shaft (Section 8).
2 Remove the column switches (Section 9, paragraph 2).
3 Disconnect the wiring harness from the switches.
4 Prise out the safety plugs and remove the column switch housing by turning it to the left and pulling (photos).
5 The double row ball-bearing can be pressed out of its housing if the two bearing fixing catches are first prised apart. Use a piece of tubing as a drift to remove the bearing.
6 Install the new bearing by reversing the removal operations. Note the bearing thrust washer (A) (Fig. 8.18).

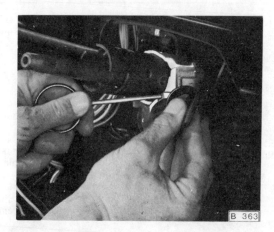

Fig. 8.19 Using a rod to depress steering column lock
retaining plunger – LHD shown (Sec 10)

10.4A Prise out the steering column switch safety plugs
(arrowed) ...

10.4B ... turn the switch assembly anti-clockwise, and withdraw it
from the column

7 Set the lock cylinder in 'I' position and depress the detent plunger using a thin rod. Remove the mechanical component of the switch.
8 Extract the two grub screws and withdraw the electrical component of the switch.
9 Remove the trim from under the dashboard and unscrew the upper pinch-bolt from the flexible coupling. Withdraw the steering shaft from the column tube.
10 To reassemble, first insert the shaft into the column tube and then engage the bottom of the shaft in the flexible coupling, making sure that the cut-out in the shaft aligns with the bolt hole in the clamp.
11 Fit the temporary plastic centering washer into the base of the column tube.
12 Install the lock cylinder and ignition lock.
13 Install the switch housing to the column tube, using new safety plugs.
14 Clip in the direction indicator and wiper switches and fix the wiring harness.
15 Fit the column shroud.
16 Fit the washer and spring on the shaft upper bearing.
17 Fit the steering wheel and tighten the nut to the specified torque using a new lockplate.
18 Pull the steering wheel/shaft upwards until the shaft upper bearing is contacted.
19 Retaining this position, tighten the coupling pinch-bolt.
20 Remove the temporary plastic centering washer.
21 Refit the dashboard trim. Check the steering centralisation as described in Section 4.

11 Steering column lock – removal and refitting

1 To renew either the ignition switch or the steering lock cylinder, first remove the lower half of the steering column shroud by undoing and removing the securing screws.
2 Refer to Chapter 4, Section 12, for details of ignition switch removal.

Steering lock cylinder

3 Disconnect the battery earth lead and, after removing the lower half of the steering column shroud, insert the ignition key and turn it to the 'I' position.
4 Using a piece of wire or a drill shank (3 mm dia), depress the lock spring retaining the cylinder and carefully withdraw the cylinder from its housing. It is important that the ignition switch is not removed or disturbed while the lock cylinder is not fitted.
5 Before fitting a new lock cylinder insert the ignition key and turn it to the 'I' position. Insert the assembly into the steering lock housing and press it down until the retaining spring engages before removing the key (photo).
6 Reconnect the battery earth lead and test the operation of the ignition switch before fitting the lower half shroud.

12 Steering angles and wheel alignment – general

1 Accurate front wheel alignment is essential to good steering and for even tyre wear. Before considering the steering angles, check that the tyres are correctly inflated, that the front wheels are not buckled, the hub bearings are not worn and that the steering linkage is in good order, without slackness or wear at the joints.
2 Wheel alignment consists of four factors:
   Camber, is the angle at which the roadwheels are set from the vertical when viewed from the front or rear of the vehicle. Positive camber is the angle (in degrees) that the wheels are tilted outwards at the top from the vertical.
   Castor, is the angle between the steering axis and a vertical line when viewed from each side of the vehicle. Positive castor is indicated when the steering axis is inclined towards the rear of the vehicle at its upper end.
   Steering axis inclination, is the angle, when viewed from the front or rear of the vehicle, between the vertical and an imaginary line drawn between the upper and lower front suspension strut mountings.
   Toe, is the amount by which the distance between the front inside edges of the roadwheel rims differs from that between the rear inside edges. If the distance between the front edges is less than that at the rear, the wheels are said to toe-in. If the distance between the front inside edges is greater than that at the rear, the wheels toe-out.
3 Due to the need for precision gauges to measure the small angles of the steering and suspension settings, it is preferable that checking of camber and castor is left to a service station having the necessary equipment. Camber and castor are set during production of the vehicle, and any deviation from the specified angle will be due to accident damage or gross wear in the suspension mountings.
4 To check the front wheel alignment, first make sure that the lengths of both tie-rods are equal when the steering is in the straight-ahead position. The tie-rods can be adjusted for length if necessary by releasing all the clamp pinch-bolts and turning the rods.
5 Obtain a tracking gauge. These are available in various forms from accessory stores, or one can be fabricated from a length of steel tubing suitably cranked to clear the sump and bellhousing and having a setscrew and locknut at one end.
6 With the gauge, measure the distance between the two wheel inner rims (at hub height) at the rear of the wheel. Push the vehicle forward to rotate the wheel through 180° (half a turn) and measure the distance between the wheel inner rims, again at hub height, at the front of the wheel. This last measurement should differ from the first by the appropriate toe-in/toe-out according to the Specifications. The vehicle must be on level ground.
7 Where the toe-in/toe-out is found to be incorrect, release the tie-rod clamp pinch-bolts and turn the tie-rods equally. Only turn them a quarter of a turn at a time before re-checking the alignment. Do not grip the threaded part of the tie-rod/balljoint during adjustment, but use an open-ended spanner on the flats provided (Fig. 8.20). It is

11.5 Ignition key positions

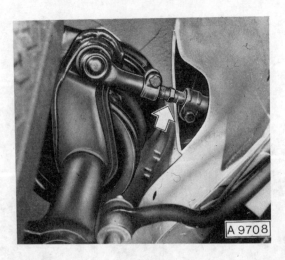

Fig. 8.20 Flats for spanner on outer tie-rod – arrowed
(Sec 12)

important not to allow the tie-rods to become unequal in length during adjustment otherwise the alignment of the steering wheel will become incorrect and tyre scrubbing will occur on turns. The maximum difference in lengths between the rods must not exceed 5 mm (0.2 in).
8   On completion, tighten the tie-rod clamps without disturbing their setting. Check that the balljoint is at the centre of its arc of travel and the openings in the clamps are aligned with the slots in the tie-rod balljoint socket, also that the clamp pinch-bolts have their nuts at the top.

13 Power steering system – bleeding

1   Fill the pump fluid reservoir to the full level with specified fluid.
2   Start the engine and allow it to idle.
3   Turn the steering slowly from one lock to the other. This will prove easier if the front roadwheels are first raised off the ground. Do not hold the steering on the full lock position in either direction for periods exceeding 10 seconds.

4   Repeat several times until the fluid level in the reservoir does not fall any further and then finally top up to the mark and switch off the engine.

14 Power steering pump drivebelt – tensioning

1   The belt should be tensioned in a similar way to that described for the alternator drivebelt in Chapter 2.
2   Before attempting to carry out any adjustment, slacken the mounting and adjuster eyebolt pivot bolts (Fig. 8.22).
3   Release the locknuts on the adjuster eyebolt and turn the nuts as necessary to tension the belt. If the belt is to be renewed, slacken off the adjustment completely so that the belt can be removed and the new one fitted over the pulley rim without excessive force being required.
4   Retighten all nuts and bolts on completion.

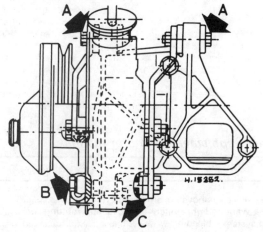

Fig. 8.21 Power steering pump mountings (Sec 14)

A   *Mounting bolts*   B   *Adjuster pivot bolt*   C   *Mounting bolt*

Fig. 8.22 Power steering pump adjuster locknuts – arrowed (Sec 14)

15 Fault diagnosis – steering

Symptom	Reason(s)
Lost motion at steering wheel	Wear in rack and pinion Wear in tie-rod end balljoints Incorrect tyre pressures
Steering wander	Wear in gear or linkage Incorrect front wheel alignment Worn front hub bearings Incorrect tyre pressures
Heavy or stiff steering	Incorrect front wheel alignment Seized balljoint Dry rack assembly Distorted shaft/column Incorrect tyre pressures
Wheel wobble and vibration	Roadwheels out of balance Roadwheel buckled Incorrect front wheel alignment
Power steering	
Lack of assistance or jerkiness	Low fluid level Slipping pump drivebelt
Noisy operation especially on turns	Air in system Low fluid level Internal wear in pump or gear

Chapter 9 Braking system

For modifications, and information applicable to later models, see Supplement at end of manual

Contents

Specifications

System type .... Four wheel hydraulic dual circuit (split diagonally). Disc front, drum rear, with servo assistance. Pressure regulating valves to rear brakes. Handbrake cable operated by floor-mounted lever to rear brakes.

Brake fluid type/specification .... Hydraulic fluid to SAE J1703F or DOT 4 (Duckhams Universal Brake and Clutch Fluid)

Brake discs
Diameter .... 236.0 mm (9.29 in)
Thickness (new):
   1.3 and 1.6 .... 12.7 mm (0.50 in)
   1.8 (ventilated) .... 20.0 mm (0.79 in)
Minimum thickness (after refinishing*):
   1.3 and 1.6 .... 10.7 mm (0.42 in)
   1.8 .... 18.0 mm (0.71 in)
Maximum run-out .... 0.1 mm (0.004 in)
*When this dimension is reached, only one more set of brake pads are permissible, then renew the discs

Disc pads
Overall thickness including backing plate .... 15.5 to 15.9 mm (0.61 to 0.63 in)
Wear limit (including backing plate) .... 7.0 mm (0.28 in)

Caliper
Piston diameter:
    1.3 and 1.6 .... 48.0 mm (1.89 in)
    1.8 .... 52.0 mm (2.04 in)

Brake drums
Internal diameter:
    Saloon and Hatchback .... 200.0 mm (7.87 in)
    Estate .... 230.0 mm (9.06 in)
Maximum internal diameter after refinishing:
    Saloon and Hatchback .... 201.0 mm (7.91 in)
    Estate .... 231.0 mm (9.09 in)
Maximum permissible out-of-round .... 0.1 mm (0.004 in)

Brake shoes
Dimensions: **Width**
    Saloon and Hatchback .... 52.0 mm (2.05 in)
    Estate .... 58.5 mm (2.30 in)
Wear limit (above rivet head) .... 0.5 mm (0.02 in)

Rear wheel cylinder
Piston diameter (minimum permissible):
    Saloon and Hatchback .... 17.39 mm (0.685 in)
    Estate .... 18.98 mm (0.748 in)
Cylinder bore (maximum permissible):
    Saloon and Hatchback .... 17.53 mm (0.690 in)
    Estate .... 19.12 mm (0.753 in)
Nominal diameter:
    Saloon and Hatchback .... 17.46 mm (0.687 in)
    Estate .... 19.05 mm (0.750 in)

Master cylinder
Piston diameter (minimum permissible):
    GMF .... 20.58 mm (0.810 in)
    ATE .... 20.49 mm (0.807 in)
Cylinder bore (nominal) .... 20.64 mm (0.813 in)

Servo unit
Type .... Vacuum operated, single diaphragm
Make .... GMF or ATE
Size .... 178, 203 or 227 mm (7.0, 8.0 or 9.0 in) according to model and year

Footbrake and handbrake free travel
Footbrake .... 6 to 9 mm (0.2 to 0.4 in)
Handbrake .... Braking effect to start at 2nd notch

Torque wrench settings

	Nm	lbf ft
Master cylinder stop bolt	6	4
Vacuum servo unit to support bracket	18	13
Vacuum servo to bulkhead	18	13
Pressure regulator to master cylinder:		
GMF type	40	30
ATE type	12	9
Caliper mounting bolts	95	70
Roadwheel bolts	90	66
Bleed screw	9	7
Caliper banjo union hollow bolt	25	18
Brake pedal support bracket to bulkhead	20	15
Pedal cross-shaft nut	18	13
Rear wheel cylinder to backplate	9	7
Master cylinder mounting nuts	18	13
Vacuum servo union nut to manifold	15	11
Hydraulic pipeline union nuts	11	8
Handbrake cable locknut	20	15
Disc splash plate guard to steering knuckle	4	3
Brake drum to hub screw	4	3
Handbrake lever to floor	20	15

1 General description

The braking system is of dual circuit (diagonally split) hydraulic type, having disc brakes at the front and drum brakes at the rear. A vacuum servo unit (booster) is fitted to all models.

The handbrake is mechanical, operating on the rear wheels only and is actuated by a floor-mounted lever.

Hydraulic pressure regulating valves are screwed into the master cylinder to prevent the rear wheels locking during heavy brake application. These valves are non-adjustable.

Routine Maintenance).

6 On pre 1984 models, check and if necessary adjust the rear brakes at the specified intervals as described in Section 8.

7 Routine maintenance of self-adjusting rear brakes is limited to inspecting the linings.

3 Disc pads – inspection and renewal

1 Raise the front of the vehicle. If the roadwheels have been balanced on the vehicle (new vehicles are balanced this way in production) then

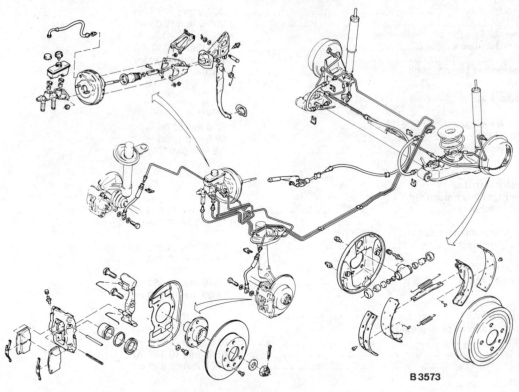

B 3573

Fig. 9.1 Braking system – left-hand drive shown (Sec 1)

The individual components of the braking systems may be one of two makes – GMF or ATE.

A handbrake ON and low fluid level warning lamp and switches are incorporated in the system.

Work on the braking system should be careful and methodical. Scrupulous cleanliness must be observed when working on the hydraulic system. Replacement parts should preferably be the maker's own, or at least of known manufacture and quality.

Warning: Braking system hazards. *Some brake friction materials still contain asbestos. Assume that all brake dust is potentially hazardous for this reason; avoid inhaling it and do not disperse it into the air. Note also that brake fluid is toxic and attacks paintwork. Do not syphon it by mouth, wash thoroughly after skin contact and wash spillage off paintwork immediately.*

2 Routine maintenance – braking system

1 Although a brake fluid warning lamp is connected to the master cylinder reservoir, it is still an extra safeguard to view the fluid level through the translucent container at the weekly check (photo).

2 The level will drop very slowly indeed due to normal pad and lining wear, but any rapid drop and the need to top up at frequent intervals will be due to a leak somewhere in the hydraulic system, which should be investigated.

3 Regularly inspect the flexible and rigid pipelines for any sign of leakage and rectify immediately should any be observed.

4 Wear in the disc pads or rear drum shoe linings should be visually checked at the intervals (specified in Routine Maintenance).

5 Renew the system fluid by bleeding at the specified intervals (see

2.1 Fluid reservoir cap and float

Fig. 9.2 Removing pad retaining pin (Sec 3)

Fig. 9.3 Disc pad springs correctly located – arrowed (Sec 3)

mark the relative position of the roadwheel to the hub so that it can be aligned correctly when refitting.

2   Inspect the thickness of the friction material on each pad. If any one is at or below the specified minimum, renew the pads as an axle set (four pads) in the following way.

3   Drive out the pad retaining pins by applying a punch to their inboard ends.

4   Remove the springs (photo).

5   Using a pair of pliers, withdraw the outboard pad (photo).

6   Remove the inboard pad. If it is very tight, move the pad sideways slightly to depress the caliper piston (photo).

7   In order to accommodate the new thicker pads, the caliper piston must be depressed fully into its cylinder using a flat bar of metal such as a tyre lever. The action of depressing the piston will cause the fluid in the reservoir to rise, so anticipate this by syphoning some off using an old (clean) hydrometer or similar.

8   Brush out the jaws of the caliper, *taking care not to inhale the dust.*

9   Insert the pads, making sure that the lining side is against the disc.

When fitting disc pads supplied by the vehicle manufacturer, it may be found that two pads out of the four have white marks on their backing plates. Where this is the case, the pads with the marks should be fitted to the piston sides of the calipers. On later ATE type brake units, a shim may be fitted between the inner brake pad and the caliper piston. Where applicable, ensure that the shim is inserted with the inner pad (photo).

10   Locate the spreader springs (Fig. 9.3), and drive in the retaining pins (photos).

11   Repeat the operations on the opposite brake.

12   Refit the roadwheels and lower the vehicle.

13   Apply the footbrake hard several times to position the pads against the discs.

14   Top up the fluid reservoir to the correct level.

15   New brake pads need to be carefully bedded in and, where possible, heavy braking should be avoided during the first 120 miles (200 km).

3.4 Removing a disc pad spring

3.5 Outboard disc pad partially withdrawn

3.6 Withdrawing the inboard disc pad

3.9 Inner disc pad and shim – ATE type brake unit

3.10A Inserting disc pad pin

3.10B Disc pads reassembled

4　Caliper (ATE type) – removal, overhaul and refitting

1　Raise the front of the vehicle and remove the brake pads (Section 3).
2　Unscrew and remove the caliper fluid union bolt. Plug the union with two suitable grommets or allow the fluid to drain into a container.
3　On earlier models, unscrew the two caliper mounting bolts and withdraw the caliper.
4　On later models remove the caliper from the mounting plate by pressing the caliper inwards at the front (towards the wheel hub) and simultaneously slide the caliper towards the centre of the car.
5　Brush away the external dirt from the caliper unit, *but take care not to inhale the dust.* Secure the caliper in the jaws of a vice. Use soft jaw protectors and take care not to damage or distort the caliper.
6　On earlier models, separate the caliper body from its bracket by sliding it off its splines (Fig. 9.4).
7　Using a screwdriver, prise off the retaining ring from the dust excluder (Fig. 9.5).
8　Remove the dust excluder (Fig. 9.6).
9　Place a thin piece of wood or hardboard on the end of the piston and apply air pressure to the fluid pipe connection on the caliper body. Only low air pressure will be required to eject the piston, such as is generated by a tyre foot pump.
10　Once the piston has been removed, pick out the seal from its groove in the cylinder, using a plastic or wooden instrument.
11　Inspect the surfaces of the piston and cylinder bore for scoring or evidence of metal-to-metal rubbing. If evident, renew the caliper complete.
12　If these components are in good condition, discard the rubber seal and dust excluder and obtain a repair kit which will contain all the necessary replaceable items.
13　On the later type caliper, the location guide rubbers can be removed for renewal if required. Extract the nylon compression sleeve from within each rubber, then carefully compress the sleeve shoulder and push it through to remove it on the inboard side (photos).
14　Clean the piston and cylinder bore with brake hydraulic fluid or methylated spirit – nothing else.
15　Commence reassembly by fitting the seal into the cylinder groove (Fig. 9.7).
16　Locate the dust excluder in its groove in the piston. Dip the piston in clean brake fluid, or apply rubber grease to its external surface, and insert it squarely into the cylinder. Check that the piston step is positioned as shown (Fig. 9.8).
17　When the piston has been partially depressed, engage the dust excluder with the rim of the cylinder and fit the retaining clip.
18　Depress the piston fully into its cylinder bore.
19　If removed from the later type caliper, refit the location rubber and insert the compression sleeve. Take care not to damage the rubber and sleeve during fitting and ensure that the shoulder of the rubber guide bush is fully engaged (photo).
20　On earlier models, secure the caliper bracket in a vice and install the guide springs (Fig. 9.9). Slide the caliper body into the bracket splines until the body and bracket are flush (Fig. 9.10).
21　Refit the caliper to the hub carrier. On earlier models, clean the threads of the mounting bolts and apply thread locking compound.

Fig. 9.4 Separating ATE caliper body from bracket (early type) (Sec 4)

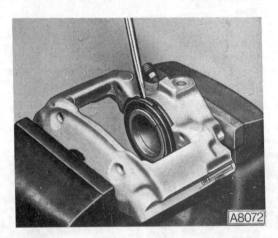

Fig. 9.5 Prising off dust excluder retaining ring (Sec 4)

Screw in the bolts, tighten to the specified torque and then fit the disc pads as described in Section 3. On later models, engage the caliper onto the location pegs and press into position (photo), then fit the disc pads.
22　Connect the fluid hose, using new seals at the union.
23　Bleed the system as described in Section 20.
24　Refit the roadwheel using the alignment marks, and lower the car to the ground. Depress the brake pedal several times to bring the pads up to the disc, then top up the master cylinder if necessary.

4.13A Extract the nylon compression sleeve ...

4.13B ... and withdraw the rubber bush from the caliper (later type)

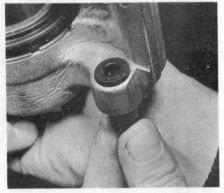

4.19 Location bush refitted to the caliper (later type)

Fig. 9.6 Removing caliper dust excluder (Sec 4)

Fig. 9.7 Engaging dust excluder in piston groove (Sec 4)

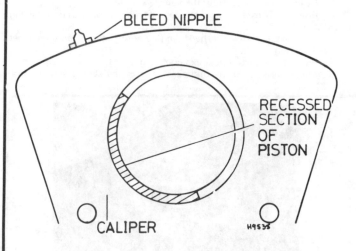

Fig. 9.8 Caliper piston recess setting diagram (Sec 4)

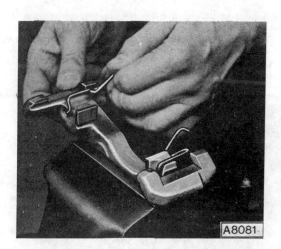

Fig. 9.9 Fitting caliper bracket guide springs (Sec 4)

Fig. 9.10 Caliper body and bracket connected flush –
arrowed (Sec 4)

4.21 Later type caliper unit (ATE type)

5.2 Remove caliper bolt cap (GMF type)

5.4 Unscrew the caliper bolt (GMF type)

5.5 Withdrawing the GMF caliper

5 Caliper (GMF type) – removal, overhaul and refitting

1 Raise the front of the vehicle and remove the roadwheels (see Section 3).
2 Prise off the mounting bolt caps (photo). Do not unscrew the two hexagon-headed bolts, as these connect the caliper body and bracket.
3 Disconnect the fluid line from the caliper and either plug with rubber grommets or allow the fluid to drain into a container.

4 Using an Allen key type wrench, unscrew the two socket-headed mounting bolts (photo).
5 Remove the caliper from the vehicle (photo).
6 Brush away external dust and remove the disc pads as described in Section 3.
7 Using a chisel, release the sliding inner dust caps from the caliper housing (Fig. 9.13).
8 Prise off the piston dust excluder (Fig. 9.14).
9 Apply pressure to the outboard ends of the sliding sleeves until

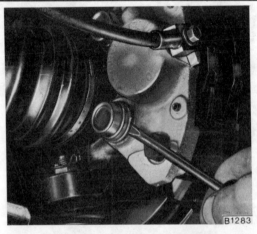

Fig. 9.11 Prising off caliper mounting bolt caps (GMF)
(Sec 5)

Fig. 9.12 Removing socket-head caliper mounting bolt
(GMF) (Sec 5)

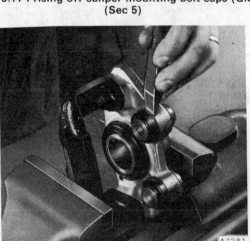

Fig. 9.13 Removing inner dust caps from sliding sleeves
(GMF) (Sec 5)

Fig. 9.14 Prising off piston dust excluder (GMF) (Sec 5)

their dust caps can be disengaged from the sleeve grooves and removed.

10 Press the sliding sleeves from the caliper housing (Fig. 9.15).

11 Carry out the operations described in Section 4, paragraphs 9 to 15.

12 When the piston has been partially inserted, engage the new dust excluder with the groove in the piston.

13 Renew the sealing rings on the sliding sleeves, applying the special grease supplied in the repair kit to the sealing ring grooves. Make sure that the sealing ring is located in the centre groove.

14 Install the sliding sleeves so that the dust cap groove is towards the caliper bracket. Do not push the sleeves fully in at this stage. Install the new dust caps for the sliding sleeves onto their caliper housing collars. Use a piece of tubing to drive them fully home.

15 Depress the piston fully and secure the dust excluder to the housing, driving it fully home with a piece of suitable tubing.

16 Refit the caliper and screw in and tighten the socket-headed mounting bolts, having first cleaned the threads and applied locking compound.

17 Fit the bolt caps.

18 Reconnect the fluid hose using new seals.

19 Refit the disc pads as described in Section 3.

20 Bleed the hydraulic system as described in Section 20.

21 Fit the roadwheels and lower the vehicle.

6 Brake disc – inspection, removal and refitting

1 Raise the front of the vehicle and remove the roadwheel (see Section 3).

2 Inspect the braking surface of the disc for deep grooving or tiny cracks. If these conditions are evident, the disc will have to be renewed or refinished. Any refinishing of both faces of the disc must not reduce the thickness of the disc below the minimum specified. Light, shallow scoring is a normal condition for brake discs.

3 If it is thought that the brake disc is distorted, check it for run-out using a dial gauge or using feeler blades between the disc and a fixed point as the disc is rotated.

4 If the run-out exceeds the specified limit, renew the disc.

5 To remove a brake disc for renewal or refinishing, first withdraw the pads as described in Section 3.

6 Extract the small retaining screw and then tilt the disc and withdraw it from the hub.

7 It is recommended that both brake discs are refinished or renewed at the same time in order to maintain even braking.

8 Refitting is a reversal of removal.

9 On vehicles which are equipped with light alloy roadwheels, a facing sleeve is mounted on the collar of the brake disc.

Fig. 9.15 Removing caliper sliding sleeves (GMF) (Sec 5)

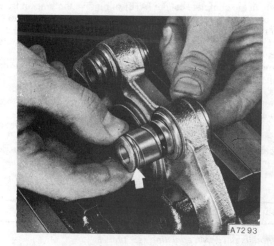

Fig. 9.16 Correct location of sliding sleeve dust cap groove – arrowed (GMF) (Sec 5)

6.6 Removing the brake disc retaining screw

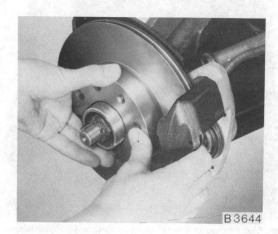

Fig. 9.17 Brake disc removal from hub (Sec 6)

Fig. 9.18 Brake disc facing sleeve (Sec 6)

Fig. 9.19 Unscrewing disc shield bolts (Sec 7)

7 Brake disc shield – removal and refitting

1   Remove the complete caliper (ATE) or remove the bracket from the
caliper body (GMF). It will not be necessary to disconnect the brake
hose at the caliper. However, with the ATE type, ensure that the caliper
is carefully supported to prevent any strain on the hose. Refer to
Section 4 or 5.
2   Remove the brake disc as described in Section 6. Then, working
through the holes in the hub flange, unscrew the disc shield fixing
bolts (Fig. 9.19).
3   Rotate the disc shield until its connecting strip can be cut through
with metal snips. Remove the shield.
4   Before fitting a new shield, cut off the web as shown. Apply some
paint to the cut edge to prevent rusting (Fig. 9.20).
5   Locate the shield so that the cut-out is at the topmost position.
Screw in the fixing bolts.
6   Refit the disc and caliper.

8 Rear brakes (pre 1984 models) – adjustment

Later models have self-adjusting rear brakes
1   Each rear brake shoe is individually adjusted by means of an
eccentric cam.

Fig. 9.20 Cutting web from disc shield (Sec 7)

2   Raise the rear of the vehicle and support it securely. Chock the front
wheels.
3   Release the handbrake fully. Apply the brake hard a couple of times
to centralise the shoes.
4   Turn one hexagon adjuster on the brake backplate while turning
the roadwheel in the normal forward direction until the wheel locks.
Then back it off until the wheel rotates freely without binding (photo).
5   Repeat the adjustment on the second adjuster and then on the two
adjusters on the opposite brake.
6   Lower the vehicle and apply the handbrake.
7   In order to combat corrosion occurring in the adjusters, apply some
lubricant round the hexagon head periodically and apply a little grease
to prevent water penetrating.

9 Rear brake shoes (pre 1984 models) – inspection and renewal

Later models are covered in Section 11

Inspection

1   It is suggested that the brake shoes are inspected when necessary
by removing the drums. This will enable a proper inspection of the
linings to be made, and additionally the wheel cylinders can be

8.4 Rear brake hexagon adjuster – arrowed (pre 1984 models)

inspected for leaks. If preferred, however, a provisional inspection of the state of wear of the rear shoe linings can be observed by removing the plug from the inspection hole in the brake backplate (Fig. 9.21).
2 Use a torch and mirror to check that the friction material has not worn down to less than the specified minimum. If it has then the shoes must be renewed.

Renewal

3 Raise the rear of the vehicle and remove the rear roadwheels (see Section 3). Chock the front wheels. Fully release the handbrake.
4 Extract the drum securing screw and remove the drum. If the drum is tight on the hub, tap it off with a plastic hammer. If the drum is grooved due to wear, the cam adjusters may have to be backed right off before the drum can be pulled off and the shoes cleared from the grooves. Sketch the location of the shoes and which way round the linings are fitted with regard to leading and trailing ends before dismanting them.
5 Disconnect the upper shoe return spring using a pair of pliers.
6 Remove the shoe steady clips. These are of spring wire type, the ends of which should be compressed to release the clip from the brake backplate.
7 Pull the shoes apart until they can be released from the bottom anchorage.
8 Detach the shoe lower return spring and remove the strut from between the shoes (Fig. 9.24).
9 Disconnect the end of the handbrake cable from the lever on the brake shoe and withdraw the shoes. Do not depress the brake pedal while the shoes are off.
10 GM still supply friction linings for fitting to original shoes. This involves drilling out the old rivets to remove the worn linings and using the new rivets supplied with the linings to reline the shoes. Riveting should be done from the centre, working out. Linings available are 5.0 mm (0.197 in) thick for normal use, and 5.6 mm (0.220 in) thick for use where drums have been reground (see also Section 14).
11 Having said all this, it is still recommended that new or factory relined shoes are used as replacements, rather than attempting to reline the shoes yourself.
12 Before installing the new shoes, brush away all dirt and dust, *taking care not to inhale it.*
13 Any signs of oil contamination on the rear brake shoes will be due to a leaking hydraulic wheel cylinder (Section 12) or to a faulty hub oil seal (Chapter 10). Remedy the leak immediately, and renew the shoes.
14 Apply a little high melting-point grease to the adjuster cams and the shoe contact high points on the brake backplate.
15 Lay the shoes out on the bench, making sure that they are correctly located with regard to handbrake lever and shoe lining leading and trailing ends (photo).

Fig. 9.21 Rear backplate inspection hole plug – arrowed (Sec 9)

Fig. 9.22 Removing brake drum securing screw (Sec 9)

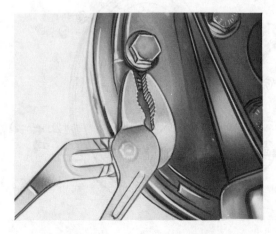

Fig. 9.23 Compressing shoe steady spring (Sec 9)

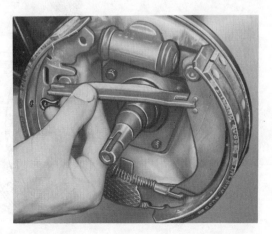

Fig. 9.24 Removing brake shoe strut (Sec 9)

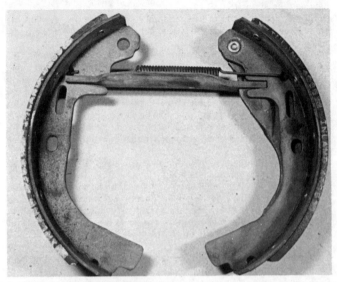

9.15 Rear brake shoes ready for fitting

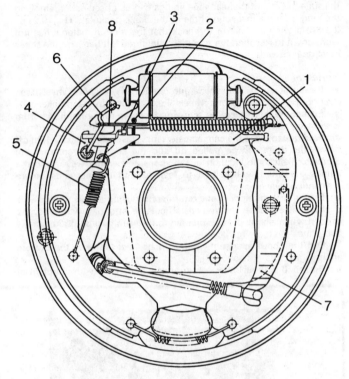

Fig. 9.25 Self-adjusting rear brake components – Saloon and Hatchback (Sec 10)

16 Fit the lower return spring.
17 Pull the shoes apart and engage their lower ends in the anchorage, then attach the handbrake cable.
18 Fit the strut and the shoe return upper spring.
19 Fit new shoe steady spring clips.
20 Refit the brake drum.
21 Adjust the shoes as described in Section 8.
22 Refit the roadwheel.
23 Repeat the operations on the opposite brake as the shoes must be renewed as axle sets (four shoes). Adjust the handbrake on completion if necessary (Section 26).

1 Strut	5 Adjuster lever return spring
2 Thermoclip	6 Return spring bracket
3 Adjuster pinion	7 Handbrake lever
4 Adjuster lever	8 Upper return spring

10 Self-adjusting rear brakes – description

All vehicles from 1984 model year are fitted with self-adjusting rear brakes. There are slight differences between the brakes fitted to Estates and those fitted to other models, but the principles of operation are the same.

The fixed strut fitted between manually adjusted brake shoes is replaced by an adjustable strut consisting of a threaded rod, an adjuster pinion and a half strut. When the shoe-to-drum clearance exceeds a certain value, a spring-loaded adjuster lever advances the pinion as the brakes are operated and the length of the strut is increased.

On all except Estate models, a thermoclip is incorporated in the adjuster strut. This clip expands as the brake drum heats up in use, so avoiding over-adjustment and subsequent lock-up as the brake drum cools.

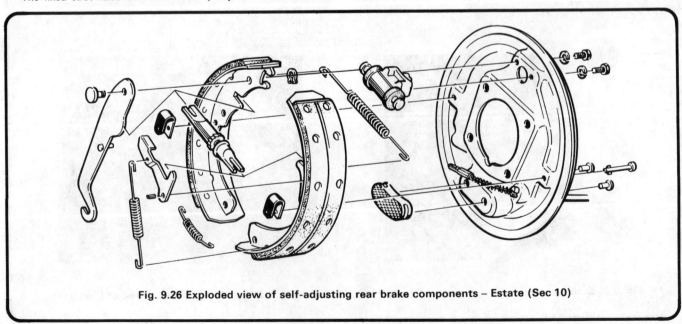

Fig. 9.26 Exploded view of self-adjusting rear brake components – Estate (Sec 10)

11 Self-adjusting rear brakes – inspection and renewal

Inspection

1   Proceed as described in paragraphs 1 and 2 of Section 9.
2   Chock the front wheels and engage a gear. Slacken the rear wheel nuts on the side being worked on, then jack up the rear of the car and remove the wheel. Release the handbrake.
3   Remove the brake drum securing screw and pull off the drum. If it is tight, collapse the brake shoes by removing the plug in the brake backplate and pushing the handbrake operating lever outwards with a screwdriver (Fig. 9.27).
4   Remove the steady pins and clips or springs and washers. Renew them if they are damaged (photos).
5   Disconnect the handbrake cable from the operating lever (photo). If there is insufficient slack in the cable, disconnect it at the equaliser.
6   The return springs may be unhooked now and the shoes removed separately, or the assembly of shoes, strut and springs may be removed together. The second course is particularly easy if the rear hub is removed, as has been done for photographic purposes here. Be careful not to damage the wheel cylinder rubber boots.
7   Clean the brake backplate, *being careful not to inhale the dust or disperse it into the air.* (Original equipment linings are now asbestos-free, but the same will not necessarily be true of aftermarket linings.)
8   Investigate and rectify any source of contamination of the linings before fitting the new shoes.
9   Dismantle the shoes, strut and springs. Note how the springs are fitted, and which way round the strut goes. Be careful not to interchange left-hand and right-hand adjuster components: on all except Estate models, the threaded rod is marked 'L' or 'R', and the other 'handed' components are colour-coded black for the left-hand side and silver for the right (photo).
10 Dismantle and clean the adjusting strut. Apply a smear of silicone-based lubricant to the adjuster threads.
11 If a new brake shoe handbrake lever was not supplied with the new

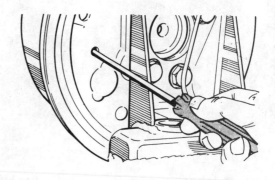

Fig. 9.27 Release the handbrake lever by pushing a screwdriver through the hole (Sec 11)

shoes, transfer the old lever. It may be secured with a pin and circlip (photo), or by a rivet which will have to be drilled out.
12 Assemble the new shoes, springs and adjuster components. Transfer the shoe return springs to their correct holes in the new shoes and locate the self-adjuster components. The threaded strut should be clean and lightly greased and fully retracted by turning the star wheel before fitting it between the shoes. Note that the shorter leg of the strut fork should be towards you. On Saloon and Hatchback variants, the cup spring securing the adjuster lever pivot pin on the shoe web should be renewed. Refer to the appropriate accompanying photographs for the reassembly details.
13 Prior to reassembling the brake shoe assemblies to their fitted positions, apply a smear of copper-based anti-seize compound, or other suitable product, to the shoe rubbing areas on the brake backplate.

11.4A Brake shoe steady clip (Estate). Twist retainer (arrowed) 90° ...

11.4B ... and remove the clip

11.5 Disconnect the handbrake cable

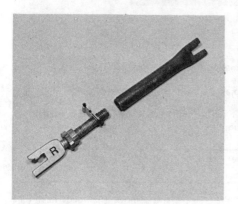

11.9 Self-adjusting strut components – right-hand side

11.11 Handbrake lever secured by pin and circlip

11.12A Fitting the adjuster lever (Estate)

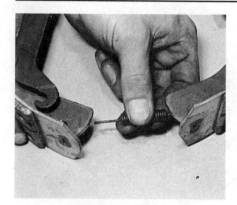

11.12B Fitting the lower return spring (Estate)

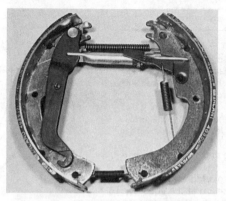

11.12C Rear brake components ready for refitting (Estate)

11.12D Self-adjusting strut correctly fitted (Saloon/Hatchback)

11.12E Fitting the upper return spring (Saloon/Hatchback)

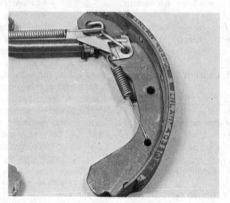

11.12F Adjuster lever spring fitted (Saloon/Hatchback)

11.14A Fitting rear brake components (Estate)

11.14B Rear brake components installed – hub removed for clarity (Saloon/Hatchback)

12.2 Brake drum retaining screw

14 Offer the shoes to the brake backplate. Be careful not to damage the wheel cylinder boots or to displace the pistons. When the shoes are in position, insert and secure the steady pins. Reconnect the handbrake cable, and refit and adjust the hub if it was removed (photos).

15 If fitting the shoes and springs together is found too difficult, it is possible to fit the shoes and secure them with the steady pins, then to introduce the adjuster strut and fit the springs and adjuster lever.

16 Back off the adjuster pinion to reduce the length of the strut until the brake drum will pass over the new linings. Make sure that the handbrake lever is correctly positioned (pin on the edge of the shoe web, not riding on top of it). Refit and secure the brake drum.

17 Repeat the operations on the other rear brake, then adjust the brakes by operating the footbrake (Saloon/Hatchback) or the handbrake (Estate) at least ten times. A clicking noise will be heard at

the drums as the automatic adjusters operate; when the clicking stops, adjustment is complete.

18 Check the handbrake adjustment and correct it if necessary (Section 26).

19 When new linings have been fitted, exercise restraint in braking for a few hundred miles until the linings have bedded-in.

12 Rear brake wheel cylinder – removal, overhaul and refitting

1 Raise the rear of the vehicle and remove the roadwheel (see Section 3).

2 Extract the securing screw and pull off the brake drum. Back off the brake adjusters if necessary (photo).

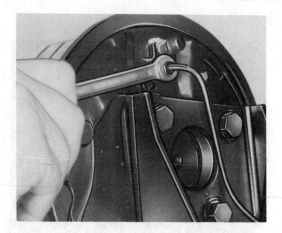

Fig. 9.28 Unscrewing rear wheel cylinder pipeline union (Sec 12)

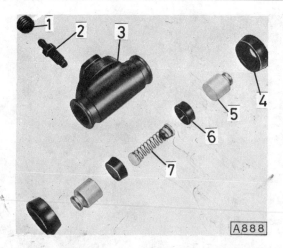

Fig. 9.29 Exploded view of a rear wheel cylinder (Sec 12)

1 Dust cap
2 Bleed screw
3 Cylinder
4 Dust excluder
5 Piston
6 Seal
7 Spring

3 Using a pair of pliers, disconnect the shoe upper return spring and push the upper ends of the shoes apart until they clear the wheel cylinder.
4 Disconnect the fluid pipe from the wheel cylinder and cap the end of the pipe as soon as the union is unscrewed to prevent loss of fluid. A bleed nipple dust cap is useful for this job.
5 Unscrew the mounting bolts and withdraw the cylinder from the backplate.
6 Clean away external dirt and pull off the rubber dust excluders from the cylinder body.
7 The pistons will normally be ejected by pressure of the coil spring but if they are not, tap the end of the cylinder on a piece of hardwood or apply low air pressure from a tyre foot pump at the pipeline connection.
8 Inspect the surfaces of the piston and the cylinder bore for rust, scoring or metal-to-metal rubbed areas. If these are evident, renew the wheel cylinder complete.
9 If these components are in good order, discard the seals and dust excluders and obtain a repair kit which will contain all the renewable items.
10 Fit the piston seals (using the fingers only to manipulate them into position) so that the spring is between them. Dip the pistons in clean hydraulic fluid and insert them into the cylinder.
11 Fit the dust excluders.
12 Refit the wheel cylinder to the backplate and connect the pipeline.
13 Engage the brake shoes with the pistons and fit the shoe return spring.
14 Fit the brake drum and adjust the shoes where applicable (see Section 8).
15 Bleed the hydraulic system as described in Section 20.
16 Refit the roadwheel and lower the vehicle.

13 Rear brake backplate – removal and refitting

1 Raise the rear of the vehicle and remove the roadwheel and the brake drum.
2 Remove the brake shoes as described in Section 9 or 11.
3 Using a screwdriver, prise up the lockplate which secures the handbrake cable in the plastic sleeve in the backplate.
4 Tap off the hub dust cap.
5 Extract the split pin and unscrew and remove the castellated nut and thrust washer.
6 Withdraw the hub from the axle shaft.
7 Disconnect the pipeline from the wheel cylinder by unscrewing the union. Cap the end of the pipe to prevent loss of fluid.
8 Unbolt and remove the wheel cylinder.
9 Unscrew the backplate mounting bolts and remove the plate with the stub axle.
10 Refitting is a reversal of removal, but observe the following points.
11 As the brake backplate bolts secure the stub axle to the rear axle flange, new bolts must be used. Reference should be made to Chapter

10, Section 16 for details of precautions and the tightening procedure.
12 Adjust the hub bearings as described in Chapter 10.
13 Adjust the brake shoes, where applicable (Section 8).
14 Bleed the hydraulic system (Section 20).

14 Brake drum – inspection and renovation

1 Whenever the rear drums are removed, brush away internal dust *taking care not to inhale it*, and inspect the lining rubbing surface. If the shoes have worn grooves in the metal, then it may be possible to re-grind the inside provided the maximum internal diameter is not exceeded (refer to Specifications). Light grooving is normal and requires no attention (see also Section 9, paragraph 10).
2 If the drum is suspected of being out-of-round, it should be renewed.

15 Brake master cylinder – removal and refitting

1 Unscrew the cap from the fluid reservoir and place it to one side complete with float and level warning switch (photo).

15.1 Master cylinder and vacuum servo unit (pre 1985 models)

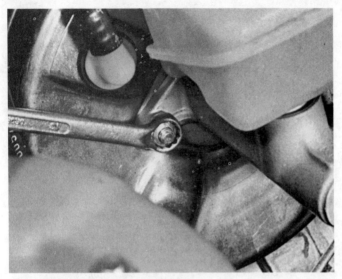

15.6 Unbolting the master cylinder from the servo unit (post 1985 models)

2   Syphon out as much fluid as possible from the reservoir using an old (clean) battery hydrometer or similar.
3   Release the cable retainer from around the master cylinder body (where applicable).
4   Disconnect the fluid pipelines from the master cylinder by unscrewing the unions.
5   Two pressure regulating valves are screwed into the master cylinder and these should now be unscrewed.
6   Unbolt the master cylinder from the brake vacuum servo unit (booster) (photo).
7   If the reason for removal was to renew the master cylinder, then retain the fluid reservoir for fitting to the new cylinder. To remove the reservoir from ATE type master cylinders, simply pull it from the rubber seals. On GMF type master cylinders, the fixing clips will first have to be pushed back with a screwdriver.
8   Refitting is a reversal of removal, use new reservoir rubber seals and tighten all bolts to the specified torque.
9   Bleed the complete hydraulic system as described in Section 20.

16 Master cylinder (ATE type) – overhaul

When overhauling the master cylinder unit, two types of repair kit are available. One is the 'loose' seal type kit and the other more recently obtainable kit is one where the secondary piston comes ready assembled in a special tube which is used for fitting the piston. Proceed as applicable according to type as follows
1   With the unit removed from the vehicle, clean away external dirt.
2   Prise the fluid reservoir from the cylinder body.
3   Extract the circlip from the end of the cylinder housing. To do this, the primary piston should be slightly depressed with a rod to relieve the tension on the circlip.
4   Withdraw the primary piston, noting which way the seals are fitted.
5   Insert a rod and depress the secondary piston so that the stop screw can be removed from the cylinder body (Fig. 9.33).
6   Withdraw the secondary piston by tapping the end of the cylinder on a block of hardwood. Note which way the seals are fitted.
7   Examine the surfaces of the pistons and the cylinder bore for rust, scoring or metal-to-metal rubbed areas. If evident, renew the master cylinder complete.
8   If the components are in good order, clean them in hydraulic fluid or methylated spirit – nothing else.
9   Obtain a repair kit which will contain all the necessary replaceable items.

Loose seal kit overhaul procedure

10 Install the new seals to the pistons, manipulating them into position with the fingers only. It is essential that the new seals are fitted the same way round as the old ones; they are tapered and will only

Fig. 9.30 Reservoir removal from ATE type master cylinder (Sec 16)

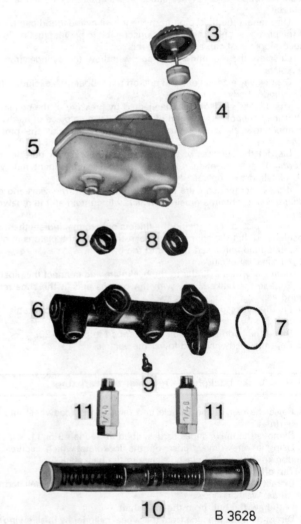

Fig. 9.31 Exploded view of ATE master cylinder (Sec 16)

3 Reservoir cap	8 Plug
4 Float guide sleeve	9 Stop screw
5 Reservoir	10 Packaged repair kit
6 Cylinder body	11 Pressure regulating valve
7 O-ring	

Fig. 9.32 Removing master cylinder primary piston (ATE) (Sec 16)

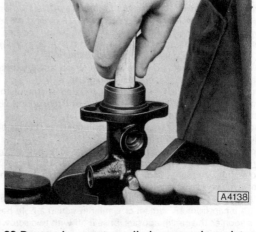

Fig. 9.33 Depressing master cylinder secondary piston (ATE) (Sec 16)

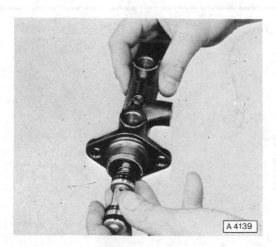

Fig. 9.34 Removing secondary piston (ATE) (Sec 16)

function correctly if fitted the right way round.

11 Reassembly is a reversal of dismantling. Take great care not to trap or cut the lips of the piston seal as the pistons are entered into the cylinder bores. Dip each component in clean hydraulic fluid before assembling. Always fit a new circlip from the repair kit.

12 Fit new rubber sealing rings and press the fluid reservoir into position on the cylinder body.

13 Pour some clean fluid into the reservoir and prime the master cylinder before installation by depressing the primary piston several times with a rod. A great deal of fluid will of course be ejected from the open ports of the cylinder.

Preassembled kit overhaul procedure

14 Lubricate the cylinder with brake fluid or brake rubber grease.

15 Clamp the cylinder in a soft-jawed vice with the bore more or less horizontal. Screw in the stop screw a little way, but not so far that it protrudes into the bore.

16 Remove the large plug from the assembly tube. Remove all the components from the short part of the tube and push the short part into the long part until they are flush.

17 Insert the assembly tube into the cylinder bore as far as the collar on the short sleeve. Use a blunt rod to push the secondary piston into the bore until it contacts the end of the cylinder. Nip up the stop screw, withdraw the rod and sleeve and tighten the stop screw fully.

18 Reposition the master cylinder in the vice with the bore opening facing upwards.

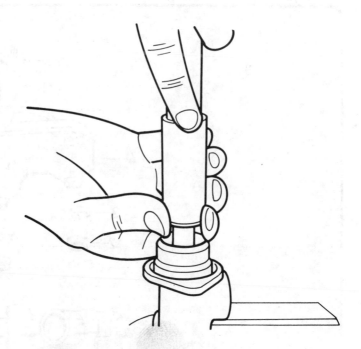

Fig. 9.35 Using the assembly tube to fit the primary piston assembly (ATE) (Sec 16)

19 Smear the primary piston skirt and seal grooves with the special grease provided in the repair kit. Fit the stop washer to the piston.

20 Adjust the assembly tube so that the end of the long part is flush with the inner shoulder of the short part.

21 Fit the front seal to the primary piston with the open end of the seal facing the front of the master cylinder. Place the assembly tube over the cylinder to compress the seal, insert the piston and tube part way into the bore and withdraw the tube.

22 Place the intermediate ring on the primary piston, then fit the other seal using the assembly tube in a similar manner.

23 Place the end washer on the primary piston, then depress the piston slightly and fit the circlip. Make sure that the circlip is properly seated and that the piston is free to move.

24 Fit new sealing rings and press the fluid reservoir into position.

25 Prime the cylinder by pouring clean brake fluid into the reservoir and working the pistons with a rod until fluid is ejected from all orifices.

17 Master cylinder (GMF type) – overhaul

When overhauling the master cylinder unit, two types of repair kit are available. One is the 'loose' seal type kit and the other more recently obtainable kit is one where the secondary piston comes ready assembled in a special tube which is used for fitting the piston. Proceed as applicable according to type as follows.

1 With the unit removed from the vehicle, clean away external dirt and remove the reservoir (Section 15, paragraph 7).
2 Insert a rod into the end of the cylinder and depress the piston until it can be held depressed by inserting a smooth pin or rod 3.0 mm (0.118 in) in diameter through the primary outlet.
3 Extract the circlip from the end of the cylinder using circlip pliers or screwdrivers. Discard the circlip (Fig. 9.37).
4 Remove the primary piston after first having pulled out the temporary retaining pin. Note which way the seals are fitted.
5 Remove the secondary piston by tapping the end of the cylinder on a piece of hardwood. Note which way the seals are fitted.
6 Dismantle the primary piston. This can be done by compressing the spring with a cap from an aerosol or similar in which a hole has been drilled. As soon as the circlip appears, prise it off with two screwdrivers and discard it.
7 Examine the surfaces of the pistons and the cylinder bore for scoring or metal-to-metal rubbed areas. If evident, renew the master

cylinder complete.
8 If the components are in good order, clean them in hydraulic fluid or methylated spirit – nothing else.
9 Obtain a repair kit which will contain all the necessary replaceable items.

Loose seal kit overhaul procedures

10 Install the seals to the pistons, manipulating them into position with the fingers only. It is essential that the new seals are fitted the same way round as the old ones; they are tapered and will only function correctly if fitted the right way round.
11 Reassemble the primary piston using a new circlip. The circlip can be fully installed into its groove in the piston by tapping it down with a piece of tubing.
12 Dip the pistons in clean hydraulic fluid and fit the secondary piston, followed by the primary piston, into the cylinder.
13 Depress and hold the primary piston as described for dismantling while a new circlip is fitted.
14 Fit new rubber sealing rings and press the fluid reservoir into position on the cylinder body.
15 Pour some clean fluid into the reservoir and prime the master cylinder before installation by depressing the primary piston several times with a rod. A great deal of the fluid will of course be ejected from the open ports of the cylinder.

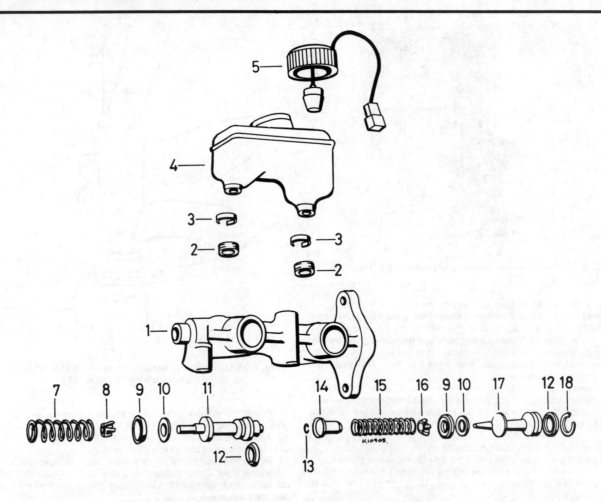

Fig. 9.36 Exploded view of GMF master cylinder (Sec 17)

1 Body	7 Spring	12 Primary seals	16 Spring retainer
2 Reservoir sealing rings	8 Spring retainer	13 Circlip	17 Primary piston
3 Circlips	9 Secondary piston seals	14 Spring sleeve	18 Circlip
4 Reservoir	10 Shim	15 Primary piston spring	
5 Cap with warning switch	11 Secondary piston		

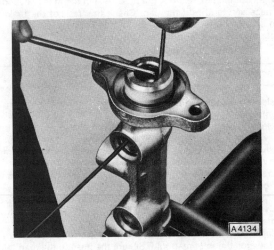

Fig. 9.37 Extracting master cylinder circlip (GMF) (Sec 17)

Fig. 9.38 Removing master cylinder primary piston circlip (GMF) (Sec 17)

Preassembled kit overhaul procedure

16 Lubricate the cylinder bore with brake fluid or brake rubber grease. Clamp the cylinder with the bore horizontal.

17 Remove the plug from the assembly tube and insert the short part of the tube into the cylinder bore as far as the shoulder on the tube. Use a blunt rod to push the piston out of the tube and into the bore; retain the pistons in the bore with the smooth rod or needle used when dismantling. Withdraw the rod and the tube.

18 Fit a new circlip to the end of the cylinder. Depress the primary piston and withdraw the retaining rod or needle. Make sure that the circlip is properly seated and that the pistons are free to move.

19 Fit new sealing rings and press the reservoir into positon.

20 Prime the cylinder, as described for the ATE type in the previous Section (paragraph 25).

18 Pressure regulating valves

1 The pressure regulating valves are screwed into the master cylinder, one valve for each diagonally split hydraulic circuit.

2 The purpose of these valves is to restrict pressure to the rear wheels during heavy braking to prevent rear wheel lock up.

3 No adjustment of the valve is possible and if it is suspected that a valve is faulty then it must be renewed. The valve operating pressure can be tested by your dealer using special equipment.

4 Refer to Section 15 for details of removal and refitting of the valves.

5 If renewing one valve, make sure that it has the same pressure reference number as the matching valve.

19 Flexible hoses and rigid pipelines – inspection and renewal

1 Periodically inspect the condition of the flexible brake hoses. If they appear swollen, chafed or when bent double with the fingers tiny cracks are visible, then they must be renewed.

2 Always uncouple the rigid pipe from the flexible hose first, then release the end of the flexible hose from the support bracket. To do this, pull out the lockplate using a pair of pliers.

3 Now unscrew the flexible hose from the caliper or connector. On calipers, a banjo type hose connector is used. When installing the hose, always use a new sealing washer.

4 When installation is complete, check that the flexible hose does not rub against the tyre or other adjacent components. Its attitude may be altered to overcome this by pulling out the clip at the support bracket and twisting the hose in the required direction by not more than one quarter turn.

5 Bleed the hydraulic system (Section 20).

Fig. 9.39 Unscrewing pipeline union at connection with flexible hose (Sec 19)

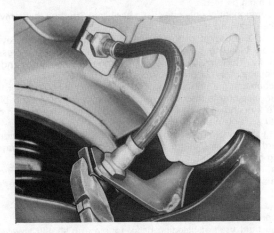

Fig. 9.40 Removing flexible hose retaining clip from support bracket (Sec 19)

Fig. 9.41 Unscrewing caliper hose banjo union bolt (Sec 19)

6   At regular intervals wipe the steel brake pipes clean and examine them for signs of rust or denting caused by flying stones.
7   Examine the fit of the pipes in their insulated securing clips and bend the tongues of the clips if necessary to secure a positive fit.
8   Check that the pipes are not touching any adjacent components or rubbing against any part of the vehicle. Where this is observed, bend the pipe gently away to clear.
9   Any section of pipe which is rusty or chafed should be renewed. Brake unions are available to the correct length and fitted with end unions from most dealers and can be made to pattern by many accessory suppliers. When installing the new pipes use the old pipes as a guide to bending and do not make any bends sharper than is necessary.
10 The system will of course have to be bled when the circuit has been reconnected.

20 Hydraulic system – bleeding

1   The two independant hydraulic circuits are as follows:

   (a) Front right-hand caliper and left rear wheel cylinder
   (b) Front left-hand caliper and right rear wheel cylinder

2   If the master cylinder or the pressure regulating valve has been disconnected and reconnected then the complete system (both circuits) must be bled.
3   If a component of only one circuit has been disturbed then only the particular circuit need be bled.
4   Due to the design of the hydraulic system and pipeline layout, satisfactory bleeding can only only be carried out using a pressure bleeding kit. These are available from motor accessory shops and are usually operated by air pressure from the spare tyre.
5   By connecting a pressurised container to the master cylinder fluid reservoir, bleeding is then carried out by simply opening each bleed nipple in turn and allowing the fluid to run out, rather like turning on a tap, until no air is visible in the fluid.
6   Using this system, the large reserve of hydraulic fluid provides a safeguard against air being drawn into the master cylinder during the bleeding operation.
7   This method is particularly effective when bleeding 'difficult' systems and when bleeding the entire system at time of routine fluid renewal.
8   Bleed the front brakes first followed by the rear ones.
9   Discard fluid bled from the system.
10 Fresh fluid used at bleeding or for topping-up should always be stored in an airtight container and remain unshaken for 24 hours before use.
11 During pressure bleeding it is permissible to depress the brake pedal slowly two or three times as an aid to expelling any trapped air.

12 When completed, recheck the fluid level in the master cylinder, top up if necessary and refit the cap. Check the 'feel' of the brake pedal which should be firm and free from any 'sponginess' which would indicate air still present in the system.

21 Vacuum servo unit hose – renewal

1   Release the union nut on the inlet manifold and disconnect the vacuum hose.
2   Release the hose from the connector at the servo unit by unscrewing the clip. If the hose is of shrink-fit type, do not apply excessive force but rather ease the elbow from the rubber grommet in the servo shell.
3   Carefully cut a new length of servo hose to length allowing for the inclusion of the non-return valve.
4   Remove the non-return valve by cutting the hose lengthwise from the valve, but take care not to damage the valve. Cut the hose from the inlet manifold and servo unit connectors.
5   Reassemble making sure that the arrows on the non-return valve point towards the inlet manifold. Secure the hose to the manifold pipe with a clip.

Fig. 9.42 Unscrewing servo vacuum hose union from inlet manifold – arrowed (Sec 21)

21.1 Servo hose connection at manifold

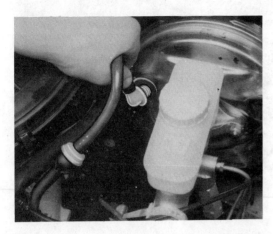

Fig. 9.43 Vacuum hose connection at servo unit (Sec 21)

22 Vacuum servo unit (booster) – testing for faulty operation

1 With the engine switched off, depress the foot brake pedal several times then hold it down. Start the engine when the pedal should be felt to move downward a little. If it does not, check the vacuum hose and connections for leaks.
2 If a leak cannot be found then an internal fault in the servo unit must be suspected. The servo unit should not be dismantled, but if faulty, renew it.

23 Vacuum servo unit – removal and refitting

Pre 1985 models
1 Remove the air cleaner from the carburettor complete with ducting and hoses.
2 Disconnect the vacuum hose from the inlet manifold by unscrewing the union nut.
3 Disconnect the vacuum hose from the servo unit.
4 Disconnect the lead for the low level warning lamp switch on the master cylinder fluid reservoir.
5 Unbolt the master cylinder from the servo unit.
6 Carefully pull the master cylinder from the servo unit as far as the flexibility of the hydraulic pipelines will allow.
7 Working inside the vehicle, remove the cover located under the facia panel to provide access to the remote control support mounting nuts and bolt located on the inner face of the bulkhead (Fig. 9.46).
8 Unscrew and remove the nuts and the bolt.
9 Disconnect the brake pedal return spring.

10 Extract the circlip from the brake pedal arm clevis pin, press out the pin to separate the pedal arm from under the servo unit pushrod.
11 Still working under the facia panel, unscrew the nuts which secure the brake pedal support bracket (Fig. 9.47).
12 Working within the engine compartment, withdraw the servo unit and the brake remote control assembly from the bulkhead (Fig. 9.48).
13 Secure the remote control rod support in a vice.
14 Prise off the spring leg of the bellcrank lever (Fig. 9.49). Then extract the circlip and take off the spring (Fig. 9.50).
15 Tap out the lock pin which retains the bellcrank pivot (Fig. 9.51).
16 Remove the bellcrank pivot.
17 Extract the circlip from the remote control rod eye pivot.
18 Remove the pivot to separate the remote control unit from the bellcrank lever at the servo unit (Fig. 9.53).
19 Unscrew the mounting nuts and disconnect the servo unit from the remote control rod support (Fig. 9.54).
20 Support the servo unit and unscrew the nut from the bellcrank lever mounting (Fig 9.55).
21 Remove the bellcrank lever by unscrewing it from the servo unit pushrod.
22 Reassembly is a reversal of dismantling, but apply grease to the bellcrank lever pivots and carry out the following adjustments. All nuts and bolts must be tightened to the specified torque wrench settings.
23 Pull the remote control rod fully towards the brake servo unit. Measure the lengths (A) of exposed thread on the rod as shown. (Fig. 9.57).
24 If adjustment is required, release the remote control rod locknut and rotate the rod. Once correctly adjusted, fit the dust excluder to the front of the pivot housing.
25 Having installed the assembly to the bulkhead, go inside the vehicle and release the pedal pushrod locknut.
26 Connect the clevis fork of the pushrod to the brake pedal arm.
27 Rotate the pushrod until the pedal arm just rests on the rubber stop.

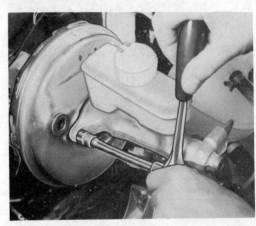

Fig. 9.44 Unbolting the master cylinder from servo unit (Sec 23)

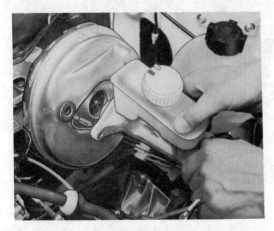

Fig. 9.45 Withdrawing master cylinder from servo unit (Sec 23)

Fig. 9.46 Remote control support mounting nuts and bolts – arrowed (Sec 23)

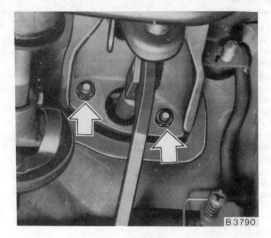

Fig. 9.47 Brake pedal support bracket nuts – arrowed (Sec 23)

Fig. 9.48 Removing remote control and servo unit from bulkhead (Sec 23)

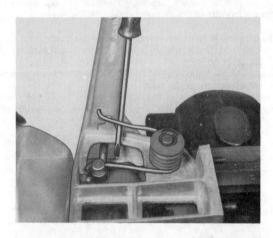

Fig. 9.49 Releasing leg of bellcrank lever spring (Sec 23)

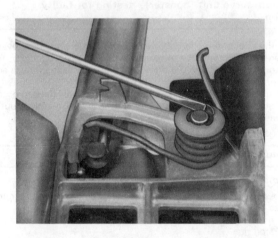

Fig. 9.50 Removing spring circlip (Sec 23)

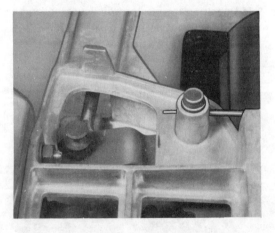

Fig. 9.51 Drive out bellcrank pivot lockpin (Sec 23)

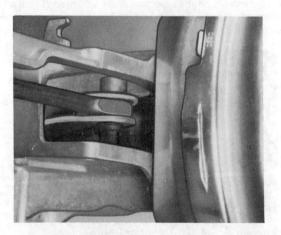

Fig. 9.52 Remote control rod pivot at servo (Sec 23)

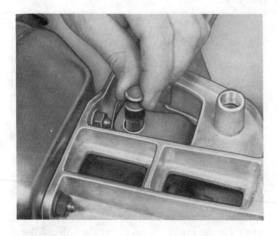

Fig. 9.53 Removing pivot at servo (Sec 23)

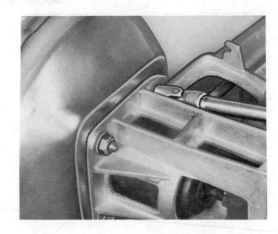

Fig. 9.54 Removing servo mounting nuts (Sec 23)

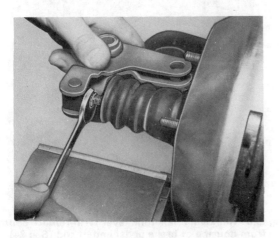

Fig. 9.55 Servo bellcrank lever nut (Sec 23)

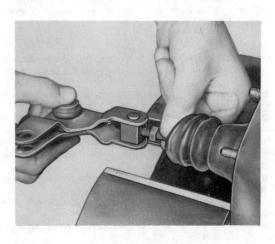

Fig. 9.56 Disconnecting bellcrank lever from servo unit pushrod (Sec 23)

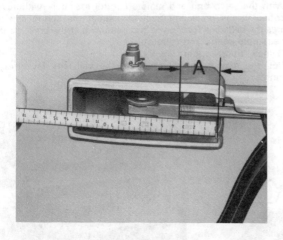

Fig. 9.57 Remote control rod thread measuring diagram (Sec 23)

A = 28.5 to 29.5 mm (1.12 to 1.16 in)

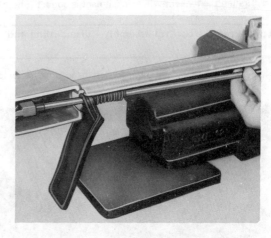

Fig. 9.58 Brake pedal pivot housing dust excluder (Sec 23)

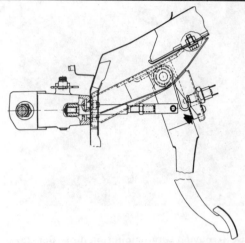

Fig. 9.59 Brake pedal setting diagram. Rubber stop is arrowed (Sec 23)

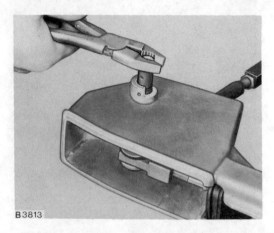

Fig. 9.60 Extracting bellcrank lever pivot pin (Sec 24)

Tighten the pushrod locknut and then fit the pedal return spring.

28 Fit the master cylinder to the servo unit and reconnect the vacuum hose and the low fluid level warning lamp.

Post 1985 models

29 From 1985 model year, the servo and master cylinder are mounted on the right-hand side of the bulkhead. To remove the servo, proceed as follows.

30 Remove the air cleaner for ease of access if necessary, and disconnect the vacuum hose from the servo (photo).

31 Remove the two nuts which secure the master cylinder to the servo. Disconnect the wires from the fluid level warning switch and carefully pull the master cylinder forwards until it clears the servo studs. Take care not to strain the hydraulic pipes; if necessary, release them from their clips on the bulkhead.

32 Inside the car, remove the cover from above the pedals. The cover is secured by clips and a strap.

33 Disconnect the return spring and the servo pushrod clevis from the brake pedal.

34 Still working inside the car, remove the four nuts which secure the servo bracket to the bulkhead.

35 Remove the servo and bracket from the engine bay by pulling the servo forwards and lifting it out. Do not displace the master cylinder further than necessary.

36 If the servo is to be renewed, unbolt it from its bracket.

37 Refit in the reverse order to removal. If a new servo has been fitted, adjust the servo pushrod at the clevis to give 1.0 mm (0.04 in) free play at the pedal. Tighten the locknut when adjustment is correct (photo).

24 Brake pedal remote control assembly – dismantling and reassembly

1 The vehicle was originally designed for left-hand drive steering,

Fig. 9.61 Removing bellcrank lever with remote control from housing at brake pedal end of rod (Sec 24)

therefore on pre 1985 right-hand drive versions, the brake pedal is connected to the vacuum servo unit by a remote control rod and bellcrank arrangement. This assembly enables force from the driver's foot to be transmitted to the left-hand side of the engine compartment where the vacuum servo unit and master cylinder are situated.

2 With the servo unit and remote control assembly withdrawn, as described in the preceding Section, extract the spring clip which secures the bellcrank lever pivot in the housing at the brake pedal end of the remote control rod (photo).

3 Remove the pivot pin (Fig. 9.60).

4 Pull the remote control rod with the bellcrank lever from the housing.

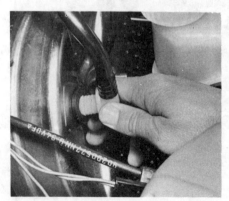

23.30 Disconnecting the servo vacuum hose (post 1985 models)

23.37 Servo clevis and locknut (arrowed). Note seal putty on bracket flange

24.2 Bellcrank lever pivot spring clip – arrowed (pre 1985 models)

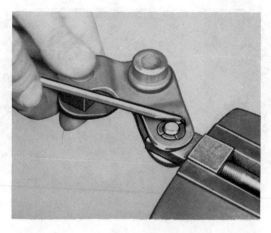

Fig. 9.62 Removing circlip to separate bellcrank lever from remote control rod (Sec 24)

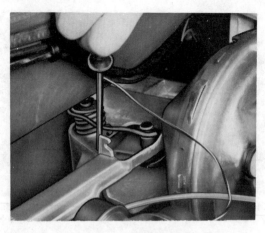

Fig. 9.63 Releasing bellcrank lever spring at servo end of remote control rod (Sec 25)

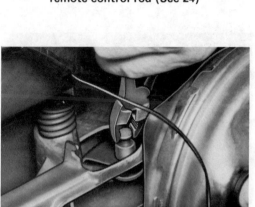

Fig. 9.64 Removing bellcrank pivot with pliers (Sec 25)

Fig. 9.65 Unscrewing remote control rod from bellcrank lever trunnion (Sec 25)

5   The bellcrank lever can be separated from the remote control rod after extracting the circlip.

6   The bellcrank lever is renewable complete with pedal pushrod.

7   Reassembly is a reversal of dismantling, apply grease to the pivots and adjust the remote control rod as described in Section 23, paragraphs 23 and 24.

25 Brake pedal remote control rod – removal and refitting

1   Removal of the brake vacuum servo unit and the remote control assembly for pre 1985 models is described in earlier Sections. The following operations will enable the remote control rod to be removed independently from the vehicle should it be necessary to renew either the rod or bellcrank levers in the event of wear occurring in pivot bolts or bushes.

2   Remove the air cleaner for ease of access if necessary.

3   Working at the servo end of the remote control rod, prise off the spring leg and release the return spring (Fig. 9.63).

4   Extract the spring clip and pull out the pivot to release the remote control rod and bellcrank lever. Use pliers to remove the pivot (Fig. 9.64).

5   Working at the brake pedal end of the remote control rod, pull off the rubber cover from the bellcrank lever housing.

6   Rotate the remote control rod to unscrew it from the trunnion on the bellcrank lever (Fig. 9.65).

7   Screw the new rod into the trunnion, making sure that the dust excluding bellows are fitted to the rod.

8   Connect the remote control rod to the bellcrank lever at the servo unit.

9   Fit the pivot and spring clip. Reconnect the spring.

10   Check and adjust the remote control rod setting as described in Section 23, paragraphs 23 and 24.

11   Refit the components removed at the commencement of operations.

26 Handbrake – adjustment

1   The handbrake will normally be kept in correct adjustment by the routine adjustment of the rear shoes. However, due to cable stretch over a period of time, the travel of the handbrake lever may become excessive and the following operations should be carried out.

2   On pre 1984 models ensure that the brake shoes are fully adjusted by means of their backplate adjusters (see Section 8).

3   Raise the rear of the vehicle so that the rear roadwheels are free to turn.

4   Pull the handbrake control lever onto its first notch.

5   Using two spanners, adjust the cable by turning the nuts on the threaded part of the cable end fitting. This is located on or above the rear axle beam. After adjusting, the brake linings should just be heard to rub when the rear wheels are turned by hand in the normal rotational direction (photo).

6   Adjustment is now correct. Keep the threads of the cable end fitting smeared with grease to prevent corrosion.

7   Lower the vehicle.

26.5A Handbrake cable equaliser/adjuster
– early models

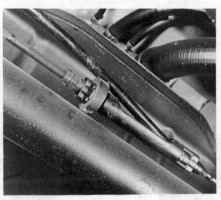

26.5B Handbrake cable equaliser/adjuster
– later models

27.4 Short handbrake cable and grommets
(arrowed) – later models

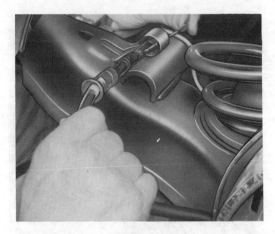

Fig. 9.66 Releasing handbrake cable from rear axle guide
(Sec 27)

Fig. 9.67 Longer cable end fitting (Sec 27)

27 Handbrake cables – renewal

1 Pull the handbrake control lever to the second notch of its ratchet.
2 Raise the rear of the vehicle and remove the roadwheels and the brake drums.

Shorter cable
3 Measure the length of exposed thread at the cable end fitting for ease of refitting and then unscrew the adjuster nut from the cable at the equaliser.
4 Detach the cable from its guide on the rear axle. On later models (1985 on) the handbrake cable guide tube was deleted and the cable routed through two grommets, held in position by a bracket welded to the rear axle. In this instance, detach the cable from the grommets (photo). **Note:** When ordering new cables. It is important to quote chassis numbers, so that the correct cables are supplied.
5 Press out the cable sleeve from the brake backplate.
6 Unhook the handbrake cable from the shoe and pull the cable through the backplate.

Longer cable.
7 Unscrew the nut from the threaded end fitting on the cable equaliser.
8 Detach the cable from the guide on the underbody. Bend the guide retaining tabs as necessary.
9 Detach the cable from the equaliser and the guide or grommets (as applicable – see paragraph 4) on the rear axle.
10 Disconnect the cable from the brake shoe.

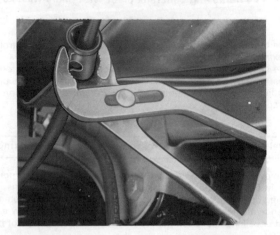

Fig. 9.68 Bend cable guide retaining tab (Sec 27)

11 Press out the cable sleeve from the backplate and withdraw the cable after disconnecting it from the extension piece on the handbrake lever pull rod (photo).

Both cables
12 Refitting of both cables is a reversal of removal. Check and adjust the cables as described in the preceding Section having first set the shorter cable end fitting to the measurement determined before removing.

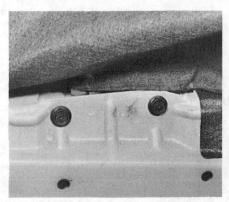

27.11 Handbrake lever control rod/cable extension piece

28.7 Handbrake lever mounting bolts

29.1 Handbrake lever withdrawn to show warning light switch location and retaining bolt (arrowed)

28 Handbrake lever – removal, overhaul and refitting

1   Disconnect the shorter handbrake cable from the equaliser on the rear axle beam, after noting the length of exposed thread at the cable end fitting.
2   Disconnect the longer cable from the extension piece.
3   Disconnect the extension piece from the handbrake control lever pull rod.
4   Remove the grommet from the pullrod.
5   Remove the front passenger seat.
6   Where necessary, release and knock out the seat sliding rails and move them towards the rear.
7   Where applicable prise free and remove the plastic cover from the handbrake lever. Access to the handbrake-to-floor mounting bolts is through slits in the carpet. If no slits are provided, either carefully cut some or release and fold back the carpet. Unbolt the handbrake lever and withdraw it with pullrod until the handbrake ON switch lead can be disconnected (photo).
8   A worn ratchet segment can be renewed by driving the sleeve from the control lever (Fig. 9.69).
9   Drive the new sleeve supplied with the segment into the lever to permit a little play between segment and lever.
10 A new pawl can be fitted if the original pivot pin is drilled out (Fig. 9.70).
11 Rivet the new pin so that the pawl is still free to move.
12 Refitting is a reversal of the removal procedure. On completion adjust the handbrake as detailed in Section 26.

29 Handbrake warning light switch – removal and refitting

1   The handbrake ON warning light microswitch is bolted to the handbrake lever (photo).
2   Access to the switch may be gained after removing the handbrake lever, as described in Section 28.
3   Undo the bolt and remove the microswitch.
4   Refit in the reverse order.

30 Brake pedal – removal and refitting

1   Working under the facia panel, disconnect the pedal return spring (Fig. 9.71).
2   Remove the clip and pull out the clevis pin to disconnect the pushrod clevis fork from the pedal arm.
3   Disconnect the electrical leads from the stop-lamp switch.
4   Pull the demister duct from the heater distributor housing.
5   Unbolt and remove the pedal support bracket.
6   Secure the support bracket in the jaws of a vice and extract the lockpin from the cross-shaft nut.
7   Unscrew and remove the nut and then pull the cross-shaft from the support bracket.
8   Withdraw the pedal and shaft spring.
9   Refitting is a reversal of removal, but apply grease to the cross-shaft and tighten nuts and bolts to the specified torque.

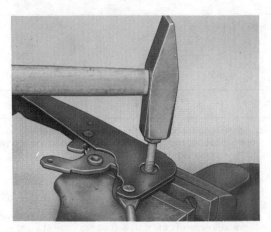
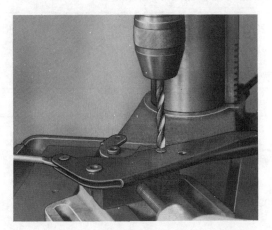

Fig. 9.69 Removing segment retaining sleeve (Sec 28)

Fig. 9.70 Drilling out handbrake lever pawl pivot pin (Sec 28)

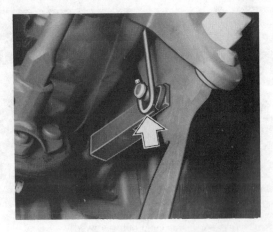

Fig. 9.71 Brake pedal return spring and clevis pin – arrowed
(Sec 30)

10 Note that the cross-shaft nut is on the right-hand side when viewed from the driver's seat and the end of the shaft spring engages in the hole in the support bracket.

31 Brake light switch – removal and refitting

1   The brake light switch is mounted on the pedal support bracket, in a 'keyhole' type mounting (photo).
2   To remove the brake light switch, disconnect the electrical leads, turn the switch through 180° so that the keys line up with the slots and remove the switch.
3   Refit in the reverse order, but pull the switch plunger out to its maximum extension before fitting the switch (photo).
4   The plunger will automatically adjust itself during use, but check that it becomes operational when the brake pedal travel exceeds 15 to 25 mm (0.6 to 1.0 in).

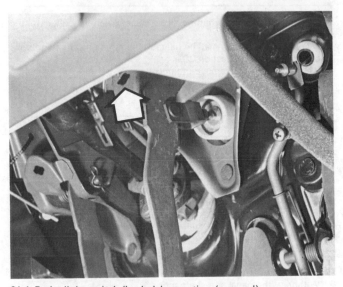

31.1 Brake light switch 'keyhole' mounting (arrowed)

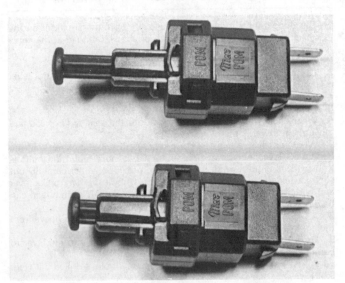

31.3 Brake light switch showing plunger fully extended (top) and retracted (bottom)

32 Fault diagnosis – braking system

Before diagnosing faults from the following chart, check that any braking irregularities are not caused by:
   Uneven and incorrect tyre pressures
   Wear in the steering mechanism
   Defects in the suspension and dampers
   Misalignment of the bodyframe

Symptom	Reason(s)
Pedal travels a long way before the brakes operate	Incorrect remote control rod/servo pushrod adjustment Brake shoes set too far from the drums (manually adjusted type) Self-adjusting mechanism faulty (when applicable) Linings badly worn Brake disc run-out excessive
Stopping ability poor, even though pedal pressure is firm	Linings, discs or drums badly worn or scored One or more wheel hydraulic cylinders seized, resulting in some brake shoes not pressing against the drums (or pads against disc) Brake linings contaminated with oil Wrong type of linings fitted (too hard) Brake shoes wrongly assembled Servo unit not functioning

Symptom	Reason(s)
Car veers to one side when the brakes are applied	Brake pads or linings on one side are contaminated with oil Hydraulic wheel cylinder on one side partially or fully seized A mixture of lining materials fitted between sides Brake discs not matched Unequal wear between sides caused by partially seized wheel cylinders
Pedal feels spongy when the brakes are applied	Air is present in the hydraulic system
Pedal feels springy when the brakes are applied	Brake lining not bedded into the drums (after fitting new ones) Master cylinder or brake backplate mounting bolts loose Severe wear in brake drums causing distortion when brakes are applied Discs out of true
Pedal travels right down with little or no resistance and brakes are virtually non-operative	Leak in hydraulic system resulting in lack of pressure for operating wheel cylinders If no signs of leakage are apparent the master cylinder internal seals are failing to sustain pressure
Binding, juddering, overheating	One or a combination of reasons given above Shoes installed incorrectly with reference to leading and trailing ends Broken shoe return spring Excessive disc run-out Drum distorted Incorrect remote control rod/servo pushrod adjustment
Lack of servo assistance	Vacuum hose disconnected or leaking Non-return valve defective or incorrectly fitted Servo internal defect

Chapter 10 Suspension

For modifications, and information applicable to later models, see Supplement at end of manual

Contents

Specifications

Front suspension

Type .... Independent with MacPherson struts and coil springs. Anti-roll bar
Suspension and steering angles .... Refer to Specifications in Chapter 8 and to the introductory Section of this Manual for wheelbase and track dimensions

Rear suspension

Type .... Semi-independent torsion beam, with trailing arms, coil springs and telescopic shock absorbers. Anti-roll bar on 1.6 and 1.8 models

Suspension angles (non-adjustable):
  Camber .... 0° to −1°
  Maximum deviation side-to-side .... 0°30′
  Toe-in .... +0°20′ to 1°00′ (2.0 to 6.0 mm)
  Maximum deviation side-to-side .... 0°15′

Roadwheels and tyres

Pressed steel type	5J or 5$\frac{1}{2}$J x 13 according to model
Light alloy type	5$\frac{1}{2}$J x 13 or 14 according to model
Tyre sizes	155 SR 13
	165 SR 13
	165 HR 13
	185/70 SR 13
	185/70 HR 13
	185/70 TR 13
	195/60 HR 14
	Dependent upon model

Tyre pressures (normal load)*

Pressures in bar (lbf/in²), cold:	Front	Rear
1.3 models:		
155 x 13 tyres	2.0 (29)	1.9 (28)
165 x 13 tyres	1.9 (28)	1.7 (25)
1.6 models up to 1985:		
All models except SR	1.9 (28)	1.7 (25)
SR	2.0 (29)	2:0 (29)
1.6 models from 1985:		
Base	2.0 (29)	1.8 (26)
L, GL and GLS	1.9 (28)	1.7 (25)
1.8 models up to 1984:		
185/70 x 13 tyres	1.9 (28)	1.8 (26)
195/60 x 14 tyres	2.0 (29)	2.0 (29)
1.8 models from 1985:		
185/70 x 13 tyres	2.0 (29)	1.8 (26)
195/60 x 14 tyres	2.1 (30)	1.9 (28)

*For high speed driving, increase pressures by 0.2 bar (3 lbf/in²). For larger loads, consult your handbook or a dealer

Torque wrench settings

Front suspension

	Nm	lbf ft
Control arm balljoint to stub axle carrier	70	52
Suspension strut top mounting nuts	20	15
Strut piston rod nut	55	41
Strut gland nut	200	148
Tie-rod balljoint to steering arm	60	44
Anti-roll bar U-clamps	20	15
Suspension control arm pivot bolts	110	81
Suspension control arm support (short type):		
Smaller bolts	110	81
Larger centre bolt	130	96
Suspension control arm support (longer type) bolts	110	81
Driveshaft to hub carrier castellated nut:		
Stage 1	100	74
Slacken then Stage 2	20	15
Stage 3	Tighten through further 90°	

Rear suspension

	Nm	lbf ft
Rear axle to underbody pivot bolts	100	74
Rear shock absorber mountings (Estate):		
Upper	20	15
Lower	55	41
Rear shock absorber lower mounting (Saloon/Hatchback):		
Up to VIN DV 144 510/D6 041 675	60	44
Later models	70	52
Level control pressure line unions	3	2
Anti-roll bar clamps	18	13
Stub axle flange to rear axle:		
Stage 1	60	44
Stage 2	Turn through further 30°	

Roadwheels

	Nm	lbf ft
Roadwheel bolts	90	66

1 General description

The front suspension consists of telescopic hydraulic struts, coil springs, anti-roll bar and a control arm.

The hub bearings are of double row ball type.

The rear suspension is of semi-independent type having a torsion beam and trailing arms with mini-block coil springs and telescopic shock absorbers.

The roadwheels may be of pressed steel or light alloy type dependent upon the particular model.

Some models are fitted with a level control system, a description of which is given elsewhere in this Chapter.

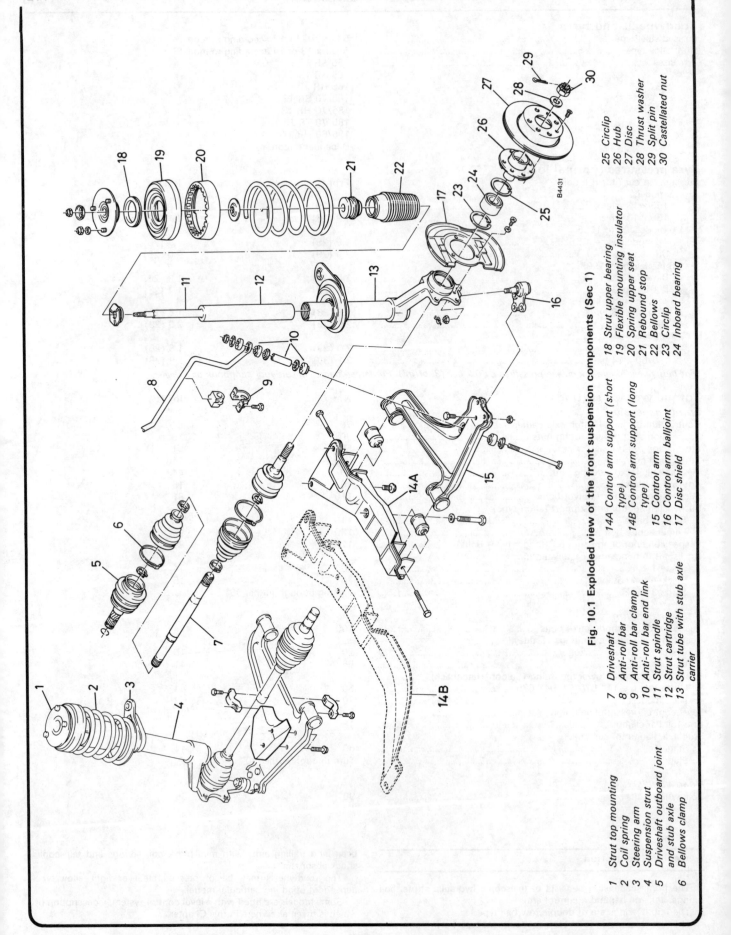

214

Fig. 10.1 Exploded view of the front suspension components (Sec 1)

1 Strut top mounting
2 Coil spring
3 Steering arm
4 Suspension strut
5 Driveshaft outboard joint and stub axle
6 Bellows clamp

7   Driveshaft
8   Anti-roll bar
9   Anti-roll bar clamp
10 Anti-roll bar end link
11 Strut spindle
12 Strut cartridge
13 Strut tube with stub axle carrier

14A Control arm support (short type)
14B Control arm support (long type)
15 Control arm
16 Control arm balljoint
17 Disc shield

18 Strut upper bearing
19 Flexible mounting insulator
20 Spring upper seat
21 Rebound stop
22 Bellows
23 Circlip
24 Inboard bearing

25 Circlip
26 Hub
27 Disc
28 Thrust washer
29 Split pin
30 Castellated nut

B4431

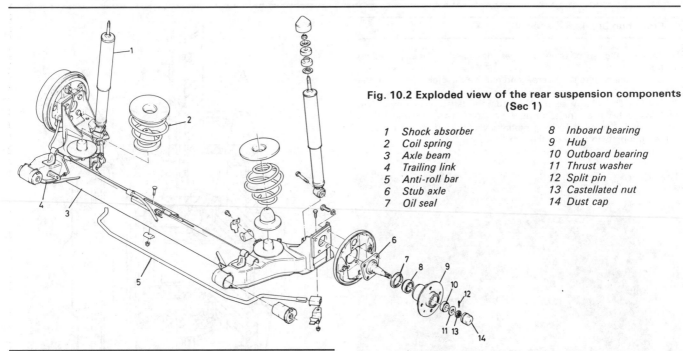

Fig. 10.2 Exploded view of the rear suspension components (Sec 1)

1	Shock absorber	8 Inboard bearing
2	Coil spring	9 Hub
3	Axle beam	10 Outboard bearing
4	Trailing link	11 Thrust washer
5	Anti-roll bar	12 Split pin
6	Stub axle	13 Castellated nut
7	Oil seal	14 Dust cap

2 Routine maintenance – suspension

Carry out the following procedures at the intervals given in Routine Maintenance at the beginning of the manual

1 Check and adjust the tyre pressures and make sure that the caps are securely fitted to the valves (photo).

2 Thoroughly examine the tyres for wear, damage and deterioration. Raise each wheel clear of the ground using a suitable jack so that a complete check can be made (photo).

3 With each wheel clear of the ground, grip each at the top and bottom and attempt to rock the wheel to assess play at the hub. Excessive play at the hub indicates wear in the hub bearings, although on front wheels check that the movement is not due to a worn lower suspension balljoint.

4 Position the car on ramps or jack it up and support on axle stands for security. Check the front and rear shock absorbers for leakage of fluid. If necessary remove and overhaul or renew the shock absorber or strut as necessary.

5 Periodically inspect the suspension mounting points for security and signs of excessive corrosion or damage; which if apparent must be attended to professionally without delay.

6 On models with a level control system fitted, check the system hoses for condition and security.

3 Front suspension strut – removal and refitting

1 Remove the centre trim plate from the roadwheel.

2 Extract the split pin from the castellated hub nut and release the nut.

3 Raise the vehicle, support securely and then remove the roadwheel (see Chapter 9, Section 3).

4 Unbolt or free the brake caliper from the stub axle carrier, slide it off the brake disc and tie it up with wire. There is no need to disconnect the hydraulic system. See Chapter 9, Section 4 or 5.

5 Unscrew the tie-rod end balljoint nut well up its threads and then, using a suitable balljoint extractor tool, disconnect the balljoint from the steering arm on the suspension strut.

6 Disconnect the control arm balljoint from the stub axle carrier in a similar way. It may be found that, owing to the limited clearance between the driveshaft joint and the balljoint nut, it is difficult to fit an extractor tool. In this case either push the driveshaft slightly out of the hub which will compress the joint and provide greater clearance for the tool or use forked wedges as an alternative.

7 Pull the stub axle carrier towards you until the driveshaft is detached from the carrier and then support the shaft on a block or jack.

Note: *Do not move the vehicle on its wheels with one or both driveshafts removed from their hubs, as damage to the front wheel hub bearings can occur.*

8 Remove the suspension strut mounting nuts from the upper turret (photo).

9 Withdraw the suspension strut, complete with coil spring, from under the front wing.

10 Refitting is a reversal of removal, tighten all nuts and bolts to the specified torque, noting the stage tightening of the castellated hub nut given in Specifications.

2.1 Check the tyre pressures regularly

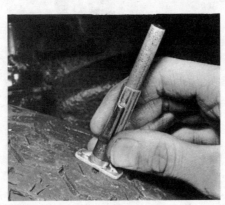

2.2 Checking tyre tread depth

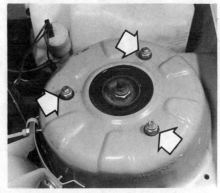

3.8 Front suspension strut top mounting nuts (arrowed)

4 Front hub bearing – renewal

1   Remove the suspension strut as described in the preceding Section.
2   Extract the countersunk screw and remove the brake disc from the hub.
3   The hub should now be removed from the carrier using one of two methods. Either use a press or puller, or screw two roadwheel bolts into the hub flange and, using progressively thicker packing pieces, tighten the bolts to force off the hub (photos).

4.3A Removing hub from carrier

4   Unbolt and remove the brake disc shield.
5   Extract the two bearing circlips (photo).
6   Using a press or bearing puller remove the bearing from the stub axle carrier, applying pressure to the outer track.
7   Before installing the new bearing, insert the circlip (A) into the stub axle carrier. Make sure that it is positively located in its groove with its tabs pointing downward (when strut is in vehicle) (Fig. 10.3).
8   Press the new bearing into position until it contacts the circlip, applying pressure to the outer track (photo).
9   Fit the remaining bearing circlip.
10 Fit the brake disc shield.
11 Press or draw (long bolt and washers) the hub, which is an interference fit, into the stub axle carrier. The bearing inner track must be supported during this operation.
12 Refit the suspension strut.

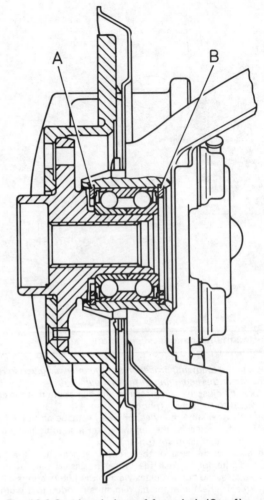

Fig. 10.3 Sectional view of front hub (Sec 4)

A and B   Bearing circlips

5 Front suspension strut – overhaul

1   The suspension struts are of renewable cartridge type which makes them very easy to recondition in the event of their losing their damping properties.
2   With the strut removed from the vehicle as described in Section 3, secure it by gripping the stub axle carrier in the jaws of a vice.

4.3B Hub removed from carrier

4.5 Extracting hub bearing circlip

4.8 Hub bearing/seal

3 Fit a suitable spring compressor tool to the spring coils. These are available at most motor accessory shops. Tighten the compressor until all the tension is removed from the spring, then, as an additional safety measure, tighten a strap or chain around the compressor (photo).

4 Unscrew and remove the strut spindle top nut and withdraw the top mounting (photos).

5 Lift off the spring upper seat. Note the detachable bearing. Remove the thrust washer and the rebound stop (photos).

6 Carefully release the spring tension by unscrewing the compressor nuts evenly.

7 Take off the compressor and the coil spring (photo).

8 Withdraw the strut bellows.

9 From the upper end of the strut, unscrew the gland nut. This is very tight and it will probably be found easier to grip the nut in a vice and to unscrew the strut from it using a long bar as shown (photos).

10 Withdraw the hydraulic damper cartridge and discard it (photo).

11 Reassemble by inserting the new cartridge and tightening the gland nut to the specified torque.

12 Locate the bellows and stop plates.

13 Locate the coil spring so that the end of its lower coil locates correctly in the channel of the seat (Fig. 10.4).

14 Fit the spring compressor and compress the spring enough to be able to fit the top mounting.

15 Fit the top mounting with bearing. Ensure that the support bearing is correctly fitted and locate the stop washers as shown (Fig. 10.5).

16 Hold the strut spindle from rotating while the mounting nut is tightened to the specified torque.

17 Carefully release the spring compressor and remove it.

5.3 Strut coil spring with compressor and strap fitted

5.4A Strut top mounting plate

5.4B Strut spring upper seat

5.5A Strut mounting plate removal from spring upper seat

5.5B Strut upper bearing

5.5C Strut thrust washer and rebound stop

5.7 Strut bellows

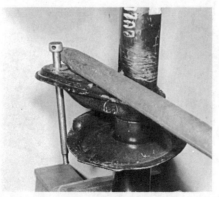

5.9A Method of unscrewing strut gland nut

5.9B Removing strut gland nut

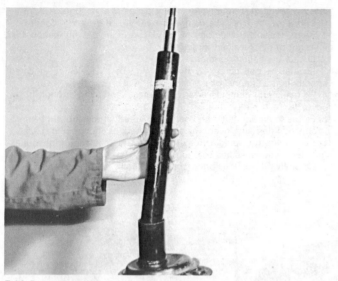

5.10 Removing strut cartridge

Fig. 10.4 Strut spring lower coil seating (Sec 5)

Arrow indicates correct spring location

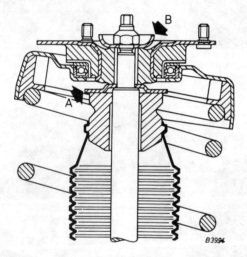

Fig. 10.5 Sectional view of upper part of front suspension strut (Sec 5)

A and B   Support bearing stop washers

6 Front suspension control arm – removal and refitting

1   The control arm may be removed independently, leaving its support attached to the vehicle.
2   Raise the front of the vehicle and remove the roadwheel (see Chapter 9, Section 3).
3   Disconnect the anti-roll bar end link.
4   Using a suitable tool, disconnect the control arm balljoint from the stub axle carrier (see Section 3, paragraph 6) (photos).
5   Unbolt the control arm pivot bolts from the support. On some later models, the control arm support differs in that it is extended and bolted to the front body crossmember; the removal of the control arm from this type of support remains the same (photo).
6   Refitting is a reversal of removal, but the pivot bolt threads in the support must be cleared of thread locking compound by screwing in a thread cutting tap (M12 x 1.75). New bolts must then be used. These are already coated with thread locking compound when supplied, but make sure that the bolts are not older than 5 years or the compound will no longer be effective. You will be able to tell the year of manufacture from the numbers on the bolt heads which represent the last two digits of the year.
7   When tightening the pivot bolts, support the control arm in the horizontal attitude and then tighten to the specified torque.
8   The right-hand control arm on 1.6 and 1.8 models is fitted with a damper weight (Fig. 10.7). This is secured by socket-headed screws (photo).

6.4A Control arm balljoint

6.4B Control arm balljoint released

6.5 Long type control arm front mounting

6.8 Right-hand control arm damper weight

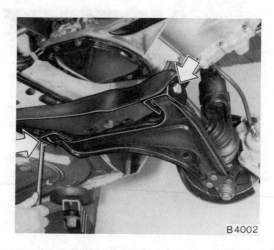

Fig. 10.6 Unbolt control arm pivot bolts – arrowed (Sec 6)

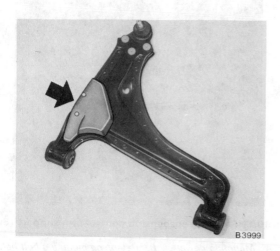

Fig. 10.7 Control arm damper weight – arrowed (Sec 6)

7 Control arm bushes – renewal

1 The flexible bushes should preferably be removed and new ones fitted using a press. However, a bolt with suitable distance pieces and washers is equally effective as a means of drawing the bushes out or in.
2 The control arm should be removed as described in the preceding Section.
3 Apply soapy water as a lubricant to the new bushes before fitting them. Make sure that the flange at each end of the flexible bush projects equally from its control arm housing. Note that the bushes are not identical; the one incorporating the internal intermediate bush must be fitted to the front of the control arm.

8 Control arm balljoint – renewal

1 With the control arm removed from the vehicle as described in Section 6, drill out the balljoint rivets using a 12.0 mm drill. Remove the balljoint.
2 Fit the replacement balljoint using the nuts and bolts supplied and making sure that the nuts are located on the underside of the control arm.

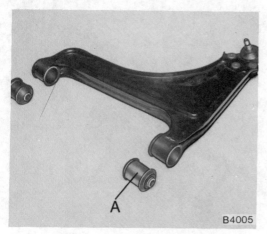

Fig. 10.8 Control arm flexible bushes (Sec 7)

A   Front bush

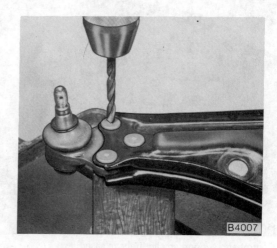

Fig. 10.9 Drilling out a control arm balljoint rivet (Sec 8)

Fig. 10.10 Control arm repair kit balljoint nut – arrowed (Sec 8)

9 Control arm support – removal and refitting

All models
1 The purpose of removing the control arm support will normally be as preparation for removal of the engine, transmission or driveshaft, and the operations described here are directed towards this end. However, if the support is being removed for renewal or repair, then the control arm should first be detached from it by unscrewing the pivot bolts.
2 Raise the front of the vehicle and remove the roadwheel.
3 Disconnect the anti-roll bar from the control arm by unscrewing the nuts on the end link of the bar.

Shorter type support – 1.3, 1.6 except GLS
4 Unscrew the two smaller bolts which attach the support to the underbody (photo).
5 Unscrew the larger bolt from the centre underside of the support, **but do not remove it.**
6 The support is located on a positioning dowel and a puller will now be required to draw it off.
7 A suitable tool can be made up by modifying a two-legged extractor as shown (photo). The important part is the shape of the heads of the anchor bolts which must be inserted into the small

rectangular cutouts in the underside of the support. These are then turned through 90° to give a firm anchorage to the tool (photo).
8 If the extractor pressure bolt is now located against the head of the larger support bolt and screwed in, the action will force the support off its dowel and leave it hanging on its partially unscrewed centre bolt (photo).
9 Remove the centre bolt and lower the support (photo).
10 Refitting is a reversal of removal, but all the bolt hole threads in the underbody must be re-tapped to clear away the old thread locking compound. Always use new bolts which will be supplied pre-coated with thread locking compound.
11 Tighten the support bolts to the specified torque (photo).

Longer type support – 1.6 GLS and 1.8
12 On these models the control arm support is held in place by six bolts and the support is not located on a dowel as previously described for the shorter type support (photos).
13 Apart from this difference, and the fact that a special removal tool will not be required, the removal and refitting operations are similar to those previously described, but prior to removing the support, make an outline marking of the mounting positions at the front and rear to ensure exact realignment when refitting.
14 The bolt threads must be cleaned and fresh thread locking compound applied before the bolts are tightened to the specified torque wrench setting.

Fig. 10.11 Refitting suspension control arm support (Sec 9)

A Mounting dowel   B Retapping mounting bolt holes

9.4 Control arm support smaller bolts released

9.7A Control arm support removal tool

9.7B Withdrawing control arm support

9.8 Short type control arm support positioning dowel

9.9 Removing control arm support larger fixing bolt

9.11 Torque tightening the control arm larger fixing bolt

9.12A Centre and rear control arm support bolts (longer type support)

9.12B Front bolts on longer type control arm support

10 Front anti-roll bar – removal and refitting

1   Raise the front of the vehicle and disconnect the anti-roll bar end links from the suspension control arms (photo).
2   Release the control arm support from the bodyframe as described in the preceding Section. Do not remove it completely, but have it hanging on the centre bolt. This will provide sufficient clearance to withdraw the anti-roll bar sideways once the bar clamps have been released from the underbody.

3   Refitting is a reversal of removal, but observe the procedure for the support bolts as described in the preceding Section.
4   Tighten the anti-roll bar end link nut to give the specified rubber cushion compression shown in Fig. 10.12.

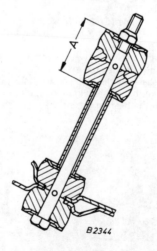

Fig. 10.12 Front anti-roll bar end link (Sec 10)

A = 38.0 mm (1.5 in)

11 Rear hub bearings – adjustment

1   Raise the rear of the vehicle. If pressed steel wheels are fitted, then there is no need to remove the roadwheel, only the wheel bolt cover

10.1 Front anti-roll bar end link

Fig. 10.13 Prising off rear hub dust cap (Sec 11)

plate. If light alloy wheels are fitted, remove the roadwheel (see Chapter 9, Section 3).

2   Prise off the small dust cap from the centre of the hub.

3   Extract the split pin from the castellated nut on the stub axle.

4   Tighten the nut to a torque of 25 Nm (18 lbf ft) while turning the roadwheel (or brake drum).

5   After tightening the nut to this initial torque, slacken the nut until the thrust washer can *just* be moved. Determine this by trying to move the washer with a screwdriver blade. Do not lever against the hub, simply apply the blade directly to the washer.

6   If the split pin holes are not aligned with the nut castellations, tighten the nut until the first available alignment occurs and check whether the thrust washer can still be moved. If it can, fit the split pin; if not, back off the nut to the next available position and then fit the split pin.

7   Check that the hub can rotate freely without binding then refit the dust cap.

12 Rear hub bearings – renewal

1   Raise the rear of the vehicle and remove the roadwheel (see Chapter 9, Section 3).

2   Remove the brake drums (Chapter 9).

3   Prise off the dust cap and extract the split pin from the castellated nut (photo).

4   Remove the nut and the thrust washer (photo).

5   Withdraw the hub from the stub axle.

6   Lever out the oil seal from the inboard end of the hub and then take out the inboard and outboard bearing inner races.

7   Press or drive out the bearing outer tracks from the hub.

8   Press or drive the new bearing outer tracks into the hub.

9   Fit the inboard bearing race and oil seal. Apply grease liberally to the bearing and the lips of the oil seal and half fill the space between the two bearing outer tracks with grease (photo).

10   Fit the hub to the stub axle, insert the outboard bearing race, the thrust washer and the nut.

11   Adjust as described in the preceding Section.

Fig. 10.14 Removing rear hub (Sec 12)

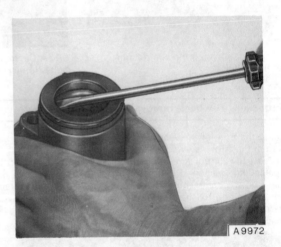

Fig. 10.15 Prising out rear hub oil seal (Sec 12)

12.3 Rear hub nut and split pin

12.4 Removing the thrust washer

12.9 Locate the new hub oil seal

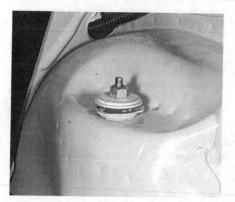

13.4A Rear shock absorber upper mounting

13.4B Rear shock absorber top mounting lower cushion

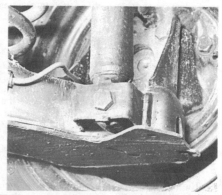

13.5 Rear shock absorber lower mounting (Saloon/Hatchback)

13.13A Rear shock absorber lower mounting (Estate)

13.13B Rear shock absorber upper mounting (Estate)

13 Rear shock absorber – removal, testing and refitting

1 Due to the design of the rear axle, it is essential that one shock absorber at a time be removed and refitted.
2 On models fitted with the level control system it is essential to depressurize the air in the system before removing the shock absorber(s) – see Section 21 (paragraph 3).

Hatchback/Saloon models
3 Open the luggage boot or tailgate and prise off the cap which covers the shock absorber top mounting.
4 Unscrew the nut(s) now exposed and take off the washer and rubber cushion (photos).
5 Drive the rear wheels up onto the ramps. If ramps are not available, raise and securely support the rear of the vehicle, but be prepared to compress the shock absorber slightly by jacking up under the axle arm (photo).
6 Disconnect the level control system union from the shock absorber where applicable (after depressurizing the air in the system).
7 Disconnect the shock absorber lower mounting from the rear axle and then withdraw it from the vehicle.

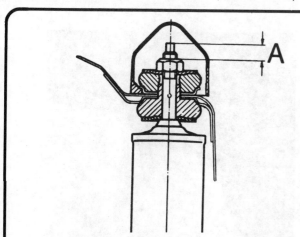

Fig. 10.16 Rear shock absorber upper mounting – standard type (Sec 13)

A = 9 mm (0.35 in)

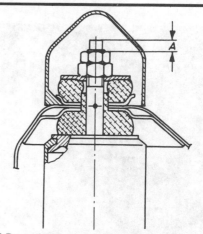

Fig. 10.17 Rear shock absorber upper mounting – two retaining nut type (Sec 13)

A = 6 mm (0.24 in)

8   To test the shock absorber unit, grip it vertically in the jaws of a vice so that it is held by its lower mounting eye.

9   Fully extend and contract the shock absorber six or seven times. Any evidence of jerky movement or lack of resistance will indicate the need for renewal.

10 Refitting is a reversal of removal. On models with level control, ensure that the shock absorber is fitted with the pressure line facing the correct way round. Tighten the lower mounting bolt to the specified torque, and the upper mounting nut to give the exposed thread length shown (Fig. 10.16, 10.17 or 10.18 as applicable).

11 Where applicable, reconnect the level control system hose to the shock absorber union, repressurize the system and check for any signs of air leaks (Section 20).

Estate models

12 The rear suspension on the Estate is similar to that on the other models. The main difference is in the shock absorber mountings: the shock absorbers are inclined at an angle to improve the load deck space.

13 Remove the mounting nuts and bolts from the top and bottom mountings, recover the spacer washers, and withdraw the shock absorber.

14 Refit in the reverse order to removal, tightening the mounting nuts to the specified torque. Note that if the top mounting stud is sheared off by over-tightening, it will have to be drilled out and tapped to accept another stud.

14 Rear anti-roll bar – removal and refitting

1   An anti-roll bar is fitted to the rear suspension system on some models. Although the mounting positions for the anti-roll bar differ on pre and post 1985 models, due to the rear axle being modified in profile, the removal, servicing and refitting procedures are the same.

2   Raise and support the vehicle at the rear.

3   Disconnect the anti-roll bar mountings from the suspension trailing arm, and from the clamps on the rear axle. Remove the bar.

4   Renew the anti-roll bar and/or its mounting bushes if they are worn, perished or damaged.

5   Refit in the reverse order of removal. Tighten the retaining bolts to the specified torque.

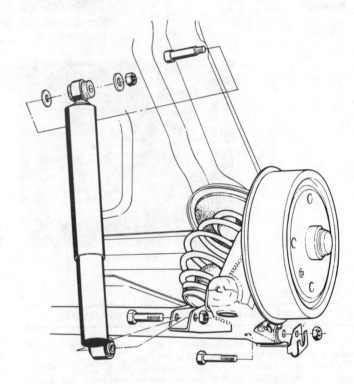

Fig. 10.19 Rear shock absorber mountings – Estate (Sec 13)

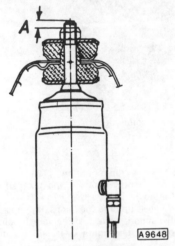

Fig. 10.18 Rear shock absorber upper mounting – load levelling type (Sec 13)

A = 6 mm (0.24 in)

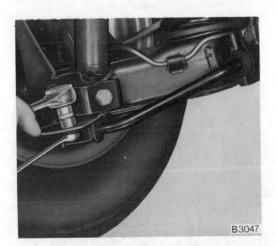

Fig. 10.20 Unbolting rear anti-roll bar from trailing arm (Sec 14)

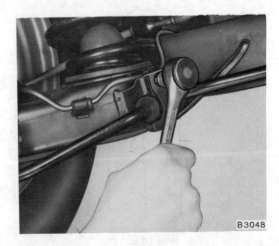

Fig. 10.21 Unbolting rear anti-roll bar from axle (Sec 14)

15 Rear coil spring – removal and refitting

1   On models fitted with the level control system (see Section 19) first depressurize the system as described in Section 21.

2   Raise the rear of the vehicle and support under the rear jacking points under the sill. Remove the roadwheels (See Chapter 9, Section 3).

3   Place a jack under the suspension trailing arm and raise it slightly.

4   Disconnect the shock absorber lower mounting and separate the shock absorber eye from the mounting bracket. Remove the jack. Disconnect and plug the brake flexible hoses if they are in danger of being strained by the movement of the rear axle (see Chapter 9 for details).

5   Disconnect the shock absorber on the other side of the vehicle in a similar way.

6   Slightly lower the jack which is still supporting the trailing arm and then remove the coil spring from the opposite side of the vehicle first, followed by the remaining one. Take out the insulating rings from the spring seats.

7   Refitting is a reversal of removal. If there is any difficulty in holding the insulators in place while the coil spring is located, use impact type adhesive. Reconnect the brake hoses and bleed the brake hydraulic system on completion where applicable (Chapter 9).

8   On models fitted with level control, repressurize the system (Section 20).

16 Rear suspension stub axle – removal and refitting

1   Remove the hub as described in Section 12.

2   Unscrew and remove the four bolts which hold the stub axle mounting flange to the axle flange. Remove the stub axle.

3   New bolts must be used at the refitting stage, these being supplied already treated with thread locking compound. Make sure that the new bolts are not older than three years as the compound will have lost its locking properties. The single number stamped on the bolt head indicates the year of manufacture. It is important that the threads of the stub axle are absolutely clear of the old thread locking compound. Ideally this should be done using a tap.

4   Tighten the bolts in the stages specified (see Specifications).

5   Refit the hub.

17 Rear axle – removal and refitting

1   Raise the rear of the vehicle, support it securely under the jacking points and remove the roadwheels (see Chapter 9, Section 3).

2   Disconnect the rear flexible brake hydraulic hoses from the rigid pipeline connections (see Chapter 9) and cap the pipes and hoses to prevent loss of fluid.

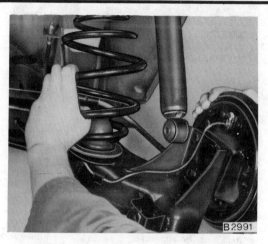

Fig. 10.22 Rear coil spring removal (Sec 15)

Fig. 10.23 Unbolting rear stub axle from axle flange (Sec 16)

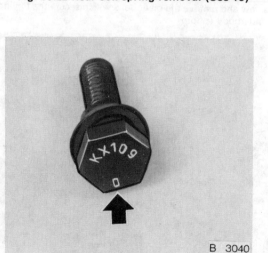

Fig. 10.24 Rear stub axle bolt manufacturing date mark – arrowed (Sec 16)

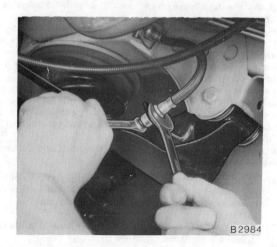

Fig. 10.25 Disconnecting a rear brake hose (Sec 17)

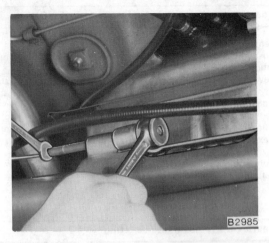

Fig. 10.26 Disconnecting shorter handbrake cable (Sec 17)

Fig. 10.27 Disconnecting longer handbrake cable (Sec 17)

Fig. 10.28 Bending open a handbrake cable guide (Sec 17)

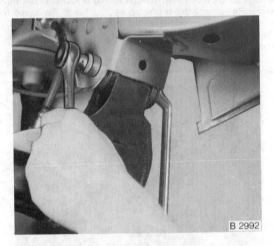

Fig. 10.29 Unscrewing a trailing arm pivot bolt (Sec 17)

3   Unscrew the self-locking nut on the shorter handbrake cable end fitting at the equaliser. Disconnect the cable from the equaliser.

4   Disconnect the longer handbrake cable from the extension piece on the lever pull rod.

5   Release the handbrake cable from the underbody guides by bending them open.

6   Remove the coil springs as described in Section 15.

7   Locate a jack, preferably of hydraulic type, under the centre of the rear axle.

8   Unscrew and remove the pivot bolts which connect the trailing arms to the underbody.

9   Lower the jack and withdraw the axle assembly from under the vehicle.

10 The axle may be dismantled as necessary by removing the brake components (Chapter 9), and the stub axle and hubs (Sections 12 and 16 of this Chapter).

11 Reassembly and refitting are reversals of removal and dismantling, but observe the following requirements:

(a) Tighten all nuts and bolts to the specified torque, but leave tightening the rear axle pivot bolts until the vehicle is free standing and laden with the equivalent of a driver and a front seat passenger

(b) Bleed the brake hydraulic system with reference to Chapter 9

(c) Adjust the handbrake (Chapter 9)

18 Trailing arm flexible bushes – renewal

1   Support the body under the jacking points. Remove the wheels

(see Chapter 9, Section 3).

2   The rear axle must be supported, preferably on a trolley jack, and the brake hose clips removed from the underbody.

3   Unscrew and remove the pivot bolts which secure the trailing arms to the underbody (photo).

18.3 Rear trailing link pivot bolt

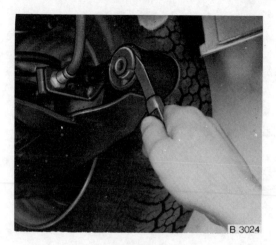

Fig. 10.30 Cutting flange from trailing arm flexible bush (Sec 18)

Fig. 10.31 One method of removing and refitting a trailing arm (Sec 18)

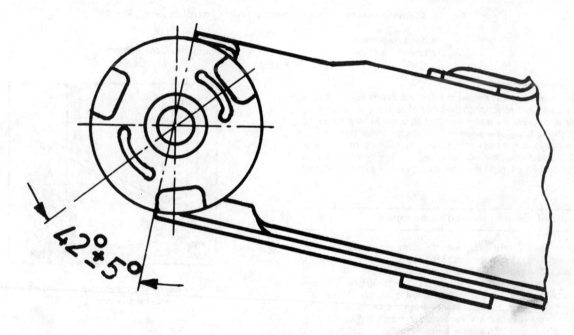

Fig. 10.32 Trailing arm flexible bush positioning (Sec 18)

4   Lower the jack very slowly and at the same time ease the brake hoses and the rigid lines, bending the latter if necessary to prevent straining them.

5   As soon as the flexible bushes in the trailing arms are clear of the underbody, support the rear axle on axle stands.

6   Using a sharp knife cut off the flange from the flexible bushes (Fig. 10.30).

7   Tap round the bush housing to free the bush.

8   Use a bolt and distance pieces to draw the bush from the trailing arm. Removal will be facilitated if the housing is heated to between 60 and 70°C (140 and 158°F). **Do not** *use a flame to do this, owing to the proximity of the fuel tank, but heat with a soldering iron or rags soaked in boiling water.*

9   Smear the new bush with grease and draw it into position, but make sure that the mouldings on the end of the bush are positioned as shown in Fig. 10.32.

10 Always renew the bushes on both trailing links at the same time.

11 Refit the axle by reversing the removal operations. Tighten bolts to the specified torque – see Section 17, paragraph 11(a).

19 Level control system – description

1   This system is only available on certain models and its function is to compensate for the effect of heavy luggage or towing loads on the vehicle's rear suspension.

2   The system operates by varying the air pressure in the rear shock absorbers. On some models the pressure in the system is regulated automatically, whilst on others (and more commonly) the pressure can be manually adjusted.

Automatic system control

3   When the fully automatic system is fitted, an electrically-driven compressor is the source of compressed air and no driver action is necessary. Response to level change is inhibited for 20 seconds or so in order to prevent the system trying to compensate for bumps in the road.

4   The layout of the automatic level control system and the location of the various components is shown in Fig. 10.33.

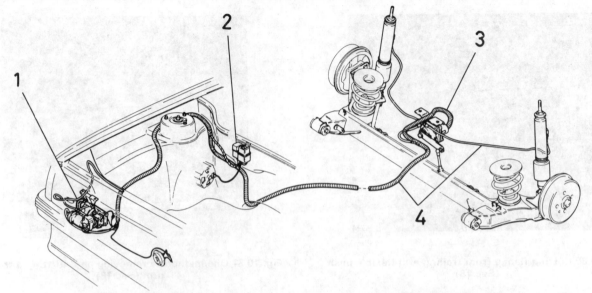

Fig. 10.33 Components of the automatic level control system (Sec 19)

1   Electric compressor
2   Relay and fuse unit

3   Load sensor
4   Air lines and electrical loom

Manual system control
5   With this more commonly fitted system, a compressed air line is connected to a union connection in the body of each shock absorber at the rear. The two hoses are interconnected to a single hose which is routed through the body side panels to an adjuster valve (similar to a tyre pressure valve) in the body at the rear. The location of this valve varies according to model, but will be in the luggage compartment or in the rain channel on the right rear corner (accessible with the boot lid open).

20 Level control system (manual) – adjustment

1   Most vehicles will be equipped with the manually adjusted system. A compressed air line is used to increase the system pressure via a valve in the load area. The procedure is as follows.
2   With the vehicle unladen, use a tyre pressure gauge on the level control valve to check that the system pressure is 0.8 bar (12 lbf/in²): adjust if necessary. Measure the distance from the centre of the rear bumper to the ground with the vehicle standing on a level surface.
3   Load the vehicle and increase the pressure in the system to restore the previously measured height. Do not exceed a pressure of 5.0 bar (73 lbf/in²).
4   After unloading the vehicle, depressurize the system to correct the height, observing the minimum pressure of 0.8 bar (12 lbf/in²). Do not drive an unladen vehicle with the system fully inflated.
5   If it is necessary to check the rear wheel alignment, this should be done with the level control system inflated to 1.0 bar (15 lbf/in²).

21 Level control system components – removal and refitting (general)

1   If a fault is suspected in the level control system it is essential that it is checked out by a Vauxhall dealer without delay. If a leak is suspected, inspect the system hoses and connections for condition and security.
2   If any part of the level control system is to be disconnected or removed, the system must first be depressurized.
3   Depressurize the level control system completely, either at the valve (manual system) or by slackening a pressure line union (automatic system).
4   If removing any of the electrical components of the automatic level control system, first disconnect the battery earth lead.
5   When refitting the system components, ensure that the line

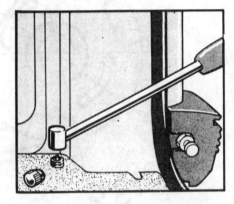

Fig. 10.34 Level control system manual inflation valve on the Estate model (Sec 20)

Fig. 10.35 Measuring the rear ride height (Sec 20)

connections ar tightened to the specified torque setting, also that the system hoses are correctly routed. Check for signs of air leaks when the system has been repressurised.

22 Rear wheel alignment

1   The rear wheel alignment and camber are set in production and are not adjustable.
2   Any deviation from the tolerances given in Specifications must be due to collision damage.

23 Wheels and tyres – general care and maintenance

Wheels and tyres should give no real problems in use provided that a close eye is kept on them with regard to excessive wear or damage. To this end, the following points should be noted.

Ensure that tyre pressures are checked regularly and maintained correctly. Checking should be carried out with the tyres cold and not immediately after the vehicle has been in use. If the pressures are checked with the tyres hot, an apparently high reading will be obtained owing to heat expansion. Under no circumstances should an attempt be made to reduce the pressures to the quoted cold reading in this instance, or effective underinflation will result.

Underinflation will cause overheating of the tyre owing to excessive flexing of the casing, and the tread will not sit correctly on the road surface. This will cause a consequent loss of adhesion and excessive wear, not to mention the danger of sudden tyre failure due to heat build-up.

Overinflation will cause rapid wear of the centre part of the tyre tread coupled with reduced adhesion, harsher ride, and the danger of shock damage occurring in the tyre casing.

Regularly check the tyres for damage in the form of cuts or bulges, especially in the sidewalls. Remove any nails or stones embedded in the tread before they penetrate the tyre to cause deflation. If removal of a nail *does* reveal that the tyre has been punctured, refit the nail so that its point of penetration is marked. Then immediately change the wheel and have the tyre repaired by a tyre dealer. Do *not* drive on a tyre in such a condition. In many cases a puncture can be simply repaired by the use of an inner tube of the correct size and type. If in any doubt as to the possible consequences of any damage found, consult your local tyre dealer for advice.

Periodically remove the wheels and clean any dirt or mud from the inside and outside surfaces. Examine the wheel rims for signs of rusting, corrosion or other damage. Light alloy wheels are easily damaged by 'kerbing' whilst parking, and similarly steel wheels may become dented or buckled. Renewal of the wheel is very often the only course of remedial action possible.

The balance of each wheel and tyre assembly should be maintained to avoid excessive wear, not only to the tyres but also to the steering and suspension components. Wheel imbalance is normally signified by vibration through the vehicle's bodyshell, although in many cases it is particularly noticeable through the steering wheel. Conversely, it should be noted that wear or damage in suspension or steering components may cause excessive tyre wear. Out-of-round or out-of-true tyres, damaged wheels and wheel bearing wear/maladjustment

also fall into this category. Balancing will not usually cure vibration caused by such wear.

Wheel balancing may be carried out with the wheel either on or off the vehicle. If balanced on the vehicle, ensure that the wheel-to-hub relationship is marked in some way prior to subsequent wheel removal so that it may be refitted in its original position.

General tyre wear is influenced to a large degree by driving style – harsh braking and acceleration or fast cornering will all produce more rapid tyre wear. Interchanging of tyres may result in more even wear, but this should only be carried out where there is no mix of tyre types on the vehicle. However, it is worth bearing in mind that if this is completely effective, the added expense of replacing a complete set of tyres simultaneously is incurred, which may prove financially restrictive for many owners.

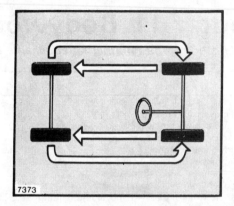

Fig. 10.36 Interchange of wheels and tyres to even out wear, as suggested by the manufacturers (Sec 23)

Front tyres may wear unevenly as a result of wheel misalignment. The front wheels should always be correctly aligned according to the settings specified by the vehicle manufacturer.

Legal restrictions apply to the mixing of tyre types on a vehicle. Basically this means that a vehicle must not have tyres of differing construction on the same axle. Although it is not recommended to mix tyre types between front axle and rear axle, the only legally permissible combination is crossply at the front and radial at the rear. When mixing radial ply tyres, textile braced radials must always go on the front axle, with steel braced radials at the rear. An obvious disadvantage of such mixing is the necessity to carry two spare tyres to avoid contravening the law in the event of a puncture.

In the UK, the Motor Vehicles Construction and Use Regulations apply to many aspects of tyre fitting and usage. It is suggested that a copy of these regulations is obtained from your local police if in doubt as to the current legal requirements with regard to tyre condition, minimum tread depth, etc.

24 Fault diagnosis – suspension

Symptom	Reason(s)
Vehicle wanders	Incorrect wheel alignment (see also Chapter 8) Worn front control arm balljoints
Heavy or stiff steering	Incorrect front wheel alignment (see Chapter 8) Incorrect tyre pressures
Wheel wobble or vibration	Roadwheels out of balance Roadwheel buckled Incorrect front wheel alignment (see Chapter 8) Faulty strut or shock absorber Weak coil spring
Excessive pitching or rolling on corners or during braking	Faulty strut or shock absorber Weak or broken coil spring

Chapter 11 Bodywork and fittings

For modifications, and information applicable to later models, see Supplement at end of manual

Contents

Specifications

Type .... All-steel welded, unitary

Model code

	Body type
81, 88	*2-door Saloon
84, 89	5-door Hatchback
86, 87	4-door Saloon
82, 83	5-door Estate

Not available from model year 1983

For vehicle dimensions and weights, refer to Introductory Section at the beginning of this Manual

Torque wrench settings

	Nm	lbf ft
Bumper mounting bolts	12	9
Tailgate strut ball-stud	20	15
Tailgate hinge bolts	20	15
Front seat U-clip bolts	20	15
Bonnet hinge bolts	20	15
Seat belt bolts	35	26

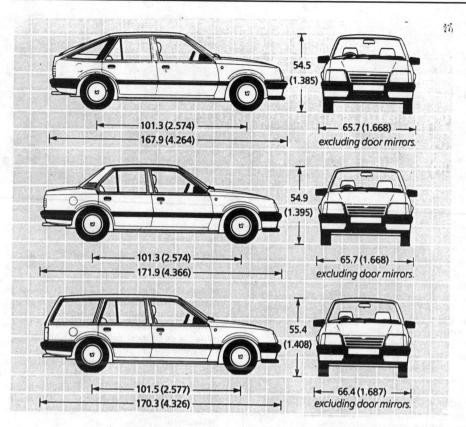

Fig. 11.1 Measuring points for body dimensions (Sec 1)

Figures given are typical (in inches/metres)

1 General description

The body and underframe are of all-welded steel construction.
Models in the range include two and four-door Saloons, a five-door Hatchback, a five-door Estate and a two-door Convertible. The only detachable 'fixed' panels are the bolt-on front wings.

2 Maintenance – bodywork and underframe

1   The general condition of a vehicle's bodywork is the one thing that significantly affects its value. Maintenance is easy but needs to be regular. Neglect, particularly after minor damage, can lead quickly to further deterioration and costly repair bills. It is important also to keep watch on those parts of the vehicle not immediately visible, for instance the underside, inside all the wheel arches and the lower part of the engine compartment.

2   The basic maintenance routine for the bodywork is washing – preferably with a lot of water, from a hose. This will remove all the loose solids which may have stuck to the vehicle. It is important to flush these off in such a way as to prevent grit from scratching the finish. The wheel arches and underframe need washing in the same way to remove any accumulated mud which will retain moisture and tend to encourage rust. Paradoxically enough, the best time to clean the underframe and wheel arches is in wet weather when the mud is thoroughly wet and soft. In very wet weather the underframe is usually cleaned of large accumulations automatically and this is a good time for inspection.

3   Periodically, except on vehicles with a wax-based underbody protective coating, it is a good idea to have the whole of the underframe of the vehicle steam cleaned, engine compartment included, so that a thorough inspection can be carried out to see what minor repairs and renovations are necessary. Steam cleaning is available at many garages and is necessary for removal of the accumulation of oily grime which sometimes is allowed to become thick in certain areas. If steam cleaning facilities are not available, there are one or two excellent grease solvents available such as Holts Engine Cleaner or Holts Foambrite which can be brush applied. The dirt can then be simply hosed off. Note that these methods should not be used on vehicles with wax-based underbody protective coating or the coating will be removed. Such vehicles should be inspected annually, preferably just prior to winter, when the underbody should be washed down and any damage to the wax coating repaired using Holts Undershield. Ideally, a completely fresh coat should be applied. It would also be worth considering the use of such wax-based protection for injection into door panels, sills, box sections, etc, as an additional safeguard against rust damage where such protection is not provided by the vehicle manufacturer.

4   After washing paintwork, wipe off with a chamois leather to give an unspotted clear finish. A coat of clear protective wax polish, like the many excellent Turtle Wax polishes, will give added protection against chemical pollutants in the air. If the paintwork sheen has dulled or oxidised, use a cleaner/polisher combination such as Turtle Extra to restore the brilliance of the shine. This requires a little effort, but such dulling is usually caused because regular washing has been neglected. Care needs to be taken with metallic paintwork, as special non-abrasive cleaner/polisher is required to avoid damage to the finish. Always check that the door and ventilator opening drain holes and pipes are completely clear so that water can be drained out (photos). Bright work should be treated in the same way as paint work. Windscreens and windows can be kept clear of the smeary film which often appears, by the use of a proprietary glass cleaner like Holts Mixra. Never use any form of wax or other body or chromium polish on glass.

Convertible

Convertible models should not be taken through a car wash, as the hood seams and the plastic rear window can be damaged. Clean the rear window with a soft damp cloth or a chamois leather. Do not use a scraper to remove frost and ice from the rear window, use a normal de-ice spray or warm water.

To clean the hood, brush it in the direction of the pile, do not use soap and water, or any other cleaning agent.

2.4A Clearing sill drain hole

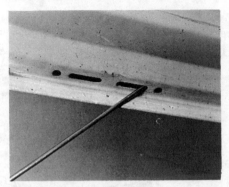

2.4B Clearing door drain hole

2.4C Bonnet scuttle drain tube

3 Maintenance – upholstery and carpets

Mats and carpets should be brushed or vacuum cleaned regularly to keep them free of grit. If they are badly stained remove them from the vehicle for scrubbing or sponging and make quite sure they are dry before refitting. Seats and interior trim panels can be kept clean by wiping with a damp cloth and Turtle Wax Carisma. If they do become stained (which can be more apparent on light coloured upholstery) use a little liquid detergent and a soft nail brush to scour the grime out of the grain of the material. Do not forget to keep the headlining clean in the same way as the upholstery. When using liquid cleaners inside the vehicle do not over-wet the surfaces being cleaned. Excessive damp could get into the seams and padded interior causing stains, offensive odours or even rot. If the inside of the vehicle gets wet accidentally it is worthwhile taking some trouble to dry it out properly, particularly where carpets are involved. *Do not leave oil or electric heaters inside the vehicle for this purpose.*

4 Minor body damage – repair

The colour bodywork repair photographic sequences between pages 32 and 33 illustrate the operations detailed in the following sub-sections.
Note: *For more detailed information about bodywork repair, the Haynes Publishing Group publish a book by Lindsay Porter called The Car Bodywork Repair Manual. This incorporates information on such aspects as rust treatment, painting and glass fibre repairs, as well as details on more ambitious repairs involving welding and panel beating.*

Repair of minor scratches in bodywork

If the scratch is very superficial, and does not penetrate to the metal of the bodywork, repair is very simple. Lightly rub the area of the scratch with a paintwork renovator like Turtle Wax New Color Back, or a very fine cutting paste like Holts Body + Plus Rubbing Compound, to remove loose paint from the scratch and to clear the surrounding bodywork of wax polish. Rinse the area with clean water.

Apply touch-up paint, such as Holts Dupli-Color Color Touch or a paint film like Holts Autofilm, to the scratch using a fine paint brush; continue to apply fine layers of paint until the surface of the paint in the scratch is level with the surrounding paintwork. Allow the new paint at least two weeks to harden; then blend it into the surrounding paintwork by rubbing the scratch area with a paintwork renovator or a very fine cutting paste, such as Holts Body + Plus Rubbing Compound or Turtle Wax New Color Back. Finally, apply wax polish from one of the Turtle Wax range of wax polishes.

Where the scratch has penetrated right through to the metal of the bodywork, causing the metal to rust, a different repair technique is required. Remove any loose rust from the bottom of the scratch with a penknife, then apply rust inhibiting paint, such as Turtle Wax Rust Master, to prevent the formation of rust in the future. Using a rubber or nylon applicator fill the scratch with bodystopper paste like Holts Body + Plus Knifing Putty. If required, this paste can be mixed with cellulose thinners, such as Holts Body + Plus Cellulose Thinners, to provide a very thin paste which is ideal for filling narrow scratches. Before the stopper-paste in the scratch hardens, wrap a piece of smooth cotton rag around the top of a finger. Dip the finger in cellulose thinners, such as Holts Body + Plus Cellulose Thinners, and then quickly sweep it across the surface of the stopper-paste in the scratch; this will ensure that the surface of the stopper-paste is slightly

hollowed. The scratch can now be painted over as described earlier in this Section.

Repair of dents in bodywork

When deep denting of the vehicle's bodywork has taken place, the first task is to pull the dent out, until the affected bodywork almost attains its original shape. There is little point in trying to restore the original shape completely, as the metal in the damaged area will have stretched on impact and cannot be reshaped fully to its original contour. It is better to bring the level of the dent up to a point which is about ⅛ in (3 mm) below the level of the surrounding bodywork. In cases where the dent is very shallow anyway, it is not worth trying to pull it out at all. If the underside of the dent is accessible, it can be hammered out gently from behind, using a mallet with a wooden or plastic head. Whilst doing this, hold a suitable block of wood firmly against the outside of the panel to absorb the impact from the hammer blows and thus prevent a large area of the bodywork from being 'belled-out'.

Should the dent be in a section of the bodywork which has a double skin or some other factor making it inaccessible from behind, a different technique is called for. Drill several small holes through the metal inside the area – particularly in the deeper section. Then screw long self-tapping screws into the holes just sufficiently for them to gain a good purchase in the metal. Now the dent can be pulled out by pulling on the protruding heads of the screws with a pair of pliers.

The next stage of the repair is the removal of the paint from the damaged area, and from an inch or so of the surrounding 'sound' bodywork. This is accomplished most easily by using a wire brush or abrasive pad on a power drill, although it can be done just as effectively by hand using sheets of abrasive paper. To complete the preparation for filling, score the surface of the bare metal with a screwdriver or the tang of a file, or alternatively, drill small holes in the affected area. This will provide a really good 'key' for the filler paste.

To complete the repair see the Section on filling and re-spraying.

Repair of rust holes or gashes in bodywork

Remove all paint from the affected area and from an inch or so of the surrounding 'sound' bodywork, using an abrasive pad or a wire brush on a power drill. If these are not available a few sheets of abrasive paper will do the job just as effectively. With the paint removed you will be able to gauge the severity of the corrosion and therefore decide whether to renew the whole panel (if this is possible) or to repair the affected area. New body panels are not as expensive as most people think and it is often quicker and more satisfactory to fit a new panel than to attempt to repair large areas of corrosion.

Remove all fittings from the affected area except those which will act as a guide to the original shape of the damaged bodywork (eg headlamp shells etc). Then, using tin snips or a hacksaw blade, remove all loose metal and any other metal badly affected by corrosion. Hammer the edges of the hole inwards in order to create a slight depression for the filler paste.

Wire brush the affected area to remove the powdery rust from the surface of the remaining metal. Paint the affected area with rust inhibiting paint like Turtle Wax Rust Master; if the back of the rusted area is accessible treat this also.

Before filling can take place it will be necessary to block the hole in some way. This can be achieved by the use of aluminium or plastic mesh, or aluminium tape.

Aluminium or plastic mesh or glass fibre matting, such as the Holts Body + Plus Glass Fibre Matting, is probably the best material to use for a large hole. Cut a piece to the approximate size and shape of the hole to be filled, then position it in the hole so that its edges are below the level of the surrounding bodywork. It can be retained in position by several blobs of filler paste around its periphery.

Aluminium tape should be used for small or very narrow holes. Pull a piece off the roll and trim it to the approximate size and shape required, then pull off the backing paper (if used) and stick the tape over the hole; it can be overlapped if the thickness of one piece is insufficient. Burnish down the edges of the tape with the handle of a screwdriver or similar, to ensure that the tape is securely attached to the metal underneath.

Bodywork repairs – filling and re-spraying

Before using this Section, see the Sections on dent, deep scratch, rust holes and gash repairs.

Many types of bodyfiller are available, but generally speaking those proprietary kits which contain a tin of filler paste and a tube of resin hardener are best for this type of repair, like Holts Body + Plus or Holts No Mix which can be used directly from the tube. A wide, flexible plastic or nylon applicator will be found invaluable for imparting a smooth and well contoured finish to the surface of the filler.

Mix up a little filler on a clean piece of card or board – measure the hardener carefully (follow the maker's instructions on the pack) otherwise the filler will set too rapidly or too slowly. Alternatively, Holts No Mix can be used straight from the tube without mixing, but daylight is required to cure it. Using the applicator apply the filler paste to the prepared area; draw the applicator across the surface of the filler to achieve the correct contour and to level the filler surface. As soon as a contour that approximates to the correct one is achieved, stop working the paste – if you carry on too long the paste will become sticky and begin to 'pick up' on the applicator. Continue to add thin layers of filler paste at twenty-minute intervals until the level of the filler is just proud of the surrounding bodywork.

Once the filler has hardened, excess can be removed using a metal plane or file. From then on, progressively finer grades of abrasive paper should be used, starting with a 40 grade production paper and finishing with 400 grade wet-and-dry paper. Always wrap the abrasive paper around a flat rubber, cork, or wooden block – otherwise the surface of the filler will not be completely flat. During the smoothing of the filler surface the wet-and-dry paper should be periodically rinsed in water. This will ensure that a very smooth finish is imparted to the filler at the final stage.

At this stage the 'dent' should be surrounded by a ring of bare metal, which in turn should be encircled by the finely 'feathered' edge of the good paintwork. Rinse the repair area with clean water, until all of the dust produced by the rubbing-down operation has gone.

Spray the whole repair area with a light coat of primer, either Holts Body + Plus Grey or Red Oxide Primer – this will show up any imperfections in the surface of the filler. Repair these imperfections with fresh filler paste or bodystopper, and once more smooth the surface with abrasive paper. If bodystopper is used, it can be mixed with cellulose thinners to form a really thin paste which is ideal for filling small holes. Repeat this spray and repair procedure until you are satisfied that the surface of the filler, and the feathered edge of the paintwork are perfect. Clean the repair area with clean water and allow to dry fully.

The repair area is now ready for final spraying. Paint spraying must be carried out in a warm, dry, windless and dust free atmosphere. This condition can be created artificially if you have access to a large indoor working area, but if you are forced to work in the open, you will have to pick your day very carefully. If you are working indoors, dousing the floor in the work area with water will help to settle the dust which would otherwise be in the atmosphere. If the repair area is confined to one body panel, mask off the surrounding panels; this will help to minimise the effects of a slight mis-match in paint colours. Bodywork fittings (eg chrome strips, door handles etc) will also need to be masked off. Use genuine masking tape and several thicknesses of newspaper for the masking operations.

Before commencing to spray, agitate the aerosol can thoroughly, then spray a test area (an old tin, or similar) until the technique is mastered. Cover the repair area with a thick coat of primer; the thickness should be built up using several thin layers of paint rather than one thick one. Using 400 grade wet-and-dry paper, rub down the surface of the primer until it is really smooth. While doing this, the work area should be thoroughly doused with water, and the wet-and-dry paper periodically rinsed in water. Allow to dry before spraying on more paint.

Spray on the top coat using Holts Dupli-Color Autospray, again building up the thickness by using several thin layers of paint. Start spraying in the centre of the repair area and then work outwards, with a side-to-side motion, until the whole repair area and about 2 inches of the surrounding original paintwork is covered. Remove all masking material 10 to 15 minutes after spraying on the final coat of paint.

Allow the new paint at least two weeks to harden, then, using a paintwork renovator or a very fine cutting paste such as Turtle Wax New Color Back or Holts Body + Plus Rubbing Compound, blend the edges of the paint into the existing paintwork. Finally, apply wax polish.

Plastic components

With the use of more and more plastic body components by the vehicle manufacturers (eg bumpers, spoilers, and in some cases major body panels), rectification of more serious damage to such items has become a matter of either entrusting repair work to a specialist in this field, or renewing complete components. Repair of such damage by the DIY owner is not really feasible owing to the cost of the equipment and materials required for effecting such repairs. The basic technique involves making a groove along the line of the crack in the plastic using a rotary burr in a power drill. The damaged part is then welded back together by using a hot air gun to heat up and fuse a plastic filler rod into the groove. Any excess plastic is then removed and the area rubbed down to a smooth finish. It is important that a filler rod of the correct plastic is used, as body components can be made of a variety of different types (eg polycarbonate, ABS, polypropylene).

Damage of a less serious nature (abrasions, minor cracks etc) can be repaired by the DIY owner using a two-part epoxy filler repair material, like Holts Body + Plus or Holts No Mix which can be used directly from the tube. Once mixed in equal proportions (or applied direct from the tube in the case of Holts No Mix), this is used in similar fashion to the bodywork filler used on metal panels. The filler is usually cured in twenty to thirty minutes, ready for sanding and painting.

If the owner is renewing a complete component himself, or if he has repaired it with epoxy filler, he will be left with the problem of finding a suitable paint for finishing which is compatible with the type of plastic used. At one time the use of a universal paint was not possible owing to the complex range of plastics encountered in body component applications. Standard paints, generally speaking, will not bond to plastic or rubber satisfactorily, but Holts Professional Spraymatch paints to match any plastic or rubber finish can be obtained from dealers. However, it is now possible to obtain a plastic body parts finishing kit which consists of a pre-primer treatment, a primer and coloured top coat. Full instructions are normally supplied with a kit, but basically the method of use is to first apply the pre-primer to the component concerned and allow it to dry for up to 30 minutes. Then the primer is applied and left to dry for about an hour before finally applying the special coloured top coat. The result is a correctly coloured component where the paint will flex with the plastic or rubber, a property that standard paint does not normally possess.

5 Door and lid hinges, locks and controls – lubrication

1 Oil the hinges of the bonnet, boot and doors with a drop or two of light oil periodically. A good time is after the car has been washed.
2 Oil the bonnet release catch pivot pin and safety catch pivot pin, periodically.
3 Do not over-lubricate door catches and strikers. Normally a little oil on the latch dovetail and a thin smear of high melting-point grease on the striker is adequate. Make sure that before lubrication they are wiped thoroughly clean and correctly adjusted.

6 Bonnet – removal and refitting

1 Open the bonnet and support it in the fully open position.
2 Mark the position of the hinges on the underside of the bonnet.
3 With the help of an assistant, support the weight of the bonnet and unbolt and remove it from the vehicle.
4 It is unlikely that the bonnet hinges will ever have to be removed but if they are, the wiper arm and linkage will first have to be withdrawn (Chapter 12) and the rivets drilled out of the hinged holder brackets.
5 Refitting is a reversal of removal, but check the bonnet alignment (even gap between edge of bonnet and wing) before finally tightening the hinge bolts.
6 When closing the bonnet, it should close smoothly and positively

7.3 Removing the bonnet release handle and holder assembly

8.1 Radiator grille lower spigot

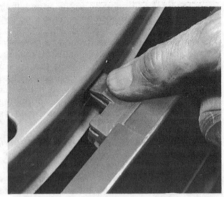

8.2 Radiator grille top clip

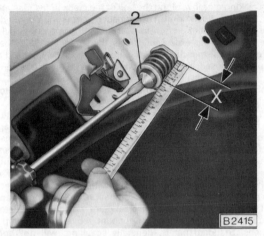

Fig. 11.2 Bonnet striker pin standard setting (Sec 6)

X = 38.0 to 40.0 mm (1.50 to 1.57 in) measured from bonnet surface to raised edge of washer (2)

with moderate hand pressure. If it does not, align the dovetail and plate and adjust the projection of the dovetail by releasing its locknut and turning it by using a screwdriver in its end slot. The standard setting is as shown in Fig. 11.2.

7 Bonnet release cable – renewal

1   Remove the cable clip from the top of the front cross rail.
2   Using a screwdriver, prise the cable end fitting out of the release slide.

3   Working inside the vehicle, pull the bonnet release handle and holder assembly sharply rearwards to disengage the holder lug from the body locating slot (photo).
4   Pull the cable assembly through its grommet in the engine compartment rear bulkhead into the engine compartment.
5   Fit the new cable by reversing the removal operations, then adjust the cable to remove any slackness by altering the cable setting at the clip on the top rail.
6   The cable should release the bonnet with a gentle pull on the control handle. If it is still stiff, check the setting of the catch dovetail as described in the preceding Section.
7   Apply some grease to the bonnet release slide and to the lock dovetail.

8 Radiator grille – removal and refitting

1   The grille is held in place at its upper edge by clips and the bottom is secured by pegs engaging in sockets (photo).
2   Disconnect the grille clips and lift the grille up and away from fhe front of the vehicle (photo).
3   Refit in the reverse order to removal.

9 Front bumper – removal and refitting

1   The bumpers are constructed of impact-resistant plastic material bolted directly to the front bodyframe and wings.
2   Reach under the front wings and unscrew the securing bolts (Fig. 11.3).
3   Withdraw the bumper.
4   If necessary, remove the number plate.
5   Refitting is a reversal of removal, engage the end slides with their brackets (Fig. 11.4).

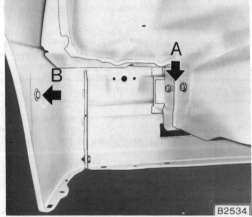

Fig. 11.3 Front bumper fixing bolts (Sec 9)
A   To bodyframe   B   To wing

Fig. 11.4 Front bumper slide (C) and bracket (D) (Sec 9)

10 Rear bumper – removal and refitting

Saloon and Hatchback

1 Remove the rear number plate lamp from the bumper as described in Chapter 12 and then disconnect the lead from it.
2 Unbolt the bumper from the support brackets located inside the lower rear body panel (Fig. 11.5).
3 Withdraw the bumper, disengaging the end slides from the brackets (Fig. 11.6).
4 Refitting is a reversal of removal.

Estate

Centre section

5 Remove the tailgate interior trim panel.
6 Remove the bolts which secure the bumper to the tailgate and remove the bumper (Fig. 11.7).
7 Refit in the reverse order to removal. Apply non-hardening sealing compound around the bolt holes before fitting the bumper.

Side section

8 Open the tailgate and remove the two bolts which secure the side section to its rear bracket (photo).
9 Slide the bumper section off rearwards. If the sliding bracket is stuck, unbolt it: access to the bolt is gained by removing the washer reservoir (right-hand side) or the rear quarter interior trim panel (left-hand side).
10 Refit in the reverse order to removal. Make sure that the interlocking pin engages correctly with the centre section.

10.8 Estate rear bumper side section retaining bolts (arrowed)

Fig. 11.5 Rear bumper mounting brackets (X) (Sec 10)

Fig. 11.6 Rear bumper end slide brackets – arrowed (Sec 10)

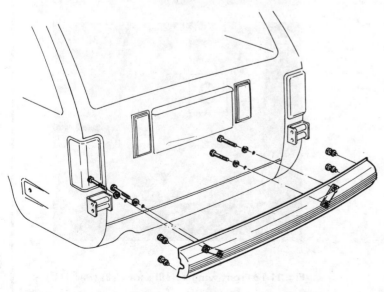

Fig. 11.7 Rear bumper centre section (Estate) (Sec 10)

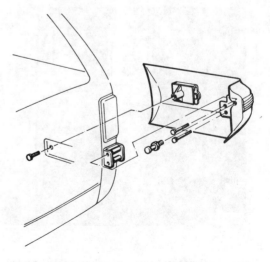

Fig. 11.8 Rear bumper side section (Estate) (Sec 10)

11 Front wing – removal and refitting

1   Remove the front roadwheel.
2   Remove the protective liner from under the wing after having unclipped it and extracted the screws which hold it in place.
3   Remove the front bumper as described in Section 9.
4   Open the bonnet and unscrew and remove the seven bolts from the top edge of the wing (Fig. 11.9).
5   Working under the wing, remove the four bolts which hold the wing to the lower front body panel (Fig. 11.10).
6   Working inside the vehicle, remove the side trim panel at the footwell to expose the two bolts at the lower part of the windscreen A-pillar (Fig. 11.11).
7   Remove the screw from the base of the pillar at the sill flange (Fig. 11.12).
8   Cut around the seams of the wing with a sharp knife to release the mastic and then life the wing away.
9   Clean away all old mastic sealer from the body mating flange and apply a thick bead of new sealer.

10   Offer the new wing into position and screw in the bolts finger tight.
11   Now align the wing with the adjacent body panels and then tighten all bolts and screws.
12   Apply protective coating to the underside of the wing and refinish the outer surface to match the body colour.
13   When the protective coating is dry, refit the bumper, the protective liner and the footwell trim panel.

12 Door trim panel – removal and refitting

1   Remove the securing clip from the window regulator handle. To do this force back the trim bezel and pull out the clip using a length of wire with a hooked end.
2   Extract the two screws and remove the armrest (photo). On later models fitted with a combined armrest/oddment tray, prise free the plastic plug for access to the rear retaining screw, then prise free and withdraw the lower section of the door pull to gain access to the three

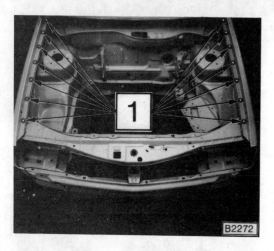

Fig. 11.9 Front wing top mounting bolts (1) (Sec 11)

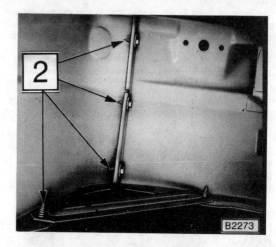

Fig. 11.10 Front wing-to-lower body panel bolts (2)
(Sec 11)

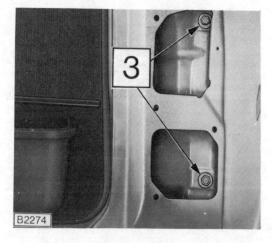

Fig. 11.11 Front wing-to-pillar bolts (3) (Sec 11)

Fig. 11.12 Front wing-to-sill screw (3) (Sec 11)

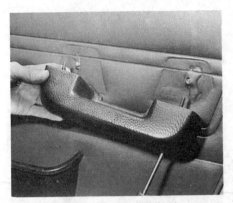

12.2A Removing door armrest (early models)

12.2B Removing door armrest/door oddment tray panel screw (later models)

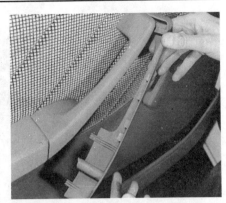

12.2C Removing door pull trim (later models)

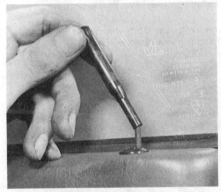

12.3 Removing door lock plunger

12.4 Door trim panel clip

12.5 Door remote control handle escutcheon

12.6 Window regulator handle ready for fitting

13.4A Window regulator mounting

13.4B Regulator arm engaged in channel

forward retaining screws (photos). Remove the door pull trim.

3   Unscrew and remove the lock plunger knob (photo).

4   Insert the fingers or a broad blade between the trim panel and the door and pull the panel from the door. Use a jerking action to do this in order to free the plastic securing clips from the holes in the door panel. The clips are rather brittle and it is a wise precaution to purchase some spare ones as replacements for any broken during the work (photo).

5   As the trim panel is withdrawn, the door lock remote control handle escutcheon plate bezel will be freed (photo).

6   Refitting is a reversal of removal, but note that the window regulator handle spring clip is fitted to the handle before the handle is fitted. The handle complete wth clip is then simply driven onto the splined shaft of the regulator by striking it with the palm of the hand (photo).

13 Window regulator – removal and refitting

1   Remove the trim panel as described in Section 12.

2   Carefully peel away the plastic waterproof sheet.

3   Temporarily refit the regulator handle and set the glass in the half open position. Chock the lower edge of the glass channel with a wooden prop.

4   Remove the regulator mounting screws and withdraw the regulator mechanism sideways through the aperture in the door panel as the regulator arm disengages from the guide channel (photos). On some later models, the regulator is secured by rivets instead of screws, in which case carefully drill out the rivets to release the mechanism.

5   Refitting is a reversal of removal, apply some molybdenum disulphide grease to the mechanism before fitting. Where applicable, use new blind rivets to secure the regulator unit.

6   Refer to Chapter 12 for details of power operated windows.

14 Door glass – removal and refitting

1   Remove the window regulator as previously described.

2   Working at the glass slot in the door, prise off the clips and remove

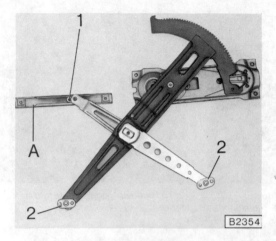

Fig. 11.13 Front door window regulator rollers (1 and 2)
and adjuster channel (A) (Sec 13)

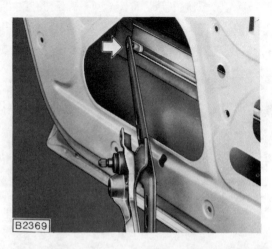

Fig. 11.14 Disconnecting rear door window regulator
(arrowed) from glass channel (Sec 13)

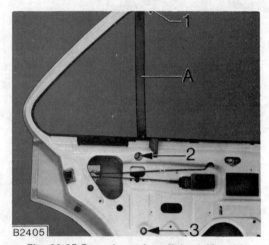

Fig. 11.15 Rear door glass fixings (Sec 14)

1   Upper fixing   3   Channel lower fixing screw
2   Channel centre fixing screw A   Glass divider channel

Fig. 11.16 Removing rear door glass divider channel
(Sec 14)
Remove in direction of arrows

Fig. 11.17 Withdrawing front door glass (Sec 14)
Remove in direction of arrow

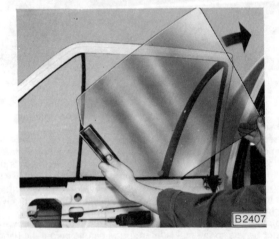

Fig. 11.18 Withdrawing rear door glass (Sec 14)
Remove in direction of arrow

the weather strips.
3 Withdraw the glass divider channel upwards from rear doors
having first released its securing screws.
4 Withdraw the glass upwards tilting it as shown to remove it (Figs.
11.17 and 11.18).

5 Refit by reversing the removal operations, but adjust the glass slide
channels as necessary to ensure smooth positive movement of the
glass.
6 Refer to Chapter 12 for details of power operated windows.

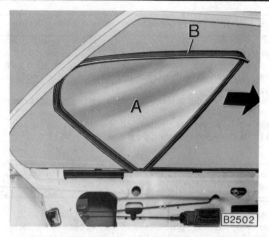

Fig. 11.19 Removing rear door fixed quarter-light (Sec 15)

A Glass   B Rubber surround
Remove in direction of arrow

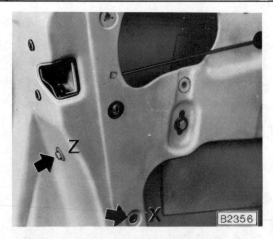

Fig. 11.20 Front door glass guide channel screws (Sec 16)

X Screws on 2-door models
Z Screws on 4-door and
   Hatchback models

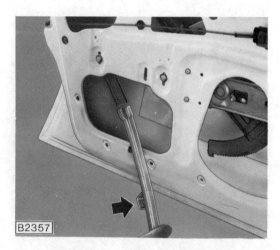

Fig. 11.21 Withdrawing glass guide channel (Sec 16)

Arrow indicates screw location

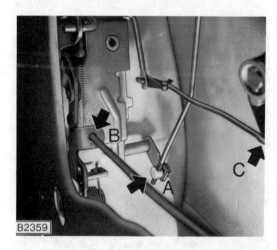

Fig. 11.22 Front door lock control rods (Sec 16)

A Rod for exterior handle   C Lock cylinder link rod
B Rod for interior remote
   control handle

15 Rear door fixed quarter-light – removal and refitting

1 Remove the door main glass as described in Section 14.
2 Pull the quarter-light complete with rubber seal out of the door frame in the direction of the arrow shown in the diagram (Fig. 11.19).
3 Refitting is a reversal of removal.

16 Front door lock – removal and refitting

1 Remove the door trim panel as described in Section 12.
2 Peel back the plastic waterproof sheet.
3 Wind up the window fully.
4 Release the window glass guide channel screws (Fig. 11.20).
5 Pull out the rubber weather strip and then withdraw the guide channels out through the apertures in the door inner panel (Fig. 11.21).
6 Disconnect the control rods from the lock by prising off the clips.
7 Working at the edge of the door, remove the lock securing screws and withdraw the lock.
8 The remote control handle can be removed from its retaining slot if it is pushed towards the front of the vehicle (photo).
9 Refitting is a reversal of removal.

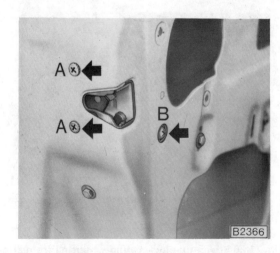

Fig. 11.23 Front door lock fixing screws (Sec 16)

A Screw with lockwasher   B Screw with plain washer

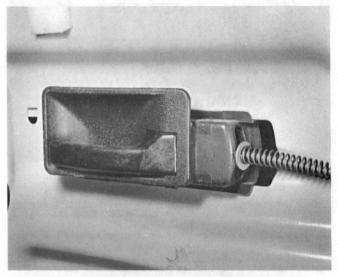

16.8 Remote control handle assembly

17 Front door exterior handle – removal and refitting

1   Remove the door trim panel as described in Section 12.
2   Peel away the plastic waterproof sheet as necessary to gain access and then disconnect the control rod (1) from the door lock (Fig. 11.24).
3   Remove the handle screws (2) and take the handle from the door panel.
4   Refitting is a reversal of removal, but adjust the control rod by means of its threaded coupling as shown in the diagram (Fig. 11.25).

18 Front door lock cylinder – removal, dismantling, reassembly and refitting

1   Remove the door trim panel as described in Section 12.
2   Peel away the waterproof sheet to give access to the lock cylinder.
3   Disconnect the control rod from the lock arm (photo).
4   Prise out the forked spring clip and remove the lock cylinder assembly.
5   To dismantle, insert the ignition key in the lock and then force a screwdriver between the housing and the arm to force off the retaining circlip (Fig. 11.26).

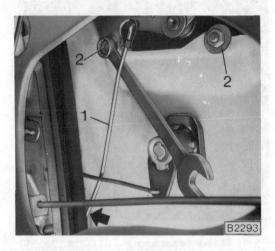

Fig. 11.24 Door exterior handle fixings (Sec 17)

1   Control rod   2   Fixing screws/nuts

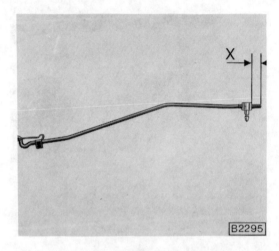

Fig. 11.25 Lock control rod setting diagram (Sec 17)

X = 8.0 mm (0.31 in)

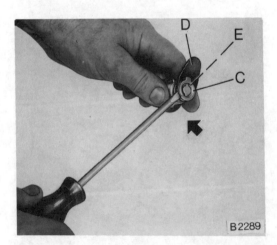

Fig. 11.26 Separating lock cylinder housing from arm (Sec 18)

C   Housing   D   Arm   E   Circlip

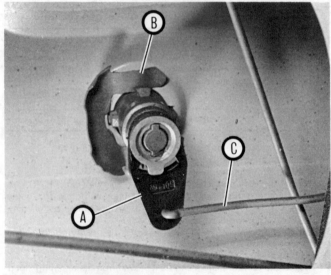

18.3 Door lock cylinder viewed from inside door showing arm (A), spring clip (B) and control rod (C)

6 Separate the components, noting their fitted sequence (Fig. 11.27).

7 Reassembly is a reversal of dismantling, but note that the ends of the spring must be crossed as shown (Fig. 11.28) also the relative position of the arm to the housing must be observed. Use a new circlip.

19 Rear door lock – removal and refitting

1 Wind up the window fully.

2 Remove the trim panel as described in Section 12.

3 Peel back the plastic waterproof sheet to give access to the lock.

4 Disconnect the control rods from the lock and the remote control handle by moving it in the direction of the front of the vehicle.

5 Working at the edge of the door, extract the securing screws and remove the door lock by swinging it around the door glass guide channel and out through the aperture in the door panel (Fig. 11.31).

6 Refit in the reverse order of removal.

20 Rear door exterior handle – removal and refitting

1 Remove the door trim panel as described in Section 12.

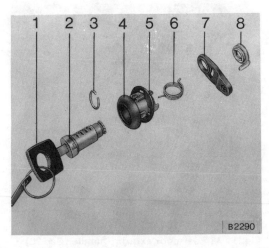

Fig. 11.27 Exploded view of lock cylinder (Sec 18)

1	Key	5	Seal
2	Cylinder	6	Spring
3	Circlip	7	Arm
4	Housing	8	End piece

Fig. 11.28 Cylinder lock spring ends correctly located – arrowed (Sec 18)

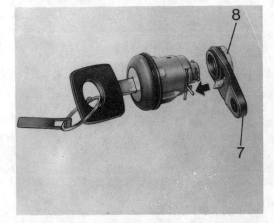

Fig. 11.29 Relationship of cylinder lock arm-to-housing showing end piece (8) and arm (7) (Sec 18)

Locate the lock arm as arrowed

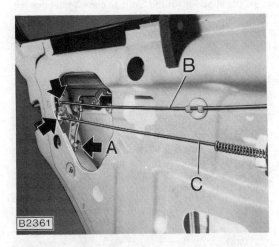

Fig. 11.30 Rear door lock (Sec 19)

A *Exterior handle control rod*   C *Remote control rod*
B *Lock plunger control rod*   *Disconnect at the arrows*

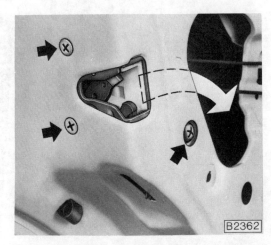

Fig. 11.31 Rear door lock removal (Sec 19)

Arrows indicate securing screws and direction of removal

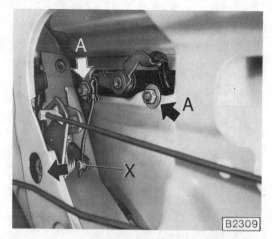

Fig. 11.32 Rear door exterior handle (Sec 20)

A *Fixing screws/nuts*   B *Control rod*

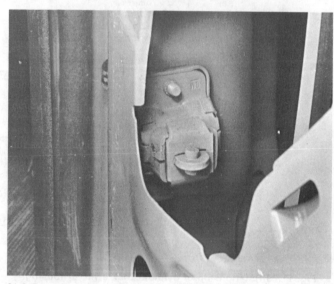

21.3 Door check strap attachment inside door edge

21.5 Door lock striker

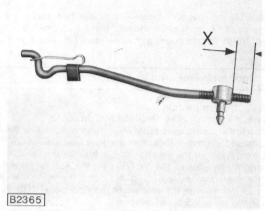

Fig. 11.33 Control rod setting diagram (Sec 20)

X = 8.0 mm (0.31 in)

2 Peel away the plastic waterproof sheet as necessary to give access to the door lock exterior handle.
3 Disconnect the control rod (X) (Fig. 11.32).
4 Unscrew the two handle fixing screws and withdraw the handle.
5 Refitting is a reversal of removal, but adjust the control rod by means of its threaded coupling to provide a dimension (X) as shown in the diagram (Fig. 11.33).

21 Door – removal and refitting

1 The door hinges are welded onto the door frame and the body pillar so that there is no provision for adjustment or alignment.
2 To remove a door, open it fully and support it under its lower edge on blocks covered with pads of rag.
3 Disconnect the door check and drive out the hinge pins. Remove the door (photo).
4 If the door can be moved up and down on its hinge due to wear in the pivot pins or holes, it may be possible to drill out the holes and fit slightly oversize pins.
5 Door closure may be adjusted by moving the socket-headed striker (photo).

22 Tailgate (Hatchback) – removal and refitting

1 Disconnect the electrical leads from the heated rear window.
2 Disconnect the hose for the tailgate washer jets.
3 Remove the supports for the luggage compartment cover.
4 Open the tailgate fully and have an assistant support it.
5 Disconnect the support strut from its mounting on the tailgate by

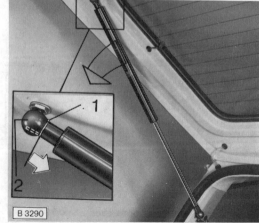

Fig. 11.34 Tailgate support strut retaining ring (1) and ball end fitting (2) (Sec 22)

Disconnect in direction of arrows

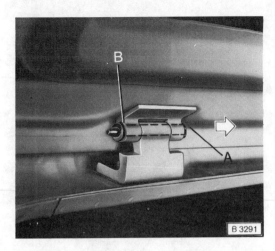

Fig. 11.35 Tailgate hinge pivot pin (A) and retaining ring (B) (Sec 22)

Remove in direction of arrow

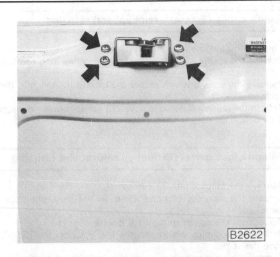

Fig. 11.36 Tailgate lock fixing screws – arrowed (Sec 23)

extracting the retaining ring from the ball end fitting.

6   Prise off the hinge pin retaining rings and then drive out the pins towards the centre line of the vehicle.

7   Lift the tailgate from the vehicle.

8   Refitting is a reversal of removal, but before fully tightening the hinge bolts adjust the tailgate to give an equal gap at each side and positive closure when shut.

23 Tailgate lock (Hatchback) – removal and refitting

1   Open the tailgate and unclip the tailgate trim panel to remove it.

2   Extract the four screws which hold the lock.

3   Prise out the forked spring clips which secure the lock cylinder housing.

4   Pull the lock cylinder outwards, complete with control linkage.

5   Remove the lock through the opening in the tailgate inner panel.

6   Refitting is a reversal of removal.

7   To dismantle the lock cylinder, refer to Section 30.

24 Tailgate struts (Hatchback and Estate) – removal and refitting

1   The strut end fittings are of ball type with a retaining ring.

2   To remove, open the tailgate fully and have an assistant support it.

3   Remove the rings and disconnect the struts.

4   Refitting is a reversal of removal.

5   The struts are gas pressurised and should not be punctured or cut open, or subjected to heat.

25 Tailgate (Estate) – removal and refitting

1   Open the tailgate and remove the ten screws which secure the bottom and sides of the trim panel.

2   Carefully free the trim panel, disengaging the fasteners from its top edge.

3   Disconnect the loudspeaker wiring (when fitted), and remove the trim panel.

4   Disconnect the wiring connectors from the tailgate electrical components, and the screen washer pipe from its nozzle. Remove the wiring harness and the pipe from the tailgate.

5   Have an assistant support the tailgate. Disconnect the support struts from the tailgate by prising free their balljoints.

6   Still with the tailgate supported, depress the hinge pin retainers and drive out the pins. Remove the tailgate.

7   Refit in the reverse order to removal.

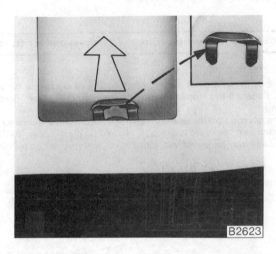

Fig. 11.37 Tailgate lock cylinder retaining clip (Sec 23)

Remove in direction of arrow

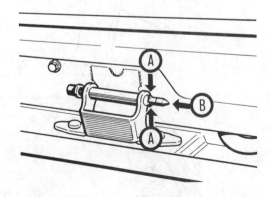

Fig. 11.38 Tailgate hinge pin removal (Estate) (Sec 25)

A   Depress retainer   B   Drive out pin

26 Tailgate lock (Estate) – removal and refitting

1 Remove the tailgate interior trim panel.
2 Release the spring clip and withdraw the connecting rod from the lock.
3 Remove the screws which secure the lock to the tailgate. Remove the lock.
4 Refit in the reverse order to removal. Check for correct operation of the lock before refitting the trim panel.

27 Tailgate lock barrel (Estate) – removal and refitting

1 Remove the tailgate interior trim panel.
2 Release the retaining clip and withdraw the connecting rod from the barrel yoke.
3 Disconnect the return spring from the barrel yoke.
4 Remove the circlip which secures the yoke to the lock barrel. Remove the yoke.
5 Remove the nut which secures the lock barrel to the tailgate. Remove the tailgate handle, which is secured by four screws, and extract the lock barrel.
6 Refit in the reverse order to removal. Check for correct operation of the lock before refitting the trim panel.

28 Load area trim panels (Estate) – removal and refitting

Load area carpet

1 The carpet in the rear section of the load area is secured by Velcro strips. Separate the strips to remove the carpet; press them home on refitting.
2 The covering on the seat backs, which becomes the load area floor when the seat backs are lowered, is secured by plastic pegs. With care these pegs may be prised out undamaged, and re-used on refitting.

Side and roof trim panels

3 Refer to Fig. 11.41 to identify the panels.

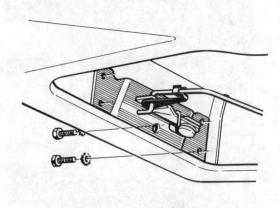

Fig. 11.39 Tailgate lock details (Sec 26)

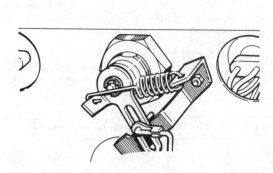

Fig. 11.40 Tailgate lock barrel details (Sec 27)

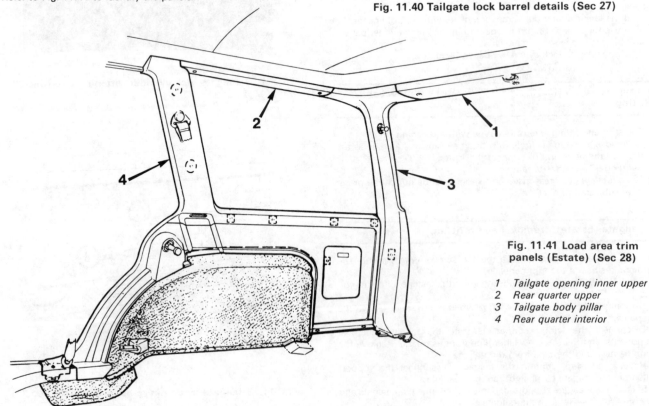

Fig. 11.41 Load area trim panels (Estate) (Sec 28)

1 Tailgate opening inner upper
2 Rear quarter upper
3 Tailgate body pillar
4 Rear quarter interior

4   In each case the various panels are secured by trim screws and/or plastic clips. Take care not to break the plastic clips when prising them free.

5   If removing the tailgate body trim panel, it will be necessary first to remove the rear carpet, the upper and rear quarter upper trim panels and the tailgate strut (see Section 24) from the side concerned.

6   When removing the rear quarter interior trim panel, also remove the rear seat belt upper mounting (if fitted).

7   Refitting is a reversal of removal. Renew any broken retaining clips.

29 Luggage boot lid – removal and refitting

1   Open the lid and mark the position of the hinges on the underside of the lid.

2   With the help of an assistant, unbolt the hinges from the lid and lift the lid away.

3   The hinges themselves should not normally be disturbed, but if they must be removed then the counterbalance springs will have to be released and removed.

4   Unhook them using a lever of sufficient length to be able to counteract the tension of the spring rods.

5   If the hinges are unbolted from the body, fit new sealing washers in order to prevent water seepage into the luggage compartment.

30 Luggage boot lid lock and cylinder – removal, dismantling and refitting

1   Open the boot lid and unscrew the lock fitting screws. Withdraw the lock (photo).

2   To remove the lock cylinder, prise the retaining clip out using a screwdriver. Withdraw the cylinder assembly.

3   To dismantle, insert the key into the cylinder and then extract the circlip (4) using a thin screwdriver (Fig. 11.44).

4   Note the fitted position of the lock components (Fig. 11.45).

5   Reassembly and refitting are reversals of removal and dismantling, but when fitting the lock to the boot lid apply pressure to the lock cylinder from the key hole end until the forked retaining clip can be felt to engage fully. Adjust the height of the striker if necessary to ensure smooth positive closure (photo).

31 Windscreen glass – removal and refitting

1   If the windscreen is to be removed and/or replaced for any reason, it is a job which is better left to an auto glass replacement specialist.

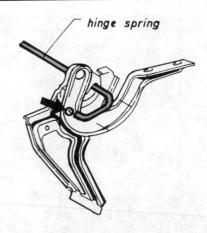

Fig. 11.42 Luggage boot lid hinge and counterbalance spring (Sec 29)

Release spring from hole (arrowed)

Fig. 11.43 Luggage boot lock cylinder retaining clip – LH arrow (Sec 30)

Other arrows indicate spring locating lugs

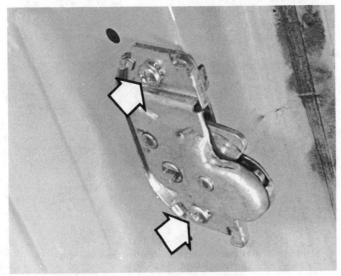

30.1 Luggage boot lid lock retaining screws (arrowed)

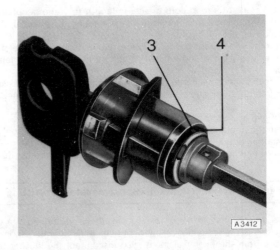

Fig. 11.44 Lock cylinder circlip (4) and washer (3) (Sec 30)

30.5 Luggage boot lid lock striker

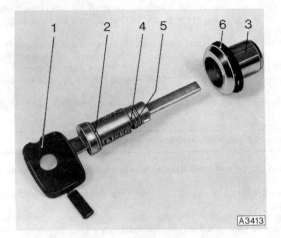

Fig. 11.45 Exploded view of luggage boot lid lock (Sec 30)

1 Key   4 Washer
2 Lock cylinder   5 Circlip
3 Housing   6 Rubber seal

They will do the job in half the time and most important, ensure that it is correctly fitted with no leakages around the surround rubber. However, if you wish to do it yourself, proceed as follows.

2 Where a windscreen is to be replaced due to shattering, the facia air vents should be covered before attempting removal. Adhesive sheeting is useful to stick to the outside of the glass to enable large areas of crystallised glass to be removed.

3 Where the screen is to be removed intact, or is of laminated type, then an assistant will be required. First release the rubber surround from the bodywork by running a blunt, small screwdriver around and under the rubber weatherstrip both inside and outside the car. This operation will break the adhesive of the sealer originally used. Take care not to damage the paintwork or catch the rubber surround with the screwdriver. Remove the windscreen wiper arms and interior mirror and place a protective cover on the bonnet. Salvage your tax disc.

4 Prise out the trim strip from the rubber surround.

5 Have your assistant push the inner lip of the rubber surround off the flange of the windscreen body aperture. Once the rubber surround starts to peel off the flange, the screen may be forced gently outward by careful hand pressure. The second person should support and remove the screen complete with rubber surround.

6 Fit a new rubber weatherseal to the glass and ensure that all old sealant is removed from the body flange. Scrape it away and then clean it off with a fuel-soaked cloth.

7 Apply a bead of sealant to the body flange all round the windscreen aperture.

8 Cut a piece of strong cord greater in length than the periphery of the glass and insert it into the body flange locating the channel of the rubber surround (Fig. 11.46).

9 Offer the windscreen to the body aperture and pass the ends of the cord, previously fitted and located at bottom centre, into the vehicle interior.

10 Press the windscreen into place, at the same time have an assistant pull the cords to engage the lip of the rubber channel over the body flange.

11 Remove any excess sealant with a paraffin-soaked rag.

12 Refit the bright moulding to the rubber surround. A special tool will facilitate this operation but take care not to tear the lips of the rubber.

13 Refit the windscreen wipers, the interior mirror and the tax disc.

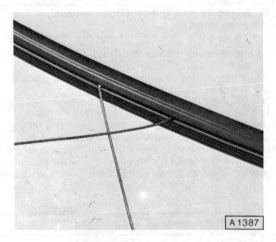

Fig. 11.46 Windscreen installing cord (Sec 31)

32 Rear window or tailgate glass – removal and refitting

1 The operations are very similar to those described for the windscreen in the preceding Section, but first remember to disconnect the leads from the heater element, also disconnect the washer hose and wiper arm (where fitted) (photo).

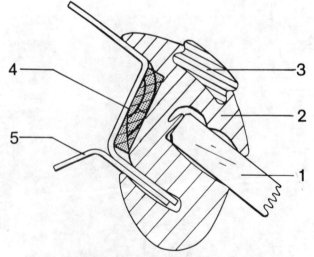

Fig. 11.47 Sectional view of windscreen sealing arrangement (Sec 31)

1 Glass   3 Trim strip
2 Rubber surround   4 Mastic (butyl) seal
   (weatherstrip)   5 Bodyframe flange

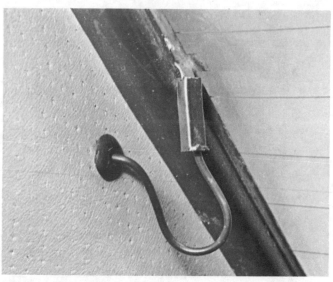

32.1 Rear screen element connection

2 On some versions, the glass is bonded directly to the bodyshell, without the use of a rubber weatherseal surround. In this case leave the removal and refitting to the experts.

33 Opening side window – removal and refitting

1 This type of window is fitted to two-door Saloon models.
2 Unscrew the window catch.
3 Disconnect the window at the hinges.
4 The toggle type lock can be removed if the pivot pin peening is drilled out and the pin then driven out.
5 Unscrew the anchor plate from the glass.
6 Reassembly and refitting are reversals of removal and dismantling, but peen the edges of the pivot pin holes to prevent the pin dropping out whilst in service.

34 Fixed side window – removal and refitting

1 This type of window is fitted to the rear quarter of Hatchback models.
2 Have an assistant ready to catch the window as it is pressed

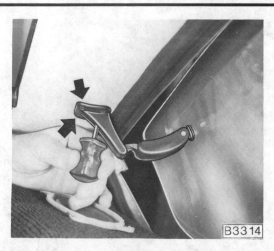

Fig. 11.48 Opening side window catch retaining screw removal (Sec 33)

Other screws arrowed

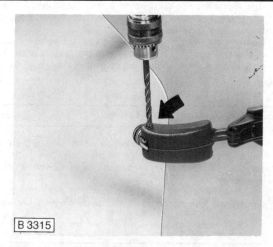

Fig. 11.49 Drilling out pivot pin hole peening – arrowed (Sec 33)

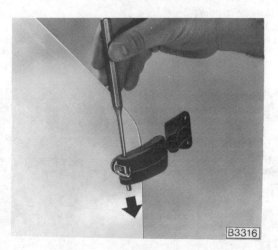

Fig. 11.50 Drive out pivot pin in direction of arrow (Sec 33)

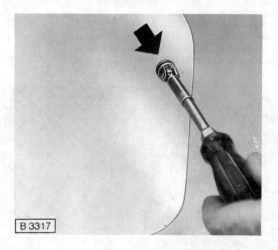

Fig. 11.51 Unscrew anchor plate from glass – arrowed (Sec 33)

Fig. 11.52 Removing fixed side window in direction of arrow (Sec 34)

Fig. 11.53 Installing fixed type side window (Sec 34)

Arrow indicates installation cord

outward by applying pressure to the inside of the glass.

3 Refit the window by using the cord method described in Section 31 for the windscreen. Have the ends of the cord crossed over, at the top front corner of the window.

4 Engage the rubber surround with the body at the bottom edge and with your assistant applying firm pressure to the outside of the glass, pull the ends of the cord to engage the lip of the rubber over the body flange.

35 Front seat – removal and refitting

1 Unbolt and remove the U-shaped clips which secure the tubular crossmembers of the seats to the floor (photo).

2 Release the seat adjuster and move the seats rearwards off their slide rails (photo).

3 Refit by reversing the removal operations, but make sure that the plastic slippers are not displaced as the seats are engaged on the runners.

36 Rear seat – removal and refitting

Saloon models

1 Pull the two loops at the base of the seat cushion to release the retainers (photo).

2 Remove the cushion.

3 Prise up the metal tabs at the base of the seat back, then lift the seat back upwards off the securing hooks (photo).

4 Refitting is a reversal of removal.

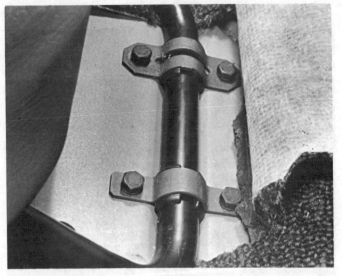

35.1 Front seat mounting bolts

Hatchback models

5 Before removing the rear seat on these models, remove the luggage compartment cover and then depress the seat back locking plungers.

6 Fold down the seat back and unbolt the seat from the floor.

7 Refitting is a reversal of removal.

35.2 Front seat slide and rake adjuster

36.1 Rear seat cushion catch (Saloon)

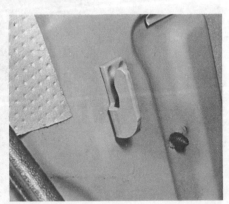

36.3 Rear seat retaining hook

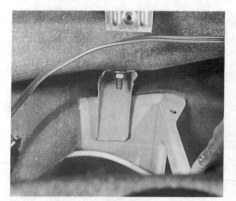

37.7 Facia mounting bracket

37.8A Facia lower mounting screw (over steering column)

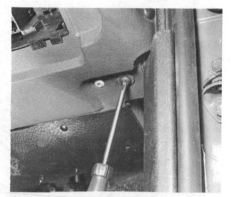

37.8B Facia lower mounting screw (underside on right, near fusebox)

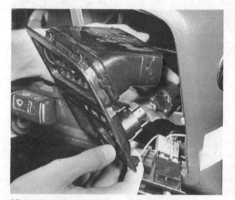

37.11 Removing fresh air vents and switch panel

39.3A Cassette/oddments box removal: undo retaining screws ...

39.3B ... remove the outer trim ...

37 Facia panel – removal and refitting

1 Disconnect the battery.
2 Remove the instrument panel as described in Chapter 12.
3 Take off the lower cover panels from under the facia panel.
4 Remove the switches, switch panels, radio, clock and other electrical accessories as described in Chapter 12.
5 Disconnect the heater control panel as described in Chapter 2.
6 Remove the glove compartment (Section 38 of this Chapter).
7 Reach through the apertures left by removal of the instrument panel and the glove compartment and unscrew the nuts from the facia retaining brackets (photo).
8 Remove the facia panel lower mounting screws (photos).
9 Remove the shrouds from the upper part of the steering column.
10 Disconnect the air ducts from the windscreen demister outlet slots.
11 Prise out the fresh air grilles and the door window demister grilles from the facia panel (photo).
12 Pull the facia panel towards you and remove it sideways from the vehicle interior.
13 Refitting is a reversal of removal.

38 Glove compartment – removal and refitting

1 Open the door of the glove compartment and unscrew and remove the fixing screws from around the edge of the liner.
2 On some models a glove compartment lamp is fitted which is actuated by a 'door open' type plunger switch. Where the lamp is fitted, withdraw the liner carefully until the electrical leads can be disconnected.
3 Refitting is a reversal of removal.

39 Centre console – removal and refitting

1 Several different types of centre console and centre oddments box

(which is situated below the heater control panel and above the centre console) may be fitted according to level of trim and equipment (Fig. 11.54).
2 All may be removed in similar fashion to that described below after first removing the oddments box and detaching any additional switches.
3 Generally, these consoles and oddments boxes are screwed and/or clipped in place, the screws being concealed under small plastic covers, which should be gently levered out to reveal the screw head (photos).
4 The centre console is secured by two self-tapping screws which are hidden under square cover plates on the top surface of the console.

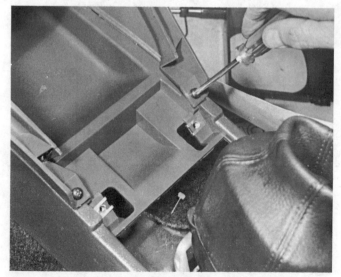

39.3C ... and remove the box retaining screws

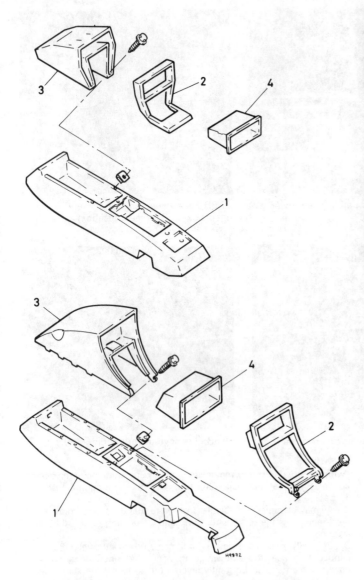

39.5 Console retaining screw viewed with cover plate removed

5   Prise out the plates with a small blade and then extract the screws (photo).
6   The console can be slid up the gear lever and swivelled out of the way, but if for any reason it must be removed completely then the gear lever knob will first have to be taken off. To do this, wrap a cloth which has been soaked in boiling water around the knob. This should expand the knob sufficiently to enable it to be pulled from the lever. *Take great care to protect your hands from the boiling water.*
7   Refitting is a reversal of removal.

40 Head restraints – removal and refitting

Standard seats

1   Using a piece of hooked wire pull out the spring clips from the head restraint mounting stems (Fig. 11.55).
2   Pull the head restraint up and out of the seat back.
3   Before fitting a head restraint, fit the clip so that its shaped section is towards the rear of the vehicle.

Sports seats

4   Press the head restraint downwards as far as it will go.
5   Have an assistant press the seat backrest at the points shown (Fig. 11.56) to release the springs. With the assistant applying pressure, pull sharply upwards on the head restraint to remove it.

Fig. 11.54 Two types of centre console assemblies (Sec 39)

1 Centre console	3 Top console
2 Cover	4 Oddments box

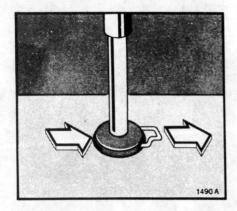

Fig. 11.55 Head restraint clip removal in direction of arrows (Sec 40)

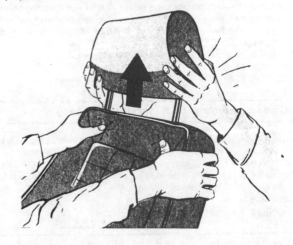

Fig. 11.56 Head restraint removal from Sports seat (Sec 40)

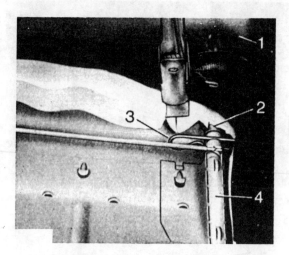

Fig. 11.57 Head restraint fitting details (Sec 40)

1   Head restraint
2   Retaining sleeve
3   Retaining spring
4   Rod

Fig. 11.58 Seat belt arrangement on 2-door model (Sec 41)

6   Refit by inserting the head restraint rods into the backrest. It should be possible to feel the retaining springs engaging with the notches in the rods.

41 Seat belts – care and maintenance

1   Periodically inspect the seat belts for fraying or other damage. If evident, renew the belt.
2   Cleaning of the belt fabric should be done with a damp cloth and a little detergent, nothing else.
3   Never alter the original belt anchorage and, if the belts are ever removed, always take careful note of the sequence of mounting components. If the washers or collars are incorrectly positioned, the belt will not swivel as it has been designed to do (photo).
4   On two-door models, the belt retractor is hidden behind the rear quarter trim panel. To gain access to the retractor, remove the trim panel.
5   This is carried out by first removing the seat cushion and then pulling the trim panel clips out of their holes by jerking the panel away with the fingers as described in Section 12 for the door panel.

42 Exterior rear view mirror glass – removal and refitting

1   Insert a wooden or plastic wedge at the outside edge of the mirror

glass and carefully lever the glass free. Disconnect the adjuster links and heater wires, as applicable, and remove the glass (photos).
2   Refit in the reverse order to removal. Be careful when pressing the glass home: the sudden movement as the ball enters its socket may cause the glass to break.

43 Exterior rear view mirror (manual) – removal and refitting

1   Working inside the vehicle, prise off the mirror remote control handle cover (photo).
2   Prise off the triangular shaped plate (photo).
3   Extract the three mirror mounting screws which are now exposed and have an assistant support the mirror head on the outside of the vehicle (photo).
4   Refitting is a reversal of removal.

Refitting after impact

5   For safety reasons, the manually adjusted exterior mirrors are designed to break free from their mountings when struck.
6   To refit a mirror which has been disengaged, offer the mirror to the linkage. Make sure that the linkage is correctly engaged, then thump the mirror base home with the hand.

41.3 Seat belt anchor bolt to floor

42.1A Remove mirror glass by levering with wooden wedge

42.1B With glass freed from balljoint, disconnect linkage

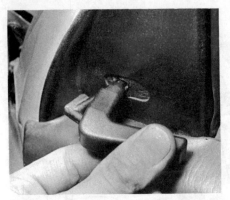

43.1 Remove exterior mirror handle cover ...

43.2 ... then remove the cover plate ...

43.3 ... and extract the mounting screws

44 Exterior rear view mirror (powered) – removal and refitting

1   Remove the door trim panel, as described in Section 12, and unplug the mirror wiring harness connector.
2   Prise off the mounting cover and remove the three mounting screws, supporting the mirror as the screws are removed. Remove the mirror from the vehicle.
3   Refit in the reverse order to removal.

45 Exterior rear view mirror motor – removal and refitting

1   Remove the mirror glass, as just described.
2   Remove the door trim panel, as described in Section 12, and unplug the mirror wiring harness connector.
3   Fold the mirror forwards and unscrew and remove the motor.
4   Refit in the reverse order to removal.

46 Sunroof (removable type) – operation

1   To raise or lower this type of sunroof (optional equipment) rotate the control knob.
2   To remove the sunroof, set it in the closed position and then use a coin to turn the screw which is located in the centre of the control knob.

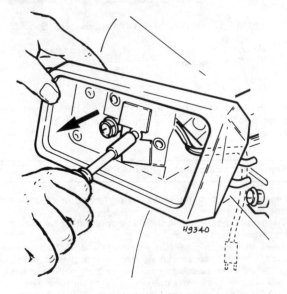

Fig. 11.59 Removing a mirror motor (Sec 45)

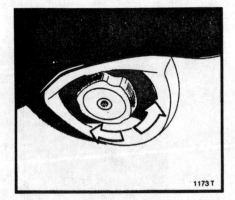

Fig. 11.60 Removable sunroof control knob (Sec 46)

Operate sunroof by rotating knob as arrowed

Fig. 11.61 Turning sunroof control knob centre screw (Sec 46)

3 Slightly raise the sunroof panel and press the release lever to disengage the safety catch (Fig. 11.62).

4 From outside the vehicle, pivot the sunroof panel and lift it from its retainers at the front edge.

5 Rotate the control knob to the fully closed position.

6 A storage bag is provided on the back of the rear seat. Store the sunroof glass panel so that its curved surface is towards the seat back and the hinge tongues pointing upward (Fig. 11.63).

7 To refit the sunroof, set the control knob to 'open' and engage the panel in the retainers and with the safety catch.

47 Sunroof (sliding type) – operation, removal and refitting

1 To open this type of sliding roof, pull the control handle out of its recess until it reaches its stop.

2 Slide the sunroof panel as required and lock it by returning the handle to its recess.

3 To remove the sliding roof, pull the control handle fully down and slide the panel rearward.

4 Extract the screws from the handle recess liner.

5 Peel down the headlining at the retaining springs.

6 Unscrew the front and rear guide plates after pulling the headlining aside (Fig. 11.65).

7 Fold the headlining upwards and towards the front of the vehicle with the retaining springs under tension.

8 Pull the sliding roof panel towards the front of the vehicle on one side until the rear slide (B) is level with the bead (C) (Fig. 11.66).

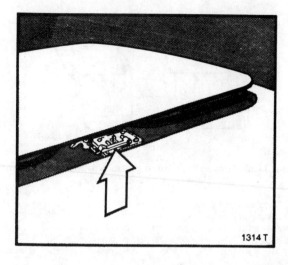

Fig. 11.62 Sunroof safety catch – arrowed (Sec 46)

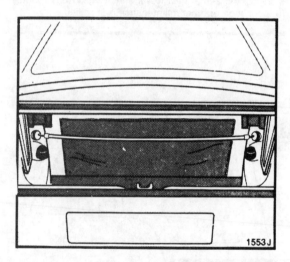

Fig. 11.63 Removable type sunroof panel stowage (Sec 46)

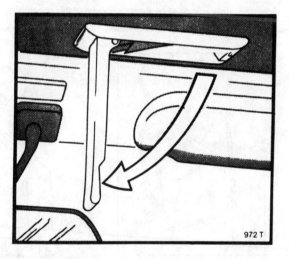

Fig. 11.64 Sliding type sunroof control handle (Sec 47)

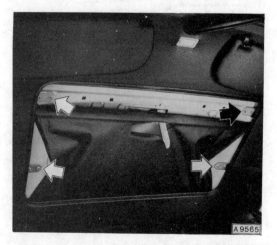

Fig. 11.65 Sliding sunroof guide plates – arrowed (Sec 47)

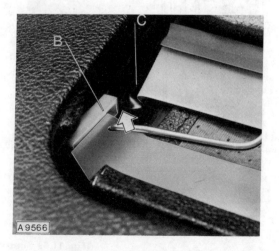

Fig. 11.66 Sunroof slide (B) and bead (C) (Sec 47)

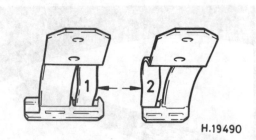

H.19490

Fig. 11.67 Sunroof retaining plates showing carrier arm clamps (1 and 2) (Sec 47)

9 Lift the sunroof panel from the vehicle.
10 Refitting is a reversal of removal, but observe the following points.
11 Apply a little grease to the roof frame slide-rails.
12 Check that both support levers point outward.
13 When refitting the retaining plates, make sure that the angled carrier arms move freely (Fig. 11.67).

48 Sunroof (slide/tilt type) – operation and maintenance

1 A slide-and-tilt glass panel sunroof is available as an optional extra on most models. It is operated by a crank handle. After depressing the

2167 T

Fig. 11.68 Sunroof crank handle – release button arrowed (Sec 48)

release button, turning the handle anti-clockwise will open the roof. Turning the handle clockwise when the roof is closed causes its rear end to tilt up for ventilation.
2 A louvred panel, known as a sunshade, can be drawn out under the glass. This should only be done when the glass is closed or in the 'tilt' position.
3 Maintenance is confined to checking periodically that the drain hoses are not blocked at their lower ends (Fig. 11.69) (photo).
4 No lubrication or other maintenance is specified.

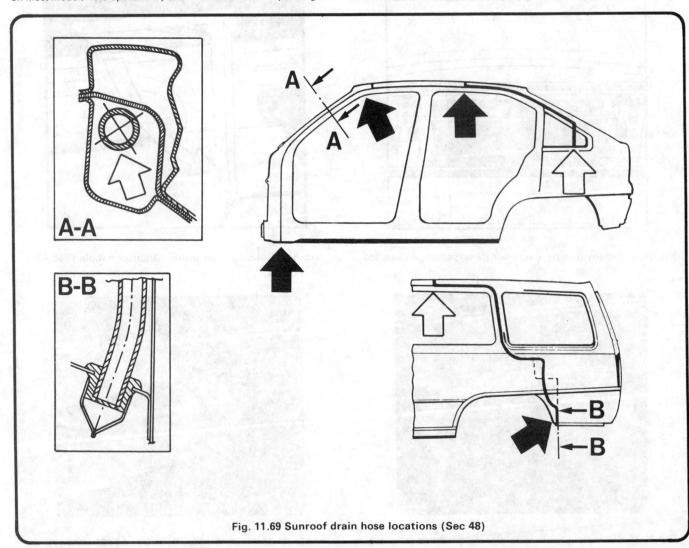

Fig. 11.69 Sunroof drain hose locations (Sec 48)

48.3 Slide and tilt sunroof drain point. Probe with wire to ensure it is clear

49 Sunroof (slide/tilt type) – component renewal in situ

1 The operations in this Section do not require the complete sunroof to be removed from the vehicle.

Glass panel

2 Close the panel and push the sunshade fully rearwards. Remove the clips from the slide block guides.
3 Unscrew the panel from the slide block guides on both sides and remove it (Fig. 11.71).
4 Before refitting a new panel, measure the distance between the attaching flanges. Bend the flanges if necessary to achieve the desired dimension (Fig. 11.72).
5 Remove the protective sheet from the new panel and fit it with the chequered edge forwards. Raise the panel into the 'tilt' position and fit it loosely to the slide block guides.
6 Before tightening the slide block guide screws, close the panel and adjust its position as shown in Fig. 11.73 then tighten the screws.

Controlled gap seal

7 The 'controlled gap seal' is the seal which surrounds the glass panel.
8 Remove the glass panel, as previously described.
9 Strip off the seal and clean off old sealing compound, being careful not to damage the glass.
10 Apply sealant (GM 90140944, or equivalent) all around the edge of the glass panel (Fig. 11.74).
11 Fit the new seal, starting at the middle of the left-hand edge and working round. Immediately refit the panel and check that the seal fits properly in the closed position. If the specified sealant has been used, it will not set for an hour or so, during which time the position of the seal can be altered slightly to provide a good fit. Make sure that the panel height adjustment is correct (paragraph 6).

Gutter

12 Remove the glass panel, as previously described.
13 Remove the two Torx screws which secure the gutter. Lift the gutter out of the cut-out in the roof (Fig. 11.75).
14 Refit the gutter to the cut-out at an angle, pushing it up to the stop on both sides so that the retaining lugs are forced into the gutter guides.
15 Refit and tighten the Torx screws.
16 Refit and adjust the glass panel.

Sunshade

17 Remove the gutter, as just described.
18 Carefully prise the four sunshade springs out of the roof guides,

using a plastic implement to avoid damage. Withdraw the sunshade from the guides (Fig. 11.76).
19 Refit in the reverse order to removal. Make sure that all the spring ends enter the guides.

Crank drive

20 Remove the central securing screw from the handle – the screw head is concealed by a plastic cover. Pull off the handle and unclip its recessed backplate, being careful not to damage the headlining.
21 Remove the two securing screws and withdraw the crank drive mechanism.
22 When refitting a new crank drive mechanism, adjust it as follows.
23 If the sunroof is open, temporarily refit the crank drive and close the roof, then remove the crank drive again.
24 Turn the drive pinion by hand – **not** with the handle – until the stop pin emerges from the housing (Fig. 11.77).
25 Refit and secure the crank drive with the stop pin facing forwards. Refit the backplate and handle.

Wind deflector

26 Remove the glass panel, as previously described.
27 Crank the handle to move the slide blocks rearwards until the wind deflector can be raised and removed.
28 Transfer the lifters and bearing blocks to the new deflector; secure them with circlips (Fig. 11.78).
29 Fit the new deflector, bring the slide blocks back to the closed position and refit the glass panel.

50 Sunroof (slide/tilt type) – removal and refitting (complete)

1 Disconnect the battery earth lead.
2 Remove the glass panel, as described in Section 49.
3 Remove the crank handle and its backplate.
4 Remove the interior lamp and grab handles. Loosen the door seals at their top edges. Remove or loosen all interior trim panels which abut the headlining, then open the tailgate and slide the headlining out rearwards, freeing it from the rear of the roof frame.
5 Disconnect the four drain hoses from the corners of the sunroof frame.
6 With the help of an assistant, remove the sunroof frame securing screws and withdraw the unit through the tailgate.
7 Before refitting, check the adjustment of the unit by turning the crank handle as far as its stop. In this position, the cable guide pin should be aligned with the notch in the roof guide (Fig. 11.79). If this is not so, remove the crank drive and adjust it, as described earlier. Align the guide pin with the notch and refit the crank drive.
8 Secure the unit to the roof – the M6 screws must be renewed, but the M5 ones can be re-used. Refit the headlining and the displaced trim, then refit and adjust the glass panel.
9 Refit the grab handles and interior light, then reconnect the battery earth lead.

51 Sunroof (slide/tilt type) – component renewal (unit removed)

1 The sunroof must be removed, as described in Section 50, before these items can be renewed.

Operating cables

2 The operating cables must always be renewed in pairs, even if only one is broken.
3 With the sunroof removed, unscrew the gutter securing screws and remove the gutter. Also remove the crank drive unit.
4 Pull the plugs out of the rear ends of the roof guides.
5 Pull the cables out of the roof guides. Separate them from the slide block guides (Fig. 11.80).
6 Offer the new cables to the roof guides. Fit the slide block guides and secure them with the guide pins and circlips. The circlips go on the outboard sides of the guides (Fig. 11.81).
7 Push the cable guides forwards until their pins are aligned, as shown in Fig. 11.79. Adjust the crank drive, as described earlier.
8 Refit the roof guide plugs and the gutter.

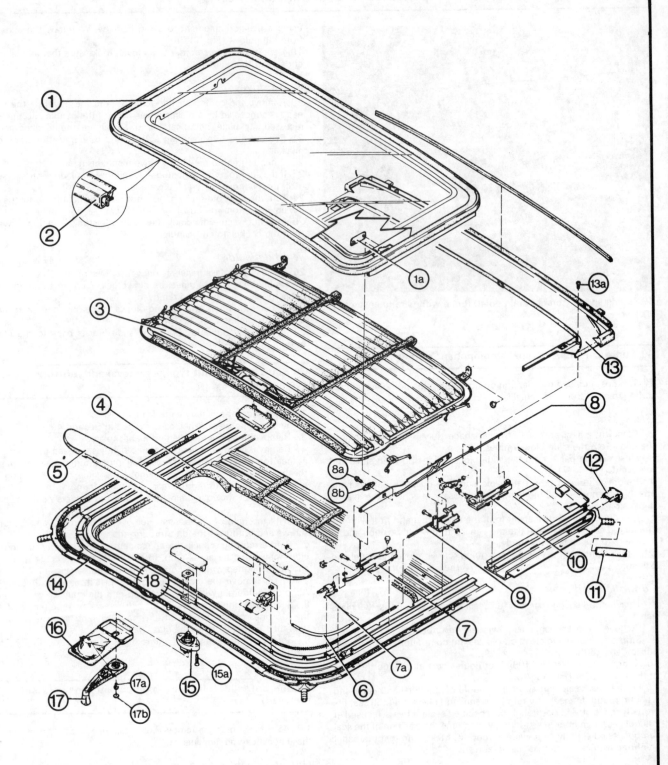

Fig. 11.70 Exploded view of the slide/tilt sunroof components (Sec 49)

1	Glass panel	7	Front guide	11	Drain hose	15a Screw
1a	Clip	7a	Slide block	12	Roof guide plug	16 Handle backplate
2	Controlled gap seal	8	Slide block guide	13	Gutter	17 Crank handle
3	Sunshade	8a	Screw	13a	Gutter screw	17a Screw
4	Seal	8b	Lockplate	14	Seal	17b Screw cover
5	Wind deflector	9	Cable	15	Crank drive	18 Frame
6	Lifter	10	Gutter guide			

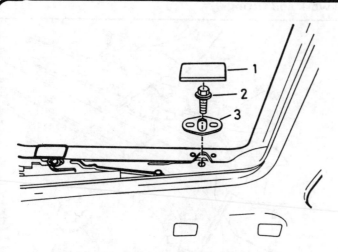

Fig. 11.71 Slide block guide bolt assembly showing cover (1), guide bolt (2) and lockplate (3) (Sec 49)

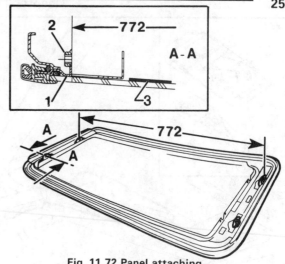

Fig. 11.72 Panel attaching flange distance (dimensions in mm) (Sec 49)

1 Flange   2 Nut   3 Protective sheet

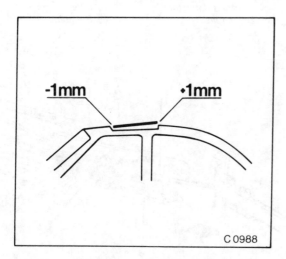

Fig. 11.73 Glass panel fitting position (Sec 49)

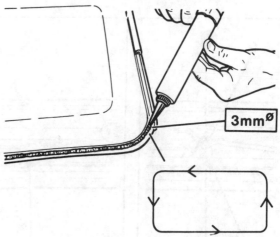

Fig. 11.74 Apply sealant to the glass panel as indicated (Sec 49)

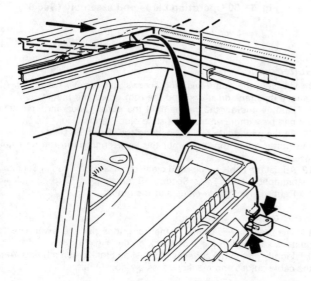

Fig. 11.75 Removing the gutter – inset shows retaining lug location (Sec 49)

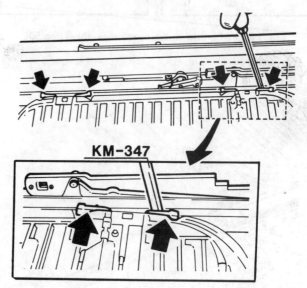

Fig. 11.76 Sunshade retaining spring locations – arrowed (Sec 49)

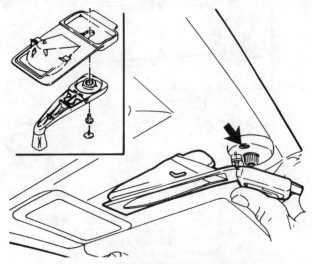

Fig. 11.77 Crank handle and drive assembly (stop pin location arrowed) (Sec 49)

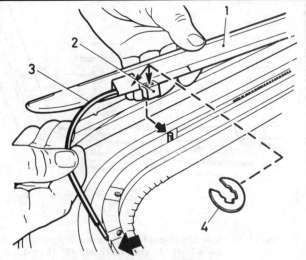

Fig. 11.78 Wind deflector mounting assembly (Sec 49)

1	Wind deflector	3	Lifter spring
2	Mount	4	Retaining clip

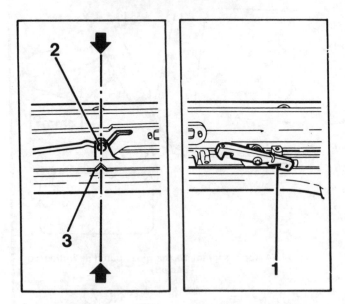

Fig. 11.79 Aligning the sunroof assembly (Sec 50)

1	Lever caught in recess	3	Adjustment notch
2	Guide pin		

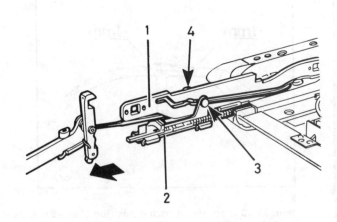

Fig. 11.80 Operating cable end assembly (Sec 51)

1	Slide block guides	3	Bolt
2	Cable	4	Retaining clip

Gutter guide

9 Unscrew the gutter securing screws and remove the gutter. Also remove the crank drive unit and the roof guide end plugs.
10 Partly withdraw the cables until the gutter guide and connecting rod can be withdrawn from the slide block guide (Fig. 11.82).
11 Fit the new guide and connecting rod. Push the slide block guide and gutter guide forwards until the lever engages in the roof guide recess.
12 Adjust the cable guides and crank drive, as described in Section 51 (paragraphs 6 and 7) and Section 49, paragraphs 22 to 25 inclusive.
13 Refit the roof guide plugs and the gutter.

Front guide

14 The procedure is similar to that for gutter guide renewal. The front guide is attached to the slide block guide (Fig. 11.83).
15 Lightly grease the surfaces of the slide block when refitting. Adjust the cable guides and crankdrive, as previously described.

Slide block

16 Proceed as for cable renewal until the slide block guide is accessible. Remove the circlip and separate the slide block from the slide block guide (Fig. 11.84).

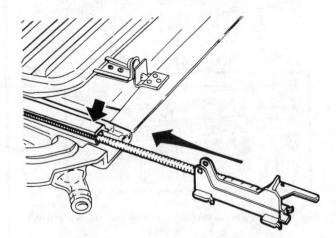

Fig. 11.81 Installing the cables (Sec 51)

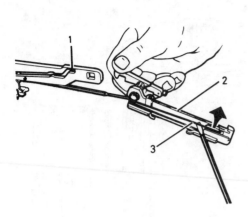

Fig. 11.82 Gutter guide assembly (Sec 51)

1   Slide block guide   2   Gutter guide   3   Connecting rod

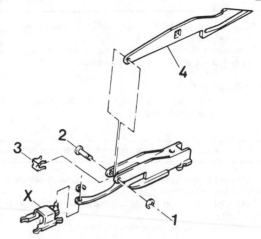

Fig. 11.83 Front guide assembly (Sec 51)

1   Circlip   4   Front guide
2   Pin   X   Slide block
3   Spring clip

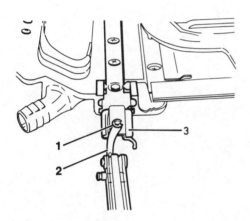

Fig. 11.84 Slide block assembly (Sec 51)

1   Retaining ring   2   Connecting rod   3   Slide block

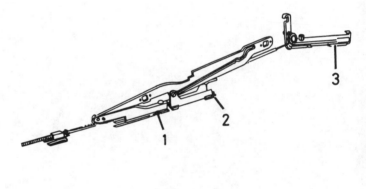

Fig. 11.85 Slide block guide assembly (Sec 51)

1   Front guide   2   Cable guide   3   Gutter guide

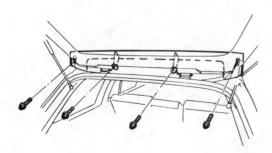

Fig. 11.86 Rear air deflector bolts (Estate) (Sec 52)

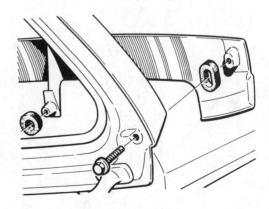

Fig. 11.87 Air deflector seal washers (Estate) (Sec 52)

17 Fit the new slide block and secure with a new circlip. Lightly grease the surfaces of the slide block.
18 Reassemble in the reverse order to dismantling; adjusting the cable guides and crank drive as previously described.

Slide block guide

19 Again, the procedure is similar to that for cable renewal. Refer to Fig. 11.85 for assembly details.

52 Rear air deflector (Estate) – removal and refitting

1   Open the tailgate and remove the four screws which secure the air deflector to the tailgate.
2   Remove the air deflector, noting the position of the sealing washers (Fig. 11.87).
3   Refit in the reverse order to removal.

53 Rear vent grille (Estate) – removal and refitting

1   The pillar vent grille is a snap fit into the body pillar. Remove it by prising it free, being careful not to damage the paintwork or the attaching lugs.
2   When fitting new grommets, use non-hardening sealing compound in the grommet holes.
3   Refit the grille by snapping it home.

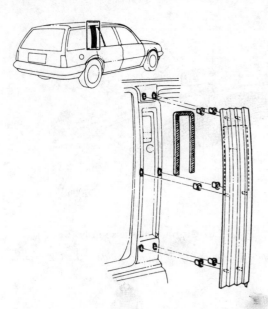

Fig. 11.88 Pillar vent grille (Estate) (Sec 53)

Chapter 12 Electrical system

For modifications, and information applicable to later models, see Supplement at end of manual

Contents

Specifications

System type	12V negative earth. Belt-driven alternator and pre-engaged starter motor
Battery capacity	36 or 44Ah
Alternator	
Type	Bosch or Delco-Remy
Output	45, 55 or 65A depending upon model
Brush wear limit:	
Bosch	5 mm (0.20 in) protrusion
Delco-Remy	11 mm (0.43 in) overall length
Wiper blades	Champion C-4501
Starter motor	
Type	Pre-engaged Bosch or Delco-Remy
Brush wear limit:	
Bosch (13S engine)	11.5 mm (0.45 in)
Bosch (16S and 18E engines)	13.0 mm (0.51 in)
Delco-Remy	5.0 mm (0.20 in)
Commutator minimum diameter:	
Bosch (13S engine)	31.2 mm (1.23 in)
Bosch (16S and 18E engines)	33.5 mm (1.32 in)
Delco-Remy	37.0 mm (1.46 in)

Fuses – early models

Number	Circuit protected	Rating (A)
1	LH parking and tail, number plate, engine compartment lamps, instrument illumination	7.5
2	RH parking and tail lamps	7.5
3	Rear foglamps	7.5
4	Interior, luggage compartment and hazard warning lamps. Clock and radio	15
5	Screen wipers and horn	30
6	Reversing lamps, cigar lighter, automatic choke, instruments	20
7	Direction indicator and stop-lamps	10
8	Heated rear screen	20
9	Heater blower	20
10	Radiator cooling fan	25
11	Spare	–

Number	Circuit protected	Rating (A)
12	Spare	–
13	Spare	–
14	Spare	–
15	Spare	–
16	Spare	–
17	Spare	–

Fuses – later models

Number	Circuit protected	Rating (A)
1	LH parking and tail lamps	7.5
2	RH parking and tail lamps	7.5
3	Spare	–
4	Interior lights, hazard warning flasher, clock, radio	15
5	Front and rear wipers and washers, horn	30
6	Reversing lights, cigarette lighter, automatic choke, instruments	20
7	Direction indicators, stop-lamps	10
8	Heated rear window	20
9	Heater blower	20
10	Radiator cooling fan	25
11	Fuel injection system	15
12	Front foglights	15
13	Auxiliary driving lights	15
14	LH main beam	10
15	RH main beam	10
16	LH dipped beam	10
17	RH dipped beam, rear foglight	10

Bulbs

Lamp	Wattage
Headlamp	60/55
Front parking lamp	4
Direction indicator lamp	21
Stop/tail lamp	21/5
Rear number plate lamp	10
Reversing lamp	21
Engine compartment lamp	10
Luggage compartment lamp	10
Glovebox	5
Instrument warning (except ignition/charge warning) lamps	1.2
Ignition/charge warning lamp	3
Cigar lighter illumination	1.2
Switch illumination	1.2
Rear foglamps	21
Ashtray lamp	1.2
Clock illumination	1.2
Selector lever index (automatic transmission)	1.2
Choke ON switch	1.2
Direction indicator side repeater lamp	5
Auxiliary driving lamps	55
Vehicle interior lamp	10

Torque wrench settings

	Nm	lbf ft
Alternator pulley nut:		
Bosch	40	30
Delco-Remy	70	52
Alternator mounting bracket bolts	40	30
Alternator pivot and adjustment bolts	34	25
Starter motor mounting bolts:		
1.3	25	18
1.6, 1.8	45	33

1 General description

The major components of the 12 volt negative earth system consist of a 12 volt battery, an alternator (driven from the crankshaft pulley), and a starter motor.

The battery supplies a steady amount of current for the ignition, lighting and other electrical circuits and provides a reserve of power when the current consumed by the electrical equipment exceeds that being produced by the alternator.

The alternator has its own regulator which ensures a high output if the battery is in a low state of charge and the demand from the electrical equipment is high, and a low output if the battery is fully charged and there is little demand from the electrical equipment.

When fitting electrical accessories to cars with a negative earth system it is important, if they contain silicon diodes or transistors, that they are connected correctly, otherwise serious damage may result to the components concerned. Items such as radios, tape players, electronic ignition systems, electronic tachometer, automatic dipping etc, should all be checked for correct polarity.

It is important that the battery leads are always disconnected if the battery is to be boost charged. Also, if body repairs are to be carried out using electrical welding equipment, the alternator must be disconnected otherwise serious damage can be caused.

2 Routine maintenance – electrical system

Carry out the following procedures at the intervals given in Routine Maintenance at the beginning of the manual.

1 Remove the battery cell covers and check the electrolyte level, as described in Section 3. Top up if necessary. Note that topping-up is not usually necessary for a low maintenance battery used under normal conditions (photo).

2 Check and, if necessary, adjust the alternator drivebelt, referring to Chapter 2 for details.

3 Periodically check for the satisfactory operation of the lights (front and rear), the windscreen wipers and washers, and the horn.

3 Battery – maintenance and inspection

1 Normal weekly battery maintenance consists of checking the electrolyte level of each cell to ensure that the separators are covered by 5 mm (0.2 in) of electrolyte. If the level has fallen, top up the battery using purified (distilled) water only. Do not overfill. If the battery is overfilled, or any electrolyte spilled, immediately wipe away the excess, as the electrolyte, which is dilute sulphuric acid, attacks and corrodes most metals it comes into contact with very quickly.

2 As well as keeping the terminals clean and covered with a light film of petroleum jelly, the top of the battery, and especially the top of the cells, should be kept clean and dry. This helps prevent corrosion and ensures that the battery does not become partially discharged by leakage through dampness and dirt.

3 Every three months remove the battery and inspect the support tray, the battery clamp and the battery terminals for corrosion. This has the appearance of white fluffy deposits and if it exists it should be cleaned off using warm water to which a little ammonia or washing soda has been added. Treat the battery terminals with petroleum jelly and other metalwork with rust preventative paint.

4 If topping-up the battery becomes excessive and there has been no leakage of electrolyte then it is likely that the battery is being overcharged and it will have to be checked by an auto-electrician. An elderly battery may need more frequent topping-up than a new one because it will take a bigger charge. There is no need to worry about this provided that it gives good service.

5 With the battery on the bench at the three monthly interval check, measure the specific gravity of the electrolyte with a hydrometer to determine the state of charge and condition of the electrolyte. There should be very little variation between individual cells and, if a variation in excess of 0.025 exists it will be due to either:

(a) *Loss of electrolyte from the battery at some time caused by spillage or a leak, resulting in a drop in the specific gravity of the electrolyte when the deficiency was made up with purified water instead of fresh electrolyte, or*

(b) *An internal short circuit caused by buckling of the plates or similar malady pointing to the likelihood of total battery failure in the near future*

6 The specific gravity of the electrolyte for fully charged and fully discharged conditions at different temperatures of the electrolyte is given below.

Fully discharged	Electrolyte temperature	Fully charged
1.098	38°C (100°F)	1.268
1.102	32°C (90°F)	1.272
1.106	27°C (80°F)	1.276
1.110	21°C (70°F)	1.280
1.114	16°C (60°F)	1.284
1.118	10°C (50°F)	1.288
1.122	4°C (40°F)	1.292
1.126	− 1.5°C (30°F)	1.296

7 On most models, a maintenance-free battery is fitted. With this battery, no topping-up is required, but the terminals and battery mounting tray must be kept clean as previously described (photo).

8 The significance of the battery condition indicator on the top of the battery should be appreciated by reference to Fig. 12.1.

9 If a yellow indicator without a green dot is observed, do not use jump start leads or attempt to use a mains charger, but consult your dealer as the battery is almost certainly unfit for further use.

2.1 Topping-up the battery

3.7 Maintenance-free type battery

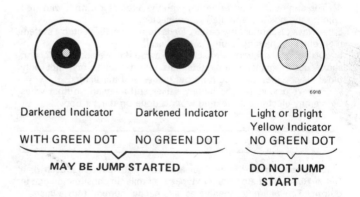

Fig. 12.1 Battery condition indicator on maintenance-free type battery (Sec 3)

4   Battery – removal and refitting

1   The battery is located on a support plate fitted to the left-hand wing valance in the engine compartment. Disconnect the negative and then the positive leads from the battery terminals after slackening the securing nuts and bolts.
2   Release the battery clamp plate and carefully lift the battery from the support plate. Hold it vertically to ensure that none of the electrolyte is spilled (photo).
3   Refitting is a direct reversal of this procedure. Reconnect the positive lead before the negative lead and smear the terminals with petroleum jelly to prevent corrosion; never use ordinary grease. Do not overtighten the terminal securing bolts, nor hammer the fittings on. The terminals are made of lead and are easily damaged.

5   Battery – charging

1   In winter time when heavy demand is placed on the battery, such as when starting from cold and when much electrical equipment is continually in use, it is a good idea to occasionally have the battery fully charged from an external source at the rate of 3.5 to 4 amps.
2   Continue to charge the battery at this rate until no further rise in specific gravity is noted over a four hour period.
3   Alternatively, a trickle charger charging at a rate of 1.5 amps can safely be used overnight.
4   Specially rapid 'boost' charges which are claimed to restore the power of the battery in one to two hours should be avoided as they can cause serious damage to the battery plates through overheating.
5   While charging the battery note that the temperature of the electrolyte should never exceed 38°C (100°F) and remember that the gas produced in the cells contains hydrogen which is flammable and explosive, so do not smoke or bring naked lights near the top of the battery.
6   Note the reservations regarding charging a maintenance-free type battery in Section 3.
7   Always disconnect the battery positive lead before connecting the mains charger to the battery.

6   Alternator – special precautions

1   If there are indications that the charging system is malfunctioning in any way, care must be taken when diagnosing faults otherwise damage of a serious and expensive nature may occur to parts which are in fact quite serviceable. The following basic requirements must be observed at all times, therefore, if damage is to be prevented.
2   All alternator systems use a negative earth. Even the simple mistake of connecting the battery the wrong way round could burn out the alternator diodes quickly.
3   Before disconnecting any wires in the system the engine and ignition circuits should be switched off. This will minimise the risk of short-circuits in the system.
4   The engine must never be run with the alternator output wire (red wire on the positive terminal) disconnected.
5   Always disconnect the battery leads from the car's electrical system if an outside charging source is being used.
6   Do not use test wire connections that could move accidentally and short-circuit against nearby terminals. Short-circuits may not only blow fuses – they can also burn out diodes and transistors.
7   Always disconnect the battery cables and alternator output wires before any electric arc-welding work is done on the car body.

7   Alternator – general description

Cars covered by this manual are fitted with either a Bosch or a Delco-Remy alternator; the two types are similar in construction and in output. The alternator generates alternating current (ac) which is rectified by diodes into direct current (dc) as this is the current needed for charging the battery.
The alternator is of the rotating field, ventilated design and comprises principally a laminated stator on which is wound the output

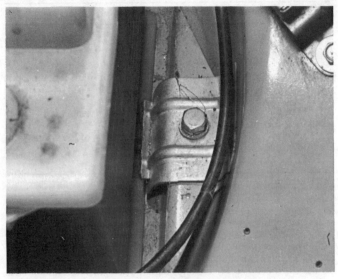
4.2 Battery fixing clamp

winding, a rotor carrying the field winding, and a diode rectifier. A voltage regulator is incorporated in the Delco-Remy alternator but on the Bosch machine it is separately mounted at the rear. The alternator generates its current in the stator windings and the rotor carries the field. The field brushes therefore are only required to carry a light current and as they run on simple slip rings they have a relatively long life. This design makes the alternator a reliable machine requiring little servicing.
The rotor is belt-driven from the crankshaft pulley through a pulley keyed to the rotor shaft. A fan adjacent to the pulley draws cooling air through the unit. Rotation is clockwise when viewed from the drive end.

8   Alternator – removal and refitting

1   Disconnect the battery leads.
2   Note the terminal connections at the rear of the alternator and disconnect the plug, multi-pin connector or terminals as appropriate (photo).
3   Undo and remove the alternator adjustment arm bolt, note the short earth wire. Slacken the lower pivot bolt and swing the alternator in

8.2 Alternator connections

8.3A Alternator adjustment link and earth cable

8.3B Alternator pivot mounting and adjustment link bolt

8.4 Alternator/engine mounting bracket

towards the engine. Lift the drivebelt off the alternator pulley (photos).
4   Remove the lower pivot bolt and lift the alternator away from the engine. Take care not to drop or knock the alternator as this can cause irreparable damage (photo).
5   Refitting the alternator is the reverse of the removal sequence. Tension the drivebelt as described in Chapter 2.

9 Alternator – fault diagnosis

Due to the specialist knowledge and equipment required to test or service an alternator it is recommended that if the performance is suspect the car be taken to an automobile electrician who will have the facilities for such work. Because of this recommendation, information is limited to the inspection and renewal of the brushes. Should the alternator not charge or the system be suspect the following points

may be checked before seeking further assistance:

(a) Check the drivebelt tension as described in Chapter 2
(b) Check condition of battery and its connections (see Section 3)
(c) Inspect all electrical cables and connections for condition and security

10 Alternator brushes – (Delco-Remy) – inspection, removal and refitting

1   Remove the alternator from the engine, as described in Section 8.
2   Scribe a line across the stator casing and front end cover to ensure correct location when reassembling.
3   Remove the three through-bolts and prise the front cover and rotor away from the rear end casing and stator. Check the condition of the

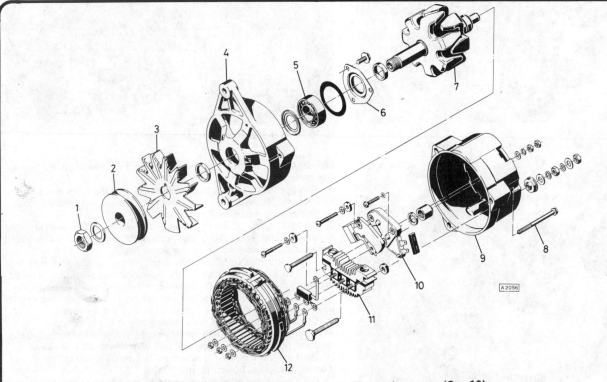

Fig. 12.2 Exploded view of Delco-Remy alternator (Sec 10)

1 Pulley nut	5 Bearing	9 Slip ring end housing/bracket	11 Diode assembly
2 Pulley	6 Bearing retainer	10 Regulator assembly	12 Stator
3 Fan	7 Rotor		
4 Drive end housing/bracket	8 Tie-bolt		

10.3A Alternator drive end bracket removed

10.3B Alternator slip rings

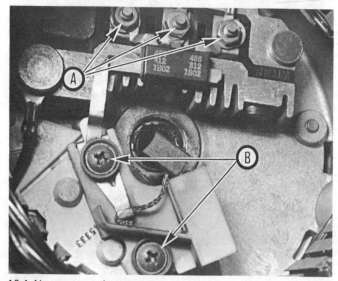

10.4 Alternator rear face
A   Stator/rectifier lead nuts (Delco-Remy)   B   Brush holder screws

10.10 Twist drill used to retract alternator brushes

10.15 Releasing alternator pulley nut

slip rings, they may require cleaning up with a fuel soaked rag or very fine glass paper (photos).

4   Remove the three nuts and washers securing the stator leads to the rectifier and lift away the stator assembly, remove the terminal screw and lift out the diode bracket (photo).

5   Undo the two screws retaining the brush holder and voltage regulator to the end casing and remove the brush holder assembly. Note insulation washers under the screw heads.

6   Check that the brushes move freely in the guides and that the length is within the limit given in the Specifications. If any doubt exists regarding the condition of the brushes the best policy is to renew them.

7   To fit new brushes, unsolder the old brush leads from the brush holder and solder on the new leads in exactly the same place.

8   Check that the new brushes move freely in the guides.

9   Before refitting the brush holder assembly, retain the brushes in the retracted position using a piece of stiff wire or a small Allen key.

10   Refit the brush holder so that the wire protrudes through the slot in the end casing as shown (photo).

11   Refit the diode bracket and stator to the casing, making sure the stator leads are in their correct positions.

12   Assemble the front casing and rotor to the stator casing ensuring that the scribe marks are aligned. Insert the three through-bolts and tighten.

13   Now carefully pull the piece of wire out of the end casing slot so that the brushes drop onto the rotor slip ring.

14 The alternator can now be refitted to the car and tested.

15 It should be remembered that if an alternator is being changed for a new or reconditioned unit then the pulley/fan assembly will be required from the original alternator. To release the pulley nut, hold the rotor shaft with an Allen key while the nut is unscrewed (photo).

11 Alternator brushes (Bosch) – inspection, removal and refitting

1 Undo and remove the two screws, spring and plain washers that secure the brush box to the rear of the brush end housing. Lift away the brush box and voltage regulator (Fig. 12.3).

2 Check that the carbon brushes are able to slide smoothly in their guides without any sign of binding.

3 Measure the length of the brushes. If they have worn below the specified limit, they must be renewed.

4 Hold the brush wire with a pair of engineer's pliers and unsolder it from the brush box. Lift away the two brushes.

5 Insert the new brushes and check to make sure that they are free to move in their guides. If they bind, lightly polish with a very fine file.

6 Solder the brush wire ends to the brush box taking care that solder is not allowed to pass to the stranded wire.

7 Whenever new brushes are fitted, new springs should also be fitted.

8 Refitting the brush box is the reverse sequence to removal.

Fig. 12.3 Alternator brush holder/regulator screws (arrowed) – Bosch (Sec 11)

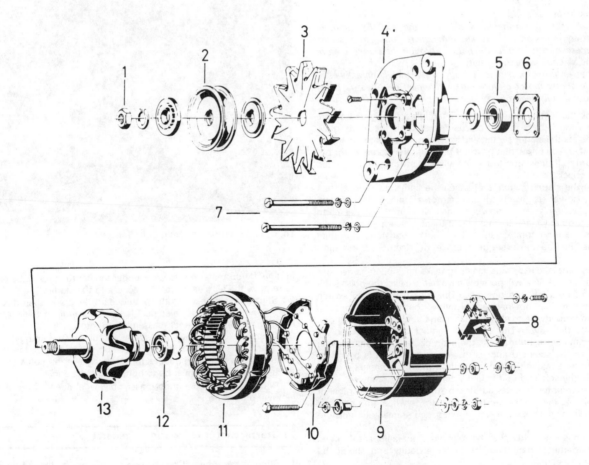

Fig. 12.4 Exploded view of Bosch alternator (Sec 11)

1 Pulley nut	5 Bearing	9 Slip ring end housing/bracket	11 Stator
2 Pulley	6 Bearing retainer	10 Collector ring endplate	12 Bearing
3 Fan	7 Tie-bolts		13 Rotor
4 Drive end bracket	8 Brush holder/regulator		

12 Starter motor – general description

The starter motor is mounted on the rear face of the crankcase and may be of either Delco-Remy or Bosch manufacture. Both makes are of the pre-engaged type, ie the drive pinion is brought into mesh with the starter ring gear on the flywheel before the main current is applied.

When the starter switch is operated, current flows from the battery to the solenoid which is mounted on the starter body. The plunger in the solenoid moves inwards, so causing a centrally pivoted lever to push the drive pinion into mesh with the starter ring gear. When the solenoid plunger reaches the end of its travel, it closes an internal contact and full starting current flows to the starter field coils. The armature is then able to rotate the crankshaft, so starting the engine.

A special freewheel clutch is fitted to the starter drive pinion so that as soon as the engine fires and starts to operate on its own it does not drive the starter motor.

When the starter switch is released, the solenoid is de-energised and a spring moves the plunger back to its rest position. This operates the pivoted lever to withdraw the drive pinion from engagement with the starter ring.

The construction of the two makes of starter motor is quite similar and the removal, refitting, dismantling, inspection and reassembly procedures detailed here will serve for both motors. Significant differences will be noted.

14.2 Starter solenoid connections

13 Starter motor – testing in the car

1   If the starter motor fails to turn the engine when the switch is operated there are five possible reasons.

    (a) The battery is faulty
    (b) The electrical connections between the switch, solenoid, battery and starter motor are somewhere failing to pass the necessary current from the battery through the starter to earth
    (c) The solenoid switch is faulty
    (d) The starter motor is mechanically or electrically defective
    (e) The starter motor pinion and/or flywheel ring gear is badly worn and in need of replacement

2   To check the battery, switch on the headlights. If they dim after a few seconds the battery is in a discharged state. If the lights glow brightly, operate the starter switch and see what happens to the lights. If they dim then you know that power is reaching the starter motor but failing to turn it. If the starter turns slowly when switched on, proceed to the next check.

3   If, when the starter switch is operated the lights stay bright, then insufficient power is reaching the motor. Remove the battery connections, starter/solenoid power connections and the engine earth strap and thoroughly clean them and refit them. Smear petroleum jelly around the battery connections to prevent corrosion. Corroded connections are the most frequent cause of electric system mal-functions.

4   When the above checks and cleaning tasks have been carried out but without success, you will possibly have heard a clicking noise each time the starter switch was operated. This was the solenoid switch operating, but it does not necessarily follow that the main contacts were closing properly (if no clicking has been heard from the solenoid, it is certainly defective). The solenoid contact can be checked by putting a voltmeter or bulb across the main cable connection on the starter side of the solenoid and earth. When the switch is operated, there should be a reading or lighted bulb. If there is no reading or no lighted bulb, the solenoid unit is faulty and should be renewed.

5   If the starter motor operates but doesn't turn the engine over then it is most probable that the starter pinion and/or flywheel ring gear are badly worn, in which case the starter motor will normally be noisy in operation.

6   Finally, if it is established that the solenoid is not faulty and 12 volts are getting to the starter, then the motor is faulty and should be removed for inspection.

14 Starter motor – removal and refitting

1   With the engine installed in the car it is easier to get to the starter motor from underneath as it is located low on the rear side of the

14.3 Starter motor mounting bolts (arrowed)

engine. If you prefer not to work under the car then it will be essential to remove the air cleaner to gain access to the starter.

2   Start by disconnecting the battery earth lead and then disconnect the solenoid and starter electrical leads. Take note of their respective locations to ensure correct reassembly (photo).

3   Unscrew and remove the starter motor unit retaining bolts and withdraw the unit from the clutch housing (photo). Note that on some models, there is an additional support bracket at the commutator end of the starter, which must be unbolted from the engine.

4   Refitting the starter motor assembly is a direct reversal of the removal procedure.

15 Starter motor renovation – general

1   Such is the inherent reliability and strength of the starter motors fitted, it is very unlikely that a motor will need dismantling until it is totally worn out and in need of replacement as a whole.

2   If, however, the motor is only a couple of years old or so and a pinion carriage, solenoid system or brush fault is suspected then remove the motor from the engine and dismantle as described in the following Sections.

Fig. 12.5 Removing solenoid retaining screws – Bosch starter (Sec 16)

Fig. 12.6 Releasing solenoid from engaging lever – Bosch starter (Sec 16)

16 Starter solenoid – removal and refitting

1 The Delco-Remy solenoid is retained by two setscrews to the pinion carriage operating mechanism casing. Remove the two setscrews, retrieve the lockwashers and remove the electrical power connection to the motor. Extract the solenoid from the end casing.
2 The Bosch starter/solenoid assembly differs from the Delco-Remy unit described above. The solenoid is retained by two screws to the end casing and is extracted after unhooking the solenoid switch shaft from the pinion carriage actuating arm mounted in the end casing.
3 Refitting of the solenoid is the reversal of removal.

17 Starter motor brushes – inspection and renewal

Bosch

1 With the starter removed from the engine and on a clean bench, begin by removing the armature end cap which is secured by two small screws on the end of the motor. Remove the armature retaining clip, washers and the rubber sealing ring which were exposed. Undo and remove the two long bolts which hold the motor assembly together. The end cover can now be removed to reveal the brushes and mounting plate (photos).
2 Take the brushes from the holder and slip the holder off the

17.1A Armature end cap (Bosch)

17.1B Starter armature clip (Bosch)

17.1C Starter motor tie-bolts (Bosch)

17.1D Removing starter motor cover (Bosch)

17.2 Brushplate holder removal (Bosch)

17.3 Bosch starter motor commutator and field coil brushes

armature shaft. Retrieve the spacer washers between the brushplate and the armature block (photo).

3 Inspect the brushes; if they are worn down to less than the minimum length given in Specifications, they should be renewed. Replacement brushes to the latest standard have no shunt wire and to fit this type first crush the old brush in a vice, or with a hammer, to remove all the carbon from the shunt wire and scrape the wire to clean it ready for soldering. Insert the wire in the hole in the new brush and spread the end out to fill the countersunk hole in the brush. Hold the

wire close under the brush with a pair of pliers to locate the wire properly for soldering and to prevent solder from penetrating the wire further than necessary as this would reduce its flexibility. A 12 to 15 watt pencil soldering iron is adequate for this job. After soldering the wire in place remove any excess solder with a file and check that the brush is an easy fit in the brush holder (photo).

4 Wipe the starter motor armature and commutator clean with a non-fluffy rag wetted with petrol.

5 Reassemble the brushes into the holder and refit the holder over the

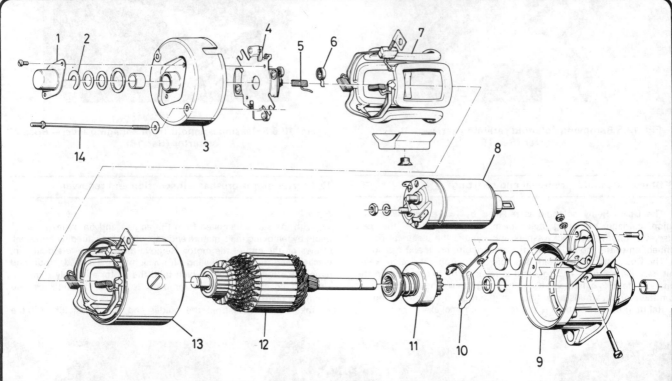

Fig. 12.7 Exploded view of Bosch starter motor (Sec 17)

1 End cap	6 Brush spring
2 Armature retaining clip	7 Field winding
3 Commutator end cover	8 Solenoid
4 Brush holder plate	9 Drive end housing
5 Brush	10 Engaging lever

11 Drive/clutch assembly
12 Armature
13 Field frame (yoke)
14 Tie-bolt

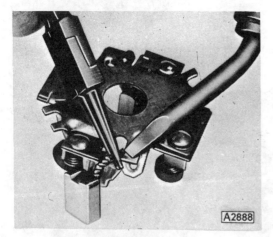

Fig. 12.8 Soldering starter motor brush leads – Bosch (Sec 17)

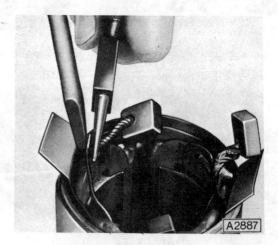

Fig. 12.9 Attaching negative brush holder leads – Bosch starter (Sec 17)

17.5 Bosch starter brush holder plate

armature shaft, remembering to fit the two washers between the holder and armature (photo).
6   Refit the motor end cover and secure with two long bolts.
7   Refit the armature shaft end cap after fitting the rubber sealing ring, washer and shaft clip.

Delco-Remy

8   With the motor removed from the engine and on a clean bench, unscrew and remove the two through-bolts from the end cover. Also remove the two small screws which secure the brush holder.
9   Remove the end cover, noting how it is keyed for the passage of the lead from the solenoid. Recover the bearing bush if it is loose; normally it will stay in the cover.
10 Remove the positive brushes (those connected to the field windings) from the brush holder, being careful not to strain the springs. Remove the brush holder from the motor.
11 Renew the brushes if they are worn to, or below, the specified minimum length. Always renew all four brushes together.
12 Renew the negative brushes (those attached to the holder) by unsoldering the old ones and soldering the new ones in place. Grip the brush lead with pliers to stop solder running up it and making it rigid.
13 Renew the positive brushes by cutting off the old ones at a suitable distance from the field windings. Solder the new brush leads to the old ones, again preventing solder from running towards the brushes.
14 Clean the commutator with a non-fluffy rag moistened with petrol. Make sure that the brushes are free in their holders.
15 Insert the negative brushes into their holders, setting the springs against the sides of the brushes so that the brushes are not yet pushed downwards.
16 Offer the brush holder to the motor. Insert and similarly restrain the positive brushes.
17 Carefully lift each brush spring so that it bears on the back of its brush; the brushes should take up their normal positions.
18 Refit the bearing bush and the end cover, making sure that the screw holes in the cover and the brush holder line up. Insert and tighten the brush holder securing screws.
19 Fit and tighten the motor through-bolts.

18 Starter motor – dismantling and reassembly

1   The complete overhaul of a starter motor is beyond the resources of the average home mechanic as special tools and equipment for testing are necessary but if the appropriate spares can be obtained repairs can be made by renewing parts. With the starter on the bench proceed as follows.

Bosch starter motor

2   Undo the two screws and remove the bearing cap from the commutator cover.

3   Prise the clip off the end of the armature and, after carefully noting the sequence of assembly, remove the washers and rubber sealing ring from the armature.
4   Mark the commutator cover relative to the starter casing and then remove the two long bolts which hold the assembly together. Remove the commutator cover.
5   Lift the brush springs to remove the positive brushes and then remove the brushplate from the assembly. Note and remove any shims that may be fitted.
6   Disconnect the field winding lead from the solenoid terminal and then undo the two retaining screws to release the solenoid from the assembly. As the solenoid is removed unhook the end fitting from the engaging lever.
7   Unscrew and remove the engaging lever pivot and then remove the end frame from the field and casing assembly. As this is done, remove the rubber plug and the engaging lever. Slide the armature out of the casing.
8   If it is required to remove the pinion or the clutch from the armature, press the retaining ring back on the shaft to enable the snap-ring to be removed. Then slide the components off the shaft (Figs. 12.12 and 12.13).
9   With the starter motor dismantled the various components can be cleaned and inspected for general wear and/or signs of damage. Use a petrol damped cloth for cleaning but avoid wetting electrical components. Dry thoroughly with a fluff-free cloth.
10 Renew worn or damaged carbon brushes as explained in Section 17.

Fig. 12.10 Disconnecting field winding lead from solenoid terminal – Bosch starter (Sec 18)

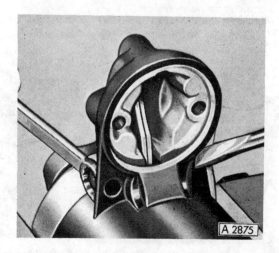

Fig. 12.11 Releasing solenoid engaging lever pivot spindle – Bosch starter (Sec 18)

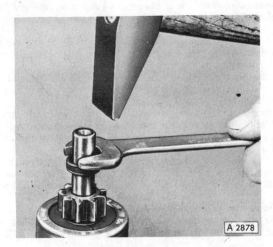

Fig. 12.12 Driving snap-ring stop collar down armature shaft – Bosch starter (Sec 18)

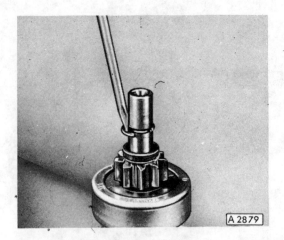

Fig. 12.13 Prising snap-ring from armature shaft – Bosch starter (Sec 18)

11 If the starter motor has shown a tendency to jam or a reluctance to disengage, then the starter pinion is almost certainly the culprit. Dirt accumulation on the shaft or on the pinion could cause this. After cleaning off any such dirt, check that the pinion can move freely in a spiral movement along the shaft. If it still tends to bind or stick, or if it is defective in any way, renew the pinion.

12 A badly worn or burnt commutator will need skimming on a lathe, but if it is only dirty or lightly marked, clean it up with a piece of fine grade glass paper wrapped round. If the commutator has to be skimmed have the job done by a specialist but make sure that the minimum diameter, as listed in the Specifications, is maintained. After skimming, the separators should be undercut using a piece of old hacksaw blade ground down to the same thickness as the separators. Undercut to a depth of about 0.5 to 0.8 mm (0.02 to 0.03 in) and then clean up with fine grade glass paper. Do not use emery on the commutator as abrasive particles could get embedded in the copper and cause rapid brush wear.

13 An armature with a bent shaft or other signs of damage must be renewed. Electrical checks should be undertaken by an auto-electrician with special equipment. Although simple continuity checks are possible with a lamp and low power source, more extensive checking is needed which is beyond the scope of the home mechanic.

14 Reassembly of the starter motor is a straightforward reversal of the dismantling sequence, but the following points should be noted:

(a) After assembling the clutch and pinion to the armature shaft, fit the retaining ring using a new snap-ring and then reposition the retainer

(c) Make sure that all shims and washers are fitted in the correct order

(d) Align the locating key and slot when assembling the case to the end frame

(d) Make sure that the carbon brushes slide freely in their holders

(e) Lightly oil all sliding parts including the armature spiral spline, the engaging lever sliding surfaces, the clutch bearing surfaces and armature bearings. Of course, no oil must contaminate the commutator or brushes

Delco-Remy starter motors

15 Mark the commutator end cover and the drive end bearing housing relative to the starter case to ensure correct reassembly and then disconnect the field winding connection from the lower stud on the solenoid.

16 Undo and remove the two tie-bolts from the commutator end cover and remove the end cover. Carefully slide the starter case off the armature and drive end bearing housing (photo).

17 Undo the two retaining screws and remove the solenoid and its spring from the drive end bearing housing. Extract the clip from the engaging lever spindle and tap the spindle out of the housing. This will allow the armature and the engaging lever to be removed together and the engaging lever can then be removed from the armature assembly.

18 The remainder of the dismantling and reassembly procedures for this starter are the same as those described in paragaphs 8 to 14, to which reference should now be made. When the solenoid has been refitted to the drive end bearing housing, use a little plastic sealing compound to seal the slot in the housing to prevent water from getting into the starter. Then continue the reassembly as described.

18.16 Removing end cover (Delco-Remy)

18.17A Removing starter solenoid and spring (Delco-Remy)

18.17B Engaging pivot spindle clip (Delco-Remy)

18.17C Removing pivot spindle (Delco-Remy)

18.17D Separating drive end housing (Delco-Remy)

18.17E Exploded view of Delco-Remy starter motor

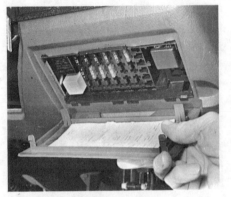

19.1 Detaching fuse box cover

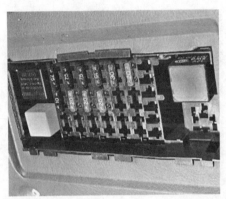

19.2 Fuses and relays

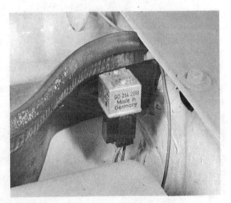

20.4 Relay in engine compartment of 1.8 SRi model

19 Fuses

1 The fuses are mounted in a panel located at the lower right-hand corner of the facia under a removable cover. The circuits protected are marked on the inside of the cover (photo).
2 To inspect or change a fuse simply remove the cover by prising it off. These cars use a special type of fuse and spares will have to be obtained from your local dealer (photo).
3 Before renewing a blown fuse, trace and rectify the cause and always use a fuse of the correct value as listed in the Specifications. Never substitute a fuse of a higher rating or use such things as a piece of wire, metal foil or a pin to act as a makeshift, as more serious damage or even fire may result.

20 Relays

1 These are located on the fuse block and are of the plug-in type.
2 Depending upon the specification of the vehicle, a relay is fitted to cover the heated rear window, the direction indicator/hazard warning system, rear foglamps and windscreen wiper dwell.
3 On certain models, relays for driving lamps and a headlamp warning buzzer may be fitted and these are located at the base of the fuse block. In order to remove these, the lower panel must be removed from under the facia.
4 Some models also have relays located in the engine compartment. This type is detached by disconnecting the wires and undoing the retaining screw (photo).

21 Switches – removal and refitting

1 Before removing a switch, disconnect the battery negative lead.

Fig. 12.14 Relays on fusebox (Sec 20)

A   Direction indicator
B   Heated rear screen
C   Headlamp
D   Lights on warning buzzer
E   Wiper delay
F   Rear foglamp

Heater blower switch

2 The blower switch is retained by spring tabs which should be depressed with a knife blade inserted behind the switch bezel as the switch is pulled out of the panel.
3 If there is any difficulty in releasing the switch, an alternative method may be used by withdrawing the switch panel after extracting the panel securing screws (photo).
4 Disconnect the switch wiring plug.

21.3 Switch panel securing screw removal

21.5 Heater blower/heated rear window/hazard warning switches and mounting panel

21.7 Lighting switch panel screw

21.11A Depressing steering column switch retaining tabs

21.11B Removing a steering column switch

21.13 Courtesy lamp switch

Heated rear window switch

5   Access to the switch is obtained after first extracting the switch panel screws and pulling the panel from the facia (photo).

Lighting switch

6   The spring-loaded tabs which retain the switch should be depressed by inserting a blade behind the switch bezel, and the switch then pulled out of the facia panel until its wiring plug can be disconnected.

7   Alternatively, the switch panel can be withdrawn after extracting the securing screws (photo). Removal of the switch panel also gives access to the instrument lighting dimmer switch, fitted to some models.

Hazard warning lamp switch

8   Access to the switch is as described for the heated rear window switch.

Steering column switches

9   Extract the securing screws and remove the lower shroud from the upper part of the steering column.

10   Remove the upper shroud. It should be possible to prise the shroud over the steering lock bezel, but if there is any difficulty, the lock can be removed if its retaining plunger is depressed with a thin rod. The ignition key must be in position 1.

11   Depress the switch retaining tabs and withdraw the switch far enough to be able to disconnect the wiring plug. Remove the switch (photos).

Courtesy lamp switch

12   This is located in the door pillar and is of plunger type.

13   To remove the switch, extract the fixing screw and withdraw it from the pillar (photo).

14   If the switch is to be removed, tape the wires to the pillar to prevent them slipping into the interior of the pillar.

15   Apply petroleum jelly to the moving parts of the switch before refitting in order to prevent corrosion.

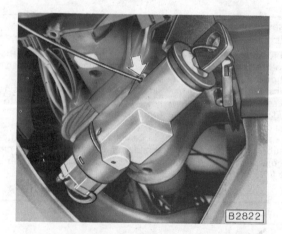

Fig. 12.15 Releasing ignition lock cylinder (Sec 21)

Arrow indicates thin rod depressing plunger

Rear foglamp switch

16   Access to this switch and its adjacent switches is best obtained by extracting the fixing screws and pulling the complete switch panel from the facia (photo). Access to the two fixing screws can be achieved by removing the left-hand plastic blanking plate.

17   The wiring plugs and the switches can then be released by prising aside the tabs of their retaining clips.

Luggage area light switch (Estate)

18   Remove the tailgate interior trim panel (Chapter 11, Section 15).

19   Depress the switch plunger and disconnect the wire from the back of the switch. Press the switch body out of the tailgate (photo).

21.16 Rear foglamp switch panel

21.19 Removing the luggage area light switch (Estate)

21.21A Removing the powered exterior mirror adjuster switch

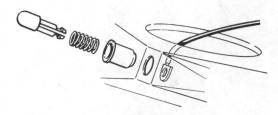

Fig. 12.16 Luggage area light switch – Estate (Sec 21)

Power operated window switches
20 When fitted these are located on the top face of the centre console.
21 To remove, prise free the switch concerned, then lift it clear and detach the wiring connections from it (photo).

Exterior mirror adjustment switch
22 Access to the switch is as described for the power operated window switches.

All switches
23 Refitting is the reversal of removal; check for correct switch operation before refitting. Switches which are retained by spring tabs only need to be pushed home.

21.21B Exterior mirror adjuster switch lead connectors

Fig. 12.17 Power operated window switches (Sec 21)

22 Starter inhibitor switch (automatic transmission) – adjustment

1 The starter inhibitor switch should prevent the starter motor operating in any selector position other than 'N' or 'P'. If this is not the case, adjust as follows.
2 Remove the selector lever cover, which is secured by four screws, and select 'P'.
3 Loosen the two screws which secure the starter inhibitor switch. Turn the switch against the direction of travel of the lever until the engine can be started.
4 Tighten the screws and check that the engine can only be started in positions 'P' and 'N'. If the correct adjustment is difficult to achieve, place a washer of thickness 1 to 2 mm (0.04 to 0.08 in) under the switch rear mounting bracket, then try again.
5 Refit the selector lever cover when adjustment is correct.

23 Horn(s) and switch

1 Where a single horn is fitted, it is located just ahead of the radiator. If twin horns are fitted, the second horn is attached to a bracket on the left-hand side underneath near the radiator (photos).
2 No maintenance is required except to occasionally check the security of the mounting bracket bolts and connecting lead.
3 The horn operating button is removable by prising it from the hub of the steering wheel using a thin blade or screwdriver (photo).

23.1A Single horn location

23.1B Second horn location – twin horns

23.3 Horn button removal

24.1 Clock withdrawal

25.3 Cigar lighter mounting plate/ashtray housing screw

24 Clock – removal and refitting

1 The clock can be withdrawn from the facia panel by depressing the spring-loaded tabs which retain it (photo).
2 Disconnect the wiring spade connectors.
3 Refitting is a reversal of removal.

25 Cigar lighter – removal and refitting

1 Disconnect the battery.

2 Remove the lighter element from its socket.
3 Extract the retaining screw and remove the ashtray housing until the electrical leads can be pulled off the cigar lighter socket terminals (photo).
4 Remove the lighter socket from the ashtray housing.
5 Refitting is a reversal of removal, but make sure that the earth lead (A) is located under the lug (B) of the lighter socket (Fig. 12.19).

26 Instrument panel – removal and refitting

1 Disconnect the battery.

Fig. 12.18 Clock connections – arrowed (Sec 24)

Fig. 12.19 Cigar lighter connections (Sec 25)

A   Earth lead   B   Lug

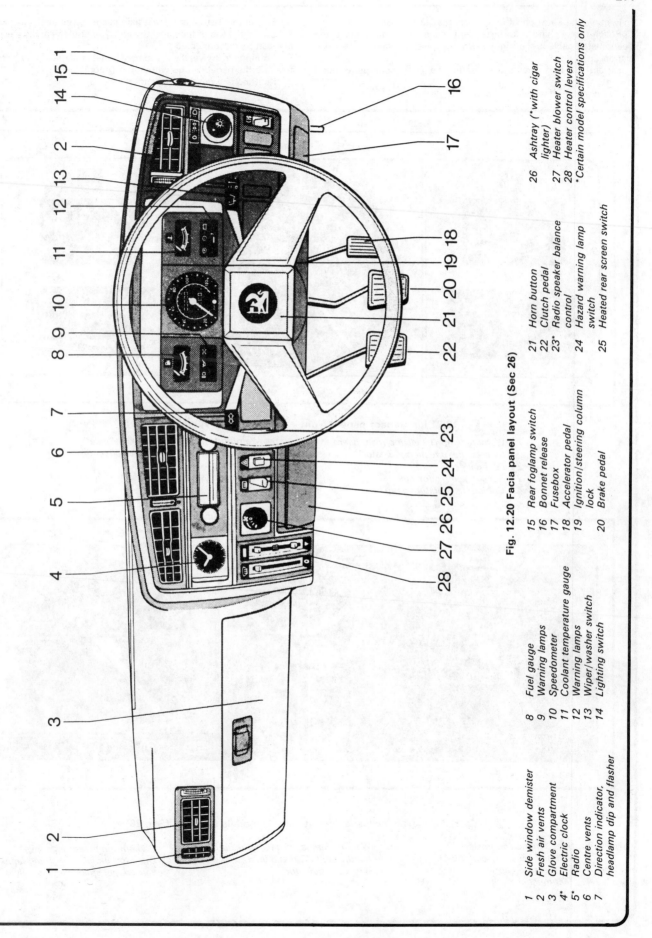

Fig. 12.20 Facia panel layout (Sec 26)

1 Side window demister
2 Fresh air vents
3 Glove compartment
4* Electric clock
5* Radio
6 Centre vents
7 Direction indicator, headlamp dip and flasher

8 Fuel gauge
9 Warning lamps
10 Speedometer
11 Coolant temperature gauge
12 Warning lamps
13 Wiper/washer switch
14 Lighting switch

15 Rear foglamp switch
16 Bonnet release
17 Fusebox
18 Accelerator pedal
19 Ignition/steering column lock
20 Brake pedal

21 Horn button
22 Clutch pedal
23* Radio speaker balance control
24 Hazard warning lamp switch
25 Heated rear screen switch

26 Ashtray (*with cigar lighter)
27 Heater blower switch
28 Heater control levers
*Certain model specifications only

2 Remove the cover panel from under the facia panel.
3 Reach up behind the instrument panel and disconnect the speedometer cable by prising down the plastic retainer (see also Section 28).
4 Extract the two screws from under the instrument panel hood (photo).
5 Withdraw and remove the hood.

6 Extract the instrument panel fixing screws (photo).
7 Swivel the top of the panel towards you until the multi-plugs at the rear can be disconnected.
8 Continue to swivel the instrument panel until the lugs at its base are free and the panel can be withdrawn (photo).
9 Refitting is a reversal of removal.

Fig. 12.21 Instrument panel layout – base models (typical) (Sec 26)

1 Warning lamp (headlamp main beam, oil pressure, direction indicator)
2 Fuel gauge
3 Speedometer/odometer
4 Coolant temperature gauge
5 Warning lamp (handbrake ON, brake fluid, ignition/charge, *trailer direction indicator)
*Certain model specifications only

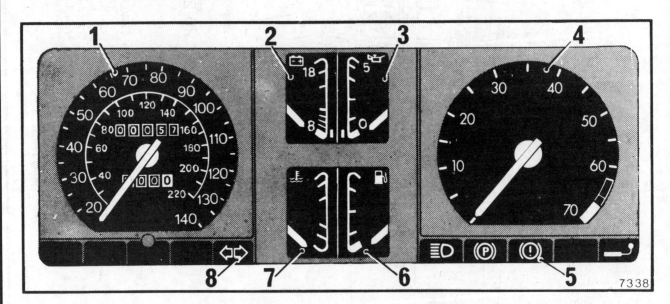

Fig. 12.22 Instrument panel layout – other models (typical) (Sec 26)

1 Speedometer/odometer
2 Voltmeter (battery condition)
3 Oil pressure gauge
4 Tachometer
5 Warning lamps (headlamp main beam, handbrake ON, brake fluid, *trailer direction indicator)
6 Fuel gauge
7 Coolant temperature gauge
8 Direction indicator warning lamp
*Certain model specifications only

26.4 Instrument panel hood screw

26.6 Instrument panel fixing screw

26.8 Instrument panel removed

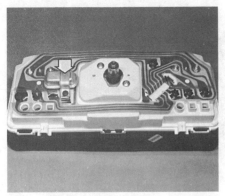

27.4 Instrument voltage stabilizer (arrowed)

28.2 Releasing speedometer drive cable

28.3 Speedometer drive cable at transmission

27 Instruments – removal and refitting

1   Once the instrument panel has been withdrawn, the individual instruments can be detached.
2   To do this, unclip and remove the bezel and transparent sheet from the front of the dials.
3   Unscrew the securing nuts and withdraw the instruments from the printed circuit board. Take care not to damage the circuit board.
4   Should the coolant temperature gauge and the fuel gauge malfunction at the same time, then this will probably be due to a faulty instrument voltage stabiliser. This can be renewed after extracting the fixing screw (photo).
5   Refitting is a reversal of removal.

28 Speedometer cable – renewal

1   Remove the cover panel from under the facia.
2   Reach up and disconnect the cable from the speedometer head by prising the retainer aside (photo). This method may prove difficult, in which case proceed from paragraph 5.
3   Disconnect the opposite end of the cable from the transmission by unbolting the retaining plate or unscrewing the knurled retaining ring according to model (photo).
4   Feed the cable through the grommet into the engine compartment and remove it.
5   If difficulty is experienced in reaching up under the instrument panel to disconnect the cable, proceed as follows.
6   Disconnect the battery earth lead.
7   Disconnect the speedometer cable at the transmission end by unscrewing the knurled nut or removing the retaining plate, as applicable.
8   Remove the instrument panel hood (two screws).
9   Remove the screw(s) which secure the instrument panel and free the panel securing lugs.

10 Draw the instrument panel forwards while an assistant feeds the speedometer cable through the bulkhead. Release the cable from the speedometer by pressing the retaining clip.
11 Withdraw the cable into the engine compartment.
12 Fit the new cable by reversing the removal procedure.

29 Bulbs – renewal

Note: *Before renewing any bulbs, ensure that the circuit concerned is switched off*

Headlamp and front parking lamp
1   Open the bonnet.
2   At the rear of the headlamp, prise the clip aside and pull off the protective cap (photo).
3   Pull off the now exposed wiring plug (photo).
4   Depress the bulb retainer and turn it through $1/8$ of a turn (photo).
5   Withdraw the retainer complete with headlamp and parking lamp bulbs (photo).
6   The headlamp bulbs are of halogen type and should not be touched with the fingers. If they are, clean their glass by wiping with a cloth moistened in methylated spirit.
7   Renew the bulb with one of similar type and refit the retainer by reversing the removal operations.

Front flasher lamp
8   Open the bonnet and reach down beside the headlamp.
9   Release the bayonet type bulbholder (photo).
10 Renew the bulb with one of similar type and refit the bulbholder.

Front foglamp
11 Remove the single screw from the bottom of the lamp and remove the lens and reflector unit.
12 Release the spring clip, free the bulb from its holder and unplug the electrical connector.

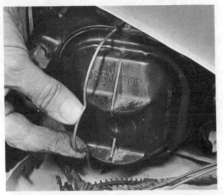

29.2 Headlamp rear cover clip

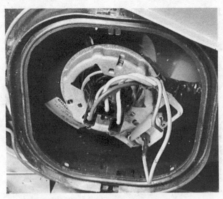

29.3 Headlamp rear cover removed

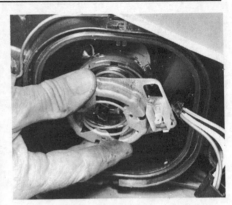

29.4 Removing bulb retainer

29.5 Bulbs and retainer removed from the headlamp

29.9 Front flasher bulb and holder removal

13 Do not touch the glass of the new bulb with the fingers; if it is accidentally touched, clean it with methylated spirit.
14 Fit the new bulb, making sure that the lugs on the reflector engage with the slots in the holder. Secure with the spring clip and refit the lens and reflector.

Rear lamp cluster (Saloon and Hatchback)
15 Access to these bulbs is obtained by unclipping the cover or carpeting within the luggage compartment and then releasing the bulbholder retaining lugs and withdrawing the bulbholder (photos).
16 Renew the bulb with one of similar type.

Rear lamp cluster (Estate)
17 Remove the four securing screws and lift off the light unit. The location of one of the screws is not immediately obvious (photo).
18 Release the bulbholder by depressing the lever on the side of the holder. Rotate the bulbholder and remove it (photo).
19 Renew the bulb and refit the bulbholder, rotating the holder until it clicks into position.
20 Refit the light unit and secure with the screws.

Rear number plate lamp (Saloon and Hatchback)
21 Insert a thin screwdriver in the notch provided and prise the lamp

Fig. 12.23 Front foglight bulb access: push spring clip legs in direction arrowed (Sec 29)

Fig. 12.24 Front foglight bulb renewal. Do not allow fingers (arrowed) to touch bulb glass (Sec 29)

29.15A Rear lamp cluster covering trim

29.15B Rear lamp bulbholder (retaining clips arrowed)

29.17 Rear light cluster (Estate) is secured by four screws – screwdriver tip is on hidden screw, others are visible

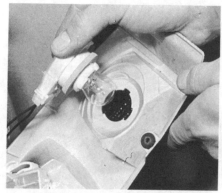

29.18 Removing bulbholder from rear light cluster (Estate)

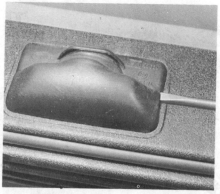

29.21A Prise free the rear number plate lamp ...

29.21B ... from the bumper aperture

29.22 Rear number plate bulb

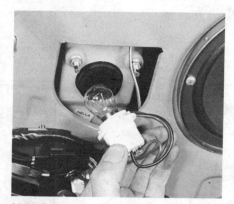

29.28 Removing a tailgate-mounted light bulb – Estate

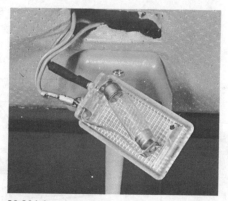

29.30A Interior lamp and bulb – standard type

from the bumper bar (photos).
22 Renew the bulb with one of similar type (photo).

Rear number plate (Estate)

23 Remove the tailgate handle, which is secured by four screws.
24 Remove the two screws which secure the lens and pull it off.
25 Pull the old bulb out of its socket and press in a new bulb.
26 Refit and secure the lens and tailgate handle.

Reversing lamps and rear foglamps (Estate)

27 Remove the tailgate interior trim panel (Chapter 11, Section 25).
28 Rotate the bulbholder and pull it to remove it (photo).
29 Renew the bulb, refit the holder and the trim panel.

Interior lamps

30 The lamp lens complete with festoon type bulbs can be removed

from the headlining above the mirror by careful prising (photos and Figs. 12.27 and 12.28).
31 Renew the bulb with one of similar type and refit the lamp. Note: If, on later models having a delay feature on the courtesy lamp, the bulb does not go out, the delay unit itself may be faulty.
32 Bulb renewal for the luggage area is carried out in a similar way (photo).

Instrument panel lamps

33 These bulbs are accessible if the instrument panel is partially withdrawn as described in Section 26.
34 There is no need to disconnect the speedometer cable provided the cable is eased through the bulkhead grommet as the panel is withdrawn.
35 Twist the bulbholders from their holes in the instrument panel and pull out the wedge type bulbs (photo).

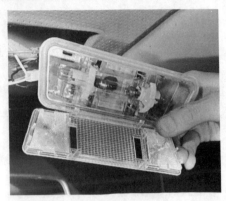

29.30B Combined interior lamp and reading lamp bulbs (unit removed for photo)

29.32 Luggage boot or area lamp

29.35 Instrument panel warning lamp bulb and holder

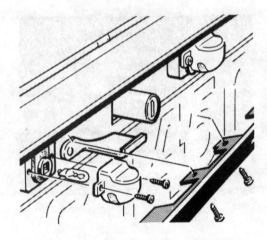

Fig. 12.25 Rear number plate light – Estate (Sec 29)

Fig. 12.26 Reversing light and rear foglight unit – Estate (Sec 29)

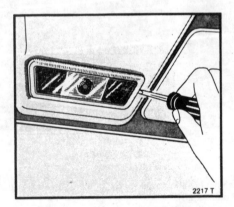

Fig. 12.27 Prise at point shown to remove standard type interior light (Sec 29)

Fig. 12.28 Prise at point shown to remove interior/reading type light lens for bulb renewal (Sec 29)

---

30 Headlamps – removal, refitting and modifications

1   To remove a headlamp unit; first disconnect the battery, then remove the radiator grille as described in Chapter 11.
2   Unscrew the two top headlamp mounting screws (photo).

3   Pull the lamp unit forward to release the lower retaining lugs (photo).
4   Press the spring clip aside on the rear cover of the lamp and take off the cover.
5   Pull out the wiring plug and withdraw the lamp unit.
6   Refitting is a reversal of removal.

30.2 Headlamp retaining screw

30.3 Headlamp unit removal

31.6 Headlamp beam adjustment screws (arrowed)

'Headlamp On' warning buzzer

7   All models from 1986 have an additional black cable in the harness to the warning buzzer.

8   This cable is for use with a new type of warning buzzer which operates only when the ignition is switched off, and should not be used on alternative buzzers.

9   When renewing a buzzer, take careful note of the wiring connections and the cable colours, to ensure buzzers are connected properly.

'Headlamp dim-dip' – modification from October 1986

10   To prevent the possibility of vehicles being driven on parking lights only and to comply with new lighting legislation, all UK models produced from the above date are fitted with a dim-dip system in the headlamp circuit. The function of the system is to ensure that the car cannot be driven on parking lights only.

11   The system is activated by a dim-dip control unit which, when activated, reduces the voltage supply to the headlamps. This system is designed as a safeguard only and normal lighting legislation requirements still apply and must be observed.

31 Headlamp beams – alignment

1   The headlight beam adjustment is most important, not only for your own safety but for that of other road users as well. Accurate beam alignment can only be obtained using optical beam setting equipment and you should regard any adjustments made without such equipment as purely temporary.

2   To make a temporary adjustment, position the car on level ground about 3 metres (10ft) in front of a vertical wall or a piece of board secured vertically. The wall or board should be square to the centre-line of the car and the car should be normally laden. Check that the tyre pressures are correct.

3   Draw a vertical line on the board or card in line with the centre line of the car.

4   Bounce the car on its suspension several times to ensure correct levelling and then accurately measure the height between the ground and the centre of the headlights.

5   Draw a horizontal line across the wall or board at the same height as the headlight centres and on this line mark a cross on either side of the centre line at the same distance apart as the headlight centres.

6   Now locate the adjusters on each headlight. There are two, diagonally opposite each other on each headlight (photo).

7   Switch the headlights on to full beam and, using the adjusters, adjust each headlamp to align the beam to shine just below the corresponding cross on the wall or board.

8   Bounce the car on its suspension again to check that the beams return to the correct position. At the same time check the operation of the dipswitch to confirm that the beams dip to the nearside. Switch off the headlights on completion.

9   Have the alignment professionally checked at the earliest opportunity.

10   Holts Amber Lamp is useful for temporarily changing the headlight colour to conform with the normal usage on Continental Europe.

32 Front foglights – adjustment

1   Adjustment of the front foglights is correct when their outer edges are parallel with the front spoiler or front bumper. In this position each beam diverges from the longitudinal axis by 10°.

2   Adjustment is made by turning the horizontal and/or vertical adjuster screws for each lamp as required. The adjuster screws are accessible through the front of the grille panel.

33 Rear light cluster – unit removal and refitting

Saloon and Hatchback

1   Remove the rear quarter trim on the side concerned to gain access to the wiring harness.

2   Unclip and withdraw the lamp bulbholder (see photo 29.15B).

3   Untwist and remove the foglamp bulbholder.

4   Undo the four retaining nuts and withdrawing the light unit from the body.

5   Refit in reverse order of removal.

Estate

6   Remove the rear quarter trim panel on the side concerned to gain access to the wiring harness. Unplug the connector for the rear light unit.

7   Remove the four securing screws and lift off the unit. Extract the grommet and remove the light unit, wiring and grommet.

8   Refit in the reverse order to removal.

34 Reversing lights and rear foglights (Estate) – unit removal and refitting

1   Remove the tailgate interior trim panel (Chapter 11, Section 25).

2   Undo the securing nuts, disconnect the wiring harness and extract the light unit from the tailgate.

3   Refit in the reverse order to removal.

35 Wiper blades and arms – removal and refitting

1   Before removing a wiper arm make sure that it is in its parked position having been switched off by the wiper switch and not the ignition key.

2   To facilitate re-alignment of the arms on the screen, stick a length of masking tape on the glass parallel to the blade before removing the arm.

3   Pull the wiper arm away from the glass, swivel the blade on the arm and then depress the catch on the U-shaped retainer and slide the blade from the wiper arm (photo).

4   Flip up the plastic cover and unscrew the arm retaining nut (photo).

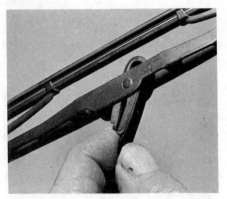

35.3 Removing a windscreen wiper blade

35.4 Wiper arm nut

36.4 Windscreen wiper motor

37.4 Removing a rear wiper motor bolt (Estate). Other bolt is out of picture to right

Fig. 12.29 Windscreen wiper arm setting – LHD shown, RHD is opposite (Sec 35)
A = 35.0 to 45.0 mm (1.4 to 1.8 in)

5   Pull the arm from the splined driving spindle.
6   Refitting is a reversal of removal, do not overtighten the nut. If tape was not applied to the glass, observe the setting dimensions in the diagram (Fig. 12.29).

36 Windscreen wiper motor and linkage – removal and refitting

1   Remove the wiper arms as described in the preceding Section.
2   Unscrew and remove the nuts from the drive spindles on the scuttle. Note the fitted sequence of seals and spacer.
3   Open the bonnet and remove the water deflector (where fitted) (Fig. 12.31).
4   Pull the wiring multi-plug from the wiper motor (photo).
5   Disconnect the motor earth cable.
6   Unscrew the motor mounting screws and withdraw the complete motor/linkage assembly from the car.
7   Disconnect the crank arm from the motor. When unscrewing the nut, counter the turning torque with an open-ended spanner applied to the crank otherwise the internal gearwheel teeth may be damaged.
8   Unbolt the wiper motor from its mounting plate.
9   Refitting is a reversal of removal, but again restrain the motor crank when tightening the crank arm nut.

37 Tailgate wiper motor – removal and refitting

1   Remove the rear wiper arm by undoing its securing nut and pulling it off. From beneath the arm remove the rubber boot, the second nut, the dust cap and the seal.
2   Remove the tailgate interior panel (Chapter 11, Section 25).
3   Disconnect the wiring connectors from the wiper motor.
4   Remove the two securing bolts and lift away the wiper motor (photo).

Fig. 12.30 Wiper drive spindle nut – arrowed (Sec 36)

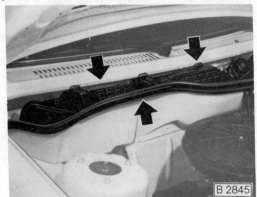

Fig. 12.31 Bulkhead water deflector (Sec 36)
Arrows indicate fixing points

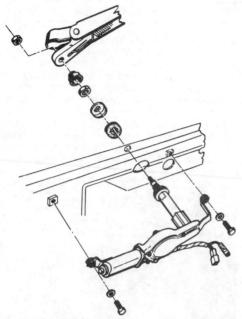

Fig. 12.32 Rear wiper motor fitting details – Estate (Sec 37)

Fig. 12.33 Tailgate wiper motor – Hatchback (Sec 37)

A Power feed lead   B Earth lead

Fig. 12.34 Tailgate wiper arm setting – Hatchback (Sec 37)

A = 20.0 mm (0.79 in)

38.1 Washer fluid reservoir

5   Refit in the reverse order to removal. Position the wiper arm so that the blade is parallel with the base of the window in the parked position, (Estate) or vertically as shown in Fig. 12.34 (Hatchback).

38 Windscreen washer system

1   This consists of a fluid reservoir mounted adjacent to the strut turret within the engine compartment, an electrically-operated pump and a steering column washer/wiper switch (photo).
2   A faulty pump can be renewed by 'rocking' it out of its sealing grommet in the fluid reservoir. Use a new seal when refitting.
3   A rubber connecting sleeve is used to join the plastic pipe to the pump nozzle as attempting to force the stiff plastic pipe onto the nozzle could cause it to fracture.
4   The washer jets should be adjusted so that the stream of fluid strikes the screen just above the wiper blades in their parked position. Use a pin to adjust the jet nozzles.

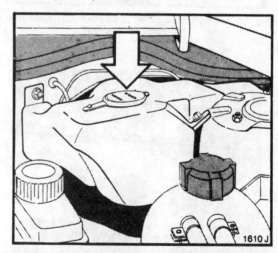

Fig. 12.35 Engine compartment washer fluid reservoir (arrowed) – large type for use with headlamp washer system (Sec 38)

39 Tailgate washer system

Hatchback

1   The arrangement is similar to that described for the windscreen washer except that the fluid reservoir and pump are located within the 'thickness' of the luggage compartment back panel.
2   Should the jet require adjustment, use a pin to do it and check that the water jet strikes the glass (vehicle stationary) at the point shown in the diagram (Fig. 12.37).

Estate

3   The rear screen washer reservoir and pump are located behind the right-hand quarter trim panel (photo).

39.3 Rear screen washer reservoir and
pump – Estate

Fig. 12.36 Tailgate washer fluid reservoir filler cap –
Hatchback (Sec 39)

Fig. 12.38 Headlamp wiper motor mounting bolts – arrowed
(Sec 40)

4   To remove the pump or reservoir, first remove the trim panel
(Chapter 11, Section 25).
5   Disconnect the electrical and fluid unions from the pump. Lift the
reservoir and pump off the retaining bracket.
6   The pump is a snap fit in the base of the reservoir. Empty the
reservoir before removing the pump.
7   Access to the washer pipe is gained by removing the appropriate
trim panels.
8   The washer jet is secured between the roof and the air deflector
assembly by two screws.
9   Refitting of all washer components is in the reverse order to
removal. Check for correct operation before refitting the trim panels.

40 Headlamp wash/wipe system

1   This is available as a factory-fitted option.
2   Where this system is fitted then a combined windscreen and
headlamp washer fluid reservoir is used, located under the bonnet.
3   The washer jet can be adjusted using a pin so that the washer fluid
strikes the headlamp glass. If required the jet unit can be removed by
carefully prising it free from the bumper (photo), then disconnecting
the hose.
4   Remove the wiper arm and blade in a similar manner to that
described for the windscreen wiper arms and blades, (photo). Access
to the wiper arm retaining nut and the wiper motor retaining nuts is
much improved by first removing the headlamp unit on the side
concerned.

Fig. 12.37 Tailgate wash jet striking pattern (Sec 39)
A = 280.0 to 380.0 mm (11.0 to 15.0 in)
B = 65.0 to 105.0 mm (2.6 to 4.1 in)

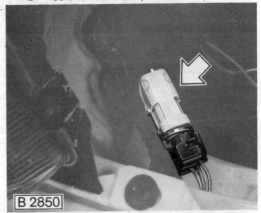

Fig. 12.39 Headlamp wiper motor lead plug – arrowed
(Sec 40)

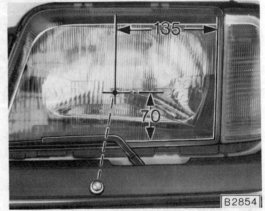

Fig. 12.40 Headlamp washer aim setting diagram (Sec 40)
Dimensions in mm

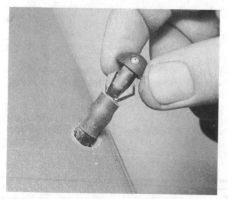

40.3 Headlamp washer jet removal

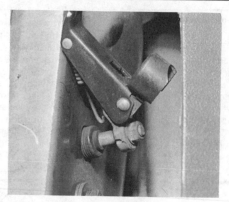

40.4 Headlamp wiper arm retaining nut

40.5 Headlamp wiper motor. Note that the motor for each side is handed (left and right) and are marked accordingly (L and R)

5   The wiper motor is located under the forward end of the wheel arch (photo). To remove the motor, detach the wiper arm and blade, then undo the two retaining bolts and withdraw the motor unit from the wheel arch side. Disconnect the wiring in the line connection.
6   Refitting of all components is a reversal of the removal procedure. Check for satisfactory operation of the wiper, washer and headlamp unit on completion.
7   Check the headlamp beam for satisfactory alignment, (Section 31). Ensure that the wiper arm is fitted so that it is in contact with the retaining plate in the parked position.
8   Adjust the washer jet (Fig. 12.40).

41 Washer fluid

1   It is recommended that only additives specially prepared for washer systems are used in the fluid reservoir. The use of household detergent or other cleaning agents is likely to damage the pump and rubber components of the system.
2   Never use cooling system antifreeze in a washer system or the paintwork will be damaged. In very cold weather, a small quantity of methylated spirit may be poured into the fluid to prevent freezing.

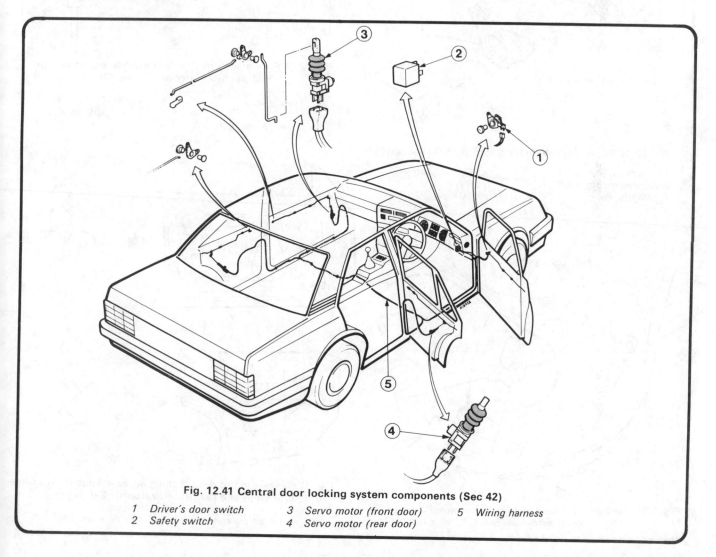

Fig. 12.41 Central door locking system components (Sec 42)

1 Driver's door switch	3 Servo motor (front door)	5 Wiring harness
2 Safety switch	4 Servo motor (rear door)	

42 Central locking system – description, and component removal and refitting

1   The central locking system ensures, by means of switches, servo motors and associated wiring, that all passenger door locks follow the position of the driver's door lock. Locking or unlocking the driver's door, from the inside or outside, produces the same state in the other door locks.

2   A safety switch below the facia panel unlocks all the doors in the event of an accident involving impact.

3   If for any reason the central locking system is disabled, the doors can still be locked and unlocked by hand.

Driver's door switch – removal and refitting

4   Remove the door trim panel (Chapter 11). Free the waterproof sheet around the switch.

5   Unplug the electrical connectors from the switch – they are different sizes so they cannot be connected wrongly.

6   Remove the centre pin and the screw which secures the switch to the door. Remove the switch components from the door, unhooking the transfer lever from the linkage.

7   Refit in the reverse order to removal. Before tightening the contact plate screw, position the plate in the middle of the travel allowed by the slot (Fig. 12.43). Check for correct operation before refitting the door trim.

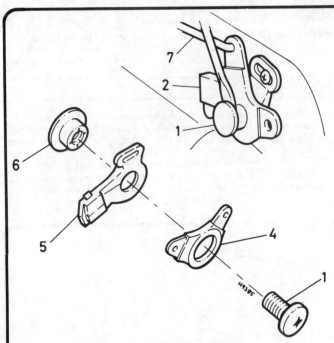

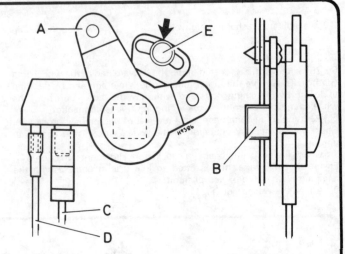

Fig. 12.43 Fitting the driver's door switch: adjust slot to mid-position (arrowed) (Sec 42)

A   Transfer lever   D   Grey lead
B   Bush   E   Contact plate screw
C   Brown/white lead

Fig. 12.42 Removing the driver's door switch (Sec 42)

1   Central pin   5   Contact plate
2   Electrical connectors   6   Bush
4   Transfer lever   7   Linkage

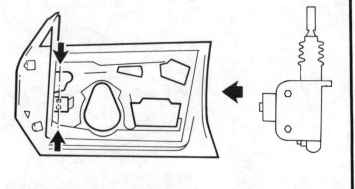

Fig. 12.45 Location of door locking servo motors in front door (top) and rear door (bottom) (Sec 42)

Fit motors in orientation indicated by arrows

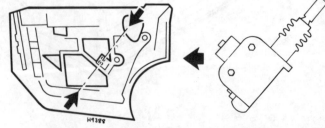

Fig. 12.44 Removing a door locking servo motor – mounting bolts arrowed (Sec 42)

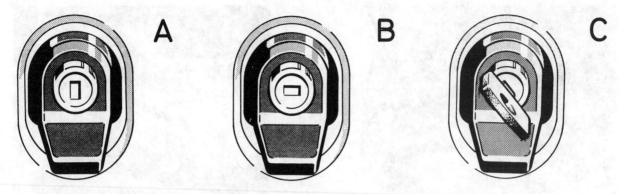

Fig. 12.46 Tailgate lock mode – central locking (Sec 42)

A   Locked – tailgate cannot be opened irrespective of central door locking selection
B   Unlocked – tailgate can only be opened if central locking is unlocked
C   Over-ride position – tailgate can be opened even if central locking is to 'locked'. Button and key twist must be depressed to release
tailgate lock
To remove key, turn back to either of positions A or B after tailgate has been opened

Servo motor – removal and refitting
8   Remove the door trim panel (Chapter 11). Free the waterproof sheet for access to the motor.
9   Remove the two bolts which secure the motor to the door. Disconnect the mechanical linkage and the electrical connector and remove the motor.
10   Refit in the reverse order to removal. Use new micro-encapsulated (self-locking) bolts. M6 x 8mm, available from a GM dealer. Check for correct function before refitting the door trim.

Tailgate lock mode – Hatchback from 1985
11   The tailgate lock barrel may be turned to one of three positions, which affects the operation of the centre locking system on the tailgate lock, as shown in Fig. 12.46.

43 Trip computer – description, and component renewal

1   A trip computer is fitted to some later models. Fuel consumption and distance data are collected and evaluated with respect to time, thus enabling the computer to provide information on fuel consumption (both instantaneous and average), average speed and range on fuel remaining. Normal time clock and stopwatch functions are available, and an external temperature sensor is also provided.
2   Refer to the owner's handbook provided with the vehicle for detailed operating instructions.
3   Although testing of the computer and its satellite components is beyond the scope of the average DIY mechanic, there is no reason why defective components should not be renewed, as described in the following paragraphs.

Component renewal
Computer relay
4   The trip computer relay is mounted on the lower face of the fusebox (Fig. 12.47).
5   Remove the lower panelling as necessary to gain access and unplug the relay from its socket.
6   Plug in the new relay and refit the panelling.
Temperature sensor
7   The temperature sensor is located under the left-hand front wing. Disconnect the wiring plug and push the sensor out of its grommet.
8   Fit the new sensor into the grommet and connect the wiring plug.
Distance sender
9   The distance sender is screwed into the speedo drive take-off on the transmission; the cable screws into the back of the sender.
10   Unscrew the speedometer cable from the sender. Disconnect the wiring plug from the sender and unscrew the sender from the transmission.

11   Fit the new sender, making sure that it is of the same type as that removed. (Senders carrying the reference 12 V 15 IMP work into the frequency divider mounted on the bulkhead; senders labelled 12 V 8 IMP work directly into the computer.) Connect the wiring plug and the speedo cable.
Computer
12   To remove the computer itself, first remove the facia switch panel.
13   Pull the computer out of the panel and disconnect the multi-plug.
14   Refit in the reverse order to removal, but note that a new computer will need to be calibrated on the vehicle. This should be done by a GM dealer.
Computer display lighting
15   Remove the computer, as first described.
16   Extract the bulbholder from the top of the computer by twisting it with pliers. Renew the capless bulb.
17   Refit the bulbholder. Check that the new bulb works (computer plugged in, instrument lighting on) before refitting the facia switch panel.

Fig. 12.47 Trip computer relay – arrowed (Sec 43)

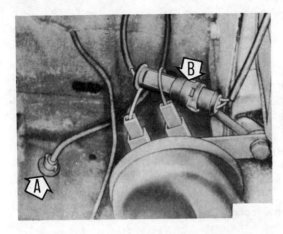

Fig. 12.48 Ambient temperature sensor (A) and wiring connector (B) (Sec 43)

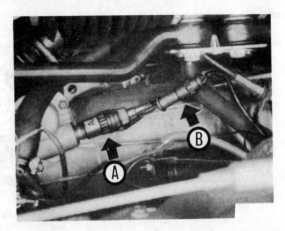

Fig. 12.49 Distance sender (A) and wiring connector (B) (Sec 43)

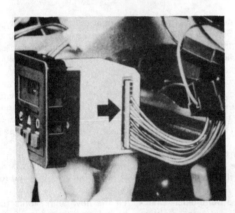

Fig. 12.50 Trip computer multi-plug (arrowed) (Sec 43)

Fig. 12.51 Removing the computer illumination bulbholder (Sec 43)

44 Electrical accessories – subsequent fitting

1   Many accessories are available either in kit form from your Vauxhall-Opel dealer or from one of the many motor accessory stores.
2   The following information is designed to provide a basic guide to fitting Vauxhall approved accessories, but it is not intended to supersede the instructions which may be supplied by other accessory manufacturers.

Cigar lighter
3   Remove the ashtray and the ashtray housing from the facia panel.
4   Route the wiring harness supplied to the fuse block.
5   Install the lamp baffle A in the ashtray housing (Fig. 12.52).
6   Fit the luminous ring to the cigar lighter.
7   Fit the lighter socket into the ashtray housing.
8   Fit the lamp socket into the luminous ring by pushing the earth connection spring A under the contact lug (Fig. 12.53).
9   Mount the lamp holder for the ashtray lamp.
10 Make the following electrical connections (Fig. 12.54):

   Black – cigar lighter positive A
   Brown – cigar lighter negative A
   Black – cigar lighter lamp positive B
   Black and brown – ashtray lamp C

11 Now connect the leads from the cigar lighter and both lamps to the spare terminal (15) on the fuse block.
12 Attach the earth wire to the right-hand side of the steering column

bracket using a self-tapping screw and star lock washer in the hole provided.
13 With the ignition ON and the lighter element pressed into its socket, the element should glow and the lamps illuminate.

Clock
14 Remove the blanking plate from the facia panel.
15 The clock wiring harness will contain a plain red and a plain grey cable.
16 Connect the red cable between the clock positive terminal and terminal (30) on the fuse block (Fig. 12.55).
17 Connect the grey cable between the clock bulbholder and terminal (58) on the fuse block.
18 Connect the earth lead between the clock and the right-hand side of the steering column bracket. Use a self-tapping screw with star lockwasher in the small hole provided (Fig. 12.56).

Choke ON warning lamp and switch
19 On later 1.3 models equipped with a manually-operated choke carburettor, a choke ON indicator may be fitted.
20 Disconnect the battery.
21 Remove the air cleaner.
22 Disconnect the choke operating cable from the carburettor.
23 Pull the cover from the underside of the facia panel (Fig. 12.57).
24 Remove the lock pin from the choke control knob.
25 Unscrew the choke control bezel nut.
26 Extract the screws and remove the facia switch panel (photo).
27 Remove the instrument panel as described in Section 26.

44.26 Removing a facia switch panel securing screw from choke control recess

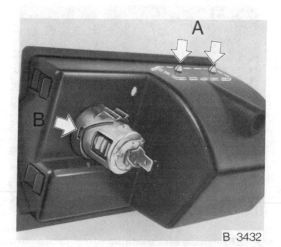

Fig. 12.52 Cigar lighter lamp baffle fixing in ashtray housing (Sec 44)

(A) lamp baffle and (B) luminous ring

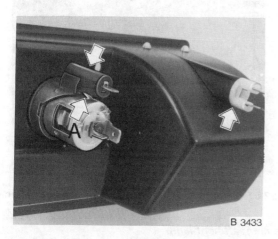

Fig. 12.53 Cigar lighter fitted (Sec 44)

A   *Earth connection spring*
Cigar lighter and ashtray lamp holders arrowed

Fig. 12.54 Cigar lighter and associated electrical connections (Sec 44)

A   *Black positive, cigar lighter*   B   *Black, cigar lighter lamp*
      Brown negative, cigar lighter   C   *Black/brown, ashtray lamp*

Fig. 12.55 Clock connections at fuse board (Sec 44)

A   *Fuse terminal 30*   B   *Fuse terminal 58*

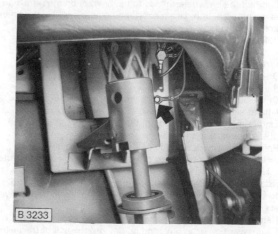

Fig. 12.56 Clock earth connection at steering column bracket (Sec 44)

Fig. 12.57 Prising off cover plate from choke control mounting plate screws (LHD) (Sec 44)

Fig. 12.58 Driving out a front seat roll pin (Sec 44)

Fig. 12.59 Handbrake ON switch – arrowed (Sec 44)

Fig. 12.60 Handbrake ON warning lamp – arrowed (Sec 44)

28 Fit bulb into the choke warning lamp position on the instrument panel.
29 Remove the existing choke cable assembly and fit the new one with switch.
30 Connect the warning lamp to terminal (15) on the fuse block.
31 Connect the choke switch wire to the lamp socket.
32 Connect the brown earth lead to the bracket on the right-hand side of the steering column. Use a self-tapping screw with star lockwasher in the hole provided.
33 Refit all removed components.

Parking brake ON warning lamp and switch
34 Disconnect the battery.
35 Remove the driver's seat.
36 Drive out the roll pins and remove the plastic overlay at the right-hand seat slide (Fig. 12.58).
37 Extract the door sill moulding, the cover from under the facia panel and the footwell side trim panel.
38 Refer to Chapter 9 and remove the handbrake lever.
39 Bolt the warning switch to the base of the lever and refit the lever (Fig. 12.59).
40 Route the wiring harness supplied between the switch and the rear of the facia by running it under the carpet, the sill and the footwell trim panel.
41 Remove the instrument panel as described earlier in this Chapter.
42 Fit the warning lamp bulb and holder into the rear of the instrument panel (Fig. 12.60).
43 Connect the end of the newly fitted lead into the multi-pin plug (Fig. 12.61).
44 With the ignition switched on, check that the warning lamp comes on when the handbrake is applied. Refit the removed components.

Glove compartment lamp
45 Route the wiring harness supplied between the fuse block and the glove compartment. Tape it securely to the rear of the facia panel.
46 Fit the bulb and holder in the glove compartment, together with the switch.
47 Connect the brown earth wire between the lamp and the hole provided in the right-hand steering column bracket. Use a self-tapping screw and lockwasher to do this.
48 Connect the black lead to the terminal (15) on the fuse block.

Luggage compartment lamp (Hatchback)
49 Cut the stale air exhaust grille inside the vehicle and mount the lamp (Fig. 12.62).
50 Connect a lead from lamp to fuse block by splicing it into the cable which comes from terminal (30). Route the cable under the carpet against the door sill riser.
51 Fit a plunger switch into the tailgate frame and connect it to both earth and feed (Fig. 12.63).

Luggage boot lamp (Saloon)
52 Fit the lamp holder and bulb (Fig. 12.64).
53 Fit the switch into the mounting hole provided at the left-hand hinge support bracket (Fig. 12.65).
54 Connect the brown earth lead to the switch.
55 Connect the red lead into the red (spare) connector in the adjacent vehicle wiring harness. If a spare connector is not fitted, run a new lead under the carpet against the sill riser to terminal (30) on the fuse block (3rd terminal from base protected by No 4 fuse).

Engine compartment lamp
56 Fit the lamp and connect the attached lead to the grey/green cable

Fig. 12.61 Handbrake ON lamp connection to multi-pin plug (Sec 44)

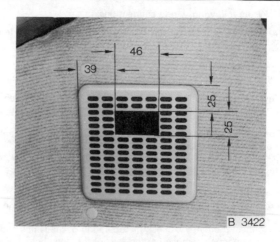

Fig. 12.62 Location for luggage compartment lamp – Hatchback (Sec 44)

Dimensions in mm

Fig. 12.63 Tailgate switch for luggage compartment lamp (Sec 44)

Securing screw arrowed

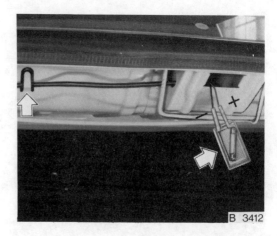

Fig. 12.64 Location for luggage boot lamp (Sec 44)

Arrows indicate lamp and cable clip

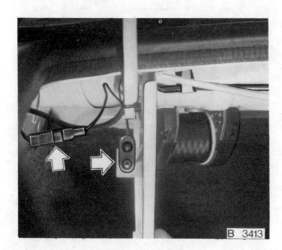

Fig. 12.65 Luggage boot lamp switch and wiring plug – arrowed (Sec 44)

connector in the adjacent wiring harness. If such a connector is not provided, run a new lead between the engine compartment lamp and the left-hand front parking lamp (Fig. 12.66).

57 Connect the earth wire to the body using a self-tapping screw with star lockwasher.

58 The engine compartment lamp is only operative when the vehicle lamps are switched on.

Auxiliary driving lamps

59 Disconnect the battery.

60 Remove the lower section of the steering column shroud.

61 Remove the cover from under the facia panel on the fusebox side.

62 Extract the fuse block mounting screws.

63 Remove the front bumper and radiator grille as described in Chapter 11.

64 Drill the driving lamp mounting holes (25.0 mm) in the bumper in accordance with the diagram (Fig. 12.67).

65 Fit the lamp brackets with reinforcement plates, spacers, nuts and washers supplied in the fitting kit.

66 Refit the bumper and grille. Connect the bracket to grille reinforcement, if supplied.

67 Drill a hole in the engine compartment rear bulkhead and route the wiring harness (with rubber grommet) through it, so that the wiring finishes near to the fuse block.

68 Connect the relay to the carrier and mount on the fuse block (Fig. 12.68).

69 Make the following wiring connections:

    (a) *Red cable, Terminal (30) to headlamp switch dipped terminal*

    (b) *White cable, Terminal (85) to headlamp switch dipped terminal*

    (c) *Earth wire to Terminal (86)*

    (d) *Terminal (87) for headlamp main beam*

70 Now connect a cable from the relay terminal (30) to the red cable of the headlamp dipped switch using a proprietary wire splicing device (Fig. 12.69).

71 Connect a cable from relay terminal (85) with the white cable of the dipped terminal (56a).

72 Connect an earth lead from terminal (86) of the relay to the steering column right-hand mounting bracket using the hole provided, a self-tapping screw and a star lockwasher.

73 Guide the power feed cable from the relay terminal (87) through the grommet in the bulkhead and route to connect with the lamp bulbholder connectors.

74 Reconnect the battery, check the operation of the lamps and then refit the components removed at the start of the operation.

75 Adjust the lamp beams by referring to Section 31.

Foglamps

76 Foglamps are usually mounted on the lower air baffle plate (spoiler).

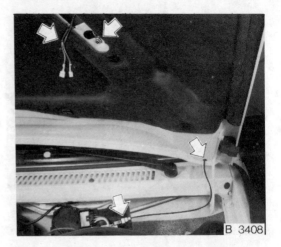

Fig. 12.66 Engine compartment lamp (Sec 44)

Arrows indicate wiring connections, earth point and grommet

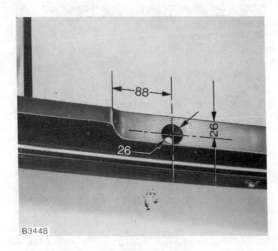

Fig. 12.67 Auxiliary lamp mounting hole diagram (Sec 44)

Dimensions in mm

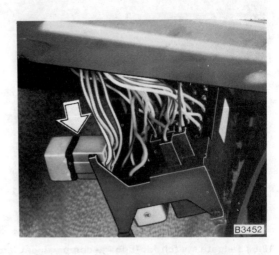

Fig. 12.68 Auxiliary lamp relay – arrowed (Sec 44)

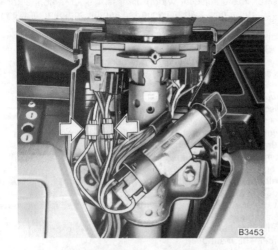

Fig. 12.69 Auxiliary lamp cable connections to headlamp dipped switch cable (Sec 44)

Wire splicing devices arrowed

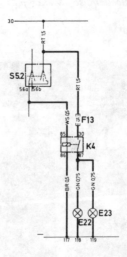

Fig. 12.70 Auxiliary lamp wiring circuit (Sec 44)

E22	LH auxiliary lamp	K4	Auxiliary lamp relay
E23	RH auxiliary lamp	S52	Low beam switch
F13	Fuse at relay		

77 Drill and mount in accordance with the diagram, using the reinforcement plates and seals supplied (Fig. 12.71).

78 Working inside the vehicle, remove the facia lower left switch plate. On vehicles with a manually-operated choke, the knob and retaining bezel will have to be removed (see earlier in this Section) and the three switch plate screws removed.

79 Fit the foglamp switch into the blank position and wire it up in the following way:

Terminal 1 – earth
Terminal 2 – cable from relay terminal (85)
Terminal 3 – cable from fuse block terminal (15)
Terminal 5 – cable from relay terminal (87)

80 Remove the cover from under the facia and also the steering column lower shroud.

81 Plug the relay into the fuse block which should be detached so that the relay wiring can be fed into the rear side of the fuse block in the following way:

Relay terminal (30) from switch terminal (58)
Relay terminal (87) lead to foglamp
Relay terminal (85) from switch terminal (2)
Relay terminal (86) from headlamp dipped switch terminal (56a)

82 Join the cable from the relay terminal (86) with the white cable which runs from the headlamp dipped beam switch terminal (56a).

83 Release the main lighting switch from the switch mounting plate and connect the cable from relay terminal (30) with the grey/green cable which runs from the lighting switch terminal (58) using a proprietary wire splicing device.

84 Connect the earth cable from terminal (1) of the foglamp switch to the right-hand mounting bracket of the steering column. A hole is provided for this using a self-tapping screw and a star lockwasher.

85 Drill a hole in the engine compartment rear bulkhead and fit a rubber grommet so that the wiring harness can be passed through.

86 Feed the cable through the grommet, connect it to terminal (87) on the relay, and to terminal (A) on the foglamp (Fig. 12.72).

87 Connect a cable from terminal (S) on the foglamp switch with the cable from the relay terminal (87) using a proprietary wire splicing device.

88 Connect the cables from the foglamp switch terminal (3) to terminal (15) on the fuse block.

89 Refit the fuse block, fit the foglamp switch into the switch plate.

90 Refit the steering column shroud and the facia under cover.

91 Connect the battery.

92 Check that the foglamps only operate when the ignition is switched on and the parking or dipped headlamps are on. When the headlamps are switched to main beam then the foglamps go out.

93 Adjust the foglamp beams.

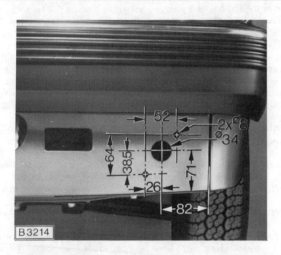

B 3214

Fig. 12.71 Foglamp mounting hole diagram (Sec 44)

Dimensions in mm

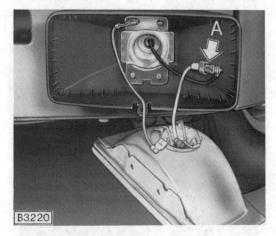

B3220

Fig. 12.72 Foglamp wiring connections (Sec 44)

A   See text

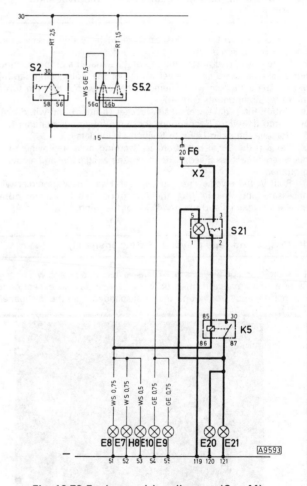

Fig. 12.73 Foglamp wiring diagram (Sec 44)

E8 Left-hand headlamp main beam	S2 Lighting switch
E20 Left-hand foglamp	S21 Foglamp switch
E21 Right-hand foglamp	S52 Headlamp low beam switch
F6 Fuse block (No 6 fuse)	X2 Fuse block (No 15 terminal)
K5 Foglamp relay	

45.2 Undoing the aerial slotted nut with a screwdriver

45 Radio aerial (optional equipment) – removal and refitting

1   Remove the wheel arch liner on the right-hand side. It is secured by one screw and some clips.
2   Undo the slotted nut on the top of the aerial. If a proper spanner is not available, use a screwdriver in one of the slots, being careful to protect the car's paintwork. Remove the slotted nut and the top half mounting components (photo).
3   Unbolt the aerial lower steady bracket (if fitted) and withdraw the aerial into the wing. Recover any loose mounting components.
4   Remove the radio (refer to Section 46 for details).
5   Release the aerial lead from its securing clips, removing trim as necessary for access. Feed the lead into the wing panel and recover the grommet.
6   Refit in the reverse order to removal. Use a new grommet where necessary and ensure that there is good metal-to-metal contact between the aerial and the underside of the wing.

46 Radios and tape players – fitting (general)

1   A radio or tape player is an expensive item to buy, and will only give its best performance if fitted properly. It is useless to expect concert hall performance from a unit that is suspended from the dashpanel by string with its speaker resting on the back seat or parcel shelf! If you do not wish to do the fitting yourself, there are many in-car entertainment specialists who will do the fitting for you.
2   Make sure the unit purchased is of the same polarity as the vehicle. Ensure that units with adjustable polarity are correctly set before commencing the fitting operations.
3   It is difficult to give specific information with regard to fitting, as final positioning of the radio/tape player, speakers and aerial is entirely a matter of personal preference. However, the following paragraphs give guidelines to follow which are relevant to all fittings:

Radio
4   Most radios are a standardised size of 7 in wide by 2 in deep. This ensures that they will fit into the radio aperture provided in these cars. Alternatively, a special console can be purchased which will fit between the dashpanel and the floor or on the transmission tunnel. These consoles can also be used for additional switches and instrumentation if required.
5   Some radios will have mounting brackets provided, together with instructions; others will need to be fitted using drilled and slotted metal strips, bent to form mounting brackets. These strips are available from most accessory shops. The unit must be properly earthed by fitting a separate earthing lead between the casing of the radio and the vehicle body.
6   Use the radio manufacturers' instructions when wiring the radio into the vehicle's electrical system. A 1 to 2 amp in-line fuse must be fitted in the radio's feed wire; a choke may also be necessary (see next Section). Take the power feed from the underside of the hazard warning switch (Fig. 12.75).
7   The type of aerial used and its fitted position, is a matter of personal preference. In general, the taller the aerial the better the reception. It is best to fit a fully retractable aerial; especially if a mechanical car-wash is used or if you live in an area where cars tend to be vandalised. In this respect, electric aerials which are raised and lowered automatically when switching the radio on or off are convenient, but are more likely to give trouble than the manual type.
8   When choosing a position for the aerial, the following points should be considered:

(a)   The aerial lead should be as short as possible; this means that the aerial should be mounted at the front of the car
(b)   The aerial must be mounted as far away from the distributor and HT leads as possible
(c)   The part of the aerial which protrudes beneath the mounting point must not foul the roadwheels, or anything else
(d)   If possible, the aerial should be positioned so that the coaxial lead does not have to be routed through the engine compartment
(e)   The plane of the panel on which the aerial is mounted should not be so steeply angled that the aerial cannot be mounted vertically (in relation to the end-on aspect of the car). Most aerials have a small amount of adjustment available

Fig. 12.74 Radio location (Sec 46)

Fig. 12.75 Radio feed connection to hazard warning switch – arrowed (Sec 46)

Fig. 12.76 Aerial location on front wing (Sec 46)

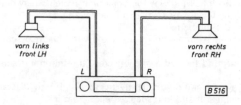

vorn links
front LH *vorn rechts*
front RH

L   R

B 516

Fig. 12.78 Dual front speaker layout (Sec 46)

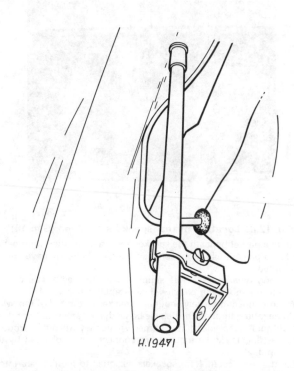

H.19491

Fig. 12.77 Aerial lower support and cable grommet to cavity
at right footwell (Sec 46)

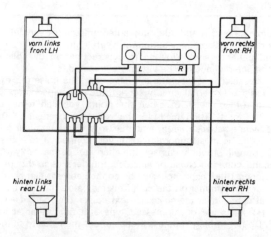

vorn links
front LH *vorn rechts*
front RH

L   R

hinten links
rear LH *hinten rechts*
rear RH

Fig. 12.79 Quadruple speaker layout with front/rear balance
(Sec 46)

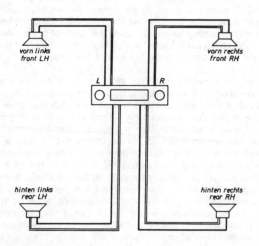

vorn links
front LH *vorn rechts*
front RH

L   R

hinten links
rear LH *hinten rechts*
rear RH

Fig. 12.80 Quadruple speaker layout (Sec 46)

9   Having decided on a mounting position, a relatively large hole will have to be made in the panel. The exact size of the hole will depend upon the specific aerial being fitted, although generally, the hole required is of 19 mm (^{3}/4 in) diameter. On metal bodied cars, a tank-cutter of the relevant diameter is the best tool to use for making the hole. This tools needs a small diameter pilot hole drilled through the panel, through which the tool clamping bolt is inserted. When the hole has been made the raw edges should be de-burred with a file and then painted to prevent corrosion.

10 Fit the aerial according to the manufacturer's instructions. If the aerial is very tall, or if it protrudes beneath the mounting panel for a considerable distance, it is a good idea to fit a stay beneath the aerial and the vehicle frame. This stay can be manufactured from the slotted

and drilled metal strips previously mentioned. The stay should be securely screwed or bolted in place. For best reception, it is advisable to fit an earth lead between the aerial and the vehicle body.

11 It will probably be necessary to drill one or two holes through bodywork panels in order to feed the aerial lead into the interior of the car. Where this is the case, ensure that the holes are fitted with rubber grommets to protect the cable and to stop possible entry of water.

12 Positioning and fitting of the speaker depends mainly on its type. Generally, the speaker is designed to fit directly into the facia fresh air grilles already provided in the car. Where this is the case, fitting the speaker is just a matter of removing the protective grille from the aperture and screwing or bolting the speaker in place. Take great care not to damage the speaker diaphragm whilst doing this. It is a good

Fig. 12.81 Location of rear speakers – Saloon (Sec 46)

idea to fit a gasket beneath the speaker frame and the mounting panel. In order to prevent vibration, some speakers will already have such a gasket fitted.

13 If a pod type speaker was supplied with the radio, this can be secured to the mounting panel with self-tapping screws.

14 When connecting a rear mounted speaker to the radio, the wires should be routed through the vehicle beneath the carpets or floor mats, preferably along the side of the floorpan where they will not be trodden on by passengers. Make the relevant connections as directed by the radio manufacturer.

15 For the best results from speakers designed to be recessed into a panel, mount them so that the back of the speaker protrudes into an enclosed chamber within the car (eg door interiors or the boot cavity).

16 To fit recessed type speakers in the front doors, first check that there is sufficient room to mount the speakers in each door without it fouling the latch or window winding mechanism. Hold the speaker against the skin of the door, and draw a line around the periphery of the speaker. With the speaker removed draw a second cutting line, within the first, to allow enough room for the entry of the speaker back, but at the same time providing a broad seat for the speaker flange. When you are sure that the cutting line is correct, drill a series of holes around its periphery. Pass a hacksaw blade through one of the holes and then cut through the metal between the holes until the centre section of the panel falls out.

17 De-burr the edges of the hole and then paint the raw metal to prevent corrosion. Cut a corresponding hole in the door trim panel – ensuring that it will be completely covered by the speaker grille. Now drill a hole in the door edge and a corresponding hole in the door surround. These holes are to feed the speaker lead through – so fit grommets. Pass the speaker leads through the door trim, door skin and out through the holes in the side of the door and door surround. Refit the door trim panel and then secure the speaker to the door using self-tapping screws. If the speaker is fitted with a shield to prevent water dripping on it, ensure that this shield is at the top.

18 By now you will have several yards of additional wiring in the car, use PVC tape to secure this wiring out of harm's way. Do not leave electrical leads dangling. Ensure that all new electrical connections are properly made (wires twisted together will not do) and completely secure.

19 The radio should now be working, but before you pack away your tools it will be necessary to trim the radio to the aerial. If specific instructions are not provided by the radio manufacturer, proceed as follows: Find a station with a low signal strength on the medium-wave band, slowly turn the trim screw of the radio in or out until the loudest reception of the selected station is obtained. The set is then trimmed to the aerial.

Tape players

20 Fitting instructions for cassette stereo tape players are the same as when fitting a radio. Tape players are not usually prone to electrical interference like radios, although it can occur, so positioning is not so critical. If possible, the player should be mounted on an even keel. Also it must be possible for a driver wearing a seat belt to reach the unit in order to change or turn over tapes.

Factory-fitted radio

21 If the vehicle is equipped with a factory-fitted radio, then it may be

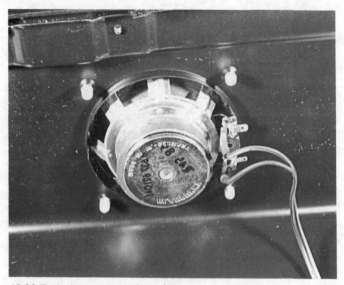

46.26 Typical rear mounted speaker

removed in the following way for repair or as a preliminary operation to removal of the facia panel (refer to Chapter 11).

22 Disconnect the battery.

23 Remove the ashtray and the central switch plate (6 screws) from the facia panel.

24 Reach around the radio and unscrew the mounting screws from the brackets.

25 Withdraw the radio sufficiently far to be able to disconnect the power, aerial, earth and loudspeaker leads from it.

26 On some models, rear mounted speakers are located in the rear shelf side panels (photo).

47 Radios and tape players – suppression of interference (general)

To eliminate buzzes and other unwanted noises cost very little and is not as difficult as sometimes thought. With a modicum of common sense and patience and following the instructions in the following paragraphs, interference can be virtually eliminated.

The first cause for concern is the generator. The noise this makes over the radio is like an electric mixer and the noise speeds up when you rev up (if you wish to prove the point, you can remove the drivebelt and try it). The remedy for this is simple; connect a 1.0µF – 3.0µF capacitor between earth, and the *large* (B+) terminal on the alternator. This is most important for if you connect it to the small terminal, you will probably damage the alternator permanently.

A second common cause of electrical interference is the ignition system. Here a 1.0µF capacitor must be connected between earth and the 'SW' or '+' terminal on the coil. This may stop the tick-tick-tick sound that comes over the speaker. Next comes the spark itself. The ignition HT leads are of suppressed type and no further action is required. Do not fit plug suppressor caps or cut the leads to fit in-line suppressors.

At this stage it is advisable to check that the radio is well earthed, also the aerial and to see that the aerial plug is pushed well into the set and that the radio is properly trimmed (see preceding Section). In addition, check that the wire which supplies the power to the set is as short as possible and does not wander all over the car. It is a good idea to check that the fuse is of the correct rating. For most sets this will be about 1 to 2 amps.

At this point the more usual causes of interference have been suppressed. If the problem still exists, a look at the causes of interference may help to pinpoint the component generating the stray electrical discharges.

The radio picks up electromagnetic waves in the air; now some are made by radio stations and other broadcasters and some, not wanted, are made by the car. The home made signals are produced by stray electrical discharges floating around in the car. Common producers of these signals are electric motors; ie, the windscreen wipers, electric screen washers, electric window winders, heater fan or an electric

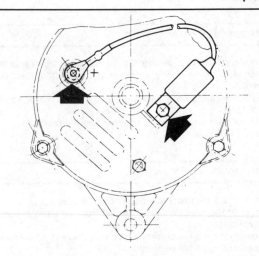

Fig. 12.82 Radio suppressor fitted to Delco-Remy alternator (Sec 47)

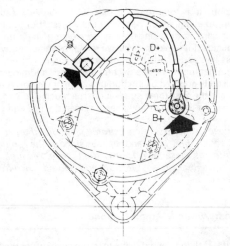

Fig. 12.83 Radio suppressor fitted to Bosch alternator (Sec 47)

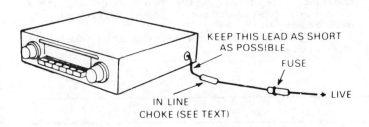

Fig. 12.84 Radio in-line choke (Sec 47)

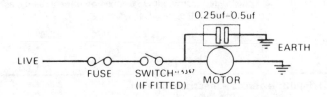

Fig. 12.85 Electrical motor suppression (Sec 47)

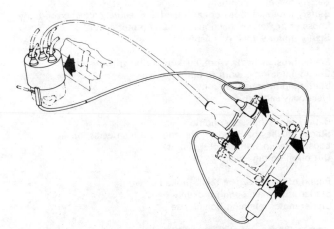

Fig. 12.86 Ignition coil suppressor and distributor screening – arrowed (Sec 47)

aerial if fitted. Other sources of interference are flashing turn signals, and instruments. Turn signals are not normally suppressed. In recent years, radio manufacturers have included in the line (live) of the radio, in addition to the fuse, an 'in-line' choke. If your installation lacks one of these put one in (Fig. 12.84).

All the foregoing components are available from radio shops or accessory shops. For a transistor radio, a 2A choke should be adequate. If you have an electric clock fitted this can be suppressed by connecting a 0.5μF capacitor directly across it as shown for a motor in Fig. 12.85.

If, after all this, you are still experiencing radio interference, first assess how bad it is, for the human ear can filter out unobstrusive unwanted noises quite easily. But if you are still adamant about eradicating the noise, then continue.

As a first step, a few 'experts' seem to favour a screen between the radio and the engine. This is OK as far as it goes, literally! – for the whole set is screened and if interference can get past that then a small piece of aluminium is not going to stop it.

A more sensible way of screening is to discover if interference is coming down the wires. First, take the live lead; interference can get between the set and the choke (hence the reason for keeping the wires short). One remedy here is to screen the wire and this is done by buying screened wire and fitting that. The loudspeaker lead could be screened also to prevent pick-up getting back to the radio – although this is unlikely.

Without doubt, the worst source of radio interference comes from the ignition HT leads, even if they have been suppressed. The ideal way of suppressing these is to slide screening tubes over the leads themselves. As this is impractical, we can place an aluminium shield over the majority of the lead areas.

Now for the really difficult cases. Here are a few tips to try out. Where metal comes into contact with metal, an electrical disturbance is caused which is why good clean connections are essential. To remove interference due to overlapping or butting panels you must bridge the join with a wide braided earth strap. The most common moving parts that could create noise and should be strapped are, in order of importance:

(a) Silencer-to-underbody
(b) Exhaust pipe-to-engine block and underbody
(c) Air cleaner-to-body
(d) Front and rear bumpers-to-body
(e) Steering column-to-body
(f) Bonnet and boot lids-to-body

These faults are most pronounced when the engine is idling or labouring under load. Although the moving parts are readily connected with nuts, bolts, etc, these do tend to rust and corrode, thus creating a high resistance interference source.

If you have a 'ragged' sounding pulse when mobile, this could be wheel or tyre static. This can be cured by buying some anti-static powder and sprinkling inside the tyres.

In conclusion, it is pointed out that it is relatively easy, and therefore cheap, to eliminate 95 per cent of all noises, but to eliminate the final 5 per cent is time and money consuming. It is up to the individual to decide if it is worth it. Please remember also, that you will not get concert hall performance out of a cheap radio.

Finally at the beginning of this Section are mentioned tape players: these are not usually affected by interference but in a very bad case, the best remedies are the first three suggestions plus using a 3 to 5 amp choke in the 'live' line and in difficult cases screen the live and speaker wires.

Note: *If you car is fitted with electronic ignition, then it is not recommended that either the spark plug resistors or the ignition coil capacitor be fitted as these may damage the system. Most electronic ignition units have built-in suppression and should, therefore, not cause interference.*

48 Heated rear window – maintenance

1   Care should be taken to avoid damage to the element for the heated rear window or tailgate.
2   Avoid scratching with rings on the fingers when cleaning, and do not allow luggage to rub against the side of the glass.
3   Do not stick labels over the element on the inside of the glass.
4   If the element grids do become damaged, a special conductive paint is available from most motor factors to repair it.
5   Do not leave the heated rear window switched on unnecessarily, as it draws a high current from the electrical system.

49 Power operated exterior mirror

1   On some models, two electrically adjustable exterior mirrors are fitted which are controlled by a four-way switch mounted on the centre console.
2   The switch controls both passenger and driver's mirror according to switch setting.
3   A facility is built into the circuit for heating the mirror.
4   The circuit includes a 20A fuse.

50 Power operated windows

1   This facility is a standard feature on some models.
2   Operation of the windows is controlled from switches mounted in the centre console.
3   In the event of a fault occurring, first check the circuit fuse and then the wiring connections for security.
4   Access to the door-mounted electric motors is obtained after removing the door trim panel as described in Chapter 11.
5   Disconnect the battery and then disconnect the wiring plugs from the motor.
6   Withdraw the motor mounting screws, or drill out the rivets, and release the window operating arm from the glass channel as described for manually-operated windows in Chapter 11. Withdraw the motor/arm assembly.
7   It is not recommended that the motor should be overhauled, but obtain a new sealed unit.

51 Fault diagnosis – electrical system

Symptom	Reason(s)
No voltage at starter motor	Battery discharged Battery defective internally Battery terminals loose or earth lead not securely attached to body Loose or broken connections in starter motor circuit Starter motor switch or solenoid faulty
Voltage at starter motor – faulty motor	Starter brushes badly worn, sticking, or brush wires loose Commutator dirty, worn or burnt Starter motor armature faulty Field coils earthed
Electrical defects	Battery in discharged condition Starter brushes badly worn, sticking, or brush wires loose Loose wires in starter motor circuit Dirt or oil on drivegear
Starter motor noisy or rough in engagement	Pinion or flywheel gear teeth broken or worn Starter drive main spring broken Starter motor retaining bolts loose
Alternator not charging*	Drivebelt loose and slipping, or broken Brushes worn, sticking, broken or dirty Brush springs weak or broken

If all appears to be well but the alternator is still not charging, take the car to an automobile electrician for checking of the alternator and regulator

Battery will not hold charge for more than a few days	Battery defective internally Electrolyte level too low or electrolyte too weak due to leakage Plate separators no longer fully effective Battery plates severely sulphated Drivebelt slipping Battery terminal connections loose or corroded Alternator not charging properly Short in lighting circuit causing continual battery drain Internal regulator unit not working correctly
Ignition light fails to go out, battery runs flat in a few days	Drivebelt loose and slipping, or broken Alternator faulty

Symptom	Reason(s)

Failure of individual electrical equipment to function correctly is dealt with below

Symptom	Reason(s)
Fuel gauge gives no reading (refer also to Chapter 3)	Fuel tank empty Electric cable between tank sender unit and gauge earthed or loose Fuel gauge case not earthed Fuel gauge supply cable interrupted Fuel gauge unit broken
Fuel gauge registers full all the time	Electric cable between tank unit and gauge broken or disconnected
Horn operates all the time	Horn push either earthed or stuck down Cable to horn push earthed
Horn fails to operate	Blown fuse Cable or cable connection loose, broken or disconnected Horn has an internal fault
Horn emits intermittent or unsatisfactory noise	Cable connections loose Horn incorrectly adjusted
Lights do not come on	If engine not running, battery discharged Light bulb filament burnt out or bulbs broken Wire connections loose, disconnected or broken Light switch shorting or otherwise faulty
Lights come on but fade out	If engine not running, battery discharged
Lights give very poor illumination	Lamp glasses dirty Reflector tarnished or dirty Lamps badly out of adjustment Incorrect bulb with too low wattage fitted Existing bulbs old and badly discoloured Electrical wiring too thin not allowing full current to pass
Lights work erratically, flashing on and off, especially over bumps	Battery terminals or earth connections loose Lights not earthing properly Contacts in light switch faulty
Wiper motor fails to work	Blown fuse Wire connections loose, disconnected or broken Brushes badly worn Armature worn or faulty Field coils faulty
Wiper motor works very slowly and takes excessive current	Commutator dirty, greasy or burnt Drive to spindles too bent or unlubricated Drive spindle binding or damaged Armature bearings dry or unaligned Armature badly worn or faulty
Wiper motor works slowly and takes little current	Brushes badly worn Commutator dirty, greasy or burnt Armature badly worn or faulty
Wiper motor works but wiper blades remain static	Linkage disengaged or faulty Drive spindle damaged or worn Wiper motor gearbox parts badly worn
Wipers do not park correctly after wash/wipe sequence	Faulty relay
No wash/wipe sequence and/or no intermittent wipe	Faulty relay
Wipers work continuously when switched to intermittent wipe	Faulty motor
Wipers do not park correctly	Faulty relay or motor (careful diagnosis is required)
Wiper motor starts spontaneously	Coil secondary (HT) winding defective (open-circuit) Alternator voltage regulator defective* Washer pump wires too close to HT leads Carburettor solenoid cut-off valve loose or defective Poor earth connection at wiper motor mounting screw

Fitting a suppression capacitor to the alternator is the first line of attack if this is the source of the problem. Failing this, it may be necessary to renew the voltage regulator

Key to Fig. 12.87

No	Description	Grid reference	No	Description	Grid reference
E1	RH parking light	47	K28	Running lights relay	240, 241
E2	RH tail light	48	K29	Electric aerial relay	259 to 267
E3	Number plate light	49	K30	Heated rear window relay	142 to 144
E4	LH parking light	44	K31	Fuel pump relay	206 to 208
E5	LH tail light	45	K35	Heated exterior mirror delay relay	335 to 338
E6	Engine compartment light	52	K36	Computer relay	312 to 314
E7	RH high beam	60	K39	Time delay relay	247 to 249
E8	LH high beam	59	M1	Starter motor	7
E9	RH low beam	63	M2	Windscreen wiper motor	119
E10	LH low beam	62	M3	Heater fan motor	89
E11	Instrument lights	51	M4	Radiator fan motor	17
E12	Selector lever light	100	M5	Washer pump	117
E13	Boot light	81	M6	LH headlight wiper motor	130
E14	Courtesy light	92	M7	RH headlight wiper motor	135
E15	Glovebox light	105	M8	Rear window wiper motor	140
E16	Cigarette lighter light	102	M9	Rear window washer pump	145
E17	RH reversing light	108	M10	Air conditioning fan motor	288
E18	LH reversing light	107	M12	Starter motor (Diesel)	168 to 171
E19	Heated rear window	40	M14	LH front door window motor	273, 275
E20	LH foglight	158	M15	RH front door window motor	276, 278
E21	RH foglight	159	M21	Fuel pump	211
E22	LH spot light	151	M26	Electric aerial motor	259, 267
E23	RH spot light	153	M27	Auxiliary fan motor (air conditioning)	299
E24	Rear foglight	163	M28	LH exterior mirror adjustment	318 to 320
E25	LH heated front seat	181 to 184	M30	LH exterior mirror adjustment and heating	325 to 328
E30	RH heated front seat	186 to 189	M31	RH exterior mirror adjustment and heating	332 to 335
E31	Symbol insert light	166	P1	Fuel gauge	22
E32	Clock light	98	P2	Temperature gauge	20
E33	Ashtray light	103	P3	Clock	96
E34	Heater control light	167	P4	Fuel sensor	22, 310
E38	Computer light	309	P5	Temperature sensor	20
E39	RH rear foglight	162	P7	Tachometer	113
F1 to F18	Fuses in fusebox	Various	P8	Oil pressure gauge	115
F19	Fuse (window motors)	274	P9	Voltmeter	114
F21	Fuse (air conditioning)	286	P10	Oil pressure sensor	115
F25	Voltage stabiliser	19	P11	Airflow meter	235
G1	Battery	1	P12	Temperature probe (coolant)	235
G2	Alternator	14	P13	Outside air temperature sensor	312
H1	Radio	95	P14	Distance sensor	303, 304
H2	Horn	109	P15	Fuel flowmeter	305, 306
H3	Turn signal warning light	76	R2	Automatic choke	202
H4	Oil pressure warning light	27	R3	Cigarette lighter	101
H5	Handbrake/brake fluid warning light	26	R5	Glow plugs	175, 176
H6	Hazard warning system warning light	72	R6	Air conditioning fan resistor	292
H7	No-charge warning light	15	S1	Starter motor switch	6, 7
H8	Main beam warning light	61	S2	Light switch	52
H9	RH stop-light	67	S2.1	Courtesy light switch	90
H10	LH stop-light	65	S3	Heater fan switch	86 to 89
H11	RH front turn signal light	76	S4	Heated rear window switch	39
H12	RH rear turn signal light	78	S5.2	Headlight dip switch	57
H13	LH front turn signal light	73	S5.3	Turn signal switch	78
H14	LH rear turn signal light	75	S7	Reversing light switch	107
H16	Preheater warning light	173	S8	Stop-light switch	65
H17	Trailer turn signal warning light	199	S9.2	Windscreen wiper switch (intermittent)	117 to 121
H18	Dual horns	110	S9.3	Rear window wiper switch (intermittent)	143, 144
H19	Headlights on warning buzzer	280, 283	S10	Automatic transmission switch	7
H20	Choke on warning light	55	S11	Brake fluid level switch	24
H23	Radio with electric aerial	269	S13	Handbrake warning light switch	26
K1	Heated rear window relay	39	S14	Oil pressure switch	27
K2	Flasher unit	69	S15	Boot lid switch	81
K4	Spotlight relay	149	S16	RH courtesy light switch	93
K5	Foglight relay	156	S17	LH courtesy light switch	92
K6	Air conditioning relay	285, 286	S18	Glovebox light switch	105
K7	Air conditioning fan relay	288, 289	S21	Foglight switch	156
K8	Windscreen wiper intermittent relay	120 to 123	S22	Rear foglight switch	163, 164
K9	Headlamp washer relay	129	S23	Boot lid release switch	204
K10	Trailer flasher unit	200, 201	S24	Air conditioning fan switch	288 to 291
K15	Fuel injection timing control	213 to 225	S25	Air conditioning switch	292 to 294
K20	Ignition module	8 to 10	S27	Pressure switch	295
K24	Radiator fan relay	298, 299	S28	Compressor cut-off switch	295
K25	Preheater relay	174 to 178	S29	Radiator fan switch	17, 300

Key to Fig. 12.87 (continued)

No	Description	Grid reference
S30	LH heated seat switch	180, 181
S37	LH front door window motor switch	272 to 275
S38	RH front door window motor switch	276 to 279
S44	Throttle valve switch	235
S46	Heated seat switch	184 to 186
S47	Doors open/headlamps on warning switch	283
S50	Choke on warning switch	55
S52	Hazard light switch	69 to 75
S60	Clutch pedal switch	246
S67	LH exterior mirror adjustment switch	317 to 320
S68	Exterior mirror switch	323 to 332
U1	Day running lights transformer	241 to 245
U3	Computer	304 to 313
U3.1	Clock switch	311
U3.2	Function selector switch	311
U3.3	Reset/stopwatch/adjustment switch	311

No	Description	Grid reference
X1	Trailer socket	191 to 197
X2	Auxiliary connector	95, 100, 55, 181, 185, 204, 266, 274, 280, 309, 322
Y1	Air conditioning compressor	295
Y2	Revolution acceleration solenoid valve	291
Y3	Boot lid release solenoid	204
Y4	Headlight washer solenoid valve	134
Y5	Diesel solenoid valve	179
Y6	Auxiliary air slide valve	235
Y7	Fuel injectors	235
Y10	Distributor	12
Y11	Hall sensor	9, 10
Y17	Idle cut-off solenoid valve	203
Y18	Dashpot solenoid valve	246, 249

Not all items fitted to all models

Colour code
BL Blue
BR Brown
GE Yellow
GN Green
GR Grey
HBL Light blue
LI Lilac
RT Red
SW Black
VI Violet
WS White

Abbreviations
ABS Anti-lock braking
BR Trip computer
EMP Receiver (radio)
EST Electronic spark timing (ignition advance)
EV61 Electronic carburettor
EZ61 Microprocessor spark timing system
EZF EST
EZV Electronic carburettor
HEI High energy ignition system
MZV Microprocessor-controlled ignition system
SAS Overrun cut-off
SSS Stop-start system
TBI Throttle body injection
TFL Day running lights
TSZ HEI

Wiring identification
eg GE WS 1.5
GE Basic colour
WS Identification colour
1.5 Section (mm²)

Explanatory note
The following wiring diagrams are laid out using a grid reference system, with the bottom line being the earth track. Using grid reference 55 at the bottom of Fig. 12.87 as an example, follow the line upwards past switch S50 to lamp H20, through connector X2 and finally to a number in a box (20). Referring back to grid reference 20 at the bottom of the diagram, it will be seen that a number 55 in a box aligns with this reference near the top of the diagram. The line from this boxed number is a continuation of grid reference 55 and shows the live feed to lamp H20 through the 20 amp fuse F6.

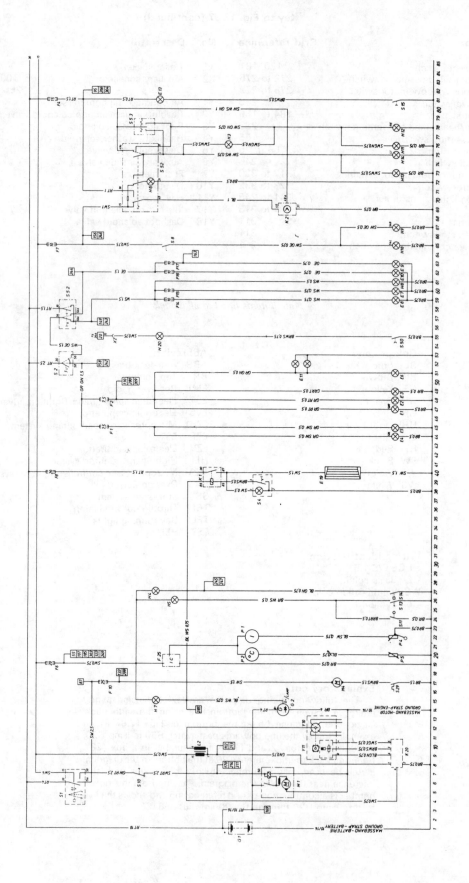

Fig. 12.87 Wiring diagram for models up to 1983

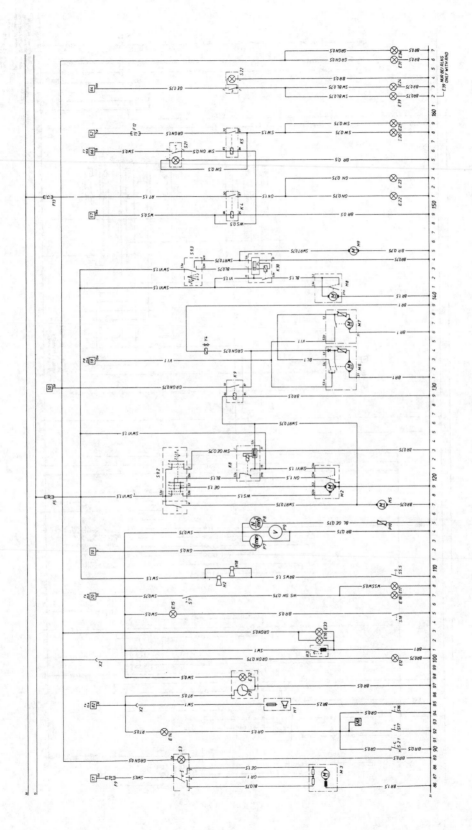

Fig. 12.87 Wiring diagram for models up to 1983 (continued)

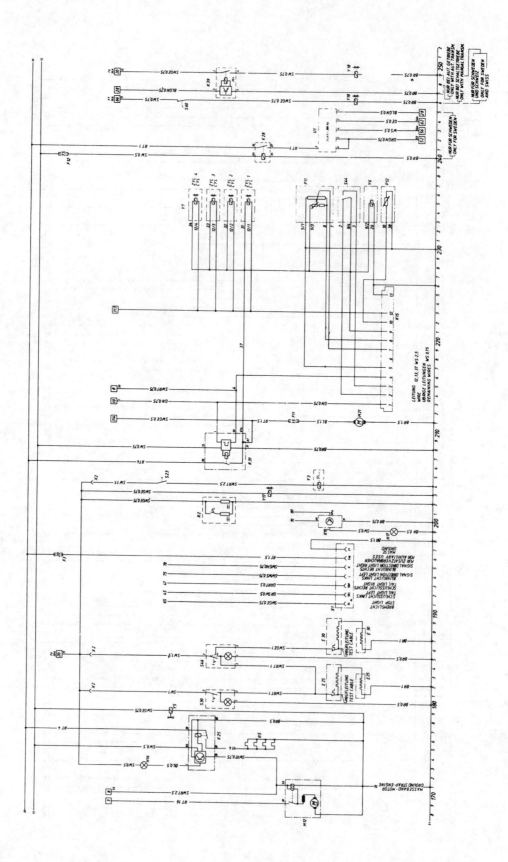

Fig. 12.87 Wiring diagram for models up to 1983 (continued)

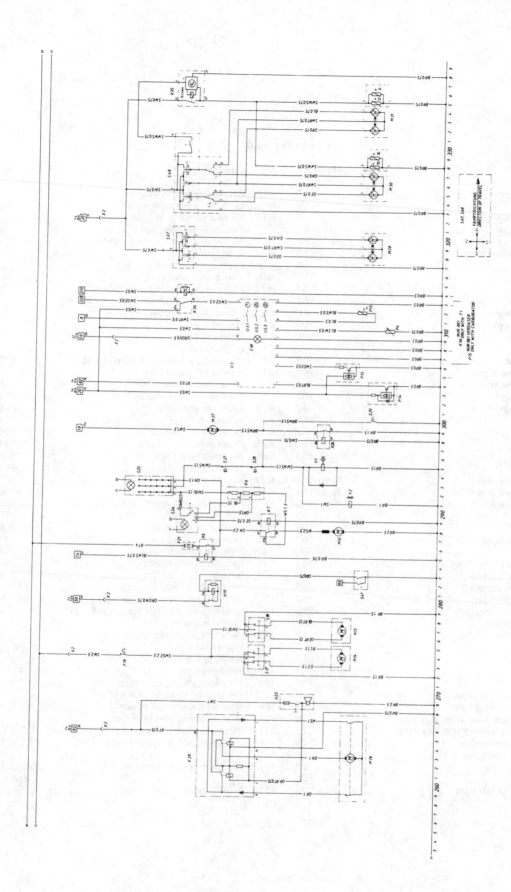

Fig. 12.87 Wiring diagram for models up to 1983 (continued)

Key to Fig. 12.88

No	Description	Grid reference	No	Description	Grid reference
E1	RH parking light	47	H12	RH rear turn signal light	78
E2	RH tail light	48	H13	LH front turn signal light	73
E3	Number plate light	49	H14	LH rear turn signal light	75
E4	LH parking light	44	H16	Preheater warning light	173
E5	LH tail light	45	H17	Trailer turn signal warning light	199
E6	Engine compartment light	52	H18	Dual horns	110
E7	RH high beam	60	H19	Headlights on warning buzzer	280, 283
E8	LH high beam	59	H20	Choke on warning light	55
E9	RH low beam	63	H23	Radio with electric aerial	269
E10	LH low beam	62	H25	Mirror heater warning light	330
E11	Instrument lights	51	K1	Heated rear window relay	39
E12	Selector lever light	100	K2	Flasher unit	69
E13	Boot light	81	K4	Spotlight relay	149
E14	Courtesy light	92	K5	Foglight relay	156
E15	Glovebox light	105	K8	Windscreen wiper intermittent relay	120 to 123
E16	Cigarette lighter light	102	K9	Headlamp washer relay	129
E17	RH reversing light	108	K10	Trailer flasher unit	200, 201
E18	LH reversing light	107	K15	Fuel injection timing control	213 to 225
E19	Heated rear window	40	K19	Level control relay	378, 379
E20	LH foglight	158	K20	Ignition module	8 to 10
E21	RH foglight	159	K21	Level control sensor	375 to 378
E22	LH spot light	151	K25	Preheater relay	174 to 178
E23	RH spot light	153	K28	Running light relay	240, 241
E24	Rear foglight	163	K29	Electric aerial relay	259 to 267
E25	LH heated front seat	181 to 184	K30	Heated rear window relay	142 to 144
E30	RH heated front seat	186 to 189	K31	Fuel pump relay	206 to 208
E31	Symbol insert light	166	K35	Heated exterior mirror delay relay	335 to 338
E32	Clock light	98	K36	Computer relay	312 to 314
E33	Ashtray light	103	K37	Central locking relay	366 to 370
E34	Heater control light	167	K39	Time delay relay	247 to 249
E38	Computer light	309	K45	Mixture preheater relay	360, 361
E39	RH rear foglight	162	K46	Ignition timing control	345 to 350
F1 to F18	Fuses in fusebox	Various	K52	Ignition module	342, 343
F19	Fuse (window motors)	274, 385	L2	Ignition coil (Hall sensor)	9
F20	Fuse (central locking)	367	L3	Ignition coil (inductive sensor)	343, 344
F22	Fuse (mixture preheater)	360	L4	Ignition coil (inductive sensor, EZ 61)	411, 412
F24	Fuse (level control)	379	M1	Starter motor	7
F25	Voltage stabiliser	19	M2	Windscreen wiper motor	119
G1	Battery	1	M3	Heater fan motor	89
G2	Alternator	14	M4	Radiator fan motor	17
H1	Radio	95	M5	Washer pump	117
H2	Horn	109	M6	LH headlight wiper motor	130
H3	Turn signal warning light	76	M7	RH headlight wiper motor	135
H4	Oil pressure warning light	27	M8	Rear window wiper motor	140
H5	Handbrake/brake fluid warning light	26	M9	Rear window washer pump	145
H6	Hazard warning system warning light	72	M12	Starter motor (Diesel)	168 to 171
H7	No-charge warning light	15	M14	LH front door window motor	273, 275, 394, 396
H8	Main beam warning light	61	M15	RH front door window motor	276, 278, 388, 390
H9	RH stop-light	67			
H10	LH stop-light	65	M16	LH rear door window motor	392, 394
H11	RH front turn signal light	76			

Key to Fig. 12.88 (continued)

No	Description	Grid reference	No	Description	Grid reference
M17	RH rear door window motor	396, 398	S22	Rear foglight switch	163, 164
M18	Front door locking motor	369, 372	S23	Boot lid release switch	204
M19	LH rear door locking motor	369, 372	S29	Radiator fan switch	17
M20	RH rear door locking motor	369, 372	S30	LH heated seat switch	180, 181
M21	Fuel pump	211	S31	LH rear door courtesy light switch	91
M22	Level control compressor	379	S32	RH rear door courtesy light switch	93
M26	Electric aerial motor	259 to 267	S37	LH front door window motor switch	272 to 275, 374 to 377
M28	LH exterior mirror adjustment	318 to 320			
M30	LH exterior mirror adjustment and heating	325 to 328	S38	RH front door window motor switch, or rear window isolating switch	276 to 279, 383
M31	RH exterior mirror adjustment and heating	332 to 335	S39	LH rear door window motor switch	392 to 394
P1	Fuel gauge	22	S40	RH rear door window motor switch	366, 367
P2	Temperature gauge	20	S41	Central locking door switch	366, 367
P3	Clock	96	S44	Throttle valve switch	235
P4	Fuel sensor	22, 310	S46	Heated seat switch	184 to 186
P5	Temperature sensor	20	S47	Doors open/headlamps on warning switch	283
P7	Tachometer	113	S50	Choke on warning switch	55
P8	Oil pressure gauge	115	S52	Hazard light switch	69 to 75
P9	Voltmeter	114	S60	Clutch pedal switch	264
P10	Oil pressure sensor	115	S66	Vacuum switch	348
P11	Airflow meter	235	S67	LH exterior mirror adjustment switch	·317 to 320
P12	Temperature probe (coolant)	235	S68	Exterior mirror switch	323 to 332
P13	Outside air temperature sensor	312	S73	Temperature switch	361
P14	Distance sensor	303, 304, 356, 357	S74	Engine temperature switch	351
			S75	Oil temperature switch	351
P15	Fuel flowmeter	305, 306	S77	Distance switch	353 to 356
R2	Carburettor preheater	199	S78	RH front door window motor switch	388 to 391
R3	Cigarette lighter	101	S79	LH rear door remote window motor switch	392 to 395
R5	Glow plugs	175, 176	S80	RH rear door remote window motor switch	396 to 399
R7	Mixture preheater	360	U1	Day running lights transformer	241 to 245
R12	Automatic choke	202	U3	Computer	304 to 313
S1	Starter motor switch	6, 7	U3.1	Clock switch	311
S2.1	Light switch	52, 53	U3.2	Function selector switch	311
S2.2	Courtesy light switch	90	U3.3	Reset/stopwatch/adjustment switch	311
S3	Heater fan switch	86 to 89	X1	Trailer socket	190 to 197
S4	Heated rear window switch	39	X2	Auxiliary connector	55, 95, 100, 181, 185, 204, 266, 274, 280, 322, 367, 385
S5.2	Headlight dip switch	57			
S5.3	Turn signal switch	78	Y3	Boot lid release solenoid	204
S5.5	Horn switch	109	Y4	Headlight washer solenoid valve	134
S7	Reversing light switch	107	Y5	Diesel solenoid valve	179
S8	Stop-light switch	65	Y6	Auxiliary air slide valve	235
S9.2	Windscreen wiper switch (intermittent)	117 to 121	Y7	Fuel injectors	235
S9.3	Rear window wiper switch (intermittent)	143, 144	Y9	Level control solenoid	377
S10	Automatic transmission switch	7	Y10	Distributor	12
S11	Brake fluid level switch	24	Y11	Hall sensor	9, 10, 345, 346
S13	Handbrake warning light switch	26	Y15	Inductive sensor	410, 411
S14	Oil pressure switch	27	Y17	Idle cut-off solenoid valve	203
S15	Boot light switch	81	Y18	Dashpot solenoid valve	246, 249
S16	RH courtesy light switch	93	Y22	Distributor	348
S17	LH courtesy light switch	92	Y23	Distributor	415
S18	Glovebox light switch	105			
S21	Foglight switch	156			

Not all items fitted to all models
For colour code, see key to Fig. 12.87

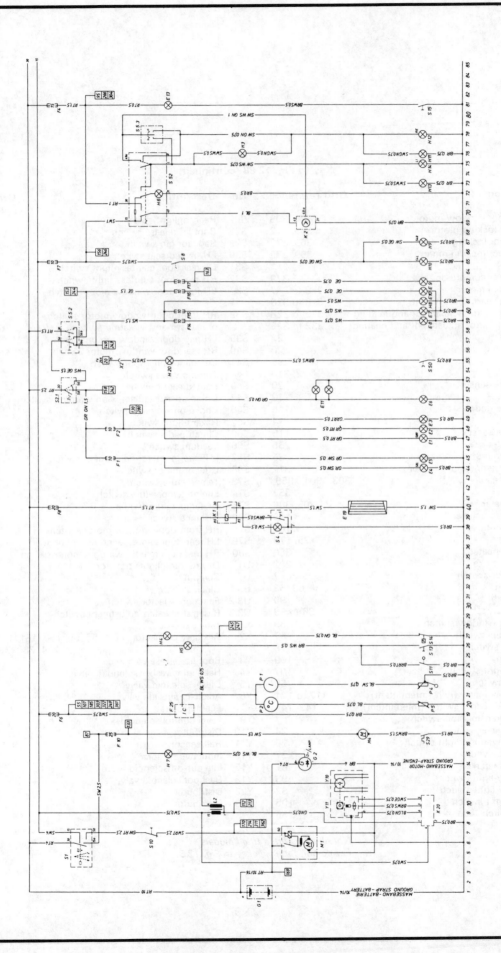

Fig. 12.88 Wiring diagram for 1984 models

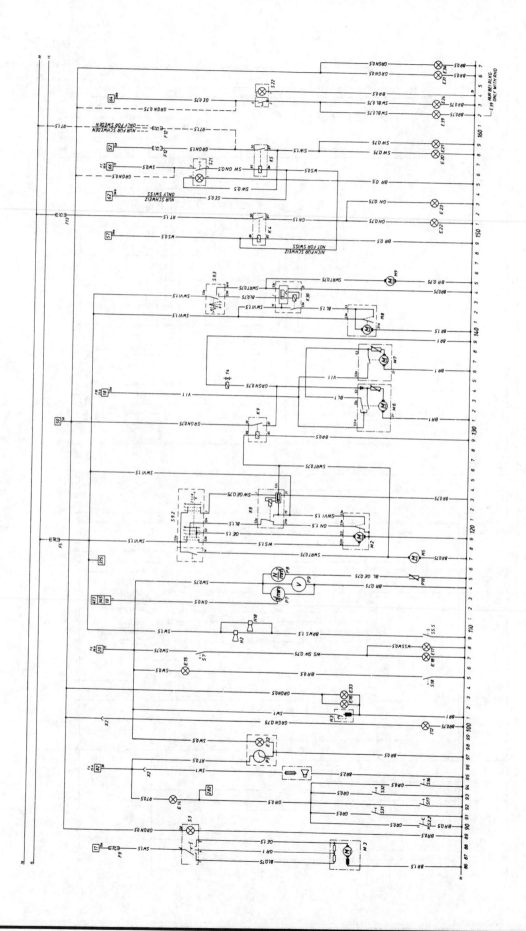

Fig. 12.88 Wiring diagram for 1984 models (continued)

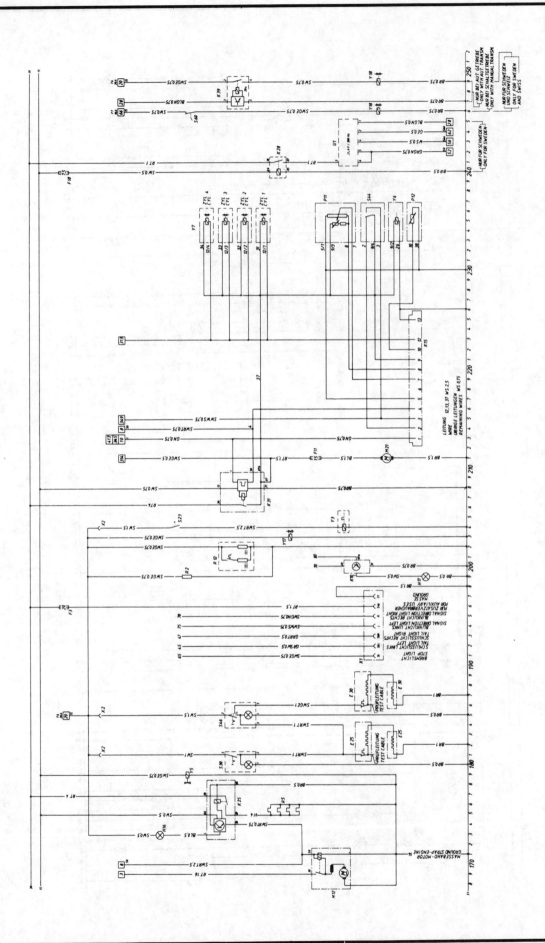

Fig. 12.88 Wiring diagram for 1984 models (continued)

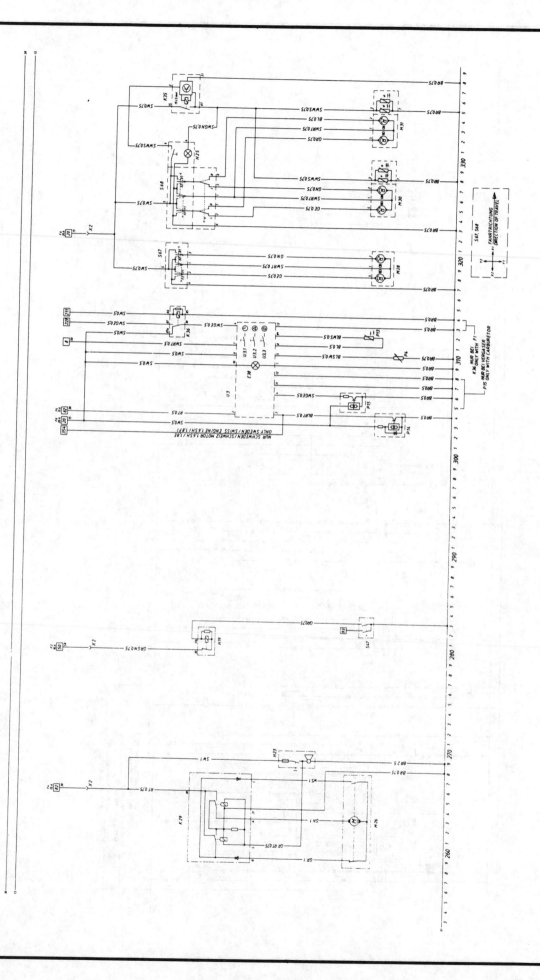

Fig. 12.88 Wiring diagram for 1984 models (continued)

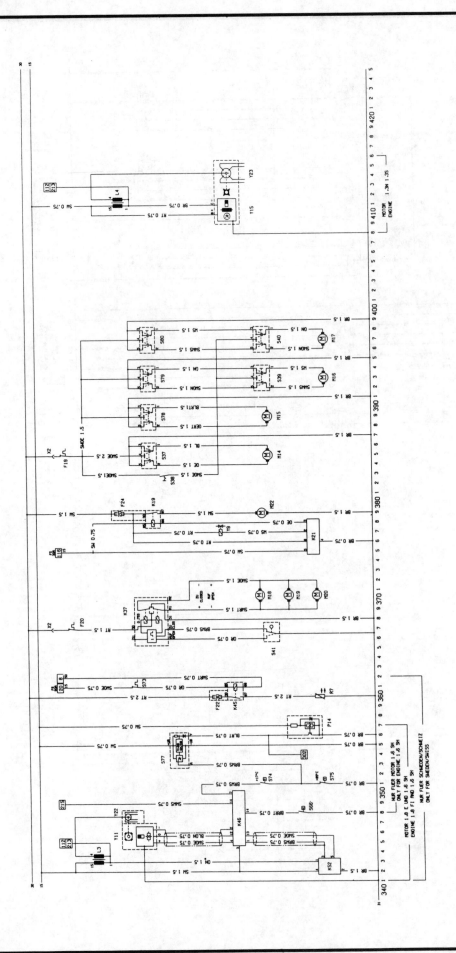

Fig. 12.88 Wiring diagram for 1984 models (continued)

Key to Fig. 12.89

No	Description	Grid reference	No	Description	Grid reference
E1	RH parking light	241	H13	LH front turn signal light	284
E2	RH tail light	242	H14	LH rear turn signal light	285
E3	Number plate light	243	H16	Preheater warning light	170
E4	LH parking light	236	H17	Trailer turn signal warning light	280
E5	LH tail light	237	H18	Dual horns	345
E6	Engine compartment light	245	H19	Headlights on warning buzzer	291
E7	RH high beam	252	H20	Choke on warning light	224
E8	LH high beam	251	H23	Radio with electric aerial	310, 311
E9	RH low beam	255	H25	Mirror heater warning light	383, 392
E10	LH low beam	254	K1	Heated rear window relay	209, 210
E11	Instrument lights	246	K2	Flasher unit	281
E12	Selector lever light	247	K4	Spotlight relay	270, 271
E13	Boot light	293	K5	Foglight relay	263, 264
E14	Courtesy light	294	K8	Windscreen wiper intermittent relay	317 to 320
E15	Glovebox light	225	K9	Headlamp washer relay	324, 325
E16	Cigarette lighter light	230	K10	Trailer flasher unit	280, 281
E17	RH reversing light	226	K15	Fuel injection timing control	181 to 191
E18	LH reversing light	227	K19	Level control relay	350, 351
E19	Heated rear window	210	K20	Ignition module	112 to 116, 423
E20	LH foglight	262			
E21	RH foglight	263	K21	Level control sensor	347 to 350
E22	LH spot light	269	K25	Preheater relay	170 to 173
E23	RH spot light	270	K28	Running lights relay	·354, 355
E24	Rear foglight (LH on some models)	258	K29	Electric aerial relay	306 to 310
E25	LH heated front seat	370	K30	Heated rear window relay	339 to 341
E30	RH heated front seat	374	K31	Fuel pump relay	177 to 179
E31	Symbol insert light	245	K35	Heated exterior mirror delay relay	397, 399
E32	Clock light	301	K36	Computer relay	413 to 415
E33	Ashtray light	231	K37	Central locking relay	361 to 365
E34	Heater control light	245	K39	Time delay relay	160, 162
E38	Computer light	408	K42	Stop/start control unit	419 to 427
E39	RH rear foglight	258	K43	Stop/start relay	427, 428
E41	Courtesy light (with delay)	297, 298	K45	Mixture preheater relay	136, 137
F1 to F18	Fuses in fusebox	Various	K46	Ignition timing control	144 to 149
F19	Fuse (window motors)	439	K52	Ignition module	141, 142, 143
F22	Fuse (mixture preheater)	136	L2	Ignition coil (Hall sensor)	113, 114, 142, 143, 423
F24	Fuse (level control)	351	L3	Ignition coil (inductive sensor)	122 to 123, 423
F25	Voltage stabiliser	213	M1	Starter motor	106, 107
G1	Battery	101	M2	Windscreen wiper motor	315 to 318
G2	Alternator	109, 110	M3	Heater fan motor	203 to 205
H1	Radio	304	M4	Radiator fan motor	202
H2	Horn	344	M5	Washer pump	314
H3	Turn signal warning light	286	M6	LH headlight wiper motor	327 to 330
H4	Oil pressure warning light	222	M7	RH headlight wiper motor	332 to 334
H5	Handbrake/brake fluid warning light	221	M8	Rear window wiper motor	337 to 339
H6	Hazard warning system warning light	283	M9	Rear window washer pump	342
H7	No-charge warning light	110	M12	Starter motor (Diesel)	168, 169
H8	Main beam warning light	253	M14	LH front door window motor	438, 440
H9	RH stop-light	278	M15	RH front door window motor	442, 444
H10	LH stop-light	277	M16	LH rear door window motor	446, 448
H11	RH front turn signal light	288	M17	RH rear door window motor	450, 452
H12	RH rear turn signal light	289	M18	Front door locking motor	364 to 367

Key to Fig. 12.89 (continued)

No	Description	Grid reference	No	Description	Grid reference
M19	LH rear door locking motor	364 to 367	S30	LH heated seat switch	369, 370
M20	RH rear door locking motor	364 to 367	S31	LH rear door courtesy light switch	297
M21	Fuel pump	177	S32	RH rear door courtesy light switch	298
M22	Level control compressor	351	S37	LH front door window motor switch	438 to 441
M26	Electric aerial motor	306 to 308	S38	Rear window isolating switch	437
M28	LH exterior mirror adjustment		S39	LH rear door window motor switch	446, 448
M30	LH exterior mirror adjustment and heating	378 to 390	S40	RH rear door window motor switch	450, 452
			S41	Central locking door switch	361, 362
M31	RH exterior mirror adjustment and heating	394 to 397	S44	Throttle valve switch	197
			S46	Heated seat switch	373, 374
M37	Boot lid/tailgate locking motor	364, 367	S47	Doors open/headlamps on warning switch	291, 292
P1	Fuel gauge	214	S50	Choke on warning switch	224
P2	Temperature gauge	215	S52	Hazard light switch	281 to 285
P3	Clock	302	S60	Clutch pedal switch	158
P4	Fuel sensor	214	S66	Vacuum switch	147
P5	Temperature sensor	215	S68.1	Exterior mirror adjustment switch	377 to 380, 385 to 289
P7	Tachometer	217			
P11	Airflow meter	197	S68.2	Exterior mirror heater switch	383, 392
P12	Temperature probe (coolant)	197	S68.3	Exterior mirror left/right switch	386 to 390
P13	Outside air temperature sensor	412, 413	S73	Temperature switch	137
P14	Distance sensor	155, 156, 404, 405	S74	Engine temperature switch	150
P15	Fuel flowmeter	406, 407	S75	Oil temperature switch	150
R2	Carburettor preheater	129	S77	Distance switch	152 to 155
R3	Cigarette lighter	229	S78	RH front door window motor switch	442 to 445
R5	Glow plugs	172, 173	S79	LH rear door remote window motor switch	446 to 449
R7	Mixture preheater	136			
R11	Instrument lights dimmer	245	S80	RH rear door remote window motor switch	450 to 453
R12	Automatic choke	131, 132			
S1	Starter motor switch	106 to 108	S85	Stop/start clutch pedal switch	419
S2.1	Light switch	241 to 243, 429, 430	S86	Stop/start switch	418, 419
S2.2	Courtesy light switch	294	U1	Day running lights transformer	355 to 359
S3	Heater fan switch	203 to 206	U3	Computer	405 to 414
S4	Heated rear window switch	208, 209	U3.1	Clock switch	412
S5.2	Headlight dip switch	253, 154, 431	U3.2	Function selector switch	412
S5.3	Turn signal switch	287, 288	U3.3	Reset/stopwatch/adjustment switch	412
S5.5	Horn switch	344	X1	Trailer socket	238, 240, 247, 274, 275, 276, 286, 290
S7	Reversing light switch	227	X2	Auxiliary connector	248, 224, 232, 304, 362, 370, 375, 439
S8	Stop-light switch	278			
S9.2	Windscreen wiper switch (intermittent)	314 to 318	Y3	Boot lid release solenoid	232
S9.3	Rear window wiper switch (intermittent)	340, 341	Y4	Headlight washer solenoid valve	325
S10	Automatic transmission switch	107	Y5	Diesel solenoid valve	174
S11	Brake fluid level switch	220	Y6	Auxiliary air slide valve	197
S13	Handbrake warning light switch	221	Y7	Fuel injectors	197
S14	Oil pressure switch	222	Y9	Level control solenoid	349
S15	Boot lid switch	293	Y10	Distributor	118
S16	RH courtesy light switch	295	Y11	Hall sensor	114 to 116, 144, 145
S17	LH courtesy light switch	296	Y15	Inductive sensor	121 to 122, 429
S18	Glovebox light switch	225	Y17	Idle cut-off solenoid valve	130
S21	Foglight switch	265 to 267	Y18	Dashpot solenoid valve	158, 162
S22	Rear foglight switch	259, 260	Y22	Distributor	148
S23	Boot lid release switch	232	Y23	Distributor	125, 432
S29	Radiator fan switch	202			

Not all items fitted to all models
For colour code, see key to Fig. 12.87

317

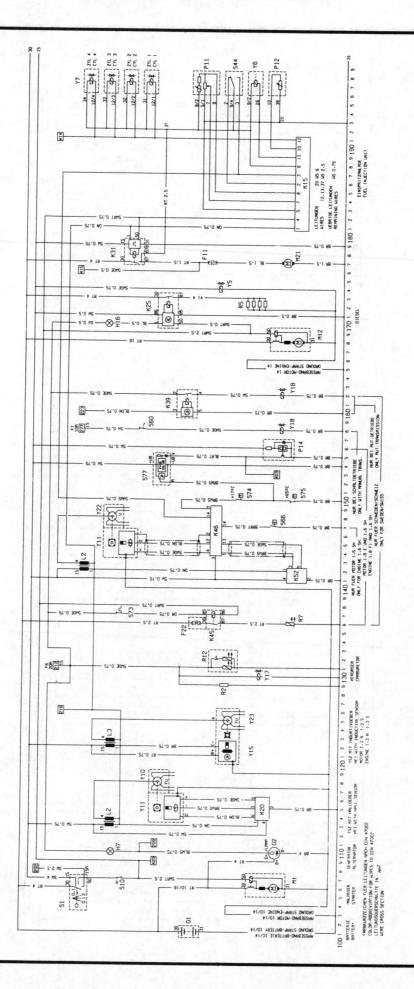

Fig. 12.89 Wiring diagram for 1985 models

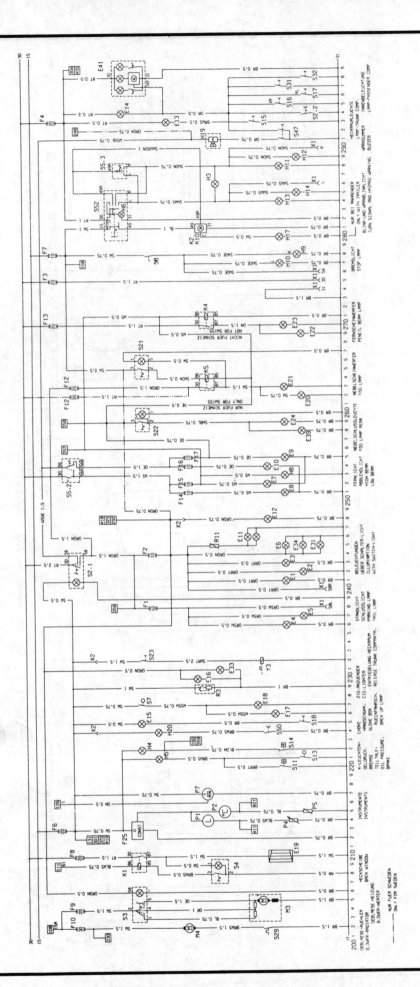

Fig. 12.89 Wiring diagram for 1985 models (continued)

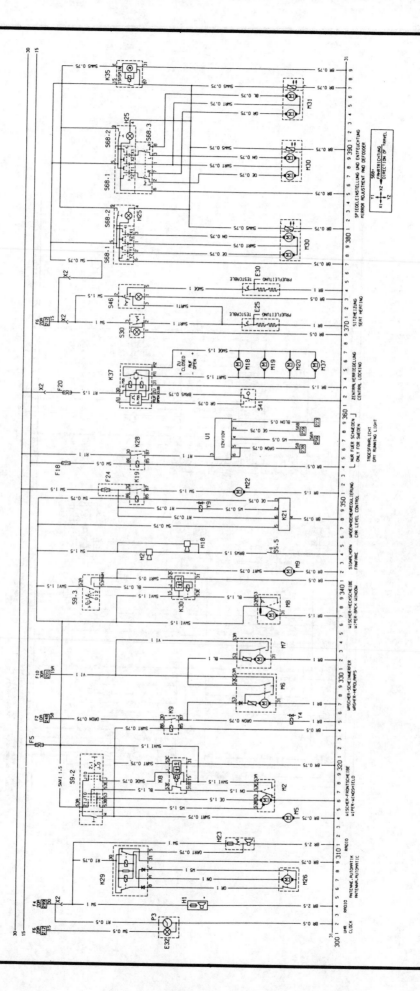

Fig. 12.89 Wiring diagram for 1985 models (continued)

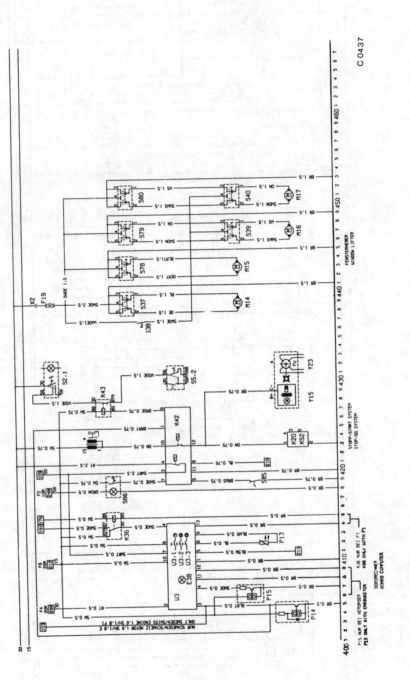

Fig. 12.89 Wiring diagram for 1985 models (continued)

C 0437

Key to Fig. 12.90

No	Description	Grid reference	No	Description	Grid reference
E1	LH parking light	236	H14	LH rear turn signal light	289
E2	LH tail light	237	H16	Preheater warning light	170
E3	Number plate light	243	H17	Trailer turn signal warning light	280
E4	RH parking light	241	H18	Dual horns	345
E5	RH tail light	242	H19	Headlights on warning buzzer	291, 292
E6	Engine compartment light	245	H20	Choke on warning light	224
E7	LH high beam	251	H23	Radio with electric aerial	310, 311
E8	RH high beam	252	H25	Mirror heater warning light	383, 393
E9	LH low beam	254	H33	LH repeater turn signal light	283
E10	RH low beam	255	H34	RH repeater turn signla light	287
E11	Instrument lights	246	K1	Headed rear window relay	209, 210
E12	Selector lever light	248	K2	Flasher unit	281
E13	Boot light	293	K4	Spotlight relay	270, 271
E14	Courtesy light	294	K5	Foglight relay	263, 264
E15	Glovebox light	225	K8	Windscreen wiper intermittent relay	317 to 320
E16	Cigarette lighter light	230	K9	Headlamp washer relay	324, 325
E17	LH reversing light	226	K10	Trailer flasher unit	280, 281
E18	RH reversing light	227	K15	Fuel injection timing control	181 to 191, 475 to 487
E19	Heated rear window	210	K19	Level control relay	350, 351
E20	LH foglight	262	K20	Ignition module	112 to 116
E21	RH foglight	263	K21	Level control sensor	347 to 350
E22	LH spot light	269	K25	Preheater relay	170 to 173
E23	RH spot light	270	K29	Electric aerial relay	306 to 310
E24	Rear foglight (LH on some models)	259	K30	Heated rear window relay	339 to 341
E25	LH heated front seat	370	K31	Fuel pump relay	177 to 179, 471 to 473
E30	RH heated front seat	374	K35	Heated exterior mirror delay relay	397, 399
E31	Symbol insert light	245	K36	Computer relay	413 to 415
E32	Clock light	301	K37	Central locking relay	361 to 365
E33	Ashtray light	231	K39	Time delay relay	160, 162
E34	Heater control light	245	K42	Stop/start control unit	419 to 427
E38	Computer light	408	K43	Stop/start relay	427, 428
E39	RH rear foglight	258	K45	Mixture preheater relay	136, 137
E41	Courtesy light (with delay)	297, 298	K46	Ignition timing control	144, 149, 460 to 467
F1 to F18	Fuses in fusebox	Various	K52	Ignition module	141, 142, 457, 458
F19	Fuse (window motors)	435	K58	Fuel pump relay (TBI)	
F20	Fuse (central locking)	362	K59	Day running light relay	354 to 359
F22	Fuse (mixture preheater)	136	L2	Ignition coil (Hall sensor)	113, 114, 142, 143, 458
F24	Fuse (level control)	351	L3	Ignition coil (inductive sensor)	122, 123, 423
F25	Voltage stabiliser	213	M1	Starter motor	106, 107
G1	Battery	101	M2	Windscreen wiper motor	315 to 318
G2	Alternator	109, 110	M3	Heater fan motor	203 to 205
H1	Radio	304	M4	Radiator fan motor	202
H2	Horn	344	M5	Washer pump	314
H3	Turn signal warning light	286	M6	LH headlight wiper motor	327 to 330
H4	Oil pressure warning light	222	M7	RH headlight wiper motor	332 to 334
H5	Handbrake/brake fluid warning light	221	M8	Rear window wiper motor	337 to 339
H6	Hazard warning system warning light	283	M9	Rear window washer pump	342
H7	No-charge warning light	110	M12	Starter motor (Diesel)	168, 169
H8	Main beam warning light	253	M14	LH front door window motor	438, 440
H9	LH stop-light	227	M15	RH front door window motor	442, 444
H10	RH stop-light	278	M16	LH rear door window motor	446, 448
H11	LH front turn signal light	284	M17	RH rear door window motor	450, 452
H12	LH rear turn signal light	285	M19	LH rear door locking motor	364, 367
H13	RH front turn signal light	288	M20	RH rear door locking motor	364, 367

Key to Fig. 12.90 (continued)

No	Description	Grid reference
M21	Fuel pump	177, 471
M22	Level control compressor	351
M26	Electric aerial motor	306 to 308
M30	LH exterior mirror adjustment and heating	378 to 381
		387 to 390
M31	RH exterior mirror adjustment and heating	394 to 397
M32	Front door locking motor	364, 367
M33	Idle control unit	
M37	Boot lid/tailgate locking motor	364, 367
P1	Fuel gauge	214
P2	Temperature gauge	215
P3	Clock	302
P4	Fuel sensor	214
P5	Temperature sensor	215
P7	Tachometer	217
P11	Airflow meter	197, 494
P12	Temperature probe (coolant)	197, 494
P13	Outside air temperature sensor	412, 413
P14	Distance sensor	155, 156, 404, 405
P15	Fuel flowmeter	406, 407
P32	Heated Lambda sensor	494
R2	Carburettor preheater	129
R3	Cigarette lighter	229
R5	Glow plugs	172, 173
R7	Mixture preheater	136
R11	Instrument lights dimmer	245
R12	Automatic choke	131, 132
S1	Starter motor switch	106 to 108
S2.1	Light switch	241 to 243, 429 to 430
S2.2	Courtesy light switch	294
S3	Heater fan switch	203 to 206
S4	Heated rear window switch	208, 209
S5.2	Headlight dip switch	253, 254, 431
S5.3	Turn signal switch	287, 288
S7	Reversing light switch	227
S8	Stop-light switch	278
S9.2	Windscreen wiper switch (intermittent)	314 to 318
S9.3	Rear window wiper switch (intermittent)	340, 341
S10.1	Automatic transmission switch	107
S11	Brake fluid level switch	220
S13	Handbrake warning light switch	221
S14	Oil pressure switch	222
S15	Boot light switch	293
S16	RH courtesy light switch	295
S17	LH courtesy light switch	296
S18	Glovebox light switch	225
S21	Foglight switch	265 to 267
S22	Rear foglight switch	259, 260
S23	Boot lid release switch	232
S29	Radiator fan switch	202
S30	LH heated seat switch	369, 370
S31	LH rear door courtesy light switch	297
S32	RH rear door courtesy light switch	298
S37	LH front door window motor switch	438 to 441
S38	Rear window isolating switch	437
S39	LH rear door window motor switch	446, 448
S40	RH rear door window motor switch	450, 452
S41	Central locking door switch	361, 362
S44	Throttle valve switch	197, 494
S46	Heated seat switch	373, 374
S47	Doors open/headlamps on warning switch	291, 292
S50	Choke on warning switch	224
S52	Hazard light switch	281 to 285
S60	Clutch pedal switch	158
S64	Horn switch	344
S66	Vacuum switch	147
S68	Exterior mirror switch	
S68.1	Exterior mirror adjustment switch	377 to 380, 385 to 389
S68.2	Exterior mirror heater switch	383, 392
S68.3	Exterior mirror left/right switch	386 to 390
S73	Temperature switch	137
S74	Engine temperature switch	150
S75	Oil temperature switch	150
S77	Distance switch	152 to 155
S78	RH front door window motor switch	442 to 445
S79	LH rear door remote window motor switch	446 to 449
S80	RH rear door remote window motor switch	450 to 453
S85	Stop/start clutch pedal switch	419
S86	Stop/start switch	418, 419
U3	Computer	405 to 414
U3.1	Clock switch	412
U3.2	Function selector switch	412
U3.3	Reset/stopwatch/adjustment switch	412
X1	Trailer socket	238, 240, 274, 275, 276, 286, 290
X2	Auxiliary connector	224, 232, 248, 304, 362, 370, 375, 435
Y3	Boot lid release solenoid	232
Y4	Headlight washer solenoid valve	325
Y5	Diesel solenoid valve	174
Y6	Auxiliary air slide valve	197, 494
Y7	Fuel injectors	197, 494
Y9	Level control solenoid	349
Y10	Distributor	118
Y11	Hall sensor	114 to 116, 460 to 462
Y15	Inductive sensor	121 to 122, 429
Y17	Idle cut-off solenoid valve	130
Y18	Dashpot solenoid valve	158, 162
Y22	Distributor	148, 464
Y23	Distributor	125, 432

Not all items fitted to all models
For colour code, see key to Fig. 12.87

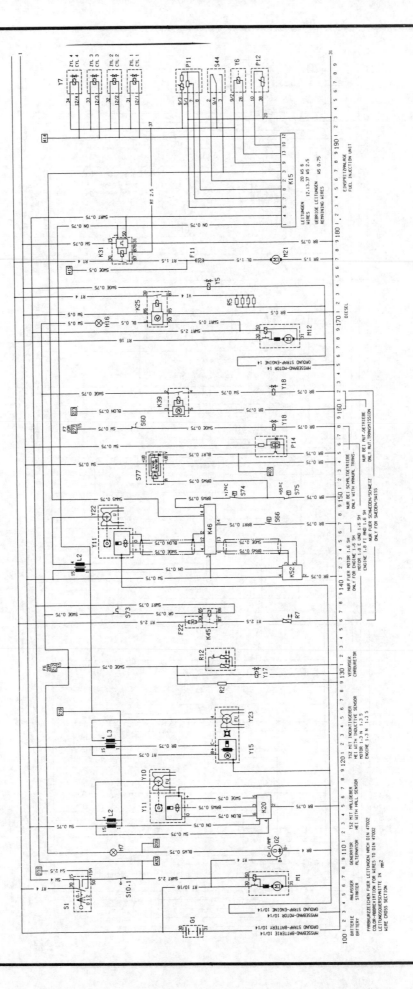

Fig. 12.90 Wiring diagram for 1986 models

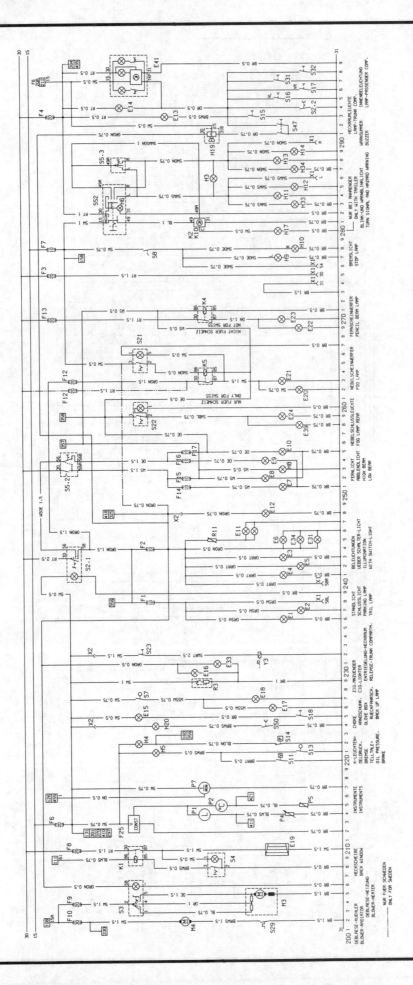

Fig. 12.90 Wiring diagram for 1986 models (continued)

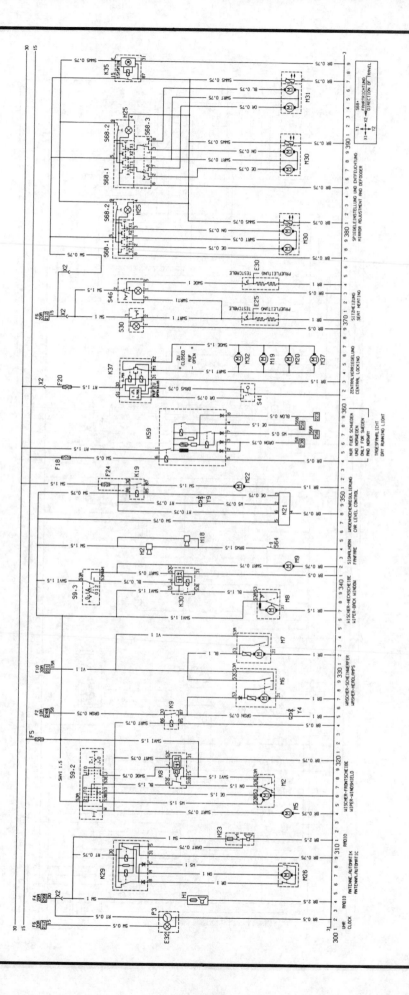

Fig. 12.90 Wiring diagram for 1986 models (continued)

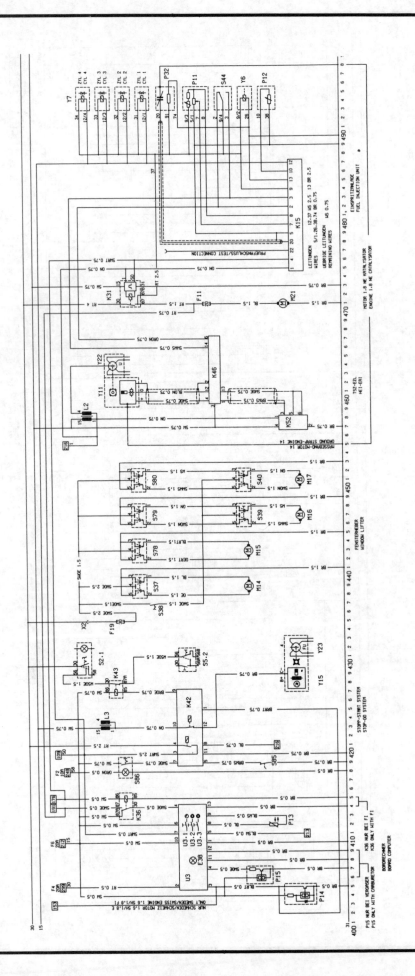

Fig. 12.90 Wiring diagram for 1986 models (continued)

Chapter 13 Supplement:
Revisions and information on later models

Contents

1 Introduction

This Supplement contains information which is additional to, or a revision of, material in the first twelve Chapters of the manual.

Much of the information deals with the changes made to the model range from 1987 on, including the introduction of the 2.0 litre engine. Also covered are revisions to the engine, cooling system, fuel and exhaust systems, and ignition system on all later models.

The Sections in the Supplement follow the same order as the Chapters to which they relate. The Specifications are all grouped together for convenience, but they follow the Chapter order also.

It is recommended that before any particular operation is undertaken, reference is made to the appropriate Section(s) of the Supplement. In this way, any changes to procedures or components can be noted before referring to the main Chapters.

2 Specifications

The Specifications given below are revisions of, or supplementary to, those appearing elsewhere in this manual. Unless given here, all specifications for the 2.0 models are the same as those for the 1.8 models given in the Specifications at the beginning of each relevant Chapter

Engine (1.6, 1.8 and 2.0, 1987 on)
General
Engine code:
    1.6 .... 16SH
    1.8 .... 18SE
    2.0 .... 20NE or 20SEH
Compression ratio:
    20NE .... 9.2 : 1
    20SEH .... 10.0 : 1

Crankshaft
Big-end running clearance:

20NE, 20SEH .... 0.006 to 0.031 mm

Camshaft
Identification code:

18SE .... E

20NE .... J

20SEH .... K

Pistons and rings

Piston grades – 16SH

	Diameter (mm)	Marking
Production grade 1	79.94	5
	79.95	6
	79.96	7
	79.97	8
Production grade 2	79.98	99
	79.99	00
	80.00	01
Production grade 3	80.01	02
	80.02	03
	80.03	04
	80.04	05
	80.05	06
Production grade 4	80.06	07
	80.07	08
	80.08	09
	80.09	1
Oversize (0.5 mm)	80.46	7 + 0.5
	80.47	8 + 0.5
	80.48	9 + 0.5
	80.49	0 + 0.5

Piston grades – 18SE:

	Diameter (mm)	Marking
Production grade 2	84.755 to 84.765	8
	84.765 to 84.775	99
	84.775 to 84.785	00
	84.785 to 84.795	01
	84.795 to 84.805	02
Oversize (0.5 mm)	85.275 to 85.285	7 + 0.5

Piston grades – 20NE, 20SEH:

	Diameter (mm)	Marking
Production grade 2	85.995 to 85.965	8
	85.965 to 85.975	99
	85.975 to 85.985	00
	85.985 to 85.995	01
	85.995 to 86.005	02
Oversize (0.5 mm)	86.445 to 86.455	7 + 0.5

Piston-to-bore clearance:

18SE, 20NE, 20SEH .... 0.01 to 0.03 mm

Cylinder head
Valve seat width:

18SE, 20NE, 20SEH:

Inlet .... 1.0 to 1.5 mm

Exhaust .... 1.7 to 2.2 mm

Valves
Valve stem-to-guide clearance:

18SE, 20NE, 20SEH:

Inlet .... 0.018 to 0.052 mm

Exhaust .... 0.038 to 0.072 mm

Valve guide installed height:

18SE, 20NE, 20SEH .... 83.50 to 83.80 mm

Valve stem diameter:

18SE, 20NE, 20SEH:

Inlet .... 6.998 to 7.012 mm

Exhaust .... 6.978 to 6.992 mm

Valve guide bore diameter:

18SE, 20NE, 20SEH .... 7.030 to 7.050 mm

Fuel and exhaust systems

Fuel injection system application (1.8 and 2.0, 1987 on)

18SE .... Bosch L3 Jetronic fuel injection system

20NE, 20SEH .... Bosch Motronic engine management system

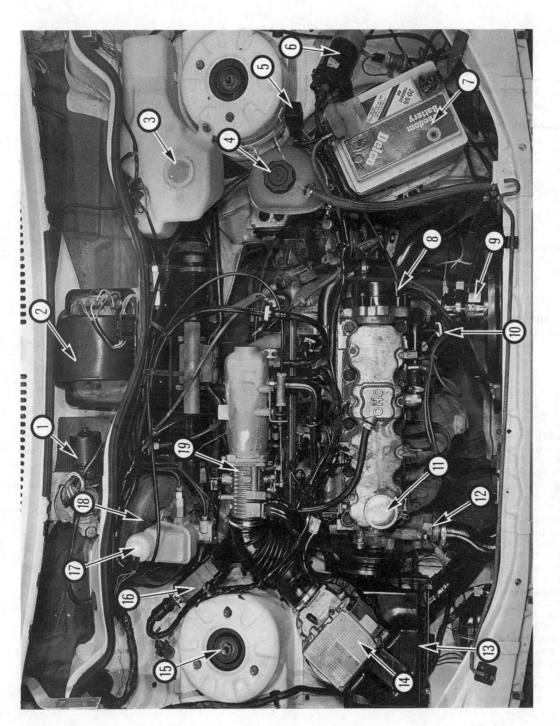

Underbonnet view of a 1987 1.8 model, with 18SE engine and L3 Jetronic fuel injection

1 Wiper motor
2 Heater blower motor
3 Washer fluid reservoir
4 Cooling system expansion tank
5 Fuel system relay
6 Ignition coil
7 Battery
8 Distributor
9 Radiator cooling fan
10 Engine oil dipstick
11 Oil filler cap
12 Thermostat housing
13 Air cleaner
14 Airflow sensor
15 Suspension strut mounting
16 Ignition system control unit
17 Brake fluid reservoir
18 Brake vacuum servo unit
19 Throttle valve housing

Adjustment data
Idle speed:
    18SE .... 800 to 900 rpm
    20NE, 20SEH .... 720 to 780 rpm*
Exhaust gas CO content at idle:
    13S, 16S, 16SH .... 1.0 to 1.5%
    18E .... 0.5% maximum
    18SE .... 1.0% maximum
    20NE, 20SEH .... 1.0% maximum*
Non-adjustable, for reference purposes only

Ignition system
Type and application (1.8 and 2.0, 1987 on)
18SE .... EZ61 (microprocessor spark timing system)
20NE, 20SEH .... Motronic system

Spark plugs (all models, 1987 on)
Type .... Champion RN7YCC or RN7YC
Electrode gap .... 0.7 to 0.8 mm (0.028 to 0.032 in)

Braking system
Brake shoes
Dimensions (1987 on):   **Width**
    Saloon and Hatchback .... 45.0 mm (1.77 in)
    Estate .... 50.0 mm (1.97 in)

Rear wheel cylinder (2.0, 1987 on)
Piston diameter (minimum permissible) .... 18.98 mm (0.748 in)
Cylinder bore (maximum permissible) .... 19.12 mm (0.753 in)
Nominal diameter .... 19.05 mm (0.751 in)

Suspension
Tyre pressures (1987 on)
Pressures in bar (lbf/in²), cold: **Front**   **Rear**

	Front	Rear
155 x 13 tyres	2.0 (29)	1.8 (26)
165 x 13 tyres	1.9 (28)	1.7 (25)
185 x 13 tyres	2.0 (29)	1.8 (26)
195 x 14 tyres	2.1 (30)	1.9 (28)

For full-load operation or high speed driving, increase pressures by 0.2 bar (3.0 lbf/in²)

Electrical system
Fuses – later models

Number	Circuit protected	Rating (A)
1	LH parking and tail lamps	10
2	RH parking and tail lamps	10
3	Spare	20
4	Interior lights, hazard warning flasher, clock, radio	20
5	Front and rear wipers and washers, horn	30
6	Reversing lights, cigarette lighter, automatic choke, instruments	20
7	Direction indicators, stop-lamps	10
8	Heated rear window	20
9	Heater blower	20
10	Radiator cooling fan	30
11	Fuel injection system	20
12	Front foglights	20
13	Auxiliary driving lights	20
14	LH main beam	10
15	RH main beam	10
16	LH dipped beam, rear foglight	10
17	RH dipped beam	10
18	Spare	10
19	Electric door windows	30
20	Central locking system	30

Weights and capacities – 1987 on
Weights
Kerb weight:
    2.0 CD Saloon .... 1103 kg (2432 lb)
    2.0 SRi Saloon .... 1143 kg (2520 lb)
    2.0 CD Hatchback .... 1145 kg (2525 lb)
    2.0 SRi Hatchback .... 1185 kg (2613 lb)

Permissible caravan/trailer towing weight:	Braked trailer	Unbraked trailer
2.0 (all models)	1300 kg (2867 lb)	500 kg (1103 lb)

Capacities (approximate)

Engine oil (with filter change):
  1.8 and 2.0 .... 4.0 litres (7.0 pints)
Cooling system:
  1.3 .... 6.7 litres (11.8 pints)
  1.6 .... 7.7 litres (13.6 pints)
  1.8 .... 7.5 litres (13.2 pints)
  2.0 .... 6.9 litres (12.1 pints)
Manual transmission:
  F13.4 .... 1.7 litres (3.0 pints)
  F13.5 .... 1.8 litres (3.2 pints)

---

3 Engine

Engine – modifications from 1987 (general)

1 For the 1987 model year, significant changes were made to the 1.6 and 1.8 litre engines, and a new 2.0 litre unit was introduced. The modified engines may be quickly identified by the location of the oil filler cap, which is now situated at the timing belt end of the camshaft cover. Additionally, the timing belt upper cover is retained by spring clips, instead of the bolts used on the earlier engines.

2 The main modifications to the later engines are as follows.

3 **Cylinder block:** This has been reinforced to reduce vibration and engine noise, as well as reducing bore and bearing distortion.

4 **Cylinder head:** The combustion chamber profile has been altered, to increase the combustion chamber area in the cylinder head, and on fuel injected engines, changes have also been made to the inlet porting. Additionally, the coolant capacity in the cylinder head water jacket has been reduced, to shorten the warm-up period.

5 **Crankshaft:** The crankshaft No 1 counterweight now has a segmented disc (1.8 engines) or a toothed lockwasher (2.0 engines) to provide the ignition and fuel system control units with engine speed/crankshaft position information.

6 **Connecting rods and gudgeon pins:** The diameter and width of the connecting rod small end eye has been changed, and narrower gudgeon pins are fitted. For optimum engine balance, the connecting rods are divided into sixteen weight categories.

7 Additional changes have been made to the pistons and rings, valves and valve springs, camshaft and oil pump.

8 Apart from the operations described in this Supplement, all other servicing, repair and overhaul procedures are the same as for earlier engines, and the information given here should be used in conjunction with that in Chapter 1.

2.0 engine – general

9 This engine is identical in design to the 1.8 litre unit, and the servicing, repair and overhaul procedures for that engine are also applicable to the 2.0 variant. Specification differences applicable to the 2.0 engine are given in the Specifications at the beginning of this Supplement. Where specifications are not given, assume them to be the same as those given for the 1.8 engine.

Camshaft toothed belt (1.6, 1.8 and 2.0, 1987 on) – renewal

Note: *Accurate adjustment of the toothed belt entails the use of a tension checking gauge, which is a Vauxhall special tool. An approximate setting can be achieved using the method described in this Section, but ideally, the tension should be checked by a dealer on completion*

10 Disconnect the battery earth lead, and for improved access, remove the air cleaner assembly, as described in Chapter 3.

11 Drain the cooling system, as described in Chapter 2.

12 Slacken the alternator adjustment link and mounting bolts (photo), push the alternator in towards the engine, and slip the drivebelt off the pulleys.

13 Release the retaining clips, and remove the toothed belt upper cover (photo).

14 Using a socket or spanner on the crankshaft pulley bolt, turn the crankshaft until No 1 piston is at its firing point. This is indicated by the notch in the crankshaft pulley being in line with the pointer on the oil pump housing, and the notch on the camshaft sprocket being in line with the pip on the inner circumference of the toothed belt inner cover (photos).

15 Raise and support the front of the car, then remove the right-hand front roadwheel.

16 Using a suitable Allen key, unscrew four bolts securing the crankshaft pulley to the toothed belt sprocket, and remove the pulley (photos).

17 Release the retaining clips, and remove the toothed belt intermediate cover from the vicinity of the coolant pump (photo).

18 Using a suitable Allen key or socket bit, slacken the three coolant pump securing bolts, then swivel the pump to release the tension on the toothed belt. The pump can be moved using the cast projection on the side of the pump body (photos).

19 If the belt is to be re-used, mark its running direction using chalk, then ease the belt off the three sprockets (photo).

20 Inspect the condition of the belt, and renew it if there is any sign of cracking, splitting, oil contamination or general deterioration.

21 Without disturbing the set position of the crankshaft and camshaft, locate the new belt over the sprockets. Apply some tension to the belt by moving the coolant pump, then temporarily tighten the coolant pump bolts.

22 Place the crankshaft pulley in position (without the retaining bolts), and check that the timing marks are still aligned as described in paragraph 14. Now turn the crankshaft through two complete revolutions, in the normal direction of rotation, and check that the marks can be re-aligned with their respective pointers. If not, release the belt tension, and alter the position of the belt on the camshaft sprocket until the marks can be correctly aligned.

23 Slacken the coolant pump bolts, and move the pump to tension the belt. The tension will be approximately correct when it is just possible to twist the belt through 90° by hand, at a point midway between the camshaft and crankshaft sprockets on the straight side of the belt. When the adjustment is correct, tighten the coolant pump bolts, turn the crankshaft through one full turn, and check the tension again. Repeat this procedure until the correct tension is obtained.

24 Refit the toothed belt intermediate cover to the coolant pump.

25 Refit the crankshaft pulley, and secure with the four bolts tightened to the specified torque.

26 Place the toothed belt upper cover in position, and secure with the retaining clips.

27 Refit the alternator drivebelt, and adjust its tension as described in Chapter 2.

28 Refit the roadwheel and lower the car to the ground.

29 Refit the air cleaner as described in Chapter 3, refill the cooling system as described in Chapter 2, then reconnect the battery earth lead.

Camshaft front oil seal (1.6, 1.8 and 2.0, 1987 on) – renewal

30 Remove the camshaft toothed belt as previously described.

31 Where applicable, detach the breather hose, then undo the bolts and remove the camshaft cover. Note the position of the cable clips under the retaining bolts to aid reassembly. Remove the cover gasket.

32 Undo the centre retaining bolt, and remove the sprocket from the camshaft (photo). To prevent the camshaft turning while the bolt is undone, engage a spanner with the flats provided between Nos 3 and 4 camshaft lobes.

33 Undo the crankshaft sprocket central bolt without disturbing the set position of the crankshaft. To prevent the crankshaft turning as the bolt is undone, it may be sufficient to engage a gear and apply the footbrake (manual gearbox only); a better way is to remove the flywheel bottom cover plate, and lock the ring gear with a large screwdriver or tyre lever.

34 Withdraw the sprocket from the crankshaft. If it is tight, refit the bolt two or three turns, and draw the sprocket off using a two-legged puller (photos).

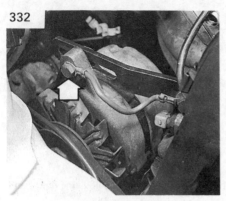

3.12 Alternator adjustment link bolt (arrowed)

3.13 Removing the toothed belt upper cover

3.14A Align the timing notch on the camshaft sprocket (arrowed) ...

3.14B ... with the pip on the toothed belt inner cover (arrowed)

3.16A Unscrew the four crankshaft pulley retaining bolts ...

3.16B ... and remove the pulley

3.17 Removing the toothed belt intermediate cover

3.18A Slacken the coolant pump upper bolt (A), front bolt (B) ...

3.18B ... and rear bolt (C), then move the pump by means of the cast projection (D)

3.19 Slip the toothed belt off the sprockets

3.32 Removing the sprocket from the camshaft

3.34A Use a puller, if necessary, to release the crankshaft sprocket ...

3.34B ... then remove the sprocket from the crankshaft

3.35A Remove the Woodruff key (arrowed) ...

3.35B ... followed by the spacer

35 Carefully ease out the Woodruff key, then remove the spacer(s) behind the key (photos).

36 Undo the two upper bolts securing the toothed belt rear cover to the camshaft housing, and release the electrical lead from the upper retaining clip. Undo the two lower bolts securing the rear cover to the oil pump housing, and remove the cover from below (photos).

37 Punch or drill a small hole in the centre of the oil seal. Screw in a self-tapping screw, and pull on the screw with pliers to extract the seal.

38 Clean out the oil seal seat in the camshaft housing, then lubricate the lips and side surfaces of the new seal with engine oil.

39 Fit the seal with its sealing lips inwards, and use a piece of tube and a mallet to drive it home. Take care not to damage the seal lips during fitting; if a protective sleeve is supplied with the new seal, it should be used.

40 Refit the toothed belt rear cover, and secure it with the four bolts.

41 Place the spacer(s) over the crankshaft, refit the Woodruff key and the toothed belt sprocket. Refit the sprocket retaining bolt, and tighten it to the specified torque (photo).

42 Refit the camshaft sprocket, and secure it with the retaining bolt, tightened to the specified torque.

43 Using a new gasket if necessary, refit the camshaft cover. Tighten the retaining bolts progressively and in a diagonal sequence, to the specified torque. Reconnect the breather hose.

44 Fit and adjust the camshaft toothed belt, using the procedure described earlier in this Section.

Camshaft (1.6, 1.8 and 2.0, 1987 on) – removal and refitting

45 Camshaft removal and refitting procedures are contained in the next sub-section dealing with removal and refitting of the cylinder head. The camshaft housing retaining bolts also secure the cylinder head, and therefore, once these bolts are removed, it is highly likely that the gasket seal will be broken. For this reason, the complete cylinder head removal and refitting procedure must be carried out, when attending to the camshaft.

Cylinder head (1.6, 1.8 and 2.0, 1987 on) – removal and refitting

Note: *The following procedure describes the removal and refitting of the cylinder head, complete with manifolds, on fuel injected engines. The operations also apply to carburettor engines, but where necessary, refer to Chapter 3 for details of fuel and electrical connections at the carburettor and inlet manifold.*

46 The cylinder head must only be removed when the engine is cold, otherwise there is a risk of distortion.
47 Disconnect the battery earth lead.
48 Remove the air cleaner assembly as described in Chapter 3.
49 Drain the cooling system as described in Chapter 2.
50 Disconnect the radiator and heater hoses from the cylinder head and inlet manifold.
51 Disconnect the spark plug HT leads, identifying them if necessary, then remove the distributor cap. On 1.6 engines, remove the distributor as described in Chapter 4.
52 Undo the bolt securing the crankcase breather pipe to the side of the cylinder head (photo).
53 Slacken the breather pipe connecting hose at the camshaft housing, withdraw the engine oil dipstick, and undo the two breather pipe retaining bolts on the block. Detach the hose, and remove the breather pipe assembly (photos).
54 Disconnect the throttle cable at the carburettor or throttle housing as applicable.
55 Disconnect the electrical leads and wiring multi-plugs from the carburettor, fuel injection system components, manifold and cylinder head as applicable. Label all the wiring as it is removed, to avoid confusion when reassembling; where necessary, refer to Chapter 3 or later sections of this Supplement for further information. With all the wiring disconnected, it should be possible to move the complete engine wiring loom to one side, clear of the engine.
56 Disconnect and plug the fuel lines from the carburettor and fuel injection system as applicable. Also on carburettor models, remove the fuel pump.
57 Disconnect the brake servo vacuum hose at the inlet manifold (photo).
58 Disconnect the exhaust downpipe from the manifold.
59 Disconnect the hoses at the auxiliary air valve (photo) then remove the valve from the camshaft housing.
60 Undo the bolts and remove the camshaft cover (photo). Recover the gasket.
61 Slacken the alternator adjustment link and mounting bolts, push

the alternator in towards the engine, and slip the drivebelt off the pulleys.
62 Remove the toothed belt covers, and slacken the belt tension as described in paragraphs 13 to 18, earlier in this Section.
63 Slip the toothed belt off the camshaft sprocket, then undo the centre retaining bolt and remove the sprocket from the camshaft. To prevent the camshaft turning while the bolt is undone, engage a spanner with the flats provided between Nos 3 and 4 camshaft lobes.
64 Undo the two bolts securing the toothed belt rear cover to the camshaft housing (photo).
65 Remove the cylinder head bolts in the reverse order to that shown in Fig. 13.1; slacken all the bolts by a quarter-turn each, and then by half-turn increments, still using the same sequence, until all tension is removed from the bolts. This procedure is important to avoid distortion of the cylinder head or camshaft housing.
66 Ease the toothed belt rear cover away from the camshaft housing, then lift the housing upwards and off the locating dowels (photo).
67 Remove the rocker arms and thrust pads from the cylinder head. Withdraw the hydraulic valve lifters, and immerse them in a container of clean engine oil to avoid any possibility of them draining. Keep all components in their original order (photos).
68 Lift off the cylinder head (photo). If it is stuck, tap it gently upwards with a hide or plastic mallet. Remove the cylinder head gasket.
69 If further dismantling of the cylinder head is to be carried out, refer to the procedures given in Chapter 1.
70 Clean the cylinder head and cylinder block free from carbon by careful scraping. Cover the coolant passages and other openings with masking tape or rag, to prevent dirt and carbon falling in. Mop out oil from the bolt holes; hydraulic pressure could crack the block when the bolts are screwed in if oil is left in the holes.
71 When all is clean, locate a new cylinder head gasket on the block so that the word 'OBEN' can be read from above (photo).
72 If the crankshaft has been turned whilst the cylinder head was removed, re-position the crankshaft so that No 1 piston is at its firing point.

3.36A Toothed belt rear cover lower retaining bolts (arrowed)

3.36B Removing the toothed belt rear cover

3.41 Tighten the sprocket retaining bolt to the specified torque

3.52 Undo the crankcase breather pipe retaining bolt (arrowed)

3.53A Detach the breather pipe connecting hose at the camshaft housing

3.53B Removing the breather pipe assembly

3.57 Brake servo vacuum hose connection at the manifold (arrowed)

3.59 Hose connections at the auxiliary air valve

3.60 Removing the camshaft cover

3.64 Toothed belt rear cover-to-camshaft housing retaining bolts

3.66 Removing the camshaft housing from the cylinder head

3.67A Remove the rocker arms ...

3.67B ... followed by the thrust pads ...

3.67C ... then withdraw the valve lifters

3.68 Removing the cylinder head

73 With the mating surfaces scrupulously clean, locate the cylinder head on the block, so that the locating dowels engage in their holes.
74 Refit the hydraulic lifters, thrust pads and rocker arms to the cylinder head, in their original order. If new hydraulic lifters are being used, initially immerse each one in a container of clean engine oil, and compress it (by hand) several times to charge it.
75 Temporarily refit the camshaft sprocket to the camshaft, and check that the timing mark on the sprocket is at the 12 o'clock position. Re-position the camshaft if necessary, then remove the sprocket.
76 Apply jointing compound to the mating faces of the cylinder head and camshaft housing, and refit the housing to the cylinder head.
77 Refit the cylinder head bolts and tighten them in a spiral pattern, as shown in Fig. 13.1 to the stages given in the Specifications. Note that the bolts are tightened initially to the Stage 1 torque wrench setting (photo), and then to an angular measurement in four further stages. The required angular measurement can be marked on a card, and then placed over the bolt as a guide to the movement of the bolt.

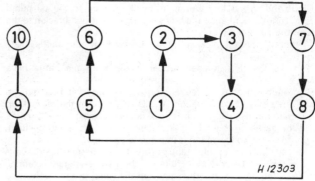

Fig. 13.1 Cylinder head bolt tightening sequence – work in the spiral pattern shown (Sec 3)

3.71 Fit the new gasket with the word 'OBEN' uppermost

Alternatively, an angular torque gauge can be used to accurately determine the required movement (photo). Gauges of this type are readily available from motor factors at modest cost, or it may be possible to hire one from larger DIY outlets.

78 Refit the two bolts securing the toothed belt rear cover to the camshaft housing.

79 Refit the camshaft sprocket, and secure with the centre retaining bolt, tightened to the specified torque (photo).

80 Check that the camshaft sprocket and crankshaft pulley timing marks are still in the correct positions as described earlier, then refit and tension the toothed belt as described in paragraphs 21 to 27 earlier in this Section.

81 Fit the camshaft cover, using a new gasket.

82 Fit and tension the alternator drivebelt, as described in Chapter 2.

83 The remainder of the refitting details are a reversal of the removal procedures. On completion, refill the cooling system, as described in Chapter 2.

84 When the engine is started and has reached normal operating temperature, check and if necessary adjust the idle speed (where applicable), and re-tighten the cylinder head bolts to the Stage 5 setting.

Sump (1.6, 1.8 and 2.0, 1987 on) – removal and refitting

85 Unscrew the drain plug, and allow the engine oil to drain into a suitable container. Refit the plug after draining.

86 Raise and support the front of the car.

87 Disconnect the exhaust downpipes from the manifold and at the ball coupling, and remove the front exhaust section from the vehicle.

88 Undo the bolts and remove the flywheel cover plate (photo).

89 Progressively slacken, then remove the sump fixing bolts.

90 Lower the sump from under the vehicle (photo).

91 If the sump is being removed for access to the crankshaft and bearings, remove the oil pick-up pipe and sump baffle plate as follows.

92 Undo the two bolts securing the pick-up pipe to the oil pump housing (photo), and undo the bolt securing the support bracket to the edge of the crankcase.

93 Withdraw the oil pick-up pipe, followed by the baffle plate (photo).

94 Remove the double-sided rubber gasket from the baffle plate (photo).

95 Thoroughly clean the sump, and obtain a new gasket if the old one shows any signs of deterioration. The O-ring seal on the oil pick-up pipe should be renewed as a matter of course (photo).

96 Fit the gasket to the baffle plate, then locate the plate in position, using two sump bolts to hold it in place temporarily.

97 Refit the oil pick-up pipe, and secure it with the two flange bolts and the support bracket bolt. Remove the two temporary retaining bolts from the baffle plate, then offer up the sump. Fit the bolts, and tighten them progressively, and in a diagonal sequence, to the specified torque.

98 Refit the flywheel cover plate and the exhaust front section.

99 Lower the car to the ground, and fill the engine with oil.

Oil pump (1.6, 1.8 and 2.0, 1987 on) – removal and refitting

100 Remove the camshaft toothed belt and belt covers, as described in paragraphs 30 to 36 earlier in this Section.

101 Remove the sump, as described in the previous sub-section.

102 Remove the oil filter, and disconnect the oil pressure switch wire from the oil pump housing (photo).

103 Undo the retaining bolts and withdraw the oil pump housing from the locating dowels on the cylinder block (photos). Remove the gasket.

104 If further dismantling of the oil pump is to be undertaken, refer to Chapter 1.

105 Clean away all traces of old gasket from the pump housing and cylinder block mating faces.

106 Apply jointing compound to the new gasket, and position it over the cylinder block dowels (photo).

107 To protect the oil seal lips when refitting the pump housing, wrap some tape around the step in the crankshaft, and grease the seal lips thoroughly.

108 Carefully place the housing in position and unwind the tape.

109 Refit the retaining bolts, and tighten them to the specified torque.

110 Fit a new oil filter, and reconnect the oil pressure switch wire.

111 Refit the sump as described in the previous sub-section.

112 Refit the toothed belt as described in paragraphs 40 to 44 earlier in this Section.

Crankshaft front (pulley end) oil seal (1.6, 1.8 and 2.0, 1987 on) – removal and refitting

113 Remove the camshaft toothed belt and belt covers, as described in paragraphs 30 to 36 earlier in this Section.

114 Punch or drill a small hole in the front face of the oil seal, and screw in a self-tapping screw. Pull on the screw with pliers to extract the seal.

115 Apply some tape over the step in the crankshaft, and grease the seal lips thoroughly.

116 Using a piece of tubing and a mallet, tap the seal into position.

117 Refit the toothed belt as described in paragraphs 40 to 44 earlier in this Section.

Engine (2.0) – removal and refitting

118 The engine removal and refitting details are much the same as for earlier engines as described in Chapter 1. Where references are made to fuel and ignition system components, refer to the relevant Sections of this Supplement for further information.

3.77A Tighten the cylinder head bolts initially to the Stage 1 torque wrench setting ...

3.77B ... then to an angular measurement in four further stages

3.79 Hold the camshaft, and tighten the sprocket bolt to the specified torque

3.88 Removing the flywheel cover plate

3.90 Removing the sump

3.92 Oil pick-up pipe retaining bolts (arrowed)

3.93 Removing the baffle plate

3.94 Removing the double-sided rubber gasket from the baffle plate

3.95 Oil pick-up pipe O-ring seal

3.102 Oil pressure switch wire connection (arrowed)

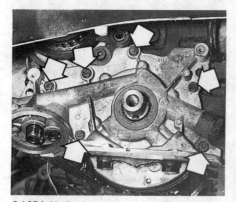

3.103A Undo the oil pump housing retaining bolts (arrowed) ...

3.103B ... and withdraw the housing

3.106 Position a new housing gasket over the locating dowels

4 Cooling system

Coolant pump (1.6, 1.8 and 2.0, 1987 on) – removal and refitting
1   Release the camshaft toothed belt tension as described in Section 3, paragraphs 9 to 18.
2   Slip the toothed belt off the coolant pump sprocket, then remove the three pump mounting bolts.
3   Withdraw the pump from its location (photo), and hook out the O-ring seal if it has remained in the cylinder block.
4   If the pump is to be renewed, it will be necessary to remove the toothed belt intermediate rear cover from the old pump and transfer it to the new pump. To do this, apply sideways pressure to the cover while rotating it relative to the pump body. The cover will disengage from the pump body flange as it is rotated (photo). Fit the cover to the new pump in the same way.
5   Thoroughly clean the pump location in the cylinder block and the pump body if the original pump is to be refitted.
6   Apply a liberal coating of silicone grease to the rubbing surfaces of the pump body and the cylinder block, then fit a new O-ring seal to the pump.
7   Place the pump in position, and fit the retaining bolts finger-tight only at this stage.

8   Refit and tension the camshaft toothed belt, as described in Section 3, paragraphs 21 to 29.

Thermostat housing (1.6, 1.8 and 2.0, 1987 on) – removal and refitting
9   Removal and refitting procedures for the thermostat are unchanged on later models, but if it is wished to remove and refit the thermostat housing, the camshaft toothed belt and belt rear cover must be removed for access.
10 To do this, carry out the operations described in Section 3, paragraphs 30 to 36. The bolts securing the thermostat housing can then be undone, and the housing and sealing ring removed.
11 Using a new sealing ring, refit the thermostat housing, then carry out the operations described in Section 3, paragraphs 40 to 44.

Radiator electric cooling fan – modifications
12 On later models, the cooling fan shroud has been modified, and the method of attachment to the radiator altered.
13 The shroud is now secured by two bolts at the top, and by two locating lugs at the bottom (photos). With the upper bolts removed, the shroud and fan assembly are lifted upwards to disengage the lower lugs.
14 Apart from this, the relevant procedures in Chapter 2 remain applicable.

4.3 Coolant pump removal

4.4 Removing the toothed belt intermediate cover from the coolant pump

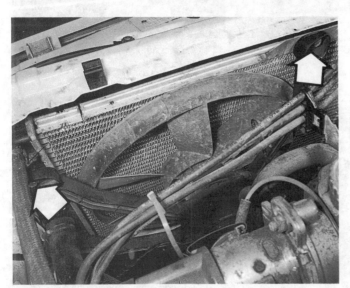

4.13A Later type cooling fan shroud upper retaining bolts (arrowed) ...

4.13B ... and lower locating lugs (arrowed)

5 Fuel and exhaust systems

Fuel injection systems – later models
Bosch L3 Jetronic system – description
1 A Bosch L3 Jetronic fuel injection system is fitted to 1.8 models from 1987 onwards.
2 The system is based on the LE system used previously, but it has a digital control system, rather than the analogue system used on the LE type. The L3 system control unit is housed within the engine compartment as part of the airflow sensor assembly, and the system wiring layout differs to suit.
Bosch Motronic system – description
3 The Motronic fuel injection system is fitted to all 2.0 models.
4 The system is a further development of the LE Jetronic system used on earlier models, but differs in that it also controls the ignition firing point and spark advance. By combining the control of the fuel and ignition systems, the engine performance is improved in terms of power, economy and reliability. Other advantages are that the system is maintenance-free, and incorporates a self-diagnosis system in which any faults that may occur will be registered and indicated for identification by a flashing code signal from the instrument panel (when activated by a service mechanic). In this way, any system faults can be quickly diagnosed and repaired.
5 Since the Motronic control unit also regulates the ignition spark advance, the conventional mechanical and vacuum advance control items are not required, and the ignition distributor is used only as a high voltage distribution unit. The ignition point on Motronic models is controlled in accordance with the engine temperature, the air inlet temperature, the throttle opening, and the engine speed.
6 An inductive pulse sensor is fitted to the side of the cylinder block, and a sensor disc is attached to the crankshaft. As the teeth of the sensor disc pass the pulse sensor during engine rotation, the air gap between them alternates in accordance with the engine speed, and this signal is then transmitted to the control unit. The information transmitted from the pulse sensor, together with the engine temperature sensor, also serves to enable the control unit to regulate the ignition advance angle.
7 The Motronic system also incorporates an idle speed adjuster device. This unit is mounted between the camshaft cover and the throttle housing, and its function is to provide an electrically-operated airflow control system past the throttle valve when it is in the idle position. The airflow is regulated as required by means of an electric motor driving a rotary spool. The idle speed adjuster is regulated automatically as required, in accordance with signals received from the control unit. No manual adjustment of the idle speed is possible.
8 The control unit is located at the side of the front footwell on the driver's side, behind the side trim panel.

L3 and Motronic fuel injection systems – general
9 Except for the following items in this Section, any maintenance and repair tasks to be undertaken on either of these systems will be the same as those described for the earlier LE Jetronic fuel injection system, in Chapter 3. The precautionary notes in Section 21 of Chapter 3 also apply to later models, but note the following additions:

(a) Any faults registered on the integral diagnosis system will be deleted when the battery is disconnected
(b) Do not short-circuit the ignition coil terminal 1 to earth, or allow it to contact the battery positive connections, or the control unit will be damaged
(c) When fitting a car alarm to Motronic injection models, the alarm relay must not receive interference from other electrical sources (ignition leads, etc)

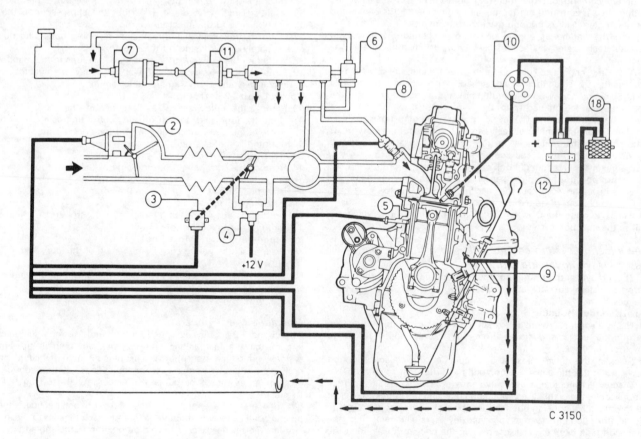

C 3150

Fig. 13.2 Bosch L3 Jetronic fuel injection system layout and components (Sec 5)

2 Airflow sensor and control unit	5 Coolant temperature sensor	8 Fuel injector	11 Fuel filter
3 Throttle valve switch	6 Fuel pressure regulator	9 Inductive pulse sensor	12 Ignition coil
4 Auxiliary air valve	7 Fuel pump	10 Distributor	18 Ignition HEI trigger box

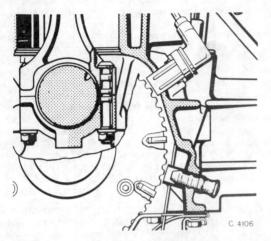

Fig. 13.3 Inductive pulse sensor location – Motronic (Sec 5)

Idle speed and mixture (L3 and Motronic systems) – adjustment

10 The idle speed and mixture settings can only be adjusted on the L3 Jetronic system. As mentioned previously, the idle speed on Motronic systems is controlled by the idle speed adjuster unit, and no other external adjustment is possible. The idle mixture (CO level) setting is also non-adjustable, being regulated entirely by the system control unit.

11 Before carrying out the following adjustments, ensure that the ignition system is in good order, the air cleaner element is clean, and that the engine itself is in good mechanical condition.

12 With the engine at normal operating temperature, connect an accurate tachometer in accordance with its manufacturer's instructions.

13 Allow the engine to idle, and compare the idle speed with that given in the Specifications. If adjustment is necessary, turn the idle speed adjusting screw on the throttle housing as necessary, until the specified speed is obtained (photo).

14 To check the mixture (CO level), connect an exhaust gas analyser or other proprietary mixture analysis device in accordance with its manufacturer's instructions. With the engine idling at the specified speed, read the CO level, and compare it with that specified.

15 If adjustment is required, hook out the black tamperproof cap from the control unit on the airflow sensor, and turn the mixture adjusting screw as necessary to obtain the specified reading (photo).

16 On completion, re-adjust the idle speed if necessary.

17 Failure to bring the CO level within the specified range indicates a fault in the injection system, or a well-worn engine.

Fuel injection system components (L3 and Motronic systems) – removal and refitting

18 The removal and refitting procedures given in Chapter 3 for the LE Jetronic system are still applicable, except for the following differences.

Throttle valve housing

19 Using a small screwdriver, extract the retaining circlip, and release the throttle cable end fitting from the throttle housing linkage (photos).

20 Slacken the hose clips, and disconnect the flexible ducting between the throttle valve housing and the airflow sensor (photo).

21 Disconnect the auxiliary air valve hose, or idle speed adjuster hose as applicable, the crankcase ventilation hose, and the coolant hoses at the throttle valve housing connections (photo). If the engine is warm, release the cooling system pressure by carefully removing the expansion tank cap before disconnecting the coolant hoses. Plug the hoses after removal, to minimise coolant loss.

22 Disconnect the wiring plug from the throttle valve switch at the rear of the housing.

23 If removing the throttle valve housing on its own, undo the four nuts and remove the housing from the manifold.

24 If removing the throttle valve housing together with the inlet manifold, the items in the following paragraphs must also be detached.

25 Disconnect the brake servo hose and the auxiliary air valve hose from the manifold.

26 Disconnect and plug the fuel hoses from the fuel distribution pipe. Also undo the bolt and release the fuel hose clip from beneath the throttle valve housing (photo).

27 Disconnect the throttle cable from the support bracket by releasing the E-clip from the groove in the outer cable (photo).•

28 Release the wiring loom by disconnecting all the additional plugs and earth connections. These include:

    (a) Airflow sensor
    (b) Coolant temperature sensor
    (c) Fuel injectors
    (d) Auxiliary air valve
    (e) Idle speed adjuster (Motronic)
    (f) Camshaft cover earth connection

29 Unscrew the inlet manifold fixing nuts, and lift off the throttle housing and manifold as a complete assembly. Recover the manifold gasket.

30 Refitting is a reversal of removal, but use new gaskets and top up the cooling system on completion.

Throttle valve switch

31 The procedure is the same as described in Chapter 3, but note that the switch is located on the opposite side of the throttle valve housing, nearest to the engine compartment bulkhead (photo).

Fuel injectors

32 Disconnect the battery earth lead, and perform the following operations with the engine cold, and in a well-ventilated area.

33 Undo the two bolts securing the throttle cable support bracket to the manifold.

34 Disconnect the brake servo vacuum hose and auxiliary air valve hose at the manifold.

35 Disconnect the wiring plugs from the fuel injectors (photo).

36 Using a small screwdriver, prise out the clips securing the fuel distribution pipe to the injectors (photo).

37 Undo the four fuel distribution pipe retaining bolts, and pull the pipe squarely upwards and off the injectors.

38 Withdraw the fuel injectors from their locations in the manifold.

39 Refitting is the reversal of removal, but renew the injector sealing O-rings if they show any signs of deterioration.

Control unit L3 Jetronic

40 Remove the airflow sensor, as described in Chapter 3.

41 Undo the four bolts and lift off the control unit cover.

42 Remove the cover insert, and lift out the control unit.

43 Refitting is the reversal of removal.

Control unit (Motronic)

44 Remove the trim panel from the side of the front footwell on the driver's side.

45 Disconnect the wiring plug from the control unit by pressing aside the retaining spring.

46 Undo the three screws and remove the control unit.

47 Refitting is the reversal of removal.

Idle speed adjuster (Motronic)

48 Disconnect the wiring plug from the end of the idle speed adjuster (photo).

49 Slacken the hose clips, detach the air hoses, and remove the adjuster.

50 Refitting is the reversal of removal.

Unleaded fuel – general

51 1.8 and 2.0 engines equipped with L3 and Motronic fuel injection systems have a fuel octane rating adjustment plug in the ignition system wiring harness (photo). The plug, which is located on the right-hand side of the engine compartment, is set during production to give optimum engine output and efficiency when run on 98 RON (4-star) fuel.

52 To operate the engine on unleaded high octane fuel, the plug position can be reset to modify the timing characteristics of the ignition systems. This is necessary to avoid detonation (knocking and pinking) on acceleration, and possible damage to the engine during prolonged use.

53 To reset the octane plug, open its locking clip, detach and twist the plug through 180° (half a turn), then reconnect the plug.

54 If, after making the adjustment, the octane rating of the fuel used is found to be so low that excessive knocking is still present, consult your dealer for further advice.

5.13 Idle speed adjusting screw
(L3 Jetronic)

5.15 Idle mixture adjusting screw
(L3 Jetronic)

5.19A Extract the retaining circlip ...

5.19B ... and remove the throttle cable
end fitting

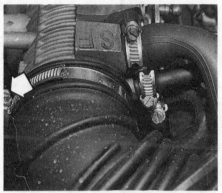

5.20 Slacken the flexible ducting hose clip
(arrowed)

5.21 Disconnect the auxiliary air valve hose
(A), the crankcase ventilation hose (B),
and the coolant hoses (C)

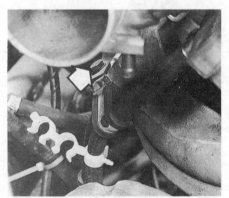

5.26 Fuel hose clip retaining bolt (arrowed)

5.27 Release the throttle cable E-clip

5.31 Throttle valve switch location
(arrowed)

5.35 Disconnect the fuel injector wiring
plugs

5.36 Prise out the fuel distribution pipe
securing clips (arrowed)

5.48 Idle speed adjuster showing wiring
plug location

5.51 Fuel octane rating adjustment plug

55 If leaded fuel is used again, top up the fuel tank with it, but do not reset the octane rating plug immediately, as a mixture of the two fuel types will initially cause the octane rating to be below the 98 RON requirement.

Inlet manifold (L3 and Motronic systems) – removal and refitting

56 Removal and refitting of the inlet manifold on engines with L3 and Motronic fuel injection systems is covered as part of the throttle valve housing removal and refitting procedure, in paragraphs 19 to 30 inclusive.

6 Ignition system

Breakerless ignition system (1.8 and 2.0, 1987 on) – general

1 The ignition system types fitted to the larger engine models from 1987 have been updated, and are as follows:

   1.8 : EZ61 system (Microprocessor spark timing system)
   2.0 : Motronic system

2 With each of these system types, the ignition timing is automatically adjusted and controlled to suit the constantly-changing operating conditions. This is achieved by a central computerized control unit, which assesses information sent to it from the various sensors and components of the system, then regulates the ignition timing as required. The distributor therefore functions merely as a high voltage distribution unit.

3 With the Motronic system, the control unit also regulates the fuel requirements, further details of which are given in Section 5.

Ignition system (1.8 and 2.0, 1987 on) – maintenance

4 The ignition system maintenance requirements on models fitted with the EZ61 and Motronic systems are minimal:

   (a) Periodically check the LT and HT wires for cleanliness, condition and security
   (b) Check and renew the spark plugs, or clean and adjust their electrode gap as necessary. Refer to Chapter 4 for details
   (c) Clean and inspect the distributor cap and rotor arm occasionally

Distributor (1.8 and 2.0, 1987 on) – removal and refitting

5 The distributor on later models fitted with EZ61 or Motronic ignition/fuel control systems differs in that vacuum and engine speed-related advance is controlled electronically by the control unit. Therefore, the distributor fitted to these models does not incorporate any vacuum or centrifugal timing advance mechanism. Removal of the unit is as follows.

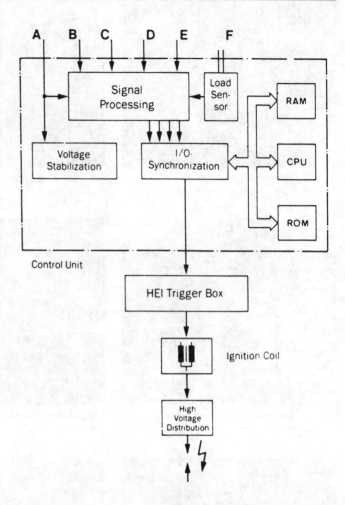

Fig. 13.4 EZ61 Microprocessor spark timing system control unit layout (Sec 6)

A	Battery voltage	F	Inlet manifold vacuum
B	Resistance coding (octane rating)	CPU	Microprocessor
		RAM	Random access memory
C	Coolant temperature	ROM	Routine operations
D	Engine speed		memory
E	Throttle valve switch position	I/O	Input/output

6 Disconnect the spark plug HT leads, and the HT lead from the ignition coil.

7 Undo the three screws securing the distributor cap, and remove the cap (photo).

8 Extract the insulator. This is an interference fit in the housing, via an O-ring seal located in a groove in its periphery, so ease out the insulator, taking care not to damage the rotor (photo).

9 Using a 3 mm Allen key, undo the two screws and remove the rotor (photos).

10 If the camshaft seal is in need of renewal, extract the seal/rotor hub by pulling it free, then carefully lever out the oil seal (photos).

11 Clean the housing, then carefully insert the new oil seal by driving it into place using a suitable tubular drift. Take care not to damage the housing.

12 Lubricate the oil seal lips, and fit the seal/rotor hub, aligning the two rotor and hub retaining bolt holes with those in the camshaft flange (photo).

13 The remainder of refitting is a direct reversal of the removal procedure. Renew the seal ring in the insulator groove if the old seal is in any way damaged, then lightly lubricate it to ease refitting (photo).

Control Unit

Fig. 13.5 Motronic system control unit arrangement (Sec 6)

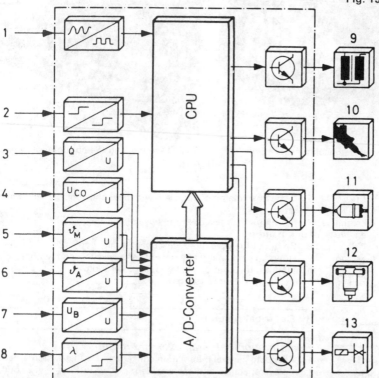

Inputs

1 Speed/ignition angle reference
2 Transmission control
3 Airflow
4 Idle speed CO potentiometer
5 Coolant temperature sensor
6 Intake air temperature
7 Battery voltage
8 Oxygen sensor (not UK models)

Outputs

9 Ignition coil
10 Fuel injector
11 Fuel pump
12 Idle speed adjuster
13 Fuel tank bleeder valve (where applicable)

6.7 Undo the distributor cap retaining screws

6.8 Extract the insulator

6.9A Undo the two rotor screws ...

6.9B ... and remove the rotor

6.10A Extract the rotor hub ...

6.10B ... and prise out the oil seal

6.12 Align the camshaft and rotor hub bolt holes

6.13 Renewing the insulator sealing ring

6.15 Disconnecting the control unit wiring plug

Ignition system control unit (1.8, 1987 on) – removal and refitting

14 The ignition system control unit, on 1.8 models fitted with the EZ61 system, is located on the right-hand side of the engine compartment, attached to the suspension strut turret.

15 To remove the control unit, release the spring retaining tags and disconnect the wiring plug (photo).

16 Undo the securing screws, and lift the unit off its mounting bracket.

17 Refitting is the reversal of removal.

---

7   Manual transmission

F13.4 and F13.5 transmissions – general

1 These transmission types have been fitted in the course of production to certain 1.3 models.

2 The F13.4 and F13.5 types are identical to the F10.4 and F10.5 transmissions described in Chapter 6, and all repair and overhaul procedures for the F10.4 and F10.5 units are therefore also applicable to the F13.4 and F13.5 types.

---

8   Bodywork

Tailgate lock components (Estate) – removal and refitting

1 On later models, the tailgate lock components have been modified, and the removal and refitting procedures are now as follows.

Lock barrel

2 Open the tailgate, and undo the screws securing the outer body trim moulding over the lock barrel (photo).

3 Remove the tailgate interior trim panel (photo).

4 Using pliers, release the return spring from the lock barrel lever (photo).

5 Extract the circlip and washer, then remove the lock barrel lever from the end of the barrel.

6 Undo the retaining nut, and withdraw the lock barrel from the tailgate.

7 Refitting is the reversal of removal.

Lock handle

8 Carry out the operations described in paragraphs 2 to 4.

9 Undo the retaining nut, remove the washer, and withdraw the handle from the control lever and tailgate (photo).

10 Refitting is the reversal of removal.

---

9   Electrical system

Radio equipment – removal and refitting

1 Adequate general information concerning the installation of radios, tape players, aerials and speakers is provided in Chapter 12, but the following specific details may be of further benefit when dealing with factory fitted radios and speakers.

2 On later models, radio/cassette units are to the latest DIN standard; they are released by inserting two special clips into the holes on each side of the unit, once the blanking plug screws have been removed. These clips are often supplied with the car; if not, they can be obtained from a car radio specialist. The clips are pressed in until they snap into place, then used to pull the radio out if its aperture. The various plugs can then be disconnected from the rear of the radio. A diagram on the rear of the unit provides information on the wiring connections, and in most cases, each of the speaker plugs and sockets are colour-coded to avoid confusion (photos).

3 In addition to the normal vehicle circuit fuse, the radio receiver itself is often fused, and the fuse is located in a holder at the rear of the unit, adjacent to the wiring sockets (photo).

4 To refit the radio, reconnect its plugs, and push it home until the retaining clips click into place. Refit the blanking plugs after removal of the clips.

5 Speakers are positioned at each end of the facia panel, and, according to model, at each end of the parcel shelf or in the tailgate.

6 Access to the facia-mounted speakers can be gained after removal

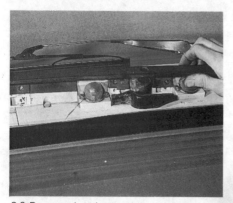

8.2 Remove the trim moulding over the lock barrel

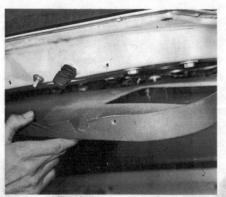

8.3 Remove the tailgate interior trim panel

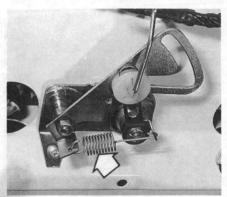

8.4 Release the return spring (arrowed) from the lock barrel lever

8.9 Lock handle removal

9.2A Unscrew the radio faceplate blanking plugs ...

9.2B ... to allow insertion of the removal clips

9.2C Wiring connections at the rear of the radio

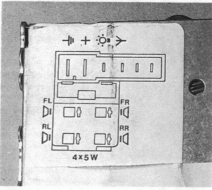

9.2D Wiring connection diagram on the radio case

9.3 Fuse holder and fuse at the rear of the radio

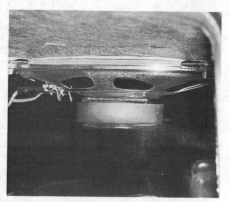

9.6 Facia-mounted speaker location, as viewed through the heater vent aperture

9.7A Remove the tailgate trim panel ...

9.7B ... for access to the rear speaker retaining screws (arrowed) on Estate models

of the relevant side heater vent (Chapter 2). Although clearance is limited, it is just possible to disconnect the wiring, release the speaker retaining nuts, and withdraw the speaker through the vent aperture (photo). If difficulty is experienced, greater working clearance can be gained if the glovebox or instrument panel are removed for the left-hand or right-hand speakers respectively.

7   Where tailgate speakers are fitted, these can be removed after removal of the tailgate trim panel. The speaker can then be unscrewed, to allow disconnection of the wiring and removal of the speaker (photos).

8   The refitting procedures for the speakers are a direct reversal of the removal operations.

Wiring diagrams commence overleaf

Key to Fig. 13.6

No	Description	Grid reference	No	Description	Grid reference
E1	LH parking light	329	H44	EZV warning light	255
E2	LH tail light	330	K1	Heated rear window relay	306, 307
E3	Number plate light	336	K2	Flasher unit	389
E4	RH parking light	334	K4	Spotlight relay	378, 379
E5	RH tail light	335	K5	Foglight relay	371, 372
E6	Engine compartment light	337	K8	Windscreen wiper intermittent relay	432 to 435
E7	LH high beam	359	K9	Headlamp washer relay	439, 440
E8	RH high beam	360	K10	Trailer flasher unit	388, 389
E9	LH low beam	362	K15	Fuel injection timing control	284 to 291
E10	RH low beam	363	K19	Level control relay	465, 466
E11	Instrument lights	338	K20	Ignition module	216 to 218
E12	Selector lever light	341	K21	Level control sensor	462 to 465
E13	Boot light	405	K25	Preheater relay	209 to 212
E14	Courtesy light	406	K29	Electric aerial relay	419 to 423
E15	Glovebox light	319	K30	Heated rear window relay	454 to 456
E16	Cigarette lighter light	324	K35	Heated exterior mirror delay relay	497, 499
E17	LH reversing light	320	K36	Computer relay	513, 515
E18	RH reversing light	321	K37	Central locking relay	558 to 562
E19	Heated rear window	307	K42	Stop/start control unit	519 to 527
E20	LH foglight	370	K43	Stop/start relay	527, 528
E21	RH foglight	371	K45	Mixture preheater relay	263, 264
E22	LH spot light	377	K47	Over-voltage protection, relay	570, 571
E23	RH spot light	378	K50	ABS timing control	574 to 588
E24	LH rear foglight	367	K53	Timing control (EV 61)	273 to 282
E25	LH heated front seat	470	K54	Carburettor control unit (EZV)	240 to 260
E26	Light switch light	334	K55	Carburettor relay (EZV)	238, 239
E30	RH heated front seat	474	K57	Control unit (TBI)	143 to 162
E31	Symbol insert light	337	K58	Fuel pump relay (TBI)	163, 164
E32	Clock light	414	K59	Day running light relay	344 to 350
E33	Ashtray light	325	K61	Control unit (Motronic)	171 to 195
E34	Heater control light	337	K62	Control unit (dim-dip lights)	353 to 357
E38	Computer light	508	K68	Fuel injection relay	196 to 199, 295 to 299
E39	RH rear foglight	366	K72	Engine revolution relay	222 to 224
E41	Courtesy light (with delay)	409, 410	K73	Ignition module (EZ 61)	270, 271
F1 to F18	Fuses in fusebox	Various	K74	Control unit (MZV)	226 to 234
F19	Fuse (window motors)	536	L2	Ignition coil (Hal sensor)	215, 216
F20	Fuse (central locking)	559	L3	Ignition coil (inductive sensor)	172, 173, 137, 138, 126, 127, 228, 229, 258, 259
F24	Fuse (level control)	466			
F25	Voltage stabiliser	310			
F31	Fuse (EZV carburettor)	238	L4	Ignition coil (inductive sensor, EZ 61)	271, 272
F32	Fuse (mixture preheater)	264	M1	Starter motor	106, 107
G1	Battery	101	M2	Windscreen wiper motor	430 to 433
G2	Alternator	110, 111, 205	M3	Heater fan motor	300 to 302
G3	Battery (Diesel)	201	M4	Radiator fan motor	114
H1	Radio	417	M5	Washer pump	429
H2	Horn	459	M6	LH headlight wiper motor	442 to 445
H3	Turn signal warning light	394	M7	RH headlight wiper motor	447 to 449
H4	Oil pressure warning light	317	M8	Rear window wiper motor	452 to 454
H5	Handbrake/brake fluid warning light	316	M9	Rear window washer pump	457
H6	Hazard warning system warning light	390	M12	Starter motor (Diesel)	207, 208
H7	No-charge warning light	111	M14	LH front door window motor	539, 541
H8	Main beam warning light	361	M15	RH front door window motor	543, 545
H9	LH stop-light	385	M16	LH rear door window motor	547, 549
H10	RH stop-light	386	M17	RH rear door window motor	551, 553
H11	LH front turn signal light	392	M18	Front door locking motor	None
H12	LH rear turn signal light	393	M19	LH rear door locking motor	561, 564
H13	RH front turn signal light	396	M20	RH rear door locking motor	561, 564
H14	RH rear turn signal light	397	M21	Fuel pump	197, 164, 295
H16	Preheater warning light	209	M22	Level control compressor	466
H17	Trailer turn signal warning light	388	M26	Electric aerial motor	419 to 421
H18	Dual horns	460	M30	LH exterior mirror adjustment and heating	478 to 481, 487 to 490
H19	Headlights on warning buzzer	430, 404			
H20	Choke on warning light	122			
H23	Radio with electric aerial	423, 424	M31	RH exterior mirror adjustment and heating	494 to 497
H25	Mirror heater warning light	483, 493			
H26	ABS warning light	589	M32	Front door locking motor	561, 564
H30	Engine warning light	149, 176	M33	Idle control unit	183, 184, 150 to 153
H33	LH repeater turn signal light	391			
H34	RH repeater turn signal light	395			

Key to Fig. 13.6 (continued)

No	Description	Grid reference
M37	Boot lid/tailgate locking motor	561, 564
P1	Fuel gauge	311
P2	Temperature gauge	312
P3	Clock	415
P4	Fuel sensor	311
P5	Temperature sensor	312
P7	Tachometer	314
P10	Oil pressure sensor	None
P11	Airflow meter	185 to 189
P12	Temperature probe (coolant)	178
P13	Outside air temperature sensor	512, 513
P14	Distance sensor	142, 143, 170, 171, 504, 505
P15	Fuel flowmeter	506, 507
P17	LH front wheel sensor (ABS)	574, 575
P18	RH front wheel sensor (ABS)	576, 577
P19	LH rear wheel sensor (ABS)	578, 579
P20	RH rear wheel sensor (ABS)	580, 581
P23	Inlet manifold vacuum sensor	156 to 158, 226 to 228
P24	Coolant temperature sensor (EV 61)	289, 231, 232
P29	Inlet manifold temperature sensor	245, 246
P30	Coolant temperature sensor	154, 155, 248, 249
P31	Main throttle potentiometer	248 to 250
P32	Heated Lambda sensor	193, 194
P33	Lambda sensor	158
P34	Throttle valve position sensor	159 to 161
P35	Crankshaft inductive sensor	189 to 191, 277, 278, 274 to 276, 257 to 259
R2	Carburettor preheater	116, 262
R3	Cigarette lighter	323
R5	Glow plugs	211, 212
R7	Mixture preheater	264
R11	Instrument lights dimmer	338
R12	Automatic choke	118
R15	Resistor	179, 160, 229, 230, 279, 280
S1	Starter motor switch	106, 107, 205, 206
S2.1	Main light switch	334 to 337, 529, 530
S2.2	Courtesy light switch	406
S3	Heater fan switch	300 to 303
S4	Heated rear window switch	305, 306
S5.2	Headlight dip switch	361, 362, 531
S5.3	Turn signal switch	395, 396
S7	Reversing light switch	321
S8	Stop-light switch	386
S9.2	Windscreen wiper switch (intermittent)	429 to 433
S9.3	Rear window wiper switch (intermittent)	455, 456
S10.1	Automatic transmission switch	107
S10.3	Park/neutral switch	154
S11	Brake fluid level switch	315
S13	Handbrake warning light switch	316
S14	Oil pressure switch	317
S15	Boot lid switch	405
S16	RH courtesy light switch	407
S17	LH courtesy light switch	408
S18	Glovebox light switch	319
S21	Foglight switch	373 to 375
S22	Rear foglight switch	367, 368
S23	Boot lid release switch	326
S29	Radiator fan switch	114
S30	LH heated seat switch	469, 470
S31	LH rear door courtesy light switch	409
S32	RH rear door courtesy light switch	410
S37	LH front door window motor switch	539 to 542
S38	Rear window isolating switch	538
S39	LH rear door window motor switch	547 to 549
S40	RH rear door window motor switch	551 to 553
S41	Central locking door switch	558, 559

No	Description	Grid reference
S44	Throttle valve switch	173, 174, 285, 286
S46	Heated seat switch	472 to 474
S47	Doors open/headlamps on warning switch	403, 404
S50	Choke on warning switch	122
S52	Hazard light switch	389 to 393
S61	Power steering pressure switch	121
S64	Horn switch	459
S68	Exterior mirror switch	None
S68.1	Exterior mirror adjustment switch	477 to 480, 485 to 489
S68.2	Exterior mirror heater switch	483, 492
S68.3	Exterior mirror left/right switch	486 to 490
S77	Distance switch	
S78	RH front door window motor switch	543 to 546
S79	LH rear door remote window motor switch	547 to 550
S80	RH rear door remote window motor switch	551 to 554
S85	Stop/start clutch pedal switch	519
S86	Stop/start switch	518, 519
S91	Oil pressure switch (TBI)	166, 167
S111	Fuel cut-off vacuum switch	224
U3	Computer	505 to 514
U3.1	Clock switch	512
U3.2	Function selector switch	512
U3.3	Reset/stopwatch/adjustment switch	512
U4	ABS system	572 to 586
U4.1	ABS relay	573 to 576
U4.2	ABS solenoid valve relay	583 to 586
U4.3	ABS pump	572
U4.4	ABS diode	585
U4.5	LH front ABS solenoid valve	578
U4.6	RH front ABS solenoid valve	580
U4.7	LH rear ABS solenoid valve	579
U4.8	RH rear ABS solenoid valve	581
X1	Trailer socket	331, 332, 382 to 384, 394 to 398
X2	Auxiliary connector	122, 341, 326, 417, 470, 475, 536, 559
X10	Ignition timing adjustment connector	233, 234
X11	5-pin connector (TBI)	146, 149, 164, 167
X13	Test connector	148, 152, 153, 175, 176, 178, 254
X15F	4-pin connector	270, 271, 291, 295
X16	4-pin connector (EZV)	255, 258, 261, 262
X17	8-pin connector (Motronic)	171, 172, 176, 181, 184, 195, 196, 198
Y1	Air conditioning compressor	
Y2	Revolution acceleration solenoid valve	
Y3	Boot lid release solenoid	326
Y4	Headlight washer solenoid valve	440
Y5	Diesel solenoid valve	213
Y6	Auxiliary air slide valve	292, 293
Y7	Fuel injectors	186 to 193, 279 to 286
Y9	Level control solenoid	464
Y10	Distributor	220
Y11	Hall sensor	216 to 218
Y14	Inductive sensor (EV 61)	133 to 137, 226 to 228
Y15	Inductive sensor	125, 126, 529
Y17	Idle cut-off solenoid valve	117
Y23	Distributor	129, 532
Y24	Distributor	140, 231
Y25	Revolution acceleration solenoid valve	121
Y26	Throttle valve positioner	238 to 244
Y27	Pre-throttle valve	252, 253
Y32	Injection valve (TBI)	144
Y33	Distributor	174, 260, 274
Y34	Tank ventilation valve	195, 196
Y39	Fuel cut-off solenoid valve	223

Not all items fitted to all models

Abbreviations

ABS	Anti-lock braking
BR	Trip computer
EMP	Receiver (radio)
EST	Electronic spark timing (ignition advance)
EV61	Electronic carburettor
EZ61	Microprocessor spark timing system
EZF	EST
EZV	Electronic carburettor
HEI	High energy ignition system
MZV	Microprocessor-controlled ignition system
SAS	Overrun cut-off
SSS	Stop-start system
TBI	Throttle body injection
TFL	Day running lights
TSZ	HEI

Explanatory note

The main wiring diagrams are laid out using a grid reference system, with the bottom line being the earth track. Using grid reference 122 at the bottom of Fig. 13.6 as an example, follow the line upwards past switch S50 to lamp H20. Here the line moves to grid reference 111 through connector X2, and finally to a number in a box (309). Referring to grid reference 309 at the bottom of the diagram on the continuation page, it will be seen that a number (111) in a box aligns with this reference, near the top of the diagram. The line from this boxed number is a continuation of grid reference 111, and shows the live feed to lamp H20 through the 20 amp fuse F6. The live feed can be traced back to its origination at ignition switch terminal 15.

Colour code

BL	Blue
BR	Brown
GE	Yellow
GN	Green
GR	Grey
HBL	Light blue
LI	Lilac
RT	Red
SW	Black
VI	Violet
WS	White

Wiring identification

eg GE WS 1.5
GE Basic colour
WS Identification colour
1.5 Section (mm²)

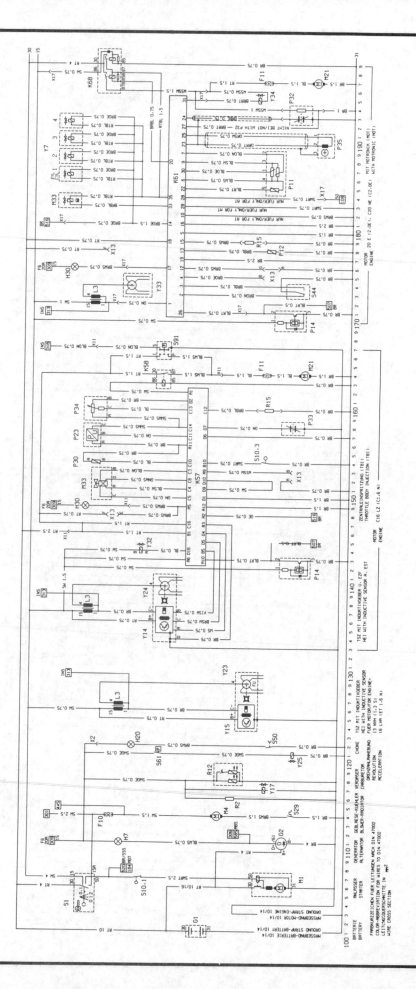

Fig. 13.6 Wiring diagram for 1987 models

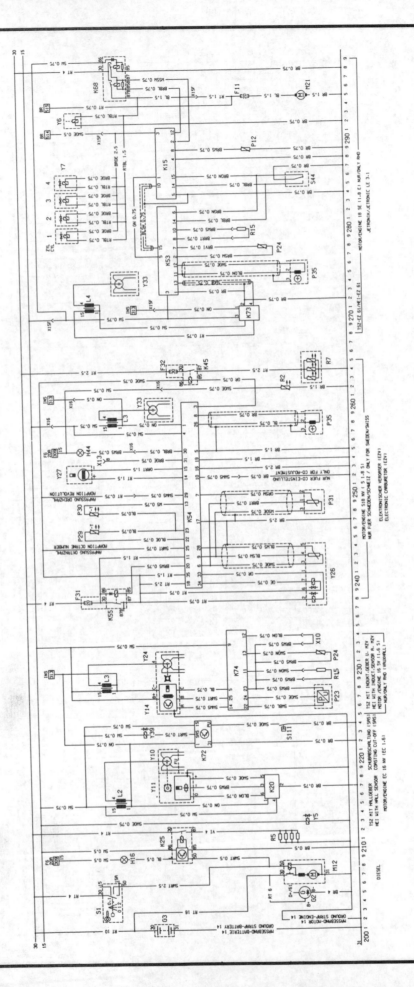

Fig. 13.6 Wiring diagram for 1987 models (continued)

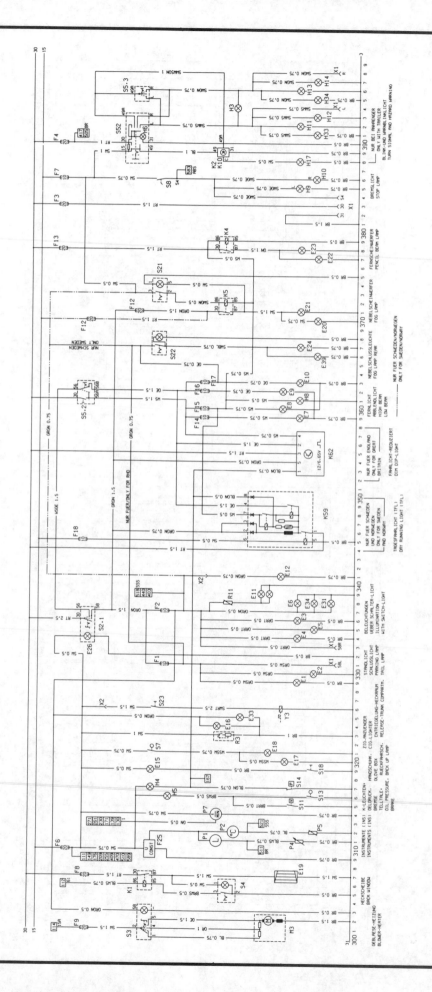

Fig. 13.6 Wiring diagram for 1987 models (continued)

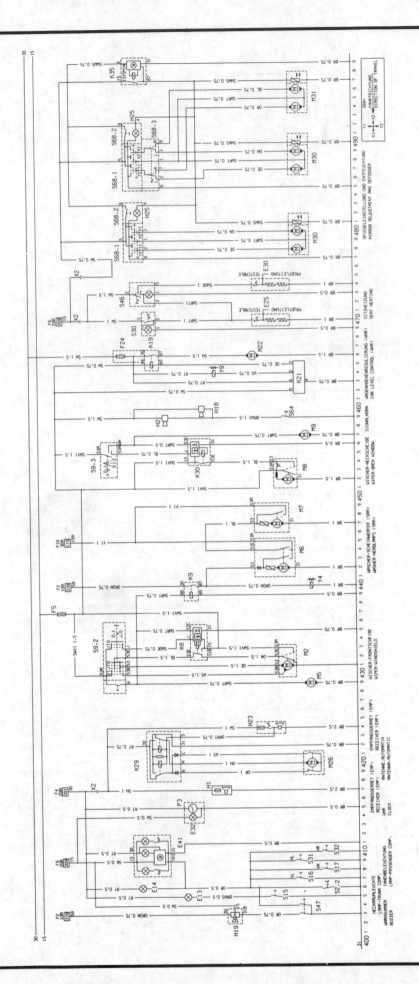

Fig. 13.6 Wiring diagram for 1987 models (continued)

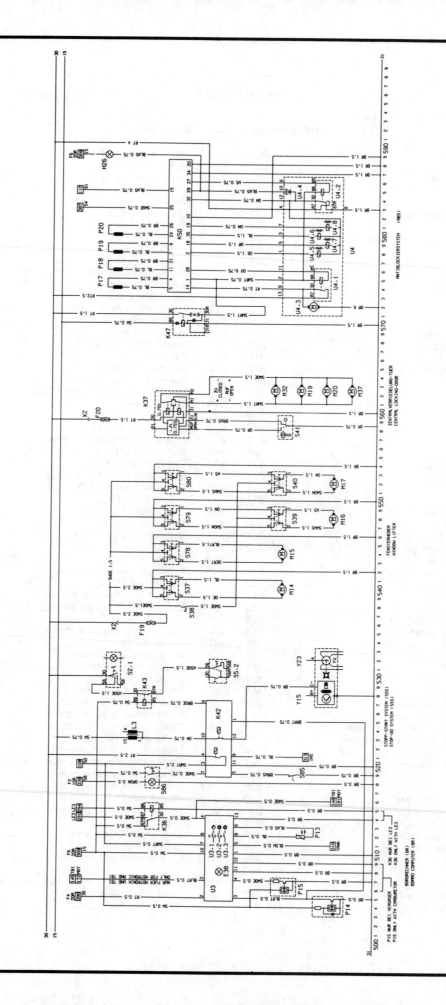

Fig. 13.6 Wiring diagram for 1987 models (continued)

Key to Fig. 13.7

No	Description	Grid reference	No	Description	Grid reference
E1	LH parking light	329	H25	Mirror heater warning light	483, 493
E2	LH tail light	330	H26	ABS warning light	589
E3	Number plate light	336	H30	Engine warning light	148, 176
E4	RH parking light	334	H33	LH repeater turn signal light	391
E5	RH tail light	335	H34	RH repeater turn signal light	395
E6	Engine compartment light	337	H44	EZV warning light	255
E7	LH high beam	359	K1	Heated rear window relay	306, 307
E8	RH high beam	360	K2	Flasher unit	389
E9	LH low beam	362	K4	Spotlight relay	378, 379
E10	RH low beam	363	K5	Foglight relay	371, 372
E11	Instrument lights	338	K8	Windscreen wiper intermittent relay	432 to 435
E12	Selector lever light	341	K9	Headlamp washer relay	439, 440
E13	Boot light	405	K10	Trailer flasher unit	388, 389
E14	Courtesy light	406	K15	Fuel injection timing control	284 to 291
E15	Glovebox light	319	K19	Level control relay	465, 466
E16	Cigarette lighter light	324	K20	Ignition module	216 to 218
E17	LH reversing light	320	K21	Level control sensor	462 to 465
E18	RH reversing light	321	K25	Preheater relay	209 to 212
E19	Heated rear window	307	K29	Electric aerial relay	419 to 423
E20	LH foglight	370	K30	Heated rear window relay	454 to 456
E21	RH foglight	371	K35	Heated exterior mirror delay relay	497, 499
E22	LH spot light	377	K36	Computer relay	513 to 515
E23	RH spot light	378	K37	Central locking relay	558 to 562
E24	LH rear foglight	367	K45	Mixture preheater relay	263, 264
E25	LH heated front seat	470	K47	Over-voltage protection, relay	570, 571
E26	Light switch light	334	K50	ABS timing control	574, 588
E30	RH heated front seat	474	K53	Timing control (EV 61)	273 to 282
E31	Symbol insert light	337	K54	Carburettor control unit (EZV)	240 to 260
E32	Clock light	414	K55	Carburettor relay (EZV)	238, 239
E33	Ashtray light	325	K57	Control unit (TBI)	143 to 161
E34	Heater control light	337	K58	Fuel pump relay (TBI)	163, 164
E38	Computer light	508	K59	Day running light relay	344 to 350
E39	RH rear foglight	366	K61	Control unit (Motronic)	171 to 195
E41	Courtesy light (with delay)	409, 410	K62	Control unit (dim-dip lights)	353 to 357
F1 to F18	Fuses in fusebox		K68	Fuel injection relay	196 to 199, 295 to 299
F19	Fuse (window motors)	536	K73	Ignition module (EZ 61)	270, 271
F20	Fuse (central locking)	559	K74	Control unit (MZV)	225 to 234
F24	Fuse (level control)	466	L2	Ignition coil (Hall sensor)	215, 216
F25	Voltage stabiliser	310	L3	Ignition coil (inductive sensor)	126, 127, 137, 138, 172, 173, 227, 228, 258, 259
F31	Fuse (EZV carburettor)	238			
F32	Fuse (mixture preheater)	264	L4	Ignition coil (inductive sensor, EZ 61)	271, 272
G1	Battery	101	M1	Starter motor	106, 107, 300, 302
G2	Alternator	110, 111, 205	M2	Windscreen wiper motor	430 to 433
G3	Battery (Diesel)	201	M4	Radiator fan motor	114
H1	Radio	417	M5	Washer pump	429
H2	Horn	459	M6	LH headlight wiper motor	442 to 445
H3	Turn signal warning light	394	M7	RH headlight wiper motor	447 to 449
H4	Oil pressure warning light	317	M8	Rear window wiper motor	452 to 454
H5	Handbrake/brake fluid warning light	316	M9	Rear window washer pump	457
H6	Hazard warning system warning light	390	M12	Starter motor (Diesel)	207, 208
H7	No-charge warning light	111	M14	LH front door window motor	539, 541
H8	Main beam warning light	361	M15	RH front door window motor	543, 545
H9	LH stop-light	385	M16	LH rear door window motor	547, 549
H10	RH stop-light	386	M17	RH rear door window motor	551, 553
H11	LH front turn signal light	392	M19	LH rear door locking motor	561, 564
H12	LH rear turn signal light	393	M20	RH rear door locking motor	561, 564
H13	RH front turn signal light	396	M21	Fuel pump	197, 164, 295
H14	RH rear turn signal light	397	M22	Level control compressor	466
H16	Preheater warning light	209	M26	Electric aerial motor	419 to 421
H17	Trailer turn signal warning light	388	M30	LH exterior mirror adjustment and heating	478 to 481, 487 to 490
H18	Dual horns	460			
H19	Headlights on warning buzzer	403, 404	M31	RH exterior mirror adjustment and heating	494 to 497
H20	Choke on warning light	122	M32	Front door locking motor	561, 564
H23	Radio with electric aerial	423, 424	M33	Idle control unit	183, 184, 149 to 152

Key to Fig. 13.7 (continued)

No	Description	Grid reference
M37	Boot lit/tailgate locking motor	561, 564
P1	Fuel gauge	311
P2	Temperature gauge	312
P3	Clock	415
P4	Fuel sensor	311
P5	Temperature sensor	312
P7	Tachometer	314
P11	Airflow meter	185 to 189
P12	Temperature probe (coolant)	178, 289
P13	Outside air temperature sensor	512, 513
P14	Distance sensor	142, 143, 170, 171, 504, 505
P15	Fuel flowmeter	506, 507
P17	LH front wheel sensor (ABS)	574, 575
P18	RH front wheel sensor (ABS)	576, 577
P19	LH rear wheel sensor (ABS)	578, 579
P20	RH rear wheel sensor (ABS)	580, 581
P23	Inlet manifold vacuum sensor	155 to 157, 225 to 227
P24	Coolant temperature sensor (EV 61)	277, 278, 231, 232
P29	Inlet manifold temperature sensor	247
P30	Coolant temperature sensor	153, 248
P31	Main throttle potentiometer	248, 250
P32	Heated Lambda sensor	193, 194
P33	Lambda sensor	157
P34	Throttle valve position sensor	158 to 160
P35	Crankshaft inductive sensor	189 to 191, 274 to 276, 257 to 259
R2	Carburettor preheater	116, 262
R3	Cigarette lighter	323
R5	Glow plugs	211, 212
R7	Mixture preheater	264
R11	Instrument lights dimmer	338
R12	Automatic choke	118
R15	Resistor	161, 162
S1	Starter motor switch	106, 107, 205, 206
S2	Light switch	
S2.1	Main light switch	334 to 337
S2.2	Courtesy light switch	406
S3	Heater fan switch	300 to 303
S4	Heated rear window switch	305, 306
S5.2	Headlight dip switch	361, 362
S5.3	Turn signal switch	395, 396
S7	Reversing light switch	321
S8	Stop-light switch	386
S9.2	Windscreen wiper switch (intermittent)	429 to 433
S9.3	Rear window wiper switch (intermittent)	455, 456
S10.1	Automatic transmission switch	107
S10.2	Reversing light switch	322
S10.3	Park/neutral switch	159
S11	Brake fluid level switch	315
S13	Handbrake warning light switch	316
S14	Oil pressure switch	317
S15	Boot lid switch	405
S16	RH courtesy light switch	407
S17	LH courtesy light switch	408
S18	Glovebox light switch	319
S21	Foglight switch	373 to 375
S22	Rear foglight switch	367, 368
S23	Boot lid release switch	326
S30	LH heated seat switch	469, 470
S31	LH rear door courtesy light switch	409
S32	RH rear door courtesy light switch	410
S37	LH front door window motor switch	539 to 542
S38	Rear window isolating switch	538

No	Description	Grid reference
S39	LH rear door window motor switch	547 to 549
S40	RH rear door window motor switch	551 to 553
S41	Central locking door switch	558, 559
S44	Throttle valve switch	173, 174, 285, 286
S46	Heated seat switch	472 to 474
S47	Doors open/headlamps on warning switch	403, 404
S50	Choke on warning switch	122
S52	Hazard light switch	389 to 393
S61	Power steering pressure switch	121
S67	Horn switch	459
S68.1	Exterior mirror adjustment switch	477 to 480, 485 to 489
S68.2	Exterior mirror heater switch	483, 492
S68.3	Exterior mirror left/right switch	486 to 490
S78	RH front door window motor switch	543 to 546
S79	LH rear door remote window motor switch	547 to 550
S80	RH rear door remote window motor switch	551 to 554
S91	Oil pressure switch (TBI)	166, 167
U3	Computer	505 to 514
U3.1	Clock switch	512
U3.2	Function selector switch	512
U3.3	Reset/stopwatch/adjustment switch	512
U4	ABS system	572 to 586
U4.1	ABS relay	573 to 576
U4.2	ABS solenoid valve relay	583 to 586
U4.3	ABS pump	572
U4.4	ABS diode	585
U4.5	LH front ABS solenoid valve	578
U4.6	RH front ABS solenoid valve	580
U4.7	LH rear ABS solenoid valve	579
U4.8	RH rear ABS solenoid valve	581
X1	Trailer socket	331, 333, 382 to 384, 394 to 398
X2	Auxiliary connector	122, 341, 326, 417, 470, 475, 536, 559
X10	Ignition timing adjustment connector	233, 234
X11	5-pin connector (TBI)	145, 148, 164, 167
X13	Test connector	175, 176, 178, 147, 153, 154, 255
X15	Connector – octane number	229, 230, 243, 244, 280 281, 154, 155, 184 to 186
X15F	4-pin connector	270, 271, 291, 295
X16	Connector – wiring harness	255, 258, 261, 262
X17	8-pin connector (Motronic)	171, 172, 176, 181
Y1	Air conditioning compressor	
Y2	Revolution acceleration solenoid valve	
Y3	Boot lid release solenoid	326
Y4	Headlight washer solenoid valve	440
Y5	Diesel solenoid valve	213
Y6	Auxiliary air slide valve	293
Y7	Fuel injectors	186 to 193, 279 to 286
Y9	Level control solenoid	464
Y10	Distributor	220
Y11	Hall sensor	216 to 218
Y14	Inductive sensor (EV 61)	133 to 137, 225 to 227
Y15	Inductive sensor	125, 126
Y17	Idle cut-off solenoid valve	117
Y23	Distributor	129
Y24	Distributor	140, 230
Y25	Revolution acceleration solenoid valve	121
Y26	Throttle valve positioner	238 to 244
Y27	Pre-throttle valve	252, 253
Y32	Injection valve (TBI)	144
Y33	Distributor	174, 260, 274
Y34	Tank ventilation valve	195, 196

Not all items fitted to all models
For colour code, see key to Fig. 13.6

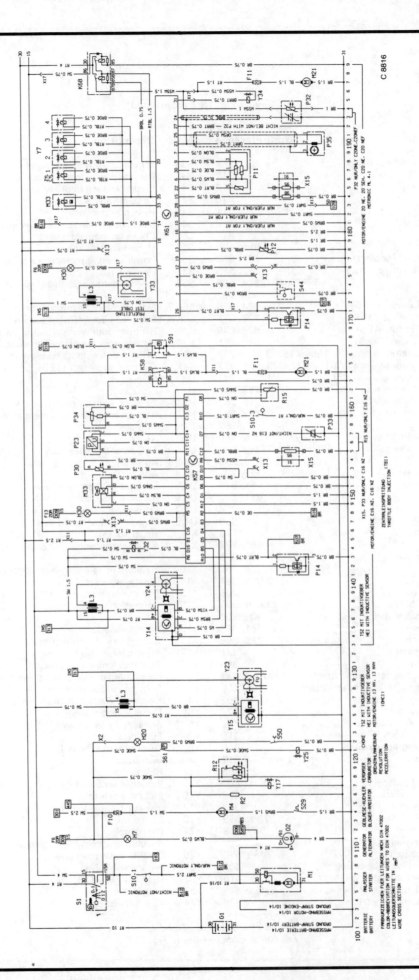

Fig. 13.7 Wiring diagram for 1988 models

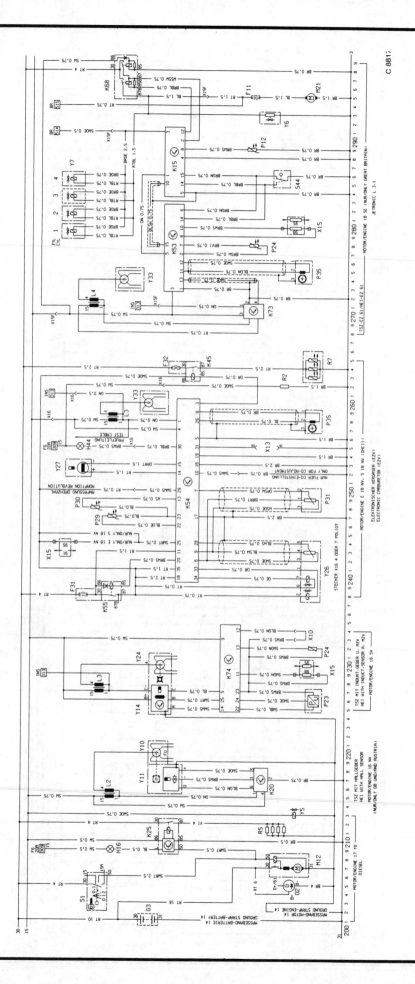

Fig. 13.7 Wiring diagram for 1988 models (continued)

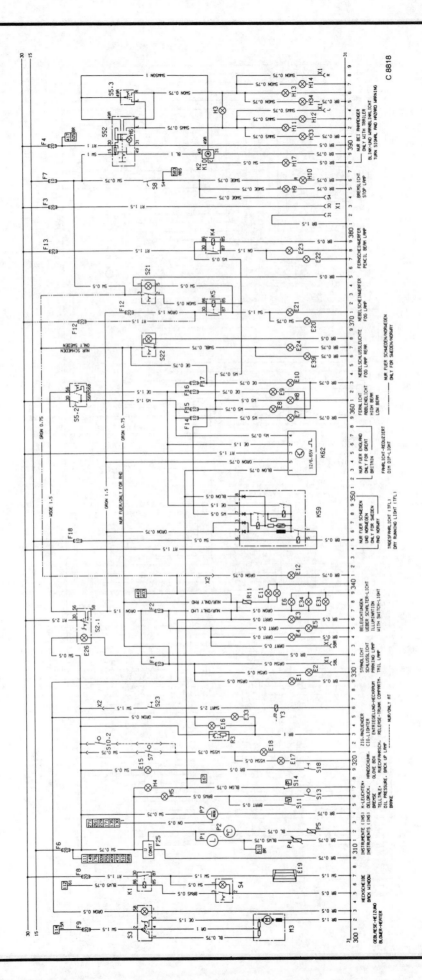

Fig. 13.7 Wiring diagram for 1988 models (continued)

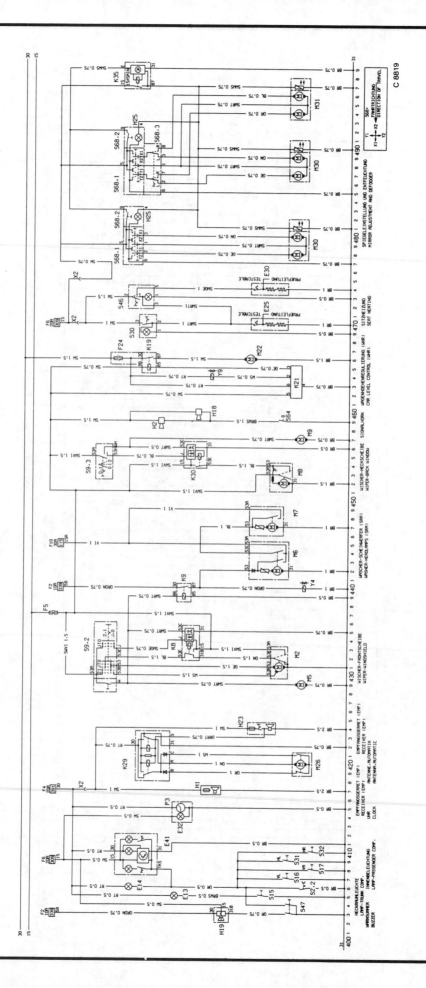

Fig. 13.7 Wiring diagram for 1988 models (continued)

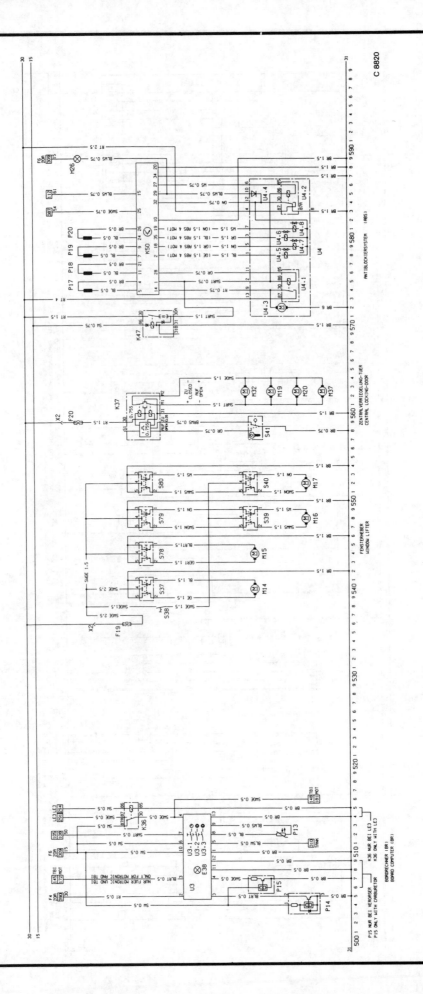

Fig. 13.7 Wiring diagram for 1988 models (continued)

Index